STUDY GUIDE
&
FULL SOLUTIONS MANUAL
Susan E. McMurry

Fundamentals of
General, Organic, and Biological
CHEMISTRY
Fourth Edition

McMurry   Castellion

Prentice
Hall

Upper Saddle River, NJ 07458

Project Manager: Kristen Kaiser
Senior Editor: Kent Porter Hamann
Editor-in-Chief: John Challice
Managing Editor: David A. George
Production Editor: James Buckley
Supplement Cover Manager: Paul Gourhan
Supplement Cover Designer: Joanne Alexandris
Manufacturing Buyer: Ilene Kahn

© 2003 by Pearson Education, Inc.
Pearson Education, Inc.
Upper Saddle River, NJ 07458

Printed in the United States of America

10 9 8 7 6 5 4 3 2 1
ISBN 0-13-047706-0

Pearson Education Ltd., *London*
Pearson Education Australia Pty. Ltd., *Sydney*
Pearson Education Singapore, Pte. Ltd.
Pearson Education North Asia Ltd., *Hong Kong*
Pearson Education Canada, Inc., *Toronto*
Pearson Educación de Mexico, S.A. de C.V.
Pearson Education—Japan, *Tokyo*
Pearson Education Malaysia, Pte. Ltd.
Pearson Education, *Upper Saddle River, New Jersey*

RH

Contents

Preface

How is food digested? What is DNA fingerprinting? How do anesthetics work?

For all of these questions, chemistry provides an answer. Chemistry, the study of matter, is essential for understanding the physical world, from acid rain to gene therapy to the ozone layer. Chemical laboratory tests are a routine part of medical care. The functioning of our bodies is a result of thousands of biochemical reactions. To study life, you must first study chemistry.

Both the textbook and this Study Guide and Solutions Manual are designed to be as helpful as possible to you in your chemistry course. The textbook contains numerous solved problems that show you techniques for solving specific types of chemistry problems. In addition, the text includes applications of the material in each chapter to contemporary science problems. This Study Guide consists of several types of study aids: detailed solutions to all textbook problems, outlines of the chapters, and self-tests.

The following suggestions may help you:

(1) Attend all classes. Although it's possible to learn chemistry just by reading the textbook and study guide, a lecturer makes difficult topics much easier to understand and ties together seemingly unrelated topics.

(2) Read the textbook. The best way to study is to skim the chapter to be covered before class, and then to read it more thoroughly after the lecturer has discussed the material. Use the textbook to help you understand subjects you find especially difficult. It is also helpful to use the chapter outlines in the Study Guide after reading the textbook.

(3) Work the problems. Start by reading carefully the Solved Problems in the textbook. Next, try to work the Practice Problems, using the steps outlined in the Solved Problems. Finally, attempt the Additional Problems at the end of the chapter. Although this Study Guide and Solutions Manual has detailed solutions to all text problems, it's better to use the solutions in this book as a last resort. You will learn more if you first struggle a bit with a problem before checking its answer, than if you look up the answer right away.

(4) Use the supplementary material in the Study Guide to help you review each chapter. The chapter outlines organize and restate both the major themes of each chapter and the detailed contents. Go over the list of key terms in the textbook to make sure that you know the meaning of each important term. Test yourself with the self-tests, which include multiple choice, sentence completions, matching, and true/false questions.

Acknowledgments

I would like to thank the following people for their assistance with this book: John McMurry (of course), Mary Castellion, Kent Porter-Hamann, Donna Young, Maria Vogt, and Alan Gahr. I am grateful to my entire family for their patience and support.

Chapter 1 – Matter, Energy, and Life

Chapter Outline

I. Matter and its properties (Sections 1.1–1.2).
   A. Matter is anything that is physically real (Section 1.1).
   B. Properties are the characteristics of matter.
      1. Physical properties are those properties that can be measured without altering the identity of a substance. Examples include mass, melting point, boiling point, color.
      2. Chemical properties must be determined by changing the identity of the substance. Examples include rusting, combustion and chemical reactivity.
      3. A physical change does not alter the identity of a substance.
      4. A chemical change is a process in which one or more substances undergoes a change in identity.
   C. States of matter (Section 1.2).
      1. The states of matter are solid, liquid and gas.
         a. Solids have definite volume and definite shape.
         b. Liquids have definite volume and indefinite shape.
         c. Gases have indefinite volume and indefinite shape.
      2. Changes of state are: melting, boiling, condensing, freezing.
II. Classification of matter (Sections 1.3–1.6).
   A. Mixtures (Section 1.3).
      1. Mixtures vary in composition and properties.
      2. Mixtures can be separated by physical methods.
   B. Pure substances.
      1. Pure substances include chemical compounds and chemical elements.
      2. Pure substances don't vary in composition and properties.
      3. Chemical compounds can be broken down to elements by chemical change.
         a. A chemical reaction represents a chemical change between pure substances (Section 1.4).
         b. In a chemical reaction, the reactants are written on the left, the products are written on the right, and an arrow connects them
      4. Chemical elements can't be broken down.
   C. Elements (Sections 1.5–1.6).
      1. There are 113 elements; 90 of them occur naturally.
      2. Elements are represented by one or two-letter symbols.
      3. The symbols for elements can be combined to produce chemical formulas.
      4. Elements are presented in a table – the periodic table
      5. Elements can be classified as metals, nonmetals or metalloids.
         a. Metals are solids that are lustrous, brittle, malleable and good conductors of heat and electricity.
         b. Nonmetals may be solid, liquid or gas and are poor conductors.
         c. Metalloids have characteristics intermediate between metals and nonmetals.

Solutions to Chapter 1 Problems

1.1   All of the listed items are made of chemicals.

1.2   *Change in physical properties*:   (a) grinding a metal surface   (d) a puddle evaporating
Change in chemical properties: (b) fruit ripening   (c) wood burning

1.3   Formaldehyde is a gas at room temperature (25°C).

1.4   At 10°C, acetic acid is a solid.

1.5   *Mixtures*: (a) concrete; (d) wood
Pure substances: (b) helium; (c) a lead weight

1.6   *Physical changes*: (a) separation by filtration; (c) mixing alcohol and water
Chemical changes: (b) production of carbon dioxide by heating limestone

1.7   (a) U = uranium;   (b) Ti = titanium;   (c) W = tungsten

1.8   (a) Na = sodium;   (b) Ca = calcium;   (c) Pd = palladium;   (d) K = potassium
(e) Sr = strontium;   (f) Sn = tin

1.9   (a) Ammonia (NH_3) contains one nitrogen atom and three hydrogen atoms.
(b) Sodium bicarbonate ($NaHCO_3$) contains one sodium atom, one hydrogen atom, one carbon atom, and three oxygen atoms.
(c) Octane (C_8H_{18}) contains eight carbon atoms and eighteen hydrogen atoms.
(d) Vitamin C ($C_6H_8O_6$) contains six carbon atoms, eight hydrogen atoms, and six oxygen atoms.

1.10

Element	Name	Number in Periodic Table
(a) Cr	chromium	24
(b) Na	sodium	11
(c) P	phosphorus	15
(d) Rn	radon	86

1.11

(a) B	boron	5
(b) Si	silicon	14
(c) Ge	germanium	32
(d) As	arsenic	33
(e) Sb	antimony	51
(f) Te	tellurium	52
(g) At	astatine	85

The metalloids occur at the boundary between metals and nonmetals.

Understanding Key Concepts

1.12   From top to bottom: helium (He), neon (Ne), argon (Ar), krypton (Kr), xenon (Xe), radon (Rn).

1.13   From top to bottom: copper (Cu), silver (Ag), gold (Au)

1.14   Blue: argon (Ar) – nonmetal
Green: arsenic (As) – metalloid
Red: yttrium (Y) – metal

1.15   The element, americium (Am), is a metal.

Chemistry and the Properties of Matter

1.16   Chemistry is the study of matter – its nature, properties and transformations.

1.17   All the listed items are composed of chemicals.

1.18   Physical changes: (a) boiling water; (c) dissolving sugar in water; (e) breaking of glass
Chemical changes: (b) decomposing water by passing a current through it; (d) exploding
of potassium when placed in water

1.19   Physical changes: (a) steam condensing; (d) breaking of a dinner plate; (e) nickel sticking
to a magnet
Chemical changes: (b) milk souring; (c) ignition of matches; (f) exploding of
nitroglycerin

States and Classification of Matter

1.20   A *gas* is a substance that has no definite shape or volume.
A *liquid* has no definite shape but has a definite volume.
A *solid* has a definite volume and a definite shape.

1.21   Melting, boiling, condensation, and freezing are all changes of state. *Melting* occurs when
a solid is heated and becomes a liquid. *Boiling* occurs when a liquid is heated and becomes
a gas. *Condensation* occurs when a gas is cooled and becomes a liquid. *Freezing* occurs
when a liquid is cooled and becomes a solid. All changes of state are physical changes.

1.22   Sulfur dioxide is a gas at 25°C.

1.23   Benzyl salicylate is a solid at 14°C and a liquid at 60°C.

1.24   Mixtures: (a) pea soup; (b) seawater; (d) urine; (f) multi-vitamin tablet
Pure substances: (c) C_3H_8; (e) lead

1.25   Mixtures: (a) blood; (c) dishwashing liquid; (d) toothpaste
Pure substances: (b) silicon; (e) gold; (f) NH_3

1.26   An *element* is a pure substance that can't be broken down chemically into simpler
substances.

A *compound* is a pure substance that has a definite composition and that can be broken
down chemically to yield elements.

1.27 A *compound* has a definite composition and properties and can be broken down into simpler substances (elements) only by chemical reactions.

A *mixture* can vary in both composition and properties, and its components can be separated by physical methods.

1.28 Element: (a) aluminum foil
Compounds: (b) table salt;   (c) water
Mixtures: (d) air;   (e) banana;   (f) notebook paper

1.29 (a) motor oil – (i) mixture; (iii) liquid
(b) copper – (ii) solid; (v) chemical element
(c) carbon dioxide – (iv) gas; (vi) chemical compound
(d) nitrogen – (iv) gas; (v) chemical element
(e) sodium bicarbonate – (ii) solid; (vi) chemical compound

1.30   *Reactant*   *Products*

Hydrogen peroxide   ⟶   water   +   oxygen
chemical compound   *chemical compound*   *element*

1.31   *Reactants*   *Products*

Sodium   +   water   ⟶   hydrogen + sodium hydroxide
element   *chemical compound*   *element*   *chemical compound*

Elements and Their Symbols

1.32 113 elements are presently known; 90 elements occur naturally.

1.33 Metallic elements are found on the left side of the periodic table.
Nonmetallic elements are found on the right side of the periodic table.
Metalloids are found in a zigzag band between the metallic elements and the nonmetallic elements.

1.34 *Metals* are elements that are solids at room temperature (except for Hg), are lustrous and malleable, and are good conductors of heat and electricity.

Nonmetals are elements that are gases or brittle solids (except for Br) and are poor conductors.

Metalloids are elements that have properties intermediate between those of metals and nonmetals.

1.35 Oxygen (O) is the most abundant element in both the Earth's crust and in the human body.

1.36 (a) Gadolinium (Gd)   (b) Germanium (Ge)   (c) Technetium (Tc)   (d) Arsenic (As)
(e) Cadmium (Cd)

1.37 (a) Zn; (b) Hg; (c) Ba; (d) Au; (e) Si; (f) C; (g) Na; (h) Pb

1.38 (a) nitrogen; (b) potassium; (c) chlorine; (d) calcium; (e) phosphorus; (f) manganese

1.39   (a) tellurium   (b) rhenium   (c) beryllium   (d) argon   (e) plutonium   (f) magnesium

1.40   The first letter of a chemical symbol is always capitalized; the second letter, if any, is never capitalized. Thus, Co stands for cobalt, and CO stands for carbon monoxide, a compound composed of carbon (C) and oxygen (O).

1.41   (a) The symbol for bromine is Br (the second letter in a symbol is never capitalized).
(b) The symbol for manganese is Mn (Mg is the symbol for magnesium).
(c) The symbol for carbon is C (Ca is the symbol for calcium).
(d) The symbol for potassium is K.

1.42   (a) Water has the formula H_2O (the number 2 is a subscript).
(b) Water is composed of hydrogen and oxygen.

1.43   (a) "Fool's gold" is a compound with the formula CuS ; the symbol for copper is Cu.
(b) The formula for "laughing gas" is NO; the symbol for nitrogen is N.

1.44   (a) $MgSO_4$: magnesium, sulfur, oxygen
(b) $FeBr_2$: iron, bromine
(c) CoP: cobalt, phosphorus
(d) AsH_3: arsenic, hydrogen
(e) $CaCr_2O_7$: calcium, chromium, oxygen

1.45   (a) C_3H_8 (b) H_2SO_4 (c) $C_9H_8O_4$
      3 carbons   2 hydrogens   9 carbons
      8 hydrogens   1 sulfur   8 hydrogens
                         4 oxygens   4 oxygens

1.46   Carbon, hydrogen, nitrogen and oxygen are present in glycine. The formula $C_2H_5NO_2$ represents ten atoms.

1.47   The formula of ribose ($C_5H_{10}O_5$) represents 20 atoms.

1.48   Ibuprofen: $C_{13}H_{18}O_2$

1.49   Penicillin V: $C_{16}H_{18}N_2O_5S$

1.50   (a) Osmium (Os) is a metal.
(b) Xenon (Xe) is a nonmetal.

1.51   (a) Tantalum (Ta) is a metal.
(b) Germanium (Ge) is a metalloid.

Applications

1.52   (no answer)

1.53   Only soluble forms of mercury are toxic. Hg_2Cl_2 passes through the body before it can be chemically converted to a soluble form, but elemental mercury vapor remains in the lungs long enough to be converted to a soluble compound.

General Questions and Problems

1.54 (a) A *physical change* is a change in the property of a substance that doesn't alter its chemical makeup. A *chemical change* alters a substance's chemical makeup.
(b) *Melting point* is the temperature at which a change of state from solid to liquid occurs. *Boiling point* is the temperature at which a change of state from liquid to gas occurs.
(c) A *reactant* is a substance that undergoes change in a chemical reaction. A *product* is a substance formed as a result of a chemical reaction.
(d) A *metal* is a lustrous malleable element that is a good conductor of heat and electricity; a *nonmetal* is an element that is a poor conductor.

1.55 (a) True; (b) False. Melting is a physical change. (c) False. The correct formula is PbO.
(d) False. The resulting product is a mixture, not a compound.

1.56 Chemical compounds: (a) H_2O_2; (d) NO; (e) $NaHCO_3$
Elements: (b) Mo; (c) C

1.57 The white solid is a chemical compound, and the brown gas and molten metal are elements.

1.58 The liquid is a mixture.

1.59 Remove the iron filings with a magnet. Add water to the remaining mixture, and filter out the sand. Evaporate the water to recover the salt.

1.60 (a) Fe; (b) Cu; (c) Co; (d) Mo; (e) Cr; (f) F; (g) S

1.61 If the undiscovered elements follow the pattern of the periodic table, element 115 would be placed below bismuth and would be a metal. Element 117 would be placed below astatine and might be either a metal or a metalloid. Element 119 would be placed below sodium and would be a metal.

Self-Test for Chapter 1

Multiple choice:

1. Which of the following is a chemical property?
(a) melting point   (b) reaction with acid   (c) hardness   (d) transparency

2. The change of state that occurs when a gas is cooled to a liquid is called:
(a) boiling   (b) melting   (c) evaporation   (d) condensation

3. Which of the following is not an element?
(a) Fluorine   (b) Freon   (c) Neon   (d) Radon

4. The chemical formula for fructose is $C_6H_{12}O_6$. How many different elements does fructose contain?
(a) 24   (b) 18   (c) 6   (d) 3

5. How many atoms does the formula for fructose represent?
(a) 24   (b) 18   (c) 6   (d) 3

6. A solution of fructose in water is a:
   (a) mixture   (b) pure substance   (c) chemical compound   (d) element

7. Which of the following is not a characteristic of a metal?
   (a) electrical conductivity   (b) malleability   (c) brittleness   (d) luster

8. All of the following have uniform composition except: (a) element   (b) solution   (c) pure substance   (d) chemical compound

Complete the following sentences:

1. Sulfur is a _____ element.

2. Color is a _____ property.

3. _____ is the symbol for the element bismuth.

4. When a substance _____, it changes from gas to liquid.

5. Matter is anything that has _____ and _____.

6. A _____ has definite volume but indefinite shape.

7. A _____ _____ doesn't vary in its properties or composition.

8. Symbols of elements are combined to produce _____ _____.

9. A _____ substance can be beaten or rolled into different shapes.

10. ____, ____, ____, and ____ are four elements present in all living organisms.

Tell whether each of the following statements is true or false:

1. Cobalt is an element essential for human life.

2. Rust formation is a chemical change.

3. A chemical compound is a pure substance.

4. The components of a solution are separable by chemical methods.

5. The formula C_2H_4O represents three atoms.

6. A metalloid has properties intermediate between metals and nonmetals.

7. The chemical symbol for silver is Si.

8. In the chemical reaction carbon + oxygen —> carbon dioxide, the reactants are elements.

9. Methyl bromide, a compound formerly used for fumigation, has a melting point of $-93.7°C$ and a boiling point of $3.6°C$ and is a liquid at room temperature.

10. Nonmetals may be solids, liquids or gases.

Chapter 2 – Measurements in Chemistry

Chapter Outline

I. Measurements (Sections 2.1–2.3).
   A. Physical quantities (Section 2.1).
      1. All physical quantities consist of a number plus a unit.
         a. SI units, the standard units for scientists, are the kilogram, the meter, and the Kelvin.
         b. Metric units are the gram, the meter, the liter and the degree Celsius.
         c. Other units, such as those for speed and concentration, can be derived from SI and metric units.
      2. Prefixes are used with units to indicate multiples of ten.
   B. Measuring mass (Section 2.2).
      1. Mass is the amount of matter in a substance.
      2. Mass differs from weight (a measure of the gravitational pull exerted on an object).
      3. The SI unit of mass is the kilogram, but in chemistry the gram and milligram are more often used.
   C. Measuring length (Section 2.3).
   The meter is the standard unit for length.
   D. Measuring volume.
      1. Volume is the amount of space that a substance occupies.
      2. Units for volume are the liter (L) and the cubic meter (m^3) - the SI unit.
II. Numbers in measurement (Sections 2.4–2.6).
   A. Significant figures (Section 2.4).
      1. All measurements have a degree of uncertainty.
      2. For any measurement, the number of digits known with certainty, plus one digit considered uncertain, is known as the number of significant figures.
      3. Rules for significant figures:
         a. Zeroes in the middle of a number are always significant.
         b. Zeroes at the beginning of a number are never significant.
         c. Zeroes at the end of a number but after a decimal point are significant.
         d. Zeroes at the end of a number but before an implied decimal point may or may not be significant.
      4. Some numbers are exact and have an unlimited number of significant figures,
   B. Scientific notation (Section 2.5).
      1. In scientific notation, a number is written as the product of a number between 1 and 10 times 10 raised to a power.
         a. For numbers greater than 10, the power of 10 is positive.
         b. For numbers less than 1, the power of 10 is negative.
      2. Scientific notation is helpful in indicating the number of significant figures in a number.
   C. Rounding off numbers (Section 2.6).
      1. Numbers must be rounded off if they contain more digits than are significant.
      2. Rounding in calculations.
         a. In multiplication or division, the result can't have more significant figures than any of the original numbers.
         b. In addition or subtraction, the result can't have more digits to the right of the decimal point than any of the original numbers.

3. Rules of rounding:
   a. If the digit to be removed is 4 or less, drop it and remove all following digits.
   b. If the digit to be removed is 5 or greater, add 1 to the digit to the left of the digit you drop.

III. Calculations (Sections 2.7–2.8).
   A. Converting a quantity from one unit to another (Section 2.7).
      1. In the <u>factor-label</u> method:
         (quantity in old units) x (conversion factor) = (quantity in new units)
         a. The conversion factor is a fraction that converts one unit to another.
         b. All conversion factors are equal to 1.
      2. In the factor-label method, units are treated as numbers.
      3. In the factor-label method, all unwanted units cancel.
   B. Problem solving (Section 2.8).
      1. Make a "ballpark" estimate of the answer.
      2. Use the factor-label method to calculate the exact answer and compare it to the estimate.
         a. Identify the information known.
         b. Identify the information needed in the answer.
         c. Use conversion factors to convert the given information to the answer.

IV. Heat (Sections 2.9–2.10).
   A. Measuring temperature (Section 2.9).
      1. Units of temperature are the degree Fahrenheit, the degree Celsius, and the Kelvin.
      2. Temperature in °C = Temperature in K − 273.15°.
      3. $°F = \left(\dfrac{9°F}{5°C} \times °C\right) + 32°F$
      4. $°C = \dfrac{5°C}{9°F} \times (°F - 32°F)$
   B. Heat and energy (Section 2.10).
      1. All chemical reactions are accompanied by a change in energy.
         a. Potential energy is stored energy.
         b. Kinetic energy is the energy of motion.
      2. Heat is the energy transferred from a hotter object to a cooler object when the two are in contact.
      3. Units of energy are the joule and the calorie.
      4. $\text{Specific heat} = \dfrac{\text{calories}}{\text{grams} \times °C}$.

V. Density and specific gravity (Sections 2.11–2.12).
   A. Density (Section 2.11).
      1. Density = mass (g) / volume (mL or cm^3).
      2. Density is temperature-dependent.
   B. Specific gravity (Section 2.12).
      1. $\text{Specific gravity} = \dfrac{\text{density of substance (g/mL)}}{\text{density of water (1 g/mL)}}$.
      2. Specific gravity has no units.

Solutions to Chapter 2 Problems

2.1   (a) mL = milliliter   (b) kg = kilogram   (c) cm = centimeter
      (d) km = kilometer   (e) μg = microgram

2.2   (a) liter = L   (b) microliter = μL   (c) nanometer = nm
      (d) megameter = Mm

2.3   (a) 1 nm = 0.000 000 001 m   (b) 1 dg = 0.1 g   (c) 1 km = 1000 m
      (d) 1 mL = 0.001 L   (e) 1 ng = 0.000 000 001 g

2.4

Number	Significant Figures	Reason
(a) 3.45 m	3	
(b) 0.1400 kg	4	Rule 3
(c) 10.003 L	5	Rule 1
(d) 35 cents	Exact	

2.5   32.6°C. The answer has 3 significant figures.

2.6   In scientific notation, a number is written as the product of a number between one and ten times ten raised to a power. In (a), 58 g = 5.8×10^1 g.

Value	Scientific Notation
(a) 58 g	5.8×10^1 g
(b) 46,792 m	4.6792×10^4 m
(c) 0.000 672 0 cm	6.720×10^{-4} cm
(d) 345.3 kg	3.453×10^2 kg

2.7

Value in Scientific Notation	Value in Normal Notation
(a) 4.885×10^4 mg	48,850 mg
(b) 8.3×10^{-6} m	0.000 008 3 m
(c) 4.00×10^{-2} m	0.0400 m

2.8   (a) 6.0×10^5 (b) 1.300×10^3 (c) 7.942×10^{11}

2.9   0.000 000 000 278 m = 2.78×10^{-10} m. (The decimal point must be moved ten places to the right.)

$$2.78 \times 10^{-10} \text{ m} \times \frac{1 \text{ pm}}{10^{-12} \text{ m}} = 2.78 \times 10^2 \text{ pm}$$

2.10   (a) 2.30 g   (b) 188.38 mL   (c) 0.009 L   (d) 1.000 kg

2.11 Remember:

(1) The sum or difference of two numbers can't have more digits to the right of the decimal point than either of the two numbers.

(2) The product or quotient of two numbers can't have more significant figures than either of the two numbers.

Calculation	Rounded to:
(a) 4.87 mL + 46.0 mL = 50.87 mL	50.9 mL
(b) 3.4 x 0.023 g = 0.0782 g	0.078 g
(c) 19.333 m − 7.4 m = 11.933 m	11.9 m
(d) 55 mg − 4.671 mg + 0.894 mg = 51.223 mg	51 mg
(e) 62,911 ÷ 611 = 102.96399	103

2.12

(a) $\dfrac{1\ L}{1000\ mL}$, $\dfrac{1000\ mL}{1\ L}$; $\dfrac{1\ mL}{0.001\ L}$, $\dfrac{0.001\ L}{1\ mL}$

(b) $\dfrac{1\ g}{0.03527\ oz}$, $\dfrac{0.03527\ oz}{1\ g}$; $\dfrac{1\ oz}{28.35\ g}$, $\dfrac{28.35\ g}{1\ oz}$

(c) $\dfrac{1\ L}{1.057\ qt}$, $\dfrac{1.057\ qt}{1\ L}$; $\dfrac{1\ qt}{0.9461\ L}$, $\dfrac{0.9461\ L}{1\ qt}$

2.13

(a) $16.0\ oz \times \dfrac{28.35\ g}{1\ oz} = 454\ g$ (b) $2500\ mL \times \dfrac{1\ L}{1000\ mL} = 2.5\ L$

(c) $99.0\ L \times \dfrac{1\ qt}{0.9461\ L} - 105\ qt$

2.14

$0.840\ quart \times \dfrac{1\ L}{1.057\ quart} \times \dfrac{1000\ mL}{1\ L} = 795\ mL$

2.15 This is a *long* unit conversion! Remember that all units must cancel at the end, except for the units needed in the final answer (meters and seconds). Nautical miles must be converted to meters, and hours must be converted to seconds. Also remember the definition of a knot – one nautical mile per hour.

$\dfrac{14.3\ naut.\ mi}{1\ hr} \times \dfrac{6076.1155\ ft}{1\ naut.\ mi.} \times \dfrac{0.3048\ m}{1\ ft} \times \dfrac{1\ hr}{60\ min} \times \dfrac{1\ min}{60\ s} = 7.36\ m/s$

2.16

(a) $7.5\ lb \times \dfrac{1\ kg}{2.205\ lb} = 3.4\ kg$

Ballpark check: Since a kilogram is approximately 2 pounds, the infant is expected to weigh about 3.5 lb. The ballpark check is close to the exact solution.

(b) $4.0 \text{ oz} \times \dfrac{29.57 \text{ mL}}{1 \text{ oz}} = 120 \text{ mL}$

Ballpark check: There are approximately 30 mL in an ounce, and the ballpark check thus gives an answer of 120 mL, which agrees with the exact solution.
Remember: The answers must have the correct number of significant figures.

2.17

$2 \times 0.324 \text{ g} \times \dfrac{1000 \text{ mg}}{1 \text{ g}} \times \dfrac{1}{135 \text{ lb}} \times \dfrac{2.205 \text{ lb}}{1 \text{ kg}} = 10.6 \dfrac{\text{mg}}{\text{kg}}$

$2 \times 0.324 \text{ g} \times \dfrac{1000 \text{ mg}}{1 \text{ g}} \times \dfrac{1}{40 \text{ lb}} \times \dfrac{2.205 \text{ lb}}{1 \text{ kg}} = 36 \dfrac{\text{mg}}{\text{kg}}$

2.18 From Section 2.9, we find the formula:

$(°F - 32°F) \times \dfrac{5°C}{9°F} = °C$

Substituting 136°F into the above formula:

$(136°F - 32°F) \times \dfrac{5°C}{9°F} = 57.8°C$

Ballpark check: The numerator in the above expression is approximately 500°C. Dividing by 9°F gives the answer 55.5°C, which approximates the exact solution.

2.19

$°F = \left(\dfrac{9°F}{5°C} \times °C\right) + 32°F$; In this problem, $°C = -38.9°$

$= (1.8°F \times -38.9°) + 32°F = -38.0°F$

$= (273.15 - 38.9)K = 234.3 \text{ K}$

2.20

$\text{Heat (cal)} = \text{mass (g)} \times \text{temperature change (°C)} \times \text{specific heat} \left(\dfrac{\text{cal}}{\text{g} \cdot °C}\right)$

$= 350 \text{ g} \times (25°C - 3°C) \times \dfrac{1.0 \text{ cal}}{\text{g} \cdot °C}$

$= 7700 \text{ cal} = 7.7 \times 10^3 \text{ cal}$

Ballpark check; The temperature change is approximately 20°C. The mass of Coca-Cola, times the temperature change equals 7000, a number close to the exact solution.

2.21

$\text{Specific heat} = \dfrac{\text{calories}}{\text{grams} \times °C}$

$\text{Specific heat} = \dfrac{161 \text{ cal}}{75 \text{ g} \times 10°C} = 0.21 \dfrac{\text{cal}}{\text{g} \cdot °C}$

2.22 Solids with densities greater than water will sink; solids with densities less than water will float.
Solids that float: ice, human fat, cork, balsa wood
Solids that sink: gold, table sugar, earth

2.23

$$12.37 \text{ g} \times \frac{1 \text{ mL}}{1.474 \text{ g}} = 8.392 \text{ mL}$$

Ballpark check: Since the density of chloroform is approximately 1.5, the volume needed is about 2/3 of the mass needed.

2.24

$$\text{Density} = \frac{\text{Mass}}{\text{Volume}} = \frac{16.8 \text{ g}}{7.60 \text{ cm}^3} = 2.21 \frac{\text{g}}{\text{cm}^3}$$

2.25 Battery acid is more dense than water.

Understanding Key Concepts

2.26 The graduated cylinder contains 34 mL; the paper clip is 2.7 cm long. Both answers have two significant figures.

2.27 The specific gravity is found by reading the liquid level on the scale of the hydrometer. The specific gravity of this solution is 0.977
(a) The answer has three significant figures.
(b) The solution is less dense than water.

2.28

The smaller graduated cylinder is more accurate for two reasons. (1) The distance between two gradations represents a smaller volume, making it easier to measure volumes more accurately. (2) The percent error is greater when a small volume is measured in a large graduated cylinder.

2.29 If two identical hydrometers are placed in ethanol and in chloroform, the hydrometer in chloroform will float higher. Since a hydrometer bulb sinks until it displaces a volume of liquid equal to its mass, it displaces a smaller volume of chloroform, the denser liquid, and the bulb floats higher.

Definitions and Units

2.30 A *physical quantity* is a physical property that can be measured; it consists of a number plus a unit.

2.31 *Mass* is the measure of the amount of matter in an object. *Weight* is the measure of the gravitational force exerted on an object by the earth, moon, or other large body.

2.32–2.33

Quantity	SI Unit	Metric Unit
Mass	kilogram (kg)	gram (g)
Volume	cubic meter (m^3)	liter (L)
Length	meter (m)	meter (m)
Temperature	kelvin (K)	degree Celsius (°C)

2.34 A cubic decimeter and a liter represent the same volume expressed in two different systems of units.

2.35 A kelvin is the same size as a Celsius degree. The lowest temperature in the SI system, 0 K, is the coldest temperature possible. In the Celsius system, 0°C is the temperature at which water freezes and is equivalent to 273.15 K.

2.36 (a) centiliter (b) decimeter (c) millimeter (d) nanoliter (e) milligram (f) cubic meter (g) cubic centimeter

2.37 (a) pg (b) cm (c) dL (d) μL (e) mL

2.38

$$1 \text{ mg } \times \frac{10^{-3} \text{ g}}{1 \text{ mg}} \times \frac{10^{12} \text{ pg}}{1 \text{ g}} = 10^9 \text{ pg}$$

$$35 \text{ ng } \times \frac{10^{-9} \text{ g}}{1 \text{ ng}} \times \frac{10^{12} \text{ pg}}{1 \text{ g}} = 3.5 \times 10^4 \text{ pg}$$

2.39

$$1 \text{ L } \times \frac{10^6 \text{ μL}}{\text{L}} = 10^6 \text{ μL} ; \quad 20 \text{ mL } \times \frac{10^3 \text{ μL}}{\text{mL}} = 2 \times 10^4 \text{ μL}$$

Scientific Notation and Significant Figures

2.40 (a) 9.457×10^3 (b) 7×10^{-5} (c) 2.000×10^{10} (d) 1.2345×10^{-2} (e) 6.5238×10^2

2.41 (a) 4870 (b) 5,501,000 (c) 0.002 540 (d) 36,800

2.42 (a) six (b) three (c) three (d) four (e) 1–5 (f) 2–3

2.43 (a) five (b) three (c) four (d) one (e) three

2.44 (a) 7,926 mi; 7,900 mi; 7,926.38 mi
(b) 7.926 381 x 10^3 mi

2.45 (a) 2.4 x 10^5 (b) 3.0 x 10^{-1} (c) 3.0
(d) 2.4 x 10^2 (e) 5.0 x 10^4 (f) 6.6 x 10^2

2.46 (a) 12.1 g (b) 96.19 cm (c) 263 mL (d) 20.9 mg

2.47 (a) 43.0 m^2 (b) 270 mi^2 (c) 184.7 mi/hr (d) 1.36 x 10^3 cm^3

Unit Conversions and Problem Solving

2.48 (a) 0.3614 cg (b) 0.0120 ML (c) 0.0144 mm (d) 60.3 ng

2.49

(a) $56.4 \text{ mi} \times \dfrac{1.609 \text{ km}}{1 \text{ mi}} = 90.7 \text{ km}$

$56.4 \text{ mi} \times \dfrac{1.609 \text{ km}}{1 \text{ mi}} \times \dfrac{1 \text{ Mm}}{10^3 \text{ km}} = 9.07 \times 10^{-2} \text{ Mm}$

(b) $2.0 \text{ L} \times \dfrac{1.057 \text{ qt}}{1 \text{ L}} = 2.1 \text{ qt}$

$2.0 \text{ L} \times \dfrac{10^3 \text{ mL}}{1 \text{ L}} \times \dfrac{1 \text{ fl oz}}{29.57 \text{ mL}} = 68 \text{ fl oz}$

(c) $7.0 \text{ ft} \times \dfrac{12 \text{ in}}{1 \text{ ft}} = 84.0 \text{ in}$; $84.0 \text{ in} + 2.0 \text{ in} = 86.0 \text{ in}$

$86.0 \text{ in} \times \dfrac{1 \text{ cm}}{0.3937 \text{ in}} = 218 \text{ cm}$; $218 \text{ cm} \times \dfrac{1 \text{ m}}{100 \text{ cm}} = 2.18 \text{ m}$

(d) $1.35 \text{ lb} \times \dfrac{1 \text{ kg}}{2.205 \text{ lb}} = 0.612 \text{ kg}$; $0.612 \text{ kg} \times \dfrac{10^4 \text{ dg}}{1 \text{ kg}} = 6.12 \times 10^3 \text{ dg}$

2.50 (a) 97.8 kg (b) 0.133 mL (c) 0.46 ng

2.51 (a) kilo (k) (b) milli (m) (c) mega (M) (d) micro (μ)

2.52

$\dfrac{100 \text{ km}}{1 \text{ hr}} \times \dfrac{0.6214 \text{ mi}}{1 \text{ km}} = 62.1 \dfrac{\text{mi}}{\text{hr}}$

$\dfrac{62.1 \text{ mi}}{1 \text{ hr}} \times \dfrac{5280 \text{ ft}}{1 \text{ mi}} \times \dfrac{1 \text{ hr}}{60 \text{ min}} \times \dfrac{1 \text{ min}}{60 \text{ s}} = 91.1 \dfrac{\text{ft}}{\text{s}}$

2.53

$$\frac{55 \text{ mi}}{1 \text{ hr}} \times \frac{1 \text{ km}}{0.6214 \text{ mi}} = 89 \frac{\text{km}}{\text{hr}}$$

$$\frac{89 \text{ km}}{1 \text{ hr}} \times \frac{10^3 \text{ m}}{1 \text{ km}} \times \frac{1 \text{ hr}}{60 \text{ min}} \times \frac{1 \text{ min}}{60 \text{ s}} = 25 \frac{\text{m}}{\text{s}}$$

2.54

$$\frac{1 \text{ cell}}{6 \times 10^{-6} \text{ m}} \times \frac{1 \text{ m}}{39.37 \text{ in}} = 4 \times 10^3 \frac{\text{cells}}{\text{in}}$$

2.55 $1 \text{ ft}^2 = (0.3048 \text{ m})^2 = 0.0929 \text{ m}^2$

$$418{,}000 \text{ m}^2 \times \frac{1 \text{ ft}^2}{0.0929 \text{ m}^2} = 4.50 \times 10^6 \text{ ft}^2$$

2.56

$$\frac{200 \text{ mg}}{1 \text{ dL}} \times \frac{10 \text{ dL}}{1 \text{ L}} \times 5 \text{ L} = 10^4 \text{ mg}; \quad 10^4 \text{ mg} \times \frac{1 \text{ g}}{10^3 \text{ mg}} = 10 \text{ g cholesterol}$$

2.57

$$6 \times 12 \text{ oz} \times \frac{29.57 \text{ mL}}{1 \text{ oz}} \times \frac{1 \text{ L}}{10^3 \text{ mL}} = 2.1 \text{ L}; \quad \frac{\$2.59}{2.1 \text{ L}} = \$1.20/\text{L for a six-pack}$$

$\$1.59/2.0 \text{ L} = \$0.80/\text{L for a 2.0 L bottle}$

2.58

$$\frac{1.2 \times 10^4 \text{ cells}}{1 \text{ mm}^3} \times \frac{10^6 \text{ mm}^3}{1 \text{ L}} \times 5 \text{ L} = 6 \times 10^{10} \text{ cells}$$

2.59

$$1200 \text{ mg} \times \frac{1.0 \text{ cup}}{290 \text{ mg}} = 4.1 \text{ cups}$$

Temperature and Heat

2.60   *Potential energy* is stored energy. *Kinetic energy* is the energy of an object in motion.

2.61   *Heat* is the kinetic energy of the particles of a substance. *Temperature* is a measure of the heat of a substance.

2.62

$$°C = \frac{5°C}{9°F} \times (°F - 32°F) = \frac{5°C}{9°F} \times (98.6°F - 32°F) = \frac{66.6°C}{1.8} = 37.0 \ °C, \text{ or } 310.2 \text{ K}$$

2.63 $273.15 \text{ K} - 195.8 = 77.4 \text{ K};$

$$°F = \left(\frac{9°F}{5°C} \times °C\right) + 32°F = \left(\frac{9°F}{5°C} \times (-195.8°C)\right) + 32°F = -352.4°F + 32°F = -320.4°F$$

2.64

$$\text{Heat (cal)} = \text{mass (g)} \times \text{temperature change (°C)} \times \text{specific heat}\left(\frac{\text{cal}}{\text{g}\cdot\text{°C}}\right)$$

$$= 30.0 \text{ g} \times (30.0\text{ °C} - 10.0\text{°C}) \times \frac{0.895 \text{ cal}}{\text{g}\cdot\text{°C}} = 537 \text{ cal}$$

$$= 0.537 \text{ kcal}$$

2.65

$$\text{Specific heat} = \frac{\text{cal}}{\text{g}\cdot\text{°C}} = \frac{23 \text{ cal}}{5.0 \text{ g} \times 50\text{°C}} = 0.092 \frac{\text{cal}}{\text{g}\cdot\text{°C}}$$

2.66

$$\text{Temperature change (°C)} = \frac{\text{heat (cal)}}{\text{mass(g)} \times \text{specific heat}\left(\frac{\text{cal}}{\text{g}\cdot\text{°C}}\right)}$$

$$\text{Temperature change (°C)} = \frac{50 \text{ cal}}{15 \text{ g} \times 0.175 \dfrac{\text{cal}}{\text{g}\cdot\text{°C}}} = 19\text{°C}$$

Since 19°C is the difference between the initial and final temperature, and since 20°C is the initial temperature, the final temperature is 20°C + 19°C = 39°C.

2.67 See problem 2.66 for help in solving this problem.

$$\text{For mercury: Temperature change (°C)} = \frac{250 \text{ cal}}{150 \text{ g} \times 0.033 \dfrac{\text{cal}}{\text{g}\cdot\text{°C}}} = 51\text{°C}$$

Final temp = 25°C + 51°C = 76°C

$$\text{For iron: Temperature change (°C)} = \frac{250 \text{ cal}}{150 \text{ g} \times 0.106 \dfrac{\text{cal}}{\text{g}\cdot\text{°C}}} = 15.7\text{°C}$$

Final temp = 25.0°C + 15.7°C = 40.7°C

Density and Specific Gravity

2.68

$$250 \text{ mg} \times \frac{1 \text{ g}}{10^3 \text{ mg}} \times \frac{1 \text{ cm}^3}{1.40 \text{ g}} = 0.179 \text{ cm}^3$$

2.69 From the expression for density, we know that 1 L of hydrogen has a mass of 0.0899 g. We need to find the number of liters that have a mass of 1.0078 g.

$$1.0078 \text{ g} \times \frac{1 \text{ L}}{0.0899 \text{ g}} = 11.2 \text{ L}$$

2.70   To find the density of lead, divide the mass of lead by the volume of the bar in cm^3.
0.500 cm x 1.55 cm x 25.00 cm = 19.375 cm^3

$$\frac{220.9 \text{ g}}{19.375 \text{ cm}^3} = 11.4 \frac{\text{g}}{\text{cm}^3}$$

2.71   This problem is similar to Problem 2.70. The volume of the wire is given by :
$V = \pi r^2 \cdot$ length = 3.1424 x $(0.120 \text{ cm})^2$ x 15.0 cm = 0.679 cm^3

$$\frac{0.3624 \text{ g}}{0.679 \text{ cm}^3} = 0.534 \frac{\text{g}}{\text{cm}^3}$$

2.72

$$\frac{3.928 \text{ g}}{5.000 \text{ mL}} = 0.7856 \frac{\text{g}}{\text{mL}}; \quad \text{specific gravity} = 0.7856$$

2.73   Specific gravity = 1.1088; density = 1.1088 g/mL

$$1.00 \text{ kg} \text{ x } \frac{1000 \text{ g}}{1 \text{ kg}} \text{ x } \frac{1 \text{ mL}}{1.1088 \text{ g}} = 902 \text{ mL}; \quad 2.00 \text{ lb} \text{ x } \frac{453 \text{ g}}{1 \text{ lb}} \text{ x } \frac{1 \text{ mL}}{1.1088 \text{ g}} = 817 \text{ mL}$$

Applications

2.74

(a) $\dfrac{1 \text{ grain}}{64.8 \text{ mg}} = \dfrac{0.0154 \text{ grain}}{1 \text{ mg}}$ (b) $\dfrac{1 \text{ fluid oz}}{8 \text{ fluidram}} = \dfrac{0.125 \text{ fluid oz}}{1 \text{ fluidram}}$

(c) $\dfrac{1 \text{ fluidram}}{3.72 \text{ mL}} = \dfrac{0.269 \text{ fluidram}}{1 \text{ mL}}$ (d) $\dfrac{1 \text{ minim}}{0.062 \text{ mL}} = \dfrac{16 \text{ minim}}{1 \text{ mL}}$

(e) $\dfrac{1 \text{ fluid oz}}{480 \text{ minim}} = \dfrac{2.08 \text{ x } 10^{-3} \text{ fluid oz}}{1 \text{ minim}}$

2.75

(a) 5 grains x $\dfrac{64.8 \text{ mg}}{1 \text{ grain}}$ = 324 mg   (b) 1.5 oz x $\dfrac{8 \text{ dram}}{1 \text{ oz}}$ = 12 dram

2.76   BMI is defined as a person's weight in kilograms, divided by the square of height in meters. Alternatively, a person's weight in pounds, divided by the square of height in inches, and multiplied by 703, also gives the same value for BMI.

2.77   A value of BMI between 26 and 29 indicates overweight, and a value of BMI over 30 indicates obesity.

2.78   Body fat acts as a shock absorber, a thermal insulator, and as an energy storehouse.

2.79

$$5.0 \text{ lb} \text{ x } \frac{454 \text{ g}}{1 \text{ lb}} \text{ x } \frac{1 \text{ mL}}{0.94 \text{ g}} = 2.4 \text{ x } 10^3 \text{ mL or } 2.4 \text{ L}$$

General Questions and Problems

2.80   One carat = 200 mg = 0.200 g

$$\frac{0.200 \text{ g}}{1 \text{ carat}} \times 44.4 \text{ carat} = 8.88 \text{ g}$$

2.81

$$^\circ C = \frac{5^\circ C}{9^\circ F}(^\circ F - 32^\circ F) = \frac{5^\circ C}{9^\circ F}(350^\circ F - 32^\circ F) = \frac{5^\circ C}{9^\circ F}(318^\circ F) = 177^\circ C$$

2.82

$$2 \times 250 \text{ mg} \times \frac{1 \text{ g}}{1000 \text{ mg}} \times \frac{1}{130 \text{ lb}} \times \frac{2.21 \text{lb}}{1 \text{ kg}} = 8.5 \times 10^{-3} \frac{\text{g}}{\text{kg}} \text{ for the woman}$$

$$\frac{8.5 \times 10^{-3} \text{g}}{1 \text{kg}} \times 40 \text{ lb} \times \frac{0.454 \text{ kg}}{1 \text{ lb}} = 0.15 \text{ g}$$

A 40-lb child would need 0.15 g, or 150 mg, of penicillin to receive the same dose as a 130-lb woman. The child would thus need about 1.2 of the 125 mg penicillin tablets.

2.83 3.9×10^{-2} g/dL iron, 8.3×10^{-3} g/dL calcium, 2.24×10^{-1} g/dL cholesterol

2.84

$$1.3 \frac{\text{g}}{\text{L}} \times 4.0 \text{ m} \times 3.0 \text{ m} \times 2.5 \text{ m} \times 1000 \frac{\text{L}}{\text{m}^3} = 3.9 \times 10^4 \text{ g}$$

$$3.9 \times 10^4 \text{ g} \times \frac{1 \text{ lb}}{454 \text{ g}} = 86 \text{ lb}$$

2.85

$$75 \frac{\text{mL}}{\text{beat}} \times 72 \frac{\text{beats}}{\text{min}} \times 60 \frac{\text{min}}{\text{hr}} \times 24 \frac{\text{hr}}{\text{day}} = 7.8 \times 10^6 \frac{\text{mL}}{\text{day}}$$

2.86

$$15 \text{ g} \times \frac{1000.0 \text{ mL}}{50.00 \text{ g}} = 300 \text{ mL}$$

2.87   (a) 13.6   (b) An iron ball bearing will float in mercury.

(c) $2.00 \text{ L} \times \frac{10^3 \text{ mL}}{1 \text{ L}} \times \frac{13.6 \text{ g}}{1 \text{ mL}} \times \frac{1 \text{ lb}}{454 \text{ g}} = 59.9 \text{ lb}$

2.88

$$\frac{85 \text{ mg}}{100 \text{ mL}} \times \frac{10^3 \text{ mL}}{1 \text{ L}} \times \frac{0.9464 \text{ L}}{1 \text{ qt}} \times \frac{1 \text{ qt}}{2 \text{ pt}} \times 11 \text{ pt} = 4.4 \text{ g}$$

$$4.4 \text{ g} \times \frac{1 \text{ lb}}{454 \text{ g}} = 0.0097 \text{ lb}$$

2.89

$$\frac{3000 \text{ mL}}{1 \text{ day}} \times \frac{5 \text{ g}}{100 \text{ mL}} \times \frac{4 \text{ kcal}}{1 \text{ g}} = 600 \text{ kcal / day}$$

2.90

$$\left(\frac{100 \text{ mL}}{1 \text{ kg}} \times 10 \text{ kg}\right) + \left(\frac{50 \text{ mL}}{1 \text{ kg}} \times 10 \text{ kg}\right) + \left(\frac{20 \text{ mL}}{1 \text{ kg}} \times 35 \text{ kg}\right) = 2200 \text{ mL}$$

2.91

$$7.5 \text{ grains} \times \frac{1 \text{ fluidram}}{10 \text{ grains}} \times \frac{3.72 \text{ mL}}{1 \text{ fluidram}} = 2.8 \text{ mL}$$

2.92

$$\text{Heat (cal)} = \text{mass (g)} \times \text{temperature change (°C)} \times \text{specific heat} \left(\frac{\text{cal}}{\text{g} \cdot \text{°C}}\right)$$

for water: specific heat $= 1.00 \text{ cal} /(\text{g}\cdot\text{°C})$;

$$\text{mass} = 3.00 \text{ L} \times \frac{10^3 \text{ mL}}{1 \text{ L}} \times \frac{1.00 \text{ g}}{1 \text{ mL}} = 3.00 \times 10^3 \text{ g};$$
$$\text{temperature change} = 90.0\text{°C} - 18.0\text{°C} = 72.0\text{°C}$$

$$\text{calories needed} = 3.00 \times 10^3 \text{ g} \times 72.0\text{°C} \times \frac{1.00 \text{ cal}}{\text{g} \cdot \text{°C}} = 2.16 \times 10^5 \text{ cal} = 216 \text{ kcal}$$

$$216 \text{ kcal} \times \frac{1.0 \text{ tbsp}}{100 \text{ kcal}} = 2.2 \text{ tbsp butter}$$

2.93

$$\frac{15.28 \text{ lb}}{1 \text{ gal}} \times \frac{454 \text{ g}}{1 \text{ lb}} \times \frac{1 \text{ gal}}{3.7856 \text{ L}} \times \frac{1 \text{ L}}{1000 \text{ mL}} = \frac{1830 \text{ g}}{1000 \text{ mL}} = 1.83 \text{ g/mL}$$

2.94

$$9.40 \times 10^{10} \text{ lb} \times \frac{1 \text{ gal}}{15.28 \text{ lb}} \times \frac{3.7856 \text{ L}}{1 \text{ gal}} = 2.33 \times 10^{10} \text{ L}$$

2.95

$$0.22 \text{ in} \times \frac{25.4 \text{ mm}}{1 \text{ in}} = 5.6 \text{ mm}$$

2.96 (a)   (b)

$$\frac{200 \text{ mg}}{100 \text{ mL}} \times \frac{1000 \text{ mL}}{1 \text{ L}} = 2 \times 10^3 \frac{\text{mg}}{\text{L}} \qquad \frac{200 \text{ mg}}{100 \text{ mL}} \times \frac{10^3 \mu\text{g}}{\text{mg}} = 2 \times 10^3 \frac{\mu\text{g}}{\text{mL}}$$

(c)

$$\frac{200 \text{ mg}}{100 \text{ mL}} \times \frac{1 \text{ g}}{1000 \text{ mg}} \times \frac{1000 \text{ mL}}{1 \text{ L}} = 2 \frac{\text{g}}{\text{L}}$$

(d)

$$\frac{200 \text{ mg}}{100 \text{ mL}} \times \frac{10^6 \text{ng}}{1 \text{ mg}} \times \frac{1 \text{ mL}}{10^3 \mu\text{L}} = 2 \times 10^3 \frac{\text{ng}}{\mu\text{L}}$$

2.97 (a) Gallium is a metal.
(b) To find the density of gallium in g/cm^3, divide the mass in grams by the volume in cm^3.
Mass of Ga: 0.2133 lb x (454 g/ lb) = 96.84 g
Volume of Ga: (1.00 in. x 2.54 cm/in.)^3 = 16.39 cm^3

$$\frac{96.84 \text{ g}}{16.39 \text{ cm}^3} = 5.91 \frac{\text{g}}{\text{cm}^3}$$

2.98 The initial temperature: 293.2 K – 273.2 K = 20.0 K = 20.0°C
The temperature change: 3.0°F/min x 8.42 min = 25.3°F = 14.1°C (since a Celsius degree is 1.8 times larger than a Fahrenheit degree)
The final temperature: 20.0°C + 14.1°C = 34.1°C

2.99 At the crossover point, °F = °C.

$$°F = \left(\frac{9°F}{5°C} \times °C\right) + 32°F \qquad \text{If } °C = °F, °F = \frac{9}{5}°F + 32°$$

The crossover temperature is °F = °C = –40°

2.100 Strategy: Use the dimensions of the cork and of the lead to find their respective volumes. Multiply the volume of each substance by its density to arrive at the mass of each.
Volume of cork: 1.30 cm x 5.50 cm x 3.00 cm = 21.45 cm^3
Volume of lead: (1.15 cm)^3 = 1.521 cm^3

Mass of cork: Mass of lead:

$$21.45 \text{ cm}^3 \times \frac{0.235 \text{ g}}{1 \text{ cm}^3} = 5.04 \text{ g cork} \qquad 1.521 \text{ cm}^3 \times \frac{11.35 \text{ g}}{1 \text{ cm}^3} = 17.26 \text{ g lead}$$

Add the two masses, and divide by the sum of the two volumes to find the density of the combination.

$$\text{Density} = \frac{5.04\text{g} + 17.26 \text{ g}}{21.45 \text{ cm}^3 + 1.521 \text{ cm}^3} = \frac{22.30 \text{ g}}{22.97 \text{ cm}^3} = 0.971 \text{ g/cm}^3$$

The combination will float because its density is less than the density of water.

Self-Test for Chapter 2

1. Write the full name of these units:
   (a) μm   (b) dL   (c) Mg   (d) L   (e) ng

2. Write the abbreviation for each of the following units:
   (a) kiloliter   (b) picogram   (c) centimeter   (d) hectoliter

3. *Quantity*   *Significant Figures?*

   (a) 1.0037 g
   (b) 0.0080 L
   (c) 0.008 L
   (d) 2 aspirin
   (e) 273,000 mi

4. Express the following in scientific notation:
   (a) 0.000 070 3 g   (b) 137,100 m   (c) 0.011 L   (d) 18,371,008 mm
   How many significant figures do each of the above quantities have?

5. Round the following to three significant figures:
   (a) 807.3 L   (b) 4,773,112 people   (c) 0.00127 g   (d) 10370 μm
   Express each of the above quantities in scientific notation.

6. Convert the following quantities:
   (a) 256 g = _____ lb   (b) 417 mm = _____ m
   (c) 2.0 gallons = _____ L   (d) 2.17 m = _____ inches
   (e) 35°C = _____ °F   (f) 298 K = _____ °C
   (g) 175 mL = _____ fl oz   (h) 175 mg = _____ oz

7. If the specific heat of gold is 0.031 cal/g °C, how many calories does it take to heat 10 g of gold from 0°C to 100°C?

8. If the density of ethanol is 0.7893 g/mL, how many grams does 275 mL of ethanol weigh?

Multiple choice:

1. Which of the following is not an SI unit?
   (a) kg   (b) L   (c) m   (d) K

2. How many significant figures does the number 4500 have?
   (a) 2   (b) 3   (c) 4   (d) any of the above

3. Which of the following quantities is larger than a gram?
   (a) 1 nanogram   (b) 1 dekagram   (c) 1 centigram   (d) 1 microgram

4. Which of the following conversion factors do you need for converting 3.2 lb/qt to kg/L?
   (a) $\dfrac{1\ kg}{2.2\ lb} \times \dfrac{1\ qt}{0.95\ L}$ (b) $\dfrac{2.2\ lb}{1\ kg} \times \dfrac{1\ qt}{0.95\ L}$ (c) $\dfrac{2.2\ lb}{1\ kg} \times \dfrac{0.95\ L}{1\ qt}$ (d) $\dfrac{1\ kg}{2.2\ lb} \times \dfrac{0.95\ L}{1\ qt}$

5. When written in scientific notation, the exponent in the number 0.000 007 316 is:
   (a) 10^{-6} (b) 6   (c) −6   (d) 10^{6}

6. Which of the following is more dense than water?
    (a) ice   (b) human fat   (c) ethyl alcohol   (d) urine

7. How many zeros are significant in the number 0.007 006?
    (a) 1   (b) 2   (c) 3   (d) 4

8. Which of the following temperatures doesn't equal the other two?
    (a) 100°F   (b) 37.8°C   (c) 297.8 K

9. To measure the amount of heat needed to raise the temperature of a given substance, you need to know all of the following except:
    (a) the mass of the substance   (b) the specific heat of the substance   (c) the density of the substance   (d) the initial and final temperature

10. For which of the following is specific gravity a useful measure?
    (a) to describe the amount of solids in urine   (b) to indicate the amount of heat necessary to raise the temperature of one gram of a substance by 1°   (c) to determine if an object will float on water

Complete the following sentences:

1. The fundamental SI units are _____, _____, _____, and _____.

2. Physical quantities are described by a _____ and a _____.

3. The amount of heat necessary to raise the temperature of one gram of a substance by one degree is the substance's _____ _____.

4. The prefix _____ indicates 10^{-9}.

5. The number 0.003 06 has _____ significant figures.

6. To convert from grams to pounds, use the conversion factor _____.

7. Two units for measuring energy are _____ and _____.

8. The method used for converting units is called the _____ _____ method.

9. _____ _____ is the density of a substance divided by the density of water at the same temperature.

10. The size of a degree is the same in both _____ and _____ units.

Tell whether the following statements are true or false:

1.   The units of specific gravity are g/mL.

2.   The number 0.07350 has four significant figures.

3.   The sum of 57.35 and 1.3 has four significant figures.

4.   The conversion factor 1.057 quarts/liter is used to convert quarts into liters.

5.   Some SI units are the same as metric units.

6.   The temperature in °C is always a larger number than the temperature in K.

7.   Raising the temperature of 10 g of water by 10°C takes less heat than raising the temperature of 10 g of gold by 10°C.

8.   Mass measures the amount of matter in an object.

9.   Ice is more dense than water.

10.   A nanogram is larger than a picogram.

Match each entry on the left with its partner on the right:

1.   5003   (a) Converts pounds to kilograms

2.   1 centimeter   (b) 0.1 grams

3. $\dfrac{2.205\ lb}{1\ kg}$ (c) Larger than one inch

4.   263 K   (d) −17.8°C

5.   1 dekagram   (e) Four significant figures

6.   0.0486   (f) SI unit of volume measure

7.   1 m^3 (g) Converts kilograms to pounds

8.   1 liter   (h) 10 grams

9.   1 decimeter   (i) −10°C

10. $\dfrac{1\ kg}{2.205\ lb}$ (j) Smaller than one inch

11.   0°F   (k) Metric unit of volume measure

12.   1 decigram   (l) Three significant figures

Chapter 3 – Atoms and the Periodic Table

Chapter Outline

I. Atomic Theory (Sections 3.1–3.3).
    A. Fundamental assumptions about atoms (Section 3.1).
        1. All matter is composed of atoms.
        2. The atoms of each element are different from the atoms of all other elements.
        3. Chemical compounds consist of elements combined in definite proportions.
        4. Chemical reactions only change the way that atoms are combined in compounds; the atoms themselves are unchanged.
    B. Nature of the atom (Sections 3.1).
        1. Atoms are very small ($\sim 10^{-11}$ m in diameter).
        2. Atoms consist of subatomic particles.
            a. A proton is positively charged and has a mass of 1.6726×10^{-24} g.
            b. A neutron has no charge and has a mass of 1.6749×10^{-24} g.
            c. An electron is negatively charged and has a mass of 9.1093×10^{-28} g.
        3. The masses of atoms are expressed in relative terms.
            a. Under this system, a carbon atom with 6 protons and 6 neutrons is given a mass of 12 atomic mass units (amu).
            b. Consequently, a proton and a neutron each have a mass of approximately 1 amu.
        4. Atoms are held together by the interplay of attractive and repulsive forces of positively charged protons and negatively charged electrons.
        5. Protons and neutrons are located in the nucleus of an atom, and electrons move around the nucleus.
    C. Composition of atoms (Section 3.2).
        1. Atoms of different elements differ from each other according to how many protons they contain.
        2. Z stands for the number of protons an atom has and is known as the atomic number.
        3. The number of electrons in an atom is the same as the number of protons.
        4. The mass number A stands for the number of protons plus the number of neutrons.
    D. Isotopes and atomic weight (Section 3.3).
        1. Isotopes are atoms of the same element that differ only in the number of neutrons.
        2. Isotopes are represented by showing the mass number as a superscript on the left side of the symbol for the chemical element; the atomic number is shown as a subscript on the left side.
        3. Most elements occur in nature as a mixture of isotopes.
        4. The atomic weight of an element can be calculated if the percent of contributing isotopes is known.
II. The Periodic Table (Sections 3.4–3.5).
    A. The periodic table is a classification of elements according to their properties (Section 3.4).
        1. Elements are arranged by increasing atomic number in 7 rows called periods.
        2. Elements are also arranged in 18 vertical columns called groups.
            a. Main group elements occur on the left and right of the periodic table.
            b. Transition-metal groups occur in the middle of the periodic table.
            c. Inner transition-metal groups are shown separately at the bottom.
        3. The elements in each group have similar chemical properties.

B. Chemical characteristics of groups of elements (Section 3.5).
   1. Group 1A – Alkali metals (Li, Na, K, Rb, Cs).
      a. Shiny, soft, low-melting.
      b. React violently with water.
   2. Group 2A – Alkaline earth metals (Be, Mg, Ca, Sr, Ba, Rd).
      a. Lustrous, shiny metals.
      b. Less reactive than metals in group 1A.
   3. Group 7A – Halogens (F, Cl, Br, I).
      a. Corrosive, nonmetals.
      b. Found in nature only in combination with other elements.
   4. Group 8A – Noble gases (He, Ne, Ar, Kr, Xe, Ra). Extremely unreactive.
C. Neighboring groups have similar behaviors.
   1. Metals.
      a. Found on the left side of the periodic table.
      b. Silvery, ductile, good conductors.
   2. Nonmetals.
      a. Found on the right side of the periodic table.
      b. Eleven of the 17 nonmetals are gases.
      c. Solid nonmetals are brittle and are poor conductors of electricity.
   3. Metalloids.
      a. Occur on the boundary between metals and nonmetals.
      b. Have intermediate chemical behavior.
III. Electrons (Sections 3.6–3.8).
  A. The properties of the elements are due to the distribution of electrons in their atoms (Section 3.6).
  B. Location of electrons .
   1. Electrons are located in specific regions about the nucleus.
   2. The energies of electrons are quantized.
   3. The locations of electrons are described by shells, subshells and orbitals.
      a. Shells.
         i. Shells describe the energy level of an electron.
         ii. Shells are related to an electron's distance from the nucleus.
      b. Subshells.
         i. Subshells describe the energy levels of electrons within each shell.
         ii. The four types of subshell are *s, p, d* and *f.*
      c. Orbitals.
         i. Orbitals are the regions of subshells in which electrons of a specific energy can be found.
         ii. An *s* subshell contains one orbital, a *p* subshell contains three orbitals, a *d* subshell contains five orbitals and an *f* subshell contains seven orbitals.
         iii. Each orbital can hold two electrons, and they must be of opposite spin.
   4. Since the exact position of electrons can't be specified, orbitals are often referred to as electron clouds.
  C. Electron configurations (Section 3.7)
   1. The specific arrangement of electrons in an atom's shells and subshells is known as its electron configuration.
   2. This arrangement can be predicted by using three rules.
      a. Electrons occupy the lowest orbitals available within each subshell
         Within each shell, the subshell energy levels increase in the order *s,p,d,f.*
      b. If two or more orbitals have the same energy, each orbital is half filled before any orbital is completely filled.
      c. Each orbital can hold only two electrons, and they must be of opposite spin.
   3. The number of electrons in each subshell is given by a superscript.

D. Electron configuration and the periodic table (Section 3.8).
   1. Properties of elements are determined by their location in the periodic table.
   2. The periodic table is divided into four regions.
      a. Elements in groups 1A and 2A are *s*-block elements because they result from filling *s* orbitals.
      b. Groups 3A–8A are *p*-block elements.
      c. Transition metals are *d*-block elements.
      d. Inner transition metals are *f*-block elements.
   3. The periodic table can be used as a reminder of the order of orbital filling.
   4. Elements within a group of the periodic table have similar electronic configurations of their valence electronic shells and thus similar chemical behavior.

Solutions to Chapter 3 Problems

3.1 Use the conversion factor that relates mass and amu.

$$2.33 \times 10^{-23} \text{ g} \times \frac{1 \text{ amu}}{1.660\ 539 \times 10^{-24} \text{ g}} = 14.0 \text{ amu}$$

3.2

$$10^5 \text{ atoms} \times \frac{197 \text{ amu}}{1 \text{ atom}} \times \frac{1.660\ 539 \times 10^{-24} \text{ g}}{1 \text{ amu}} = 3.27 \times 10^{-17} \text{ g}$$

3.3

(a) $1.0 \text{ g} \times \dfrac{1 \text{ amu}}{1.660\ 539 \times 10^{-24} \text{ g}} \times \dfrac{1 \text{ atom}}{1.0 \text{ amu}} = 6.0 \times 10^{23}$ atoms

(b) $12.0 \text{ g} \times \dfrac{1 \text{ amu}}{1.660\ 539 \times 10^{-24} \text{ g}} \times \dfrac{1 \text{ atom}}{12.0 \text{ amu}} = 6.02 \times 10^{23}$ atoms

(c) $23.0 \text{ g} \times \dfrac{1 \text{ amu}}{1.660\ 539 \times 10^{-24} \text{ g}} \times \dfrac{1 \text{ atom}}{23.0 \text{ amu}} = 6.02 \times 10^{23}$ atoms

3.4 In each of the above examples, the mass in grams equals the mass in amu, and the number of atoms in all three samples is identical.

3.5 (a) Re   (b) Li   (c) Te

3.6 Recall that the *atomic number* (Z) shows how many protons an atom contains. Uranium, with an atomic number of 92 thus contains 92 protons.
Uranium also contains 92 electrons, since the number of protons equals the number of electrons.
The *mass number* (A) shows the number of protons plus the number of neutrons. To find the number of neutrons in an atom, subtract the atomic number from the mass number.
For uranium: Mass number – atomic number = 235 – 92 = 143
The uranium atom has 143 neutrons.

3.7 From Problem 3.6, we know that $A - Z$ = number of neutrons
In this problem, $A = 52$, and the number of neutrons = 28. Thus $Z = 24$. The table of elements in the front of the book shows that chromium is the element with $Z = 24$.

3.8 Both chlorine isotopes have 17 protons. The chlorine isotope with mass number 35 has 18 neutrons, and the isotope with mass number 37 has 20 neutrons.
The atomic number is written at the lower left of the element symbol, and the mass number is written at the upper left.

$$^{35}_{17}Cl \quad \text{and} \quad ^{37}_{17}Cl$$

3.9

(a) $^{11}_{5}B$ (b) $^{56}_{26}Fe$

3.10 Aluminum is in group 3A (or 13) and period 3.

3.11 The group 1B element in period 5 is silver (Ag).
The group 2A element in period 4 is calcium (Ca).

3.12

Group 5A Element	Period
Nitrogen (N)	2
Phosphorus (P)	3
Arsenic (As)	4
Antimony (Sb)	5
Bismuth (Bi)	6

3.13 Metals: titanium (Ti), scandium (Sc)
Nonmetals: selenium (Se), argon (Ar)
Metalloids: tellurium (Te), astatine (At)

3.14 (a) Krypton – (ii) nonmetal, (iv) main group element, (v) noble gas
(b) Strontium – (i) metal, (iv) main group element
(c) Nitrogen – (ii) nonmetal, (iv) main group element
(d) Cobalt – (i) metal, (iii) transition element

3.15 The element zinc (Zn) is a metal found in period 4, group 2B (or 12).

3.16 (a) A maximum of six electrons can occupy a $3p$ subshell.
(b) A maximum of two electrons can occupy a $2s$ subshell.
(c) A maximum of six electrons can occupy a $2p$ subshell.

3.17 Ten electrons are present in this atom, which is neon.

3.18 Twelve electrons are present in this atom, which is magnesium.

3.19 To find the electron configuration of an atom, first find its atomic number. For C (carbon), the atomic number is 6; thus carbon has 6 protons and 6 electrons. Then, assign electrons to the proper orbitals. For carbon, the electron configuration is $1s^2 2s^2 2p^2$.

Element	Atomic Number	Electron Configuration
(a) C (carbon)	6	$1s^2 2s^2 2p^2$
(b) Na (sodium)	11	$1s^2 2s^2 2p^6 3s^1$
(c) Cl (chlorine)	17	$1s^2 2s^2 2p^6 3s^2 3p^5$
(d) Ca (calcium)	20	$1s^2 2s^2 2p^6 3s^2 3p^6 4s^2$

3.20   Element 14 (Si): $1s^2\, 2s^2\, 2p^6\, 3s^2\, 3p^2$
Element 36 (Kr): $1s^2\, 2s^2\, 2p^6\, 3s^2\, 3p^6\, 4s^2\, 3d^{10}\, 4p^6$

3.21   Element 33 (As): $1s^2\, 2s^2\, 2p^6\, 3s^2\, 3p^6\, 4s^2\, 3d^{10}\, 4p^3$. The $4p$ subshell is incompletely filled. Notice that only one electron occupies each orbital of the $4p$ subshell.

 $4p^3$

3.22   The atom has 31 electrons (and 31 protons) and can be identified as gallium.

3.23   In group 2A, all elements have the outer-shell configuration ns^2.

3.24   Chlorine, in group 7A (17), has seventeen electrons. Its electron configuration is $1s^2\, 2s^2\, 2p^6\, 3s^2\, 3p^5$. Two electrons are in shell 1, eight electrons are in shell 2, and seven electrons are in shell 3. The outer shell configuration is $3s^2\, 3p^5$.

3.25   The elements form group 6A (16) and have the general configuration ns^2np^4.

Understanding Key Concepts

3.26   Drawing (a) represents a p orbital (dumbbell-shaped), and drawing (b) represents an s orbital (spherical).

3.27

3.28

3.29   The element marked in red is a gas (argon – a group 8A noble gas)
The element marked in blue has atomic number 42 (molybdenum).
All elements in group 1A have chemical behavior similar to the element marked in green (cesium). These include lithium, sodium, potassium and rubidium.

3.30

two *p* electrons
in 3rd shell

$ns^2 np^5$

3.31 Nickel (Z = 28) is the element whose orbital-filling diagram is shown. Notice that it is possible to identify the element by counting its electrons, which equal the number of protons and give the value of Z.

Atomic Theory and the Composition of Atoms

3.32 (1) All matter is composed of atoms.
(2) The atoms of a given element differ from the atoms of all other elements.
(3) Chemical compounds consist of atoms combined in specific proportions.
(4) Chemical reactions change only the way that atoms are combined in compounds; the atoms themselves are unchanged.

3.33 Atoms of different elements differ in the number of protons and electrons they have.

3.34

(a) Bi: $208.9804 \text{ amu} \times \dfrac{1.660\ 539 \times 10^{-24} \text{ g}}{1 \text{ amu}} = 3.47020 \times 10^{-22} \text{ g}$

(b) Xe: $131.29 \text{ amu} \times \dfrac{1.660\ 539 \times 10^{-24} \text{ g}}{1 \text{ amu}} = 2.1801 \times 10^{-22} \text{ g}$

(c) He: $4.0026 \text{ amu} \times \dfrac{1.660\ 539 \times 10^{-24} \text{ g}}{1 \text{ amu}} = 6.6465 \times 10^{-24} \text{ g}$

3.35

(a) $\dfrac{2.66 \times 10^{-23} \text{ g}}{1 \text{ atom O}} \times \dfrac{1 \text{ amu}}{1.660\ 539 \times 10^{-24} \text{ g}} = 16.0 \text{ amu}$

(b) $\dfrac{1.31 \times 10^{-22} \text{ g}}{1 \text{ atom Br}} \times \dfrac{1 \text{ amu}}{1.660\ 539 \times 10^{-24} \text{ g}} = 78.9 \text{ amu}$

3.36

$6.022 \times 10^{23} \text{ atoms} \times \dfrac{1.660\ 539 \times 10^{-24} \text{ g}}{1 \text{ amu}} \times \dfrac{14.01 \text{ amu}}{1 \text{ atom}} = 14.01 \text{ g}$

3.37

$$6.022 \times 10^{23} \text{ atoms } \times \frac{1.660\ 539 \times 10^{-24} \text{ g}}{1 \text{ amu}} \times \frac{12.00 \text{ amu}}{1 \text{ atom}} = 12.00 \text{ g}$$

3.38

$$15.99 \text{ g } \times \frac{1 \text{ amu}}{1.660\ 539 \times 10^{-24} \text{ g}} \times \frac{1 \text{ atom}}{15.99 \text{ amu}} = 6.022 \times 10^{23} \text{ atoms}$$

3.39

$$22.99 \text{ g } \times \frac{1 \text{ amu}}{1.660\ 539 \times 10^{-24} \text{ g}} \times \frac{1 \text{ atom}}{22.99 \text{ amu}} = 6.022 \times 10^{23} \text{ atoms}$$

3.40

Particle	Mass in amu	Charge
Proton	1.007 276	+1
Neutron	1.008 665	0
Electron	$5.485\ 799 \times 10^{-4}$	−1

3.41 Protons and neutrons are found in a dense central region called the nucleus. Electrons move about the nucleus in large, specifically defined regions.

3.42 (a) Potassium (K)   (b) Tin (Sn)   (c) Zinc (Zn)

3.43 (a) Phosphorus (P)   (b) Niobium (Nb)   (c) Cobalt (Co)

3.44

Isotope	Argon-36	Argon-38	Argon-40
Number of neutrons	18	20	22

3.45

Isotope	(a) $^{27}_{13}$Al	(b) $^{28}_{14}$Si	(c) $^{11}_{5}$B	(d) $^{115}_{47}$Ag
Number of protons	13	14	5	47
Number of neutrons	14	14	6	68
Number of electrons	13	14	5	47

3.46 Symbols (a) and (c) represent isotopes because they have the same atomic number, but different mass numbers.

3.47

(a) $^{206}_{84}$Po   (b) $^{224}_{88}$Ra   (c) $^{197}_{79}$Au   (d) $^{84}_{36}$Kr

3.48 (a) Fluorine-19   (b) Neon-19   (c) Fluorine-21   (d) Magnesium-21

3.49 (a) 122   (b) 136   (c) 118   (d) 48

3.50

(a) $^{14}_{6}$C   (b) $^{39}_{19}$K   (c) $^{20}_{10}$Ne

3.51

(a) $^{20}_{10}\text{Ne}$ (b) $^{51}_{23}\text{V}$ (c) $^{56}_{26}\text{Fe}$

3.52

$^{12}_{6}\text{C}$ – six neutrons $^{13}_{6}\text{C}$ – seven neutrons $^{14}_{6}\text{C}$ – eight neutrons

3.53

$^{131}_{53}\text{I}$

3.54   Contribution from ^{63}Cu: 69.17% of 62.93 amu = 43.53 amu
Contribution from ^{65}Cu: 30.83% of 64.93 amu = 20.02 amu

_____

Atomic weight = 63.55 amu

3.55   Contribution from ^{107}Ag: 51.84% of 106.91 amu =   55.42 amu
Contribution from ^{109}Ag: 48.16% of 108.90 amu =   52.45 amu

_____

Atomic weight = 107.87 amu

The Periodic Table

3.56   The third period in the periodic table contains eight elements because eight electrons are needed to fill the *s* subshell (2 electrons)and *p* subshell (6 electrons) of the third shell.

3.57   The fourth period contains 18 elements because 18 electrons are needed to fill the *s* subshell (2 electrons) and *p* subshell (6 electrons) of the fourth shell, plus the *d* subshell (10 electrons) of the third shell.

3.58   Americium (Am; atomic number 95) is a metal.

3.59   Antimony (Sb; atomic number 51) is a metalloid.

3.60   (a) They are metals.
(b) They are transition metals.
(c) The 3*d* subshell is being filled.

3.61   (a) Calcium: (i) metal (iv) main group element (vii) alkaline earth metal
(b) Palladium: (i) metal (iii) transition element
(c) Carbon: (ii) nonmetal (iv) main group element
(d) Radon: (ii) nonmetal (iv) main group element (v) noble gas

3.62   Selenium is chemically similar to sulfur.

3.63   Gallium is chemically similar to aluminum.

3.64   The alkali metal family is composed of lithium, sodium, potassium, rubidium, cesium and francium.

3.65   Fluorine, chlorine, bromine, iodine, and astatine make up the halogen family.

Electron Configuration

3.66   A maximum of two electrons can go into an orbital.

3.67   An s orbital is spherical and centered on the nucleus. A p orbital is dumbbell-shaped, and the three p orbitals extend out from the nucleus at 90° angles to each other.

3.68   First shell – 2 electrons
Second shell – 8 electrons
Third shell – 18 electrons

3.69   The third shell contains nine orbitals: one s orbital, three p orbitals, and five d orbitals. The fourth shell contains sixteen orbitals: one s orbital, three p orbitals, five d orbitals, and seven f orbitals.

3.70   Ten electrons are present; the element is neon.

3.71   Fourteen electrons are present; the element is silicon.

3.72   (a) sulfur   (b) bromine   (c) silicon

$$\underset{3p^4}{\underline{\uparrow\downarrow}\ \underline{\uparrow}\ \underline{\uparrow}} \qquad \underset{4p^5}{\underline{\uparrow\downarrow}\ \underline{\uparrow\downarrow}\ \underline{\uparrow}} \qquad \underset{3p^{2-}}{\underline{\uparrow}\ \underline{\uparrow}}$$

3.73   *Element*   *Electron configuration*

Element	Electron configuration
(a) Mg	$1s^2\ 2s^2\ 2p^6\ 3s^2$
(b) S	$1s^2\ 2s^2\ 2p^6\ 3s^2\ 3p^4$
(c) Ne	$1s^2\ 2s^2\ 2p^6$
(d) Cd	$1s^2\ 2s^2\ 2p^6\ 3s^2\ 3p^6\ 4s^2\ 3d^{10}\ 4p^6\ 5s^2\ 4d^{10}$

3.74   The element with atomic number 20 (Ca) has two electrons in its outer shell.

3.75   The number of valence electrons for elements in a main group is the same as the group number. Thus, group 4A elements have four valence electrons.

3.76   Beryllium: $2s$ Arsenic: $4p$

3.77   Group 6A has the configuration $ns^2\ np^4$.

3.78

Element	(a) Kr	(b) C	(c) Ca	(d) K	(e) B	(f) Cl
# of valence-shell electrons	8	4	2	1	3	7

3.79   Group 7A: $ns^2\ np^5$ Group 1A: ns^1

Applications

3.80 A normal light microscope can't reach the degree of precision of a scanning tunneling microscope.

3.81 Scanning tunnelling microscopes are used in studies of surface chemistry and to determine the structures of complex biological molecules.

3.82 Hydrogen and helium are the first two elements made in stars.

3.83 A gravitational collapse of stars results in the synthesis of elements heavier than iron and produces an explosion known as a supernova.

3.84

	Higher energy	*Lower energy*
(a)	ultraviolet	infrared
(b)	gamma waves	microwaves
(c)	X rays	visible light

3.85 Ultraviolet rays are more damaging to the skin because they are of higher energy than visible light.

General Questions and Problems

3.86 Helium, neon, argon, krypton, xenon, and radon make up the noble gas family.

3.87 Hydrogen can be placed in group 1A because it has one electron in its outermost (only) electron shell. Hydrogen can be placed in group 7A because only one electron is needed to fill its outermost (only) electron shell.

3.88 Tellurium has a greater atomic weight because its nuclei contain, on the average, more neutrons than an iodine nucleus.

3.89 The new element beneath francium has the atomic number 119.

3.90 Pb: $1s^2\ 2s^2\ 2p^6\ 3s^2\ 3p^6\ 4s^2\ 3d^{10}\ 4p^6\ 5s^2\ 4d^{10}\ 5p^6\ 6s^2\ 4f^{14}\ 5d^{10}\ 6p^2$
Shell 1: 2 electrons   Shell 2: 8 electrons   Shell 3: 18 electrons
Shell 4: 32 electrons   Shell 5: 18 electrons   Shell 6: 4 electrons

3.91 Highest-energy occupied subshell: (a) Ar – $3p$ (b) Mg – $3s$ (c) Tc – $4d$ (d) Fe – $3d$

3.92 Contribution from ^{79}Br: 50.69% of 78.92 amu = 40.00 amu
Contribution from ^{81}Br: 49.31% of 80.91 amu = 39.90 amu

Atomic weight = 79.90 amu

3.93 Contribution from ^{24}Mg: 78.99% of 23.99 amu = 18.95 amu
Contribution from ^{25}Mg: 10.00% of 24.99 amu =   2.50 amu
Contribution from ^{26}Mg: 11.01% of 25.98 amu =   2.86 amu

Atomic weight = 24.31 amu

3.94 One atom of carbon weighs more than one atom of hydrogen because the mass of carbon (12 amu) is greater than the mass of hydrogen (1 amu).

3.95 10^{23} atoms of carbon weigh 12 x 10^{23} amu, and 10^{23} atoms of hydrogen weigh 1 x 10^{23} amu. Thus the weight of carbon is 12 times greater than that of hydrogen.

3.96 If 10^{23} hydrogen atoms weigh about 1 g, then 10^{23} carbon atoms will weigh about 12 g.

3.97 Using the above reasoning, we predict that 10^{23} sodium atoms will weigh about 23 grams.

3.98 The unidentified element is strontium, which occurs directly below calcium in group 2A and thus has similar chemical behavior. Strontium is a metal, has 38 protons, and is in the fifth period.

3.99 The outer-shell electrons of titanium are in the 4s orbital.

3.100 Zirconium, a metal, has an electron configuration by shell of 2 8 18 10 2.

3.101

$$8.6 \text{ mg } \times \frac{1 \text{ g}}{10^3 \text{ mg}} \times \frac{1 \text{ amu}}{1.660\ 539 \times 10^{-24} \text{ g}} \times \frac{1 \text{ atom}}{40.08 \text{ amu}} = 1.3 \times 10^{20} \text{ atoms}$$

3.102 (a) Electrons must fill the 4s subshell before entering the 3d subshell. The correct configuration:

$$1s^2\ 2s^2\ 2p^6\ 3s^2\ 3p^6\ 4s^2\ 3d^8$$

(b) Electrons must fill the 2s subshell before entering the 2p subshell. The correct configuration:

$$1s^2\ 2s^2\ 2p^3$$

(c) Silicon has fourteen electrons. The correct configuration:

$$1s^2\ 2s^2\ 2p^6\ 3s^2\ \underset{3p}{\uparrow\ \uparrow\ \_}$$

(d) The 3s electrons must have opposite spins. The correct configuration:

$$1s^2\ 2s^2\ 2p^6\ \underset{3s}{\uparrow\downarrow}$$

3.103 Count the electrons in each example to arrive at the atomic number. Then look up the answer in the periodic table.
(a) Cu   (b) Mo

3.104 The last orbital filled in element 118 is 7p.

Self-Test for Chapter 3

Multiple choice:

1. Which of the following is a metalloid?
   (a) Carbon   (b) Aluminum   (c) Silicon   (d) Phosphorus

2. Which of the following has a partially filled d subshell?
   (a) Calcium   (b) Vanadium   (c) Zinc   (d) Arsenic

3. Which of the following is not a part of atomic theory?
   (a) All metal is composed of atoms.   (b) The atoms of each element are different from the atoms of other elements.   (c) In chemical compounds, atoms are combined in specific proportions.   (d) Chemical reactions only change the way that atoms are combined.

4. How many isotopes of hydrogen are there?
   (a) one   (b) two   (c) three   (d) can't be determined

5. What holds protons and neutrons together in the nucleus?
   (a) attraction   (b) repulsion   (c) electrons   (d) internuclear forces

6. Which of the following has a mass number of 33?
   (a) $^{74}_{33}As$ (b) $^{35}_{17}Cl$ (c) $^{32}_{16}S$ (d) $^{33}_{16}S$

7. In which order are subshells usually filled?
   (a) s, p, d, f (b) d, f, p, s (c) s, p, f, d (d) s, d, p, f

8. An element with atomic number 38 is likely to be:
   (a) an alkali metal   (b) an alkaline earth metal   (c) a transition metal   (d) a metalloid

9. The element that has atomic weight = 91 and has 40 electrons is:
   (a) Protactinium   (b) Niobium   (c) Antimony   (d) Zirconium

10. The element that has electron configuration $1s^2\,2s^2\,2p^6\,3s^2\,3p^6\,4s^2\,3d^7$ is:
    (a) Copper   (b) Rhodium   (c) Arsenic   (d) Cobalt

11. An element that has electrons in its f subshell is:
    (a) Europium   (b) Technetium   (c) Antimony   (d) Xenon

12. $^{195}_{78}X$ is the symbol for:
    (a) Gold   (b) Platinum   (c) Iridium   (d) Iron

Complete the following statements:

1. A _____ orbital is dumbbell-shaped.

2. An atomic mass unit is also known as a _____.

3. The nucleus of an atom is made up of _____ and _____.

4.   The _____ _____ indicates the number of protons in an atom.

5.   The electrons in an atom are grouped by energy into _____.

6.   Elements belonging to the same _____ have similar chemical properties.

7.   The atomic number of aluminum is _____.

8.   Protons, neutrons, and electrons are known as _____ _____.

9.   Atoms having the same number of protons but different numbers of neutrons are called _____.

10.   The third shell contains _____ electrons.

11.   The word _____ means that electrons can have certain energy values and no others.

Tell whether the following statements are true or false:

1.   Bismuth is a metal.

2.   The mass of an electron is approximately 1 amu.

3.   A 4s electron is higher in energy than a 3d electron.

4.   Isotopes have the same number of protons but different numbers of neutrons.

5.   An atom's atomic number indicates the number of protons and neutrons the atom has.

6.   Elements in group 2A are more reactive than elements in group 1A.

7.   Elements in the same period have similar chemical properties.

8.   More elements are metals than are nonmetals.

9.   All compounds consist of atoms combined in specific proportions.

10.   A subshell contains only two electrons.

11.   An element can have the same number of protons, neutrons and electrons.

12.   Atomic weight always increases with atomic number.

Match the items on the left with those on the right.

1. $1s^2\, 2s^2$ (a) Mendeleev

2. Group   (b) Number of protons in an element

3. Atomic mass unit   (c) Reactive metals

4. Formulated the periodic   (d) Average mass of a large number of an
    table   element's atoms

5. Neutron   (e) Column in the periodic table

6. $^{28}_{14}\text{Si}$ (f) Row in the periodic table

7. Group 1A   (g) Element with atomic mass of 14 amu

8. Atomic number   (h) Electron configuration of beryllium

9. $^{29}_{14}\text{Si}$ (i) Element having 15 neutrons

10. Atomic weight   (j) Subatomic particle with zero charge

11. $^{14}_{7}\text{N}$ (k) Dalton

12. Period   (l) Element with atomic number 14

Chapter Outline

I. Ions (Sections 4.1–4.2).
   A. Ions are formed when a neutral atom either gains an electron (to form an anion) or loses an electron (to form a cation).
      1. Ionization energy measures the ease with which an atom gives up an electron.
         a. Energy must be supplied in order to remove an electron.
         b. Elements on the far left of the periodic table have smaller ionization energies and lose electrons more easily.
         c. Elements on the far right of the periodic table have larger ionization energies and lose electrons with difficulty.
      2. Electron affinity measures the ease with which an atom gains an electron.
         a. Energy is released when an atom gains an electron.
         b. Elements on the far right of the periodic table have larger electron affinities and gain electrons easily.
         c. Elements on the far left of the periodic table have smaller electron affinities and gain electrons less easily.
   B. Main group elements in the middle of the periodic table neither lose or gain electrons easily.
II. Formation of ionic compounds (Sections 4.3–4.6).
   A. Compounds formed between an element on the far left side of the periodic table and an element on the far right of the periodic table are electronically neutral (Section 4.3).
      1. These compounds consist of a large number of cations and anions packed together in a regular arrangement in a crystal.
      2. The bonds between ions in the crystal are known as ionic bonds.
      3. The crystal is known as an ionic solid.
   B. Properties of ionic compounds (Section 4.4)
      1. Ionic compounds are crystalline.
      2. Ionic compounds conduct electricity.
      3. Ionic compounds are high-melting.
      4. Many, but not all, ionic compounds are water-soluble.
   C. The Octet Rule (Sections 4.5–4.6).
      1. Main group elements undergo reactions that leave them with eight valence electrons – an octet (Section 4.5).
      2. The valence electrons in an ionic compound can be represented by electron dots (Section 4.6).
III. Ions of some common elements (Sections 4.7–4.9).
   A. Cations (Section 4.7)

      1. Group 1A $M\cdot \longrightarrow M^+ + e^-$

      2. Group 2A $\cdot M\cdot \longrightarrow M^{2+} + 2e^-$
      3. Group 3A Al^{3+} is the only common cation.
      4. Transition metals often form more than one cation.

B. Anions.

   1. Group 6A $:\overset{\cdot}{X}: + 2\,e^- \longrightarrow :\overset{\cdot\cdot}{\underset{\cdot\cdot}{X}}:^{2-}$

   2. Group 7A $:\overset{\cdot}{\underset{\cdot\cdot}{X}}: + e^- \longrightarrow :\overset{\cdot\cdot}{\underset{\cdot\cdot}{X}}:^{-}$

C. Group 4A, Group 5A and Group 8A elements don't usually form cations or anions.
D. Naming ions (Section 4.8).
   1. Main group cations are named by identifying the metal and then adding the word "ion".
   2. Transition metal cations are named by identifying the metal, specifying the charge and adding the word "ion".
   3. Anions are named by replacing the end of the name of the element with "-ide" and adding the word "ion".
   4. Polyatomic ions (Section 4.9).
      a. Polyatomic ions are composed of more than one atom.
      b. Subscripts in polyatomic ions indicate how many of each ion are present in the formula unit (no subscripts are necessary if only one ion is present).
      c. The names of polyatomic ions should be memorized.
IV. Ionic compounds (Sections 4.10–4.12).
   A. Formulas of ionic compounds (Section 4.10).
      1. Formulas are written so that the number of positive charges equals the number of negative charges.
         a. Cations are listed first, anions second.
         b. It is not necessary to write the charges of the ions.
         c. Use parentheses around a polyatomic ion if it has a subscript.
      2. A formula unit shows the simplest neutral unit of an ionic compound.
   B. Naming ionic compounds (Section 4.11).
      Ionic compounds are named by citing the cation and then the anion, with a space between the two words.
   C. Acids and bases (Section 4.12).
      1. Acids are compounds that provide H^+ ions in solution.
      2. Bases are compounds that provide OH^- ions in solution.
      3. Acids and bases can each provide more than one H^+ or OH^- ion in solution.

Solutions to Chapter 4 Problems

4.1   The Mg^{2+} ion is a cation.

4.2   The O^{2-} ion is an anion.

4.3   Figure 4.1 shows approximate ionization energies for argon and krypton. In line with this trend, it is predicted that the ionization energy of xenon should be somewhat less than that of krypton but greater than the ionization energy of most other elements.

4.4   (a) According to Figure 4.1a, B ($Z = 5$) loses an electron more easily than Be ($Z = 4$).
       (b) Ca ($Z = 20$) loses an electron more easily than Co ($Z = 27$).
       (c) Sc ($Z = 21$) loses an electron more easily than Se($Z = 34$).

4.5 (a) According to Figure 4.1, H gains an electron more easily than He. Because the electron affinity for He is zero, it does not accept an electron.

(b) S gains an electron more easily than Si.

(c) Na gains an electron slightly more easily than Mg. Because both electron affinities are close to zero, neither element accepts an electron readily.

4.6 Potassium (atomic number 19): $1s^2\,2s^2\,2p^6\,3s^2\,3p^6\,4s^1$
Argon (atomic number 18): $1s^2\,2s^2\,2p^6\,3s^2\,3p^6$
Potassium can attain the noble-gas configuration of argon by losing an electron from its $4s$ subshell, forming the K^+ cation.

4.7 Aluminum (atomic number 13): $1s^2\,2s^2\,2p^6\,3s^2\,3p^1$
Neon (atomic number 10): $1s^2\,2s^2\,2p^6$
Aluminum can attain the noble-gas configuration of neon by losing three electrons, two from its $3s$ subshell and one from its $3p$ subshell, resulting in the formation of the Al^{3+} ion.

4.8 Oxygen atom (atomic number 8): $1s^2\,2s^2\,2p^4$
Neon atom (atomic number 10): $1s^2\,2s^2\,2p^6$
Oxygen can attain the noble-gas configuration of neon by gaining two electrons in its $2p$ subshell.

4.9

·Ẍ·

4.10

:Ṛn: ·Pb·   :Ẍe: ·Ra·

4.11

(a) :S̈e· + 2e⁻ ⟶ :S̈e:²⁻ ;   Se + 2e⁻ ⟶ Se^{2-}

(b) ·Ba· ⟶ Ba^{2+} + 2e⁻ ;   Ba ⟶ Ba^{2+} + 2e⁻

(c) :Ḃr· + e⁻ ⟶ :B̈r:⁻ ;   Br + e⁻ ⟶ Br^-

4.12 Molybdenum, a transition metal, is more likely to form a cation than an anion.

4.13 Strontium loses two electrons to form the Sr^{2+} cation, and bromine gains an electron to form the Br^- anion. Only chromium, a transition metal, can form more than one cation.

4.14 (a) Al^{+2} is not likely to form because loss of two electrons doesn't give a cation with a noble-gas configuration. Al^{+3} is the cation that forms from the loss of three electrons from the outermost subshells of aluminum.

(b) O^- doesn't form because it is one electron short of having a noble-gas configuration. O^{2-} is the ion that is formed from oxygen.

(c) Se^{2-} has a noble-gas configuration and is produced by the gain of two electrons by selenium.

4.15 (a) Cu^{2+} copper(II) ion (cupric ion)   (b) F^- fluoride ion
(c) Mg^{2+} magnesium ion   (d) S^{2-} sulfide ion

4.16 (a) Ag^+ (b) Fe^{2+} (c) Cu^+ (d) Te^{2-}

4.17 Na^+ sodium ion K^+ potassium ion
Ca^{2+} calcium ion Cl^- chloride ion

4.18 (a) NO_3^- nitrate ion   (b) CN^- cyanide ion
(c) OH^- hydroxide ion   (d) HPO_4^{2-} hydrogen phosphate ion

4.19 (a) HCO_3^- bicarbonate ion   (b) NH_4^+ ammonium ion
(c) PO_4^{3-} phosphate ion   (d) MnO_4^- permanganate ion

4.20 (a) The two ions are Ag^+ and I^-. Since they have the same charge, only one of each ion is
needed. The formula is AgI.
(b) Ions: Ag^+, O^{2-}. Two Ag^+ ions will balance the O^{2-} ion. The formula is Ag_2O.
(c) The ions are Ag^+ and PO_4^{3-}. Three Ag^+ ions are needed to balance the PO_4^{3-} anion.
The formula is Ag_3PO_4.

4.21 (a) Na_2SO_4 (b) $FeSO_4$ (c) $Cr_2(SO_4)_3$

4.22 $(NH_4)_2CO_3$

4.23 $Al_2(SO_4)_3$, $Al(CH_3CO_2)_3$

4.24 Use the periodic table to identify the elements present, and use the rules described in
Section 4.10 to write the formulas. The formulas are K_2S (blue) and $BaBr_2$ (red).

4.25 $BaSO_4$. One barium ion is present for each sulfate ion.

4.26 Ag_2S – silver(I) sulfide. The charge on silver is +1.

4.27 (a) CuO copper(II) oxide   (b) $Ca(CN)_2$ calcium cyanide
(c) $NaNO_3$ sodium nitrate   (d) Cu_2SO_4 copper(I) sulfate
(e) Li_3PO_4 lithium phosphate   (f) NH_4Cl ammonium chloride

4.28 (a) $Ba(OH)_2$ (b) $CuCO_3$ (c) $Mg(HCO_3)_2$ (d) CuF (e) $Fe_2(SO_4)_3$
(f) $Fe(NO_3)_2$

4.29 Acids provide H^+ ions when dissolved in water.
Bases provide OH^- ions when dissolved in water.

Acids: HF $\xrightarrow{\text{dissolve in water}}$ H^+ + F^-

HCN $\xrightarrow{\text{dissolve in water}}$ H^+ + CN^-

Bases: $Ca(OH)_2$ $\xrightarrow{\text{dissolve in water}}$ Ca^{2+} + $2\ OH^-$

LiOH $\xrightarrow{\text{dissolve in water}}$ Li^+ + OH^-

4.30   Solution (a) represents HCl; the drawing shows that there are equal numbers of cations and anions in solution. Solution (b) represents H_2SO_4; two cations are present for each anion.

Understanding Key Concepts

4.31

■ elements that form only one type of cation

▨ elements that commonly form anions

□ elements that can form more than one type of cation

4.32

▥ elements that commonly form +2 ions

▤ elements that commonly form −2 ions

▨ an element that forms a +3 ion

4.33   Drawing (a) shows an ion that has one more electron than proton and thus represents an F^- ion.
Drawing (b) represents sodium, a neutral atom.
Drawing (c) represents Ca^{2+}, an ion with two more protons than electrons.

4.34   Drawing (a) represents a sodium atom, and drawing (b) represents an Na^+ ion. The Na atom is larger because its $3s$ electron lies in an orbital that is farther from the nucleus.

4.35   Drawing (a) represents a chlorine atom, and drawing (b) represents a Cl^- anion. The anion is larger because its extra electron is not as tightly held by the positively charged nucleus as are the electrons of the atom.

4.36   red – SrF_2 (strontium fluoride)   blue – Li_2S (lithium sulfide)
green – $AlBr_3$ (aluminum bromide)

4.37   Use the ratios of atoms to assign answers. Picture (a) represents PbO, because one cation is present for each anion. Picture (b) represents $ZnBr_2$, and (c) represents $CrCl_3$.

Ions and Ionic Bonding

4.38

(a) · Be ·   (b) :Ne: (c) · Sr ·   (d) · Al ·

4.39

(a) $:\overset{\cdot}{\underset{}{P}}\cdot$ (b) $:\overset{\cdot}{\underset{\cdot\cdot}{S}}\cdot$ (c) $:\overset{\cdot\cdot}{\underset{\cdot\cdot}{Cl}}\cdot$ (d) $\cdot Ba\cdot$

4.40 (a) $Ca \rightarrow Ca^{2+} + 2\,e^-$ (b) $Au \rightarrow Au^+ + e^-$
(c) $F + e^- \rightarrow F^-$ (d) $Cr \rightarrow Cr^{3+} + 3\,e^-$

4.41 (a) $N + 3\,e^- \rightarrow N^{3-}$ (b) $Li \rightarrow Li^+ + e^-$
(c) $Ti \rightarrow Ti^{2+} + 2\,e^-$ (d) $Au \rightarrow Au^{3+} + 3\,e^-$

4.42 (a) False. A cation is formed by *loss* of one or more electrons from an atom. (b), (c) False. Group 4A elements rarely form ions. (d) True.

4.43 (a) False. Ions have a regular arrangement in ionic solids.   (b) False. Ions vary in size. (c) True.   (d) False. Ionic solids have high melting points and boiling points.

Ions and the Octet Rule

4.44 The *octet rule* states that main-group atoms undergo reactions in order to achieve a noble-gas electron configuration with eight outer-shell electrons.

4.45 Electrons belonging to hydrogen and helium occupy the first shell, which can hold only two electrons. Thus, even though H^- has the configuration of a noble gas (He), it can't have an electron octet.

4.46 An ion with 34 protons and 36 electrons has a –2 charge.

4.47 An ion with 11 protons and 10 electrons has a +1 charge.

4.48 (a) $X^{2+} = Sr^{2+}$; $X = Sr$ The strontium ion has the same electron configuration as the noble gas krypton.
(b) $X^- = Br^-$; $X = Br$ The bromide ion also has the same electron configuration as the noble gas krypton.

4.49 $Z^{3+} = Cr^{3+}$. $Z = Cr$. The Z^{3+} cation has 24 protons and 21 electrons.

4.50 (a) Rb^+ $1s^2\,2s^2\,2p^6\,3s^2\,3p^6\,4s^2\,3d^{10}\,4p^6$
(b) Br^- $1s^2\,2s^2\,2p^6\,3s^2\,3p^6\,4s^2\,3d^{10}\,4p^6$
(c) S^{2-} $1s^2\,2s^2\,2p^6\,3s^2\,3p^6$
(d) Ba^{2+} $1s^2\,2s^2\,2p^6\,3s^2\,3p^6\,4s^2\,3d^{10}\,4p^6\,5s^2\,4d^{10}\,5p^6$
(e) Al^{3+} $1s^2\,2s^2\,2p^6$

4.51 (a) Ar   (b) He   (c) Ne   (d) Ne   (e) Ne

Periodic Properties and Ion Formation

4.52 (a) O   (b) Li   (c) Zn   (d) N

4.53 (a) O   (b) Br   (c) N

4.54 None of the ions are stable because all lack eight outer-shell electrons.

4.55 (a) Magnesium forms only the Mg^{2+} cation.
(b) Silicon does not form cations.
(c) Manganese, a transition metal, can form several different cations.

4.56 Cr^{2+}: $1s^2\,2s^2\,2p^6\,3s^2\,3p^6\,3d^4$
Cr^{3+}: $1s^2\,2s^2\,2p^6\,3s^2\,3p^6\,3d^3$

4.57 Co : $1s^2\,2s^2\,2p^6\,3s^2\,3p^6\,3d^7\,4s^2$
Co^{2+}: $1s^2\,2s^2\,2p^6\,3s^2\,3p^6\,3d^7$
Co^{3+}: $1s^2\,2s^2\,2p^6\,3s^2\,3p^6\,3d^6$

4.58 The ionization energy of Li^+ is much greater than that of Li. Li readily loses an electron to form an ion with eight outer-shell electrons, but Li^+ would need to lose one electron from a stable octet in order to form the Li^{2+} cation.

4.59 (a) $K \rightarrow K^+ + e^-$ loss of an electron by K
$K^+ + e^- \rightarrow K$ gain of an electron by K^+
(b) The second equation is the reverse of the first equation.
(c) Ionization energy of K = – (electron affinity of K^+)

Symbols, Formulas, and Names for Ions

4.60 (a) S^{2-} sulfide ion   (b) Sn^{2+} tin(II) ion   (c) Sr^{2+} strontium ion
(d) Mg^{2+} magnesium ion   (e) Au^+ gold(I) ion

4.61 (a) Cu^+ cuprous ion   copper(I) ion
(b) Fe^{3+} ferric ion   iron(III) ion
(c) Hg^{2+} mercuric ion   mercury(II) ion

4.62 (a) Se^{2-} (b) O^{2-} (c) Ag^+

4.63 (a) Fe^{2+} (b) Co^{2+} (c) Sn^{4+}

4.64 (a) OH^- (b) SO_4^{2-} (c) $CH_3CO_2^-$ (d) MnO_4^- (e) OCl^- (f) NO_3^-
(g) HCO_3^-

4.65 (a) NH_4^+ ammonium ion   (b) CN^- cyanide ion
(c) CO_3^{2-} carbonate ion   (d) HSO_4^- hydrogen sulfate anion or bisulfate anion

Names and Formulas For Ionic Compounds

4.66 (a) $Al(NO_3)_3$ (b) $AgNO_3$ (c) $Zn(NO_3)_2$ (d) $Ba(NO_3)_2$

4.67 (a) $SrCO_3$ (b) $Fe_2(CO_3)_3$ (c) $(NH_4)_2CO_3$ (d) $Sn(CO_3)_2$

4.68 (a) $NaHCO_3$ (b) KNO_3 (c) $CaCO_3$

4.69 (a) $Ca(OCl)_2$ (b) $CuSO_4$ (c) Na_3PO_4

4.70

	S^{2-}	Cl^-	$PO_4{}^{3-}$	$CO_3{}^{2-}$
Copper(II)	CuS	$CuCl_2$	$Cu_3(PO_4)_2$	$CuCO_3$
Ca^{2+}	CaS	$CaCl_2$	$Ca_3(PO_4)_2$	$CaCO_3$
$NH_4{}^+$	$(NH_4)_2S$	NH_4Cl	$(NH_4)_3PO_4$	$(NH_4)_2CO_3$
Ferric ion	Fe_2S_3	$FeCl_3$	$FePO_4$	$Fe_2(CO_3)_3$

4.71

	O^{2-}	$HSO_4{}^-$	$HPO_4{}^{2-}$	$Cr_2O_7{}^{2-}$
Na^+	Na_2O	$NaHSO_4$	Na_2HPO_4	$Na_2Cr_2O_7$
Zn^{2+}	ZnO	$Zn(HSO_4)_2$	$ZnHPO_4$	$ZnCr_2O_7$
$NH_4{}^+$	$(NH_4)_2O$	NH_4HSO_4	$(NH_4)_2HPO_4$	$(NH_4)_2Cr_2O_7$
Ferrous ion	FeO	$Fe(HSO_4)_2$	$FeHPO_4$	$FeCr_2O_7$

4.72 (a) $MgCO_3$ magnesium carbonate   (b) $Ca(CH_3CO_2)_2$ calcium acetate
(c) $AgCN$ silver(I) cyanide   (d) $Na_2Cr_2O_7$ sodium dichromate

4.73 (a) $Fe(OH)_3$ iron(III) hydroxide   (b) KNO_2 potassium nitrite
(c) $NaOCl$ sodium hypochlorite   (d) $Ba(MnO_4)_2$ barium permanganate

4.74 $Ca_3(PO_4)_2$ (d) is the correct formula because the six positive charges from the three Ca^{2+} ions are balanced by the six negative charges of the two $PO_4{}^{3-}$ ions.

4.75 (a) Na_2SO_4 (b) $Ba_3(PO_4)_2$ (c) $Ga_2(SO_4)_3$

Acids and Bases

4.76 An acid provides H^+ ions when dissolved in water. A base provides OH^- ions when dissolved in water.

4.77 Acids: HNO_2, HCN, CH_3CO_2H
Base: $Ca(OH)_2$

4.78

(a) HNO_2 $\xrightarrow{\text{dissolve in water}}$ H^+ + $NO_2{}^-$

(b) HCN $\xrightarrow{\text{dissolve in water}}$ H^+ + CN^-

(c) $Ca(OH)_2$ $\xrightarrow{\text{dissolve in water}}$ Ca^{2+} + $2\ OH^-$

(d) CH_3CO_2H $\xrightarrow{\text{dissolve in water}}$ H^+ + $CH_3CO_2{}^-$

4.79 (a) nitrite anion   (b) cyanide anion   (d) acetate anion

Applications

4.80 To a geologist, a mineral is a naturally occurring crystalline compound. To a nutritionist, a mineral is a metal ion essential for human health.

4.81 Salt is usually obtained by mining salt beds. It can also be obtained by evaporating sea water.

4.82 For most people, the effect of salt consumption on blood pressure elevation is slight, but a small proportion of people may suffer high blood pressure as a result of excessive salt consumption.

4.83 Most of the calcium present in the body is found in bones and teeth.

4.84 Sodium protects against fluid loss and is necessary for muscle contraction and transmission of nerve impulses.

4.85 Too little iron in the blood leads to anemia, which becomes more severe if blood is removed.

4.86

Ion	Name	Charge	Total charge
Ca^{2+}	calcium ion	2+	$10 \times (2+) = 20+$
PO_4^{3-}	phosphate ion	3–	$6 \times (3-) = 18-$
OH^-	hydroxide ion	1–	$2 \times (1-) = 2-$

The formula correctly represents a neutral compound because the number of positive charges equals the number of negative charges.

4.87 $Ca_{10}(PO_4)_6(OH)_2 + 2 F^- \rightarrow Ca_{10}(PO_4)_6F_2 + 2 OH^-$

General Questions and Problems

4.88 The hydride ion has the same electron configuration ($1s^2$) as the noble gas helium.

4.89 The H^- ion has a stable noble gas configuration, but the Li^- ion doesn't, and is thus likely to be unstable. (Notice in Figure 4.1 that the electron affinity of Li is very small, indicating that Li is unlikely to gain an electron to form Li^-.)

4.90 (a) CrO_3 (b) VCl_5 (c) MnO_2 (d) MoS_2

4.91 $Pb_3(AsO_4)_2$

4.92 (a) A gluconate ion has one negative charge.
(b) Three gluconate ions are in one formula unit of iron(III) gluconate, and the formula is $Fe(gluconate)_3$.

4.93 (a) Cu_3PO_4 copper(I) phosphate
(b) Na_2SO_4 sodium sulfate
(c) MnO_2 manganese(IV) oxide
(d) $AuCl_3$ gold(III) chloride
(e) $Pb(CO_3)_2$ lead(IV) carbonate
(f) Ni_2S_3 nickel(III) sulfide

4.94   (a) $Co(CN)_2$ (b) UO_3 (c) $SnSO_4$ (d) K_3PO_4 (e) Ca_3P_2 (f) $LiHSO_4$

4.95

Ion	Protons	Electrons	Neutrons
(a) $^{16}O^{2-}$	8	10	8
(b) $^{89}Y^{3+}$	39	36	50
(c) $^{133}Cs^+$	55	54	78
(d) $^{81}Br^-$	35	36	46

4.96   (a) X is likely to be a metal, because metals are more likely to form cations.
(b) Y is likely to be a nonmetal.
(c) The formula for the product is X_2Y_3.
(d) X is likely to be in Group 3A or Group 3B (or to be a transition metal) and Y is likely to be in Group 6A.

Self-Test for Chapter 4

Multiple choice:

1.   How many atoms does a formula unit of Li_2CO_3 contain?
     (a) 3   (b) 4   (c) 5   (d) 6

2.   How many ions are produced when a formula unit of Li_2CO_3 is dissolved in water?
     (a) 3   (b) 4   (c) 5   (d) 6

3.   Which of the following is not a property of ionic compounds?
     (a) crystalline   (b) conductor of electricity   (c) high melting   (d) 1:1 ratio of cations to anions

4.   Which of the following is the correct name for $Fe(NO_3)_3$?
     (a) Ferrous nitrate   (b) Iron nitrate   (c) Iron(III) nitrate   (d) Iron(II) nitrate

5.   Bromine has a:
     (a) large ionization energy and large electron affinity   (b) large ionization energy and small electron affinity   (c) small ionization energy and large electron affinity   (d) small ionization energy and small electron affinity

6. H_2CrO_4 is an acid that :
     (a) provides one H^+ ion when dissolved   (b) provides two H^+ ions when dissolved
     (c) provides one OH^- when dissolved   (d) H_2CrO_4 is not an acid

7.   An element that loses three electrons to attain the electron configuration of argon is:
     (a) Titanium   (b) Scandium   (c) Calcium   (d) Potassium

8.   The formula for gold(III) chloride is:
     (a) Au_3Cl (b) $AuCl$ (c) $AuCl_2$ (d) $AuCl_3$

9.   Which of the following anions is not biologically important?
     (a) Cl^- (b) Br^- (c) HCO_3^- (d) HPO_4^-

10. The redness of rubies is due to which ion?
     (a) Iron   (b) Titanium   (c) Aluminum   (d) Chromium

Complete the following sentences:

1. _____ _____ measures the ease with which an atom gives up an electron.

2. The name of K_3PO_4 is _____ _____.

3. Radium (atomic number 88) loses _____ electrons to achieve a noble-gas configuration.

4. NO_3^- is an example of a _____ ion.

5. The formulas of ionic compounds are _____ formulas.

6. Atoms of main-group elements tend to combine in chemical compounds so that they attain _____ outer-shell electrons.

7. A _____ provides OH^- ions in water.

8. _____ is the principal mineral component of bone.

9. Ionic compounds are usually _____ solids.

10. The first three elements in group _____A form neither cations nor anions.

Tell whether the following statements are true or false:

1. Zinc can form ions with different charges.

2. Na^+ and F^- have the same electron configuration.

3. Ionization energy measures the amount of energy released when an ion is formed from a neutral atom.

4. $Co(CO_3)_2$ is a possible compound.

5. A solution of H_3PO_4 contains only H^+ and $H_2PO_4^-$ ions.

6. Ionic crystals conduct electricity.

7. Cuprous ion is the same as copper(II) ion.

8. Many ionic compounds are not water-soluble.

9. Group 5A consists of metals and nonmetals.

10. Elements in group 7A have the largest ionization energies.

11. The octet rule is limited to main-group elements.

12. Both men and women suffer the same percent bone loss over their lifetimes.

Match each item on the left with its partner on the right:

1. $FeBr_2$ (a) sulfite anion

2. S^{2-} (b) electron-dot symbol

3. NH_4^+ (c) alkali metal

4. SO_3^{2-} (d) has the same electron configuration as Na^+

5. Ca   (e) iron(II) bromide

6. $FeBr_3$ (f) transition metal

7. Ar   (g) sulfate anion

8. ·Be·   (h) alkaline earth metal

9. Co   (i) has the same electron configuration as Cl^-

10. SO_4^{2-} (j) iron(III) bromide

11. Ne   (k) polyatomic cation

12. K   (l) sulfide anion

Chapter Outline

I. Covalent bonds (Sections 5.1–5.4).
   A Formation of covalent bonds (Section 5.1).
      1. Covalent bonds occur when two atoms share electrons.
      2. Electron sharing results from the overlap of orbitals of two atoms.
      3. The optimum distance between nuclei of two atoms is the bond length.
      4. Seven elements exist as diatomic molecules: H_2, N_2, O_2, F_2, Cl_2, Br_2, I_2.
   B. Covalent bonds and the periodic table (Section 5.2).
      1. Molecular compounds result when atoms form covalent bonds to another atom or to more than one atom.
      2 The octet rule states that each atom in a molecular compound shares the number of electrons necessary to achieve a noble-gas configuration.
      3 Most main-group elements form from one to four covalent bonds and obey the octet rule.
         a. Boron forms only three bonds because it has only 3 valence electrons.
         b. Sulfur and phosphorus may form 5 or 6 bonds if they use *d* orbitals.
   C. Multiple covalent bonds (Section 5.3).
      1. Some atoms can share more than one electron pair to form multiple bonds.
         a. A double bond is formed when two pairs are shared.
         b. A triple bond is formed when three pairs are shared.
      2. Even when multiple bonds occur, the atoms still obey the octet rule.
   D. Coordinate bonds occur when one atom donates both of the shared electrons (Section 5.4).
II. Formulas, structures and shapes (Sections 5.5–5.7).
   A. Formulas (Section 5.5).
      1. Molecular formulas show the numbers and kinds of atoms in one molecule of a compound.
      2. Structural formulas show how atoms are connected.
      3. Some larger organic molecules are written as condensed structures.
   B. Lewis structures are structural formulas that show electron lone pairs (Section 5.6).
      1. One approach to drawing Lewis structures involves knowing common bonding patterns.
      2. The other approach is a general method.
         a. Find the number of valence electrons for all atoms.
         b. Draw a line between each pair of connected atoms to represent an electron pair.
         c. Place lone pairs around all peripheral atoms to give them octets.
         d. Place remaining electrons around the central atom.
         e. If the central atom doesn't have an octet, use an electron pair from a neighboring atom to form a multiple bond to the central atom.
   C. Molecular shapes can be predicted by using the VSEPR model (Section 5.7).
      1. Draw a Lewis structure of the molecule, and identify the atom whose geometry you want to know.
      2. Count the number of charge clouds around the atom.
      3. Predict shape by assuming that the charge clouds orient in space so that they are as far apart as possible.
         a. If there are two charge clouds, the geometry is linear.
         b. If there are three charge clouds, the geometry is linear or bent.
         c. If there are four charge clouds, the geometry is tetrahedral, trigonal pyramidal or bent.

III. Polar covalent bonds (Sections 5.8–5.9).
    A. Polar covalent bonds occur when the electrons in a covalent bond are attracted more to one atom than another (Section 5.8).
       1. The ability of an atom to attract electrons is called electronegativity.
       2. Atoms with electronegativity differences < 1.9 form polar covalent bonds.
       3. Atoms with electronegativity differences > 1.9 form ionic bonds.
    B. Molecules containing polar covalent bonds can be polar (Section 5.9).
       1. Molecular polarity depends on both the presence of polar covalent bonds and on molecular shape.
       2. Polarity has a dramatic effect on molecular properties.
IV. Molecular compounds (Sections 5.10–5.11).
    A. Naming binary molecular compounds (Section 5.10).
       1. Name the first element in the compound, using a prefix if necessary.
       2. Name the second element, using an -ide ending and using a prefix if necessary.
    B. Properties of molecular compounds (Section 5.11).
       1. Molecular compounds are electrically neutral.
       2. Molecular compounds have low melting and boiling points.
       3. Molecular compounds may be solids, liquids or gases.

Solutions to Chapter 5 Problems

5.1

shared electron pair

Each iodine atom achieves the noble-gas configuration of xenon.

5.2   (a) PH_3 hydrogen – one covalent bond;   phosphorus – three covalent bonds
           (b) H_2Se hydrogen – one covalent bond;   selenium – two covalent bonds
           (c) HCl   hydrogen – one covalent bond;   chlorine – one covalent bond
           (d) SiF_4 fluorine – one covalent bond;   silicon – four covalent bonds

5.3   Lead is a member of group 4A and should form four covalent bonds, as do carbon and silicon. $PbCl_4$ is thus a more likely formula for a compound containing lead and chlorine than is $PbCl_5$.

5.4   (a) CH_2Cl_2. Carbon forms four covalent bonds. Two bonds form between carbon and hydrogen, and the other two form between carbon and chlorine.
           (b) BH_3. Boron forms three covalent bonds.
           (c) NI_3
           (d) $SiCl_4$

5.5   In acetic acid, all hydrogen atoms have two outer-shell electrons and all carbon and oxygen atoms have eight outer-shell electrons.

Acetic acid

5.6

H—C—C—C—C—H   Methyl ethyl ketone   H—C—C—C—C—H

Neither of the two circled atoms in the structure on the left has a complete octet, even when electrons not involved in bonding are considered. A double bond between carbon and oxygen allows all atoms to have electron octets.

5.7   C and N must be bonded to each other. After drawing the C–N bond and all bonds to hydrogens, two electrons remain; they are a lone pair on nitrogen. All atoms now have a noble-gas configuration.

CH_5N: 14 valence electrons

H—C—N—H

5.8

C_3H_8: 20 valence electrons

H—C—C—C—H

5.9

CH_2O: 12 valence electrons

H—C—H

5.10

(a) H—C—O—H

(b) :N≡C—C—H

(c) :Cl:—N—Cl: with :Cl:

5.11 (a) The molecular formula for methyl methacrylate is $C_6H_{10}O_2$.
(b) Methyl methacrylate has two double bonds and four electron lone pairs.

Methyl methacrylate

5.12   (a) For phosgene, $COCl_2$:

Step 1:   Total valence electrons –
$4 e^-$ (from C) + $6 e^-$ (from O) + $2 \times 7 e^-$ (from Cl) = $24 e^-$

Step 2:   Six electrons are involved in the covalent bonds.

$$\overset{\displaystyle O}{\underset{\displaystyle Cl-C-Cl}{|}}$$

Step 3:   The other 18 electrons are placed in nine lone pairs.

$$\overset{\displaystyle :\ddot{O}:}{\underset{\displaystyle :\ddot{C}l-C-\ddot{C}l:}{|}}$$

Step 4:   All electrons are used up in the above structure, but carbon doesn't have an electron octet, so one electron pair must be moved from oxygen to form a carbon-oxygen double bond.

Step 5:   The 24 electrons have been used up, and all atoms have a complete octet.

$$\overset{\displaystyle :\ddot{O}:}{\underset{\displaystyle :\ddot{C}l-C-\ddot{C}l:}{\|}}$$

(b) For OCl^-:

Step 1:   Total valence electrons –
$6 e^-$ (from O) + $7 e^-$ (from Cl) + $1 e^-$ (negative charge) = $14 e^-$

Step 2:   Two electrons used. O—Cl

Step 3:   Twelve additional electrons used. $:\ddot{O}-\ddot{C}l:^-$

Step 4:   The above structure uses fourteen valence electrons, and all atoms have complete octets.

(c) For H_2O_2:

Step 1: $2 e^-$ (from 2 H) + $2 \times 6 e^-$ (from O) = 14 electrons

Step 2:   Six electrons are involved in covalent bonds.   H—O—O—H

Step 3:   The other 8 electrons are placed in four lone pairs. $H-\ddot{O}-\ddot{O}-H$

Step 4:   The 14 electrons have been used up, and all atoms have complete octets.

(b) SCl_2 : 20 electrons

$$:\ddot{C}l-\ddot{S}-\ddot{C}l:$$

5.13

HNO_3 :   24 electrons

$$\overset{\displaystyle :\ddot{O}:}{\underset{\displaystyle :\ddot{O}-N-\ddot{O}-H}{\|}}$$

5.14 Carbon, the central atom, is surrounded by four bonds. Referring to Table 5.1, we see that chloroform has tetrahedral geometry.

 Chloroform

Each carbon of dichloroethylene is surrounded by three charge clouds. Dichloroethylene is planar, with 120° bond angles.

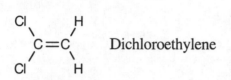 Dichloroethylene

5.15 Both ammonium ion and sulfate ion are tetrahedral.

5.16 Both molecules are bent and have bond angles of approximately 105°.

5.17

 Methionine

a. bent
b. tetrahedral
c. tetrahedral
d. planar triangular
e. pyramidal

5.18 Use Figure 5.7 to predict electronegativity:

Least electronegative ——————> *Most electronegative*

H (2.1), P (2.1) < S (2.5) < N (3.0) < O (3.5)

5.19

Electronegativity		Difference	Type of Bond
(a) I (2.5),	Cl (3.0)	0.5	polar covalent
(b) Li (1.0),	O (3.5)	2.5	ionic
(c) Br (2.8),	Br (2.8)	0	covalent
(d) P (2.1),	Br (2.8)	0.7	polar covalent

5.20

Electronegativity	Bond polarity
(a) F (4.0), S (2.5)	$\overset{\delta- \quad \delta+}{F—S}$
(b) P (2.1), O (3.5)	$\overset{\delta+ \quad \delta-}{P—O}$
(c) As (2.0), Cl (3.0)	$\overset{\delta+ \quad \delta-}{As—Cl}$

5.21

Formaldehyde is polar because of the polarity of the carbon-oxygen bond and because of the two electron lone pairs.

5.22   The $-CH_3$ portions of diethyl ether are tetrahedral. The C–O–C portion is bent, and has a bond angle of 112°. The molecule has the indicated polarity because of the polar C–O bonds and because of the two lone pairs of electrons.

5.23

The difference in electronegativity between Li (1.0) and C (2.5) indicates that the bond between them is polar covalent, with carbon the more electronegative atom. The electrostatic potential map shows that carbon is electron-rich (red) and lithium is electron-poor (blue).

5.24   (a) S_2Cl_2 Disulfur dichloride   (b) ICl   Iodine chloride
              (c) ICl_3 Iodine trichloride

5.25   (a) SeF_4 Selenium tetrafluoride   (b) P_2O_5 Diphosphorus pentoxide
              (c) BrF_3 Bromine trifluoride

Understanding Key Concepts

5.26 Drawing (a) represents an ionic compound because ions are held together by strong attractive forces in all directions. Drawing (b) represents a covalent compound because the covalent bonds that hold atoms together in a molecule are much stronger than the forces between molecules.

5.27 Drawing (a), which shows molecules composed of one sulfur atom and two oxygen atoms, depicts SO_2.

5.28 (a) tetrahedral geometry   (b) pyramidal geometry   (c) planar triangular geometry

5.29 All models except (c) represent a molecule with a tetrahedral central atom.

5.30

(a) (b)

Acetaminophen $C_8H_9NO_2$

(c) All carbons except for the starred carbon have planar triangular geometry.
The starred carbon has tetrahedral geometry.
Nitrogen has pyramidal geometry.

5.31

Vitamin C

5.32

(a) (b)

Thalidomide $C_{13}H_{10}N_2O_4$

(c) All carbons except for the starred carbons have planar triangular geometry.
The starred carbons have tetrahedral geometry.
The nitrogens have pyramidal geometry.

5.33

Acetamide

The electrostatic potential maps show that oxygen is the most electron-rich atom (red) in acetamide. The hydrogens are most electron-poor (blue).

Covalent Bonds

5.34   A covalent bond is a chemical bond in which two electrons are shared between two atoms. An ionic bond is formed by the attraction of a positively charged ion to a negatively charged ion. In an ionic bond, both electrons of the electron pair "belong" to the negatively charged ion.

5.35   When two atoms are far apart, neither feels the effect of the other. As the atoms move closer together, they are attracted to each other. Potential energy is at a minimum at a distance that is the bond length between the two atoms. If the atoms move closer to each other than the bond length, they repel each other, and potential energy increases.

5.36   (a) oxygen (i) (iv)   (b) potassium (iii)   (c) phosphorus (ii)
(d) iodine (i) (iv)   (e) hydrogen (i) (ii)   (f) cesium (iii)

5.37   Form covalent bonds: (b) carbon and fluorine, (d) silicon and fluorine

5.38   Tellurium, a group 6A element, forms two covalent bonds, as do oxygen, sulfur, and other members of group 6A.

5.39   Germanium, a group 4A element, forms four covalent bonds.

5.40   Coordinate covalent bonds: (b) $Cu(NH_3)_4^{2+}$ (c) NH_4^+

5.41   Coordinate covalent bonds: (c) H_3O^+

5.42   Since tin is a member of group 4A, it forms four covalent bonds. $SnCl_4$ is the most likely formula for a molecular compound of tin and chlorine.

5.43   A low-boiling, low-melting compound of gallium and chlorine is most likely covalent (ionic compounds are high-boiling and high-melting). Since gallium is a group 3A element, a likely formula is $GaCl_3$.

5.44   The indicated bond is coordinate covalent because both electrons in the bond come from nitrogen.

:N≡N—O: coordinate covalent

5.45 The indicated bond is coordinate covalent because both electrons in the bond come from sulfur.

Structural Formulas

5.46 (a) A *molecular formula* shows the numbers and kinds of atoms in a molecule; a *structural formula* shows how the atoms in a molecule are bonded to one another.
  (b) A *structural formula* shows the bonds between atoms; a *condensed structure* shows central atoms and the atoms connected to them written as groups but does not show bonds.
  (c) A *lone pair* of valence electrons is a pair that is not shared; a *shared pair* of electrons is shared between two atoms.

5.47 Two possible methods to distinguish between the compounds:
  (a) Take the melting point of the two compounds. The covalent solid melts at a lower temperature.
  (b) Try to dissolve the two solids in water. The ionic solid is more likely to be water-soluble than the covalent solid.

5.48 (a) N_2 – 10 valence electrons   (b) CO – 10 valence electrons
  (c) CH_3CH_2CHO – 24 valence electrons   (d) OF_2 – 20 valence electrons

5.49

  (a) : C≡O: (b) $CH_3\ddot{S}H$ (c) H—$\overset{..}{\underset{H}{O}}$—H   (d) H_3C—$\overset{..}{\underset{H}{N}}$—$CH_3$

5.50 A compound with the formula C_2H_8 can't exist because any structure drawn would violate the rules of valence.

5.51 Structure (a) is correct. Structure (b) has two carbons with incomplete octets. Structure (c) has one carbon with an incomplete octet and an oxygen bonded to three groups.

5.52

  (a)   (b)   (c)

  H—$\ddot{O}$—N=$\ddot{O}$ H—$\overset{H}{\underset{H}{C}}$—C≡N: H—$\ddot{F}$:

5.53

$$\left[\begin{array}{c} :\!\overset{\displaystyle :\!O\!:}{\underset{\displaystyle :\!\overset{..}{O}\!-\!N\!-\!\overset{..}{O}\!:}{\|}} \end{array}\right]^{-}$$

Each oxygen atom has eight protons, and nitrogen has seven, for a total of 31 protons. The structure shown for nitrate has 24 outer-shell electrons which, when added to the 8 inner-shell electrons, add up to 32 electrons. Since there is one more electron than proton, nitrate ion has a −1 charge.

5.54   (a) $CH_3CH_2CH_3$ (b) $H_2C=CHCH_3$ (c) CH_3CH_2Cl

5.55 CH_3CO_2H

Drawing Lewis Structures

5.56

(a), (b), (c), (d), (e), (f)

5.57

(a)   (b)   (c)

5.58

Ethanol

5.59

Dimethyl ether

5.60

Hydrazine

5.61

:Cl: :Cl:
   \   /
   C=C   Tetrachloroethylene contains a double bond.
   /   \
:Cl: :Cl:

5.62

S=C=S   Carbon disulfide contains two carbon-sulfur double bonds.

5.63

H—N—O—H
    |
    H

5.64 Cyanide ion has 4 inner-shell electrons, plus the 10 electrons pictured, for a total of 14 electrons. Together, carbon and nitrogen have 13 protons. Since there is one more electron than proton, cyanide ion has a charge of -1.

$$:C\equiv N:^-$$

5.65

(a) $\left[\begin{array}{c} :O: \\ \| \\ H-C-O: \end{array}\right]^-$ (b) $\left[\begin{array}{c} :O: \\ \| \\ :O-C-O: \end{array}\right]^{2-}$ (c) $\left[\begin{array}{c} :O: \\ | \\ :O-S-O: \end{array}\right]^{2-}$ (d) $\left[:S-C\equiv N:\right]^-$

Molecular Geometry

5.66 Use Table 5.1 to predict molecular geometry. **B** equals the number of bonds, and **E** equals the number of electron lone pairs:

Molecule	# of bonds	# of lone pairs	Shape	Bond angle
(a) AB_3	3	0	planar triangular	120°
(b) AB_2E	2	1	bent	120°

5.67 As in the previous problem, use Table 5.1.

Molecule	# of bonds	# of lone pairs	Shape	Bond angle
(a) AB_4	4	0	tetrahedral	109°
(b) AB_3E	3	1	pyramidal	109°
(c) AB_2E_2	2	2	bent	109°

5.68

(a)

bond angle = 109°

(b)

bond angle = 105°

(c)

bond angle = 120°

(d)

bond angle = 180°

(e)

bond angle = 120°

5.69

Molecule	# of bonding pairs around central atom	# of lone pairs	Shape	Bond angle
(a) SiF_4	4	0	tetrahedral	109°
(b) CF_2Cl_2	4	0	tetrahedral	109°
(c) SO_3	3*	0	planar triangular	120°
(d) BBr_3	3	0	planar triangular	120°
(e) NF_3	3	1	pyramidal	107°

* For determining shape, the double bond counts as one bond pair, and the number of bonds is three.

5.70

tetrahedral →   ← planar triangular

Alanine

5.71

Vinyl acetate

All carbons are planar triangular, except for the starred carbon, which is tetrahedral.

Polarity of Bonds and Molecules

5.72 The most electronegative elements are found on the upper right side of the periodic table. The least electronegative elements are found on the left side of the periodic table.

5.73 Using the periodic table, count up from element 114. Element 119 should occur under francium and accordingly should be one of the least electronegative elements, with an electronegativity of 0.8.

5.74 *Less electronegative* ———> *More electronegative*

$$K < Li < C < Br < Cl$$

5.75 *More electronegative* ———> *Less electronegative*

$$Cl > C > Cu > Ca > Cs$$

5.76

(a) $\overset{\delta+\ \ \delta-}{I—Br}$ (b) $\overset{\delta-\ \ \delta+}{O—H}$ (c) $\overset{\delta+\ \ \delta-}{C—F}$ (d) $\overset{\delta-\ \ \delta+}{N—C}$ (e) nonpolar

5.77

(a) $\overset{\delta-\ \ \delta+}{O—Br}$ (b) $\overset{\delta-\ \ \delta+}{N—H}$ (c) $\overset{\delta+\ \ \delta-}{P—O}$ (d) nonpolar   (e) $\overset{\delta-\ \ \delta+}{C—Li}$

5.78

Electronegativity		Difference	Type of bond
(a) Na (0.9) ,	F (4.0)	3.1	ionic
(b) C (2.5) ,	Cl (3.0)	0.5	polar covalent
(c) N (3.0) ,	H (2.1)	0.9	polar covalent
(d) Be (1.5) ,	Br (2.8)	1.3	polar covalent

5.79 Use Figure 5.5 to determine bond polarities

Least polar bonds ———> *Most polar bonds*

$$PH_3 < HCl < H_2O < CF_4$$

5.80 The individual bonds in BCl_3 are polar, but BCl_3 is nonpolar overall because all bond polarities cancel.

5.81

(a)   (b)   (c)   (d) nonpolar

polar   polar   polar

Names and Formulas of Molecular Compounds

5.82 (a) PI_3 phosphorus triiodide   (b) $AsCl_3$ arsenic trichloride
(c) P_4S_3 tetraphosphorus trisulfide   (d) Al_2F_6 dialuminum hexafluoride
(e) NI_3 nitrogen triiodide   (f) IF_7 iodine heptafluoride

5.83 (a) $SiCl_4$ silicon tetrachloride   (b) NaH   sodium hydride
(c) SbF_5 antimony pentafluoride   (d) OsO_4 osmium tetroxide

5.84 (a) NO_2 (b) SF_6 (c) BrI_5 (d) N_2O_3 (e) N_2O_4 (f) $AsCl_5$

5.85 (a) SeO_2 (b) XeO_4 (c) N_2S_5 (d) P_3Se_4

Applications

5.86 Carbon monoxide serves as a stimulus to production of cyclic GMP, which regulates many cellular functions. It is also involved with long-term memory and response to odors.

5.87 Carbon monoxide is toxic in high concentration because it irreversibly binds to hemoglobin and thus prevents transfer of oxygen to tissues.

5.88 A polymer is formed of many repeating units contained in a long chain.

5.89 Carbohydrates, proteins and DNA are all examples of polymers that occur in nature.

5.90 Chemical names are complicated because the name of each of the 20 million known chemicals must be unique and must contain enough information for chemists to identify the composition and structure of each chemical.

5.91 The name of a chemical gives no clue as to whether the chemical is natural or synthetic, although certain chemicals are unlikely to occur in nature.

General Questions and Problems

5.92 (a) It was thought that noble gases couldn't form bonds because they already had a full electron octet.

(b)

Xenon tetrafluoride

5.93

(a)

(b) The C=O carbon atoms have planar triangular geometry, and the other carbons have tetrahedral geometry.
(c) The C=O bonds are polar.

5.94 Consult Figure 5.4 for help.

(a) Carbon forms four bonds. The correct formula is CCl_4.
(b) Nitrogen forms three bonds. The correct formula is N_2H_4.
(c) Sulfur forms two bonds. The correct formula is H_2S.
(d) C_2OS *could* actually be correct (S=C=C=O), but compounds with such adjacent double bonds are rare. More likely is the formula COS, a structural relative of carbon dioxide (S=C=O).

5.95 (a) $CaCl_2$ (i)   (b) $Mg(NO_3)_2$ (i), (ii)   (c) BF_4^- (ii), (iii)   (d) CBr_4 (ii)

5.96

(a)

(b) Phosphonium ion is tetrahedral.

(c) Phosphorus donates its lone pair of electrons to H^+ to form a coordinate covalent bond.
(d) # of electrons: 15 (from P) + 3 (from 3 H) = 18
　　# of protons: 15 (from P) + 4 (from 4 H) = 19
PH_4^+ is positive because the number of protons exceeds the number of electrons by one.

5.97

Compound	Name
(a) $CaCl_2$	calcium chloride
(b) $TeCl_2$	tellurium dichloride
(c) BF_3	boron trifluoride
(d) $MgSO_4$	magnesium sulfate
(e) K_2O	potassium oxide
(f) FeF_3	iron(III) fluoride
(g) PF_3	phosphorus trifluoride

5.98

 Chloral hydrate

5.99

 Dichromate ion

5.100

 Oxalic acid

5.101

(a) $O=Se=O$

(b) KrF_2

5.102

(a)

(b)

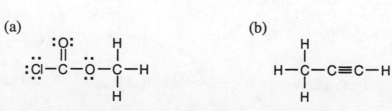

Self-Test for Chapter 5

Multiple choice:

1. Which of these diatomic molecules contains a double bond?
    (a) H_2 (b) I_2 (c) O_2 (d) N_2

2. Which of these molecules is pyramidal?
    (a) CBr_4 (b) $AlCl_3$ (c) SF_6 (d) PH_3

3. Choose the element that forms three covalent bonds and has one lone pair of electrons.
    (a) C   (b) N   (c) O   (d) F

4. How many charge clouds does the molecule H_2S have?
    (a) 2   (b) 3   (c) 4   (d) can't tell

5. Which of the following double bonds is not likely to be found in organic molecules?
    (a) O=O   (b) C=C   (c) C=O   (d) C=N

6. All of the following are true about the polyatomic ion BF_4^- except:
    (a) All atoms don't have electron octets.   (b) It has polar covalent bonds.   (c) It contains a coordinate covalent bond.   (d) It has a tetrahedral shape.

7. One of these molecules doesn't contain a polar covalent bond. Which is it?
    (a) $BeBr_2$ (b) PCl_3 (c) CO_2 (d) CS_2

8. Which of the following compounds is polar?
    (a) $BeBr_2$ (b) PCl_3 (c) CO_2 (d) CS_2

9. A name for S_2F_2 is:
    (a) Sulfur fluoride   (b) Sulfur difluoride   (c) Disulfur fluoride   (d) Disulfur difluoride

10. Which of the following is not true for molecular compounds?
    (a) They are water-soluble.   (b) They can be solids, liquids or gases.   (c) They are composed of nonmetals.   (d) They have low melting points.

Complete the following sentences:

1. An _____ element strongly attracts electrons.

2. A molecular compound that occurs in living organisms is called a _____ .

3. In Lewis structures, a line represents a _____ bond.

4. _____ and _____ are the most common triple bonds in chemical compounds.

5. The formula X_2 represents a _____ molecule.

6. A molecule whose central atom forms three bonds and has no lone pairs has a _____ _____ shape.

7. _____ orbitals in sulfur and phosphorus can be used for covalent bonds.

8. N_2 contains a _____ bond.

9.   _____ molecular compounds are formed from only two elements.

10.   Many molecular compounds are soluble in _____ liquids.

11.   Large organic molecules are often written as _____ structures.

Tell whether the following statements are true or false:

1. Br_2 is a molecular compound.

2.   Six electrons are used to form a triple bond.

3.   Coordinate covalent bonds occur only in cations or anions, not in neutral compounds.

4.   The first step in drawing a Lewis structure is to find the total number of electrons in the combined atoms.

5. $AlCl_3$ is a pyramidal molecule.

6.   The shape of ionic compounds can be predicted by the VSEPR model.

7.   Electronegativity decreases in going down the periodic table.

8. CI_4 contains polar covalent bonds.

9.   Both planar and bent molecules have bond angles of 120°.

10.   Group 7A elements can form more than one covalent bond.

11.   Bent compounds may have either 1 or 2 lone pairs.

Match each item on the left with its partner on the right:

1. BCl_3 (a) contains a pure covalent bond

2. planar molecule   (b) $BeCl_2$

3. bent molecule   (c) exception to the octet rule

4. Cl_2 (d) NH_3

5. BCl_4^- (e) contains a triple bond

6. NaI   (f) H_2O

7. $C \equiv O$ (g) contains a double bond

8. SF_6 (h) central atom doesn't have an electron octet

9. linear molecule   (i) contains an ionic bond

10. $O = C = O$ (j) $AlCl_3$

11. pyramidal molecule   (k) contains a coordinate covalent bond

12. CH_3Cl (l) contains a polar covalent bond

Chapter 6 – Chemical Reactions: Classification and Mass Relationships

Chapter Outline

I. Chemical equations (Sections 6.1–6.2).
  A. Writing chemical equations (Section 6.1).
    1. A chemical equation describes a chemical reaction.
        a. The reactants are written on the left.
        b. The products are written on the right.
        c. An arrow goes between them.
    2. The number and kinds of atoms must be the same on both sides of the equation. This is known as the Law of Conservation of Mass.
    3. Numbers that are placed in front of formulas are called coefficients.
    4. States of matter (s), (g), (l) are often placed after chemical formulas.
  B. Balancing chemical equations (Section 6.2).
    1. Write an unbalanced equation using the correct formulas for all substances.
    2. Add appropriate coefficients to balance the atoms of each type, one at a time.
    3. Check to make sure that the numbers and kinds of atoms are balanced.
    4. Make sure all coefficients are reduced to their lowest whole-number values.
II. Molar relationships (Sections 6.3–6.7).
  A. The mole (Section 6.3).
    1. Molecular weight is the sum of the atomic weights of atoms in a molecule.
    2. Formula weight is the sum of the atomic weights of atoms in a formula unit.
    3. One mole of any pure substance has a mass equal to its molecular or formula weight in grams.
        Avogadro's number (6.022×10^{23}), known as the mole, represents the number of formula units that has a mass in grams equal to its weight in amu.
  B. Mole–mass relationships (Section 6.4–6.6).
    1. Gram–mole conversions (Section 6.4).
        a. Molar mass is the mass in grams of one mole of any substance.
        b. Molar mass is a conversion factor that allows calculation of moles from grams and *vice versa*.
    2. Molar relationships from chemical equations (Section 6.5).
        a. The coefficients in an equation tell how many moles of reactant or product are involved in the reaction.
        b. The coefficients can be put in a mole ratio, which can be used as a conversion factor.
    3. Mass relationships (Section 6.6).
        a. Mole–mole conversions are made by using mole ratios.
        b. Mole–mass conversions are made by using molar mass as a conversion factor.
        c. Mass–mass conversions can be made by a mass–mole conversion of one substance, using mole ratios, and making a mole–mass conversion of the other substance.
    4. A summary of calculations using mole–mass relationships:
        a. Write the balanced equation.
        b. Choose mole–mass relationships and mole ratios to calculate the desired quantity.
        c. Set up the factor-label method to calculate the answer.
        d. Check the answer with a ballpark solution.
  C. Percent yield (Section 6.7).
    1. Percent yield = actual yield / theoretical yield x 100%
    2. Theoretical yield is found by using a mass–mass calculation.

III. Chemical reactions (Sections 6.8–6.13).
  A. Classes of chemical reactions (Section 6.8).
    1. Precipitation reactions occur when an insoluble solid is formed.
    2. Acid–base reactions occur when an acid and a base react to yield water and a salt.
    3. Redox reactions occur when electrons are transferred between reaction partners.
  B. Precipitation reactions (Section 6.9)
    1. To predict whether a precipitation reaction occurs, you must know the solubilities of the products.
    2. Table 6.1 gives general solubility rules to predict if a precipitation reaction will occur.
  C. Acid–base reactions (Section 6.10).
    1. Acid–base reactions are known as neutralization reactions because when reaction is complete the solution is neither acidic nor basic.
    2. An example: $HA(aq) + MOH(aq) \longrightarrow H_2O(l) + MA(aq)$
    3. When a carbonate or bicarbonate is one of the reactants, CO_2 is also produced.
  D. Net ionic equations (Section 6.11).
    1. A molecular equation shows reactants and products as molecules and doesn't indicate if they are ions.
    2. An ionic equation is written if ions are involved and shows all ionic reactants and products.
    3. A net ionic equation includes only the ions that undergo change and deletes spectator ions.
  E. Redox reactions (Sections 6.12–6.13).
    1. Definition of redox reactions (Section 6.12).
      a. A redox reaction occurs when electrons are transferred from one atom to another.
      b. The substance that loses electrons is oxidized and is known as the reducing agent.
      c. The substance that gains electrons is reduced and is known as the oxidizing agent.
      d. Redox reactions occur during corrosion, combustion, respiration, and photography.
    2. Recognizing redox reactions (Section 6.13).
      a. With some substances, it isn't obvious if a redox reaction has occurred.
      b. In a neutral compound, oxidation numbers are assigned to each element to indicate electron ownership.
      c. To assign oxidation numbers:
        i.   An element has an oxidation number of 0.
        ii. A monoatomic ion has an oxidation number equal to its charge.
        iii. In a molecular compound, an atom usually has the same oxidation number that it would have if it were a monoatomic ion.
        iv. The sum of the oxidation numbers in a neutral compound is zero.

Solutions to Chapter 6 Problems

6.1   (a) Solid cobalt(II) chloride plus gaseous hydrogen fluoride yield solid cobalt(II) fluoride plus gaseous hydrogen chloride.

(b) Aqueous lead(II) nitrate plus aqueous potassium iodide yield solid lead(II) iodide plus aqueous potassium nitrate.

6.2   An equation is balanced if the number and types of atoms on the left side equals the number and types of atoms on the right side.

(a) On the left: 2 H + Cl + K + O
   On the right: 2 H + Cl + K + O   The equation is balanced.

(b) On the left: 1 C + 4 H + 2 Cl
On the right: 1 C + 3 H + 3 Cl The equation is not balanced.
(c) Balanced
(d) Not balanced in H, O.

6.3   *Step 1*. Write the unbalanced equation

$$O_2 \longrightarrow O_3$$

Step 2. Balance the atoms of each type, one by one.

$$3\,O_2 \longrightarrow 2\,O_3 \quad \text{The equation is balanced.}$$

6.4   (a) $Ca(OH)_2 + 2\,HCl \longrightarrow CaCl_2 + 2\,H_2O$

(b) $4\,Al + 3\,O_2 \longrightarrow 2\,Al_2O_3$

(c) $2\,CH_3CH_3 + 7\,O_2 \longrightarrow 4\,CO_2 + 6\,H_2O$

(d) $2\,AgNO_3 + MgCl_2 \longrightarrow 2\,AgCl + Mg(NO_3)_2$

6.5   *Step 1*. $A + B_2 \longrightarrow A_2B_2$

Step 2. $2\,A + B_2 \longrightarrow A_2B_2$ The equation is balanced.

6.6   (a) For ibuprofen, $C_{13}H_{18}O_2$:

at. wt of 13 C = 13 x 12.0 amu = 156.0 amu
at. wt of 18 H = 18 x 1.0 amu =   18.0 amu
at. wt of 2 O =   2 x 16.0 amu =   32.0 amu
MW of $C_{13}H_{18}O_2$ = 206.0 amu

(b) For phenobarbital, $C_{12}H_{12}N_2O_3$:

at. wt of 12 C = 12 x 12.0 amu = 144.0 amu
at. wt of 12 H = 12 x 1.0 amu =   12.0 amu
at. wt of 2 N =   2 x 14.0 amu −   28.0 amu
at. wt of 3 O =   3 x 16.0 amu =   48.0 amu
MW of $C_{12}H_{12}N_2O_3$ = 232.0 amu

6.7   at. wt of 6 C = 6 x 12.0 amu =   72.0 amu
at. wt of 8 H = 8 x 1.0 amu =   8.0 amu
at. wt of 6 O = 6 x 16.0 amu =   96.0 amu

MW of $C_6H_8O_6$ = 176.0 amu

Since the molecular weight of ascorbic acid is 176.0 amu, 6.022×10^{23} molecules have a mass of 176 g.

$$500 \text{ mg ascorbic acid } \times \frac{1\text{ g}}{10^3\text{ mg}} \times \frac{6.022 \times 10^{23}\text{ molecules}}{176\text{ g}} = 1.71 \times 10^{21} \text{ molecules}$$

A 500 mg tablet contains 1.71×10^{21} molecules of ascorbic acid.

6.8   at. wt of 9 C = 9 x 12.0 amu =   108.0 amu
at. wt of 8 H = 8 x 1.0 amu =   8.0 amu
at. wt of 4 O = 4 x 16.0 amu =   64.0 amu

MW of $C_9H_8O_4$ =   180.0 amu

$$5.0 \times 10^{20} \text{ molecules } \times \frac{180.0 \text{ g}}{1 \text{ mol}} \times \frac{1 \text{ mol}}{6.022 \times 10^{23} \text{molecules}} = 0.15 \text{ g}$$

5.0×10^{23} molecules of aspirin weigh 0.15 g

6.9

Cytosine $C_4H_5N_3O$

at. wt of 4 C =   4 x 12.0 amu =   48.0 amu
at. wt of 5 H =   5 x 1.0 amu   =   5.0 amu
at. wt of 3 N =   3 x 14.0 amu =   42.0 amu
at. wt of 1 O =   1 x 16.0 amu =   16.0 amu

MW of $C_4H_5N_3O$ = 111.0 amu

6.10   Molar mass of C_2H_6O = 46.0 g/mol

$$10.0 \text{ g } \times \frac{1 \text{ mol}}{46.0 \text{ g}} = 0.217 \text{ mol in a 10.0 g sample}$$

Ballpark check: The sample size, 10.0 g, is about 1/5 mol, or about 0.2 mol.

$$0.10 \text{ mol } \times \frac{46.0 \text{ g}}{1 \text{ mol}} = 4.6 \text{ g in a 0.10 mol sample}$$

6.11   Molar mass of acetaminophen = 151 g

$$0.0225 \text{ mol } \times \frac{151 \text{ g}}{1 \text{ mol}} = 3.40 \text{ g}$$

5.00 g acetaminophen weighs more than 0.0225 mol.

6.12 (a) $Ni(s) + 2\ HCl(aq) \longrightarrow NiCl_2(aq) + H_2(g)$

$$9.81\ \text{mol HCl} \times \frac{1\ \text{mol Ni}}{2\ \text{mol HCl}} = 4.90\ \text{mol Ni}$$

(b) $6.00\ \text{mol Ni} \times \dfrac{1\ \text{mol NiCl}_2}{1\ \text{mol Ni}} = 6.00\ \text{mol NiCl}_2$ from $6.00\ \text{mol Ni}$

$$12.00\ \text{mol HCl} \times \frac{1\ \text{mol NiCl}_2}{2\ \text{mol HCl}} = 6.00\ \text{mol NiCl}_2 \text{ from } 12.00\ \text{mol HCl}$$

$6.00\ \text{mol NiCl}_2$ can be formed from $6.00\ \text{mol Ni}$ and $12.00\ \text{mol HCl}$.

6.13 $6\ CO_2 + 6\ H_2O \longrightarrow C_6H_{12}O_6 + 6\ O_2$

$$15.0\ \text{mol glucose} \times \frac{6\ \text{mol CO}_2}{1\ \text{mol glucose}} = 90.0\ \text{mol CO}_2$$

6.14 (a) This is a mole-to-mole problem.

$$9.90\ \text{mol SiO}_2 \times \frac{4\ \text{mol HF}}{1\ \text{mol SiO}_2} = 39.6\ \text{mol HF}$$

(b) This is a mass-to-mass problem.

$$23.0\ \text{g SiO}_2 \times \frac{1\ \text{mol SiO}_2}{60.1\ \text{g SiO}_2} \times \frac{2\ \text{mol H}_2\text{O}}{1\ \text{mol SiO}_2} \times \frac{18.0\ \text{g H}_2\text{O}}{1\ \text{mol H}_2\text{O}} = 13.8\ \text{g H}_2\text{O}$$

Ballpark check: About 1/3 mol SiO_2 is used to produce 2/3 mol H_2O. Since the molar mass of H_2O is 18 g, we expect about 12 g H_2O, which is reasonably close to the calculated answer.

6.15 For WO_3:

$$5.00\ \text{g W} \times \frac{1\ \text{mol W}}{183.8\ \text{g W}} \times \frac{1\ \text{mol WO}_3}{1\ \text{mol W}} \times \frac{231.8\ \text{g WO}_3}{1\ \text{mol WO}_3} = 6.31\ \text{g WO}_3$$

For H_2:

$$5.00\ \text{g W} \times \frac{1\ \text{mol W}}{183.8\ \text{g W}} \times \frac{3\ \text{mol H}_2}{1\ \text{mol W}} \times \frac{2.02\ \text{g H}_2}{1\ \text{mol H}_2} = 0.165\ \text{g H}_2$$

$6.31\ \text{g WO}_3$ and $0.165\ \text{g H}_2$ are needed to produce $5.00\ \text{g W}$.

Ballpark check: About 3/4 of the mass of WO_3 is composed of W. Thus, 5.00 g W comes from about 4/3 x 5.00 g W = 6.33 g WO_3, a result almost identical to the calculated result.

6.16 The molar mass of ethylene is 28.0 g/mol; the molar mass of ethyl chloride is 64.5 g/mol.

$$19.4 \text{ g ethylene} \times \frac{1 \text{ mol ethylene}}{28.0 \text{ g ethylene}} \times \frac{1 \text{ mol ethyl chloride}}{1 \text{ mol ethylene}} \times \frac{64.5 \text{ g ethyl chloride}}{1 \text{ mol ethyl chloride}}$$

$$= 44.7 \text{ g ethyl chloride}$$

$$\frac{25.5 \text{ g ethyl chloride actually formed}}{44.7 \text{ g theoretical yield of ethyl chloride}} \times 100 \% = 57.0 \%$$

Ballpark check: The amount of ethylene reactant corresponds to about 2/3 mol. The theoretical yield of product is about 2/3 mol ethyl chloride (somewhat more than 40 g). Since the actual yield is 25.5 g, the percent yield should be around 60%.

6.17 Note: to save space, ethylene oxide will be represented as EO, and ethylene glycol as EG.

$$35.0 \text{ g EO} \times \frac{1 \text{ mol EO}}{44.0 \text{ g EO}} \times \frac{1 \text{ mol EG}}{1 \text{ mol EO}} \times \frac{62.0 \text{ g EG}}{1 \text{ mol EG}} = 49.3 \text{ g ethylene glycol}$$

This quantity represents the maximum possible amount of ethylene glycol that can be produced. If the reaction occurs in 96.0% yield, then 49.3 g EG x 0.960 = 47.3 g EG is actually formed.

Ballpark check: A bit less than 3/4 mol EO is used to produce the same number of mol of EG, corresponding to about 45 g EG, close to the calculated result. The percent yield is also in close agreement.

6.18 (a) $AgNO_3(aq) + KCl(aq) \longrightarrow AgCl(s) + KNO_3(aq)$
Precipitation: Solid AgCl is formed.

(b) $2 \text{ Al}(s) + 3 \text{ Br}_2(l) \longrightarrow 2 \text{ AlBr}_3(s)$
Redox reaction: Al^{+3} is formed from Al, and Br^- is formed from Br_2.

(c) $Ca(OH)_2(aq) + 2 HNO_3(aq) \longrightarrow 2 H_2O(l) + Ca(NO_3)_2(aq)$
Acid–base neutralization

6.19 Use Table 6.1 for solubility guidelines.

Insoluble

(a) $CdCO_3$ (most carbonates are insoluble)
(c) $PbSO_4$
(e) Hg_2Cl_2

Soluble

(b) Na_2S
(d) $(NH_4)_3PO_4$

6.20 As in Worked Example 6.13, identify the products, and use Table 6.1 to predict their solubility. If the products are insoluble, a precipitation reaction will occur.

(a) $NiCl_2(aq) + (NH_4)_2S(aq) \longrightarrow 2 NH_4Cl(aq) + NiS(s)$
A precipitation reaction will occur.

(b) $2 AgNO_3(aq) + CaBr_2(aq) \longrightarrow Ca(NO_3)_2(aq) + 2 AgBr(s)$
A precipitation reaction will occur.

6.21 (a) $2\,CsOH(aq) + H_2SO_4(aq) \longrightarrow Cs_2SO_4(aq) + 2\,H_2O(l)$

(b) $Ca(OH)_2(aq) + 2\,CH_3CO_2H(aq) \longrightarrow Ca(CH_3CO_2)_2(aq) + 2\,H_2O(l)$

(c) $NaHCO_3(aq) + HBr(aq) \longrightarrow NaBr(aq) + CO_2(g) + H_2O(l)$

6.22 (a) Write the equation, including all ions.

$2\,Li(s) + Pb^{2+} + 2\,NO_3^- \longrightarrow 2\,Li^+ + 2\,NO_3^- + Pb(s)$
The nitrate ions on each side cancel.

$2\,Li(s) + Pb^{2+}(aq) \longrightarrow 2\,Li^+(aq) + Pb(s)$

(b) $OH^-(aq) + H^+(aq) \longrightarrow H_2O(l)$
K^+ and SO_4^{2-} cancel, and coefficients are reduced.

(c) $CuS(s) + 2\,H^+(aq) \longrightarrow Cu^{2+}(aq) + H_2S(g)$
The chloride ions cancel.

6.23

	Oxidized reactant/ Reducing agent	Reduced reactant/ Oxidizing agent
(a)	Fe	Cu^{2+}
(b)	Mg	Cl_2
(c)	Al	Cr_2O_3

The oxidizing agent is the reduced reactant, and the reducing agent is the oxidized reactant.

6.24 $2\,K(s) + Br_2(l) \longrightarrow 2\,KBr(s)$
Reducing agent   Oxidizing agent

6.25

Compound	Oxidation number of metal	Name
(a) VCl_3	+3	vanadium(III) chloride
(b) $SnCl_4$	+4	tin(IV) chloride
(c) CrO_3	+6	chromium(VI) oxide
(d) $Cu(NO_3)_2$	+2	copper(II) nitrate
(e) $NiSO_4$	+2	nickel(II) sulfate

6.26

Compound	Atom	Oxidation number
(a) N_2O_4	N	+4
	O	−2
(b) $HClO_4$	H	+1
	Cl	+7
	O	−2
(c) MnO_4^-	Mn	+7
	O	−2
(d) H_2SO_4	H	+1
	S	+6
	O	−2

6.27 Oxidation numbers are written above the atoms.

$$\overset{+1 \ -2}{Na_2S}(aq) \ + \ \overset{+2 \ -1}{NiCl_2}(aq) \ \longrightarrow \ 2\,\overset{+1 \ -1}{NaCl}(aq) \ + \ \overset{+2 \ -2}{NiS}(s)$$

(a) This reaction is not a redox reaction because no atoms change oxidation numbers.

$$\text{(b)} \ 2\,\overset{0}{Na}(s) \ + \ 2\,\overset{+1 \ -2}{H_2O}(l) \ \longrightarrow \ 2\,\overset{+1 \ -2 \ +1}{NaOH}(aq) \ + \ \overset{0}{H_2}(g)$$

Sodium is oxidized and hydrogen is reduced in this reaction.

$$\text{(c)} \ \overset{0}{C}(s) \ + \ \overset{0}{O_2}(g) \ \longrightarrow \ \overset{+4 \ -2}{CO_2}(g)$$

Carbon is oxidized and oxygen is reduced in this redox reaction.

$$\text{(d)} \ \overset{+2 \ -2}{CuO}(s) \ + \ 2\,\overset{+1 \ -1}{HCl}(aq) \ \longrightarrow \ \overset{+2 \ -1}{CuCl_2}(aq) \ + \ \overset{+1 \ -2}{H_2O}(l)$$

This is not a redox reaction because no atoms change oxidation number.

$$\text{(e)} \ 2\,\overset{+7 \ -2}{MnO_4^-}(aq) \ + \ 5\,\overset{+4 \ -2}{SO_2}(g) \ + \ 2\,\overset{+1 \ -2}{H_2O}(l) \ \longrightarrow \ 2\,\overset{+2}{Mn^{2+}}(aq) \ + \ \overset{+6 \ -2}{SO_4^{2-}}(aq) \ + \ 4\,\overset{+1}{H^+}(aq)$$

In this redox reaction, the oxidation number of Mn changes from +7 to +2 and the oxidation number of S changes from +4 to +6.

Understanding Key Concepts

6.28 Product mixture (d) is the only mixture that contains the same number of atoms as (a).

6.29 (c) $2\,A \ + \ B_2 \ \longrightarrow \ A_2B_2$

6.30   (d) $\longrightarrow$ (c)
reactants   products

6.31 Methionine: $C_5H_{11}NO_2S$

at. wt of 5 C = 5 x 12.0 amu =   60.0 amu
at. wt of 11 H = 11 x 1.0 amu =   11.0 amu
at. wt of   N =   =   14.0 amu
at. wt of 2 O = 2 x 16.0 amu =   32.0 amu
at. wt of   S =   =   32.1 amu

MW of $C_5H_{11}NO_2S$ = 149.1 amu

6.32 (a) $A_2 \ + \ 3\,B_2 \ \longrightarrow \ 2\,AB_3$

(b) $1.0 \text{ mol } A_2 \ \times \ \dfrac{2 \text{ mol } AB_3}{1 \text{ mol } A_2} \ = \ 2.0 \text{ mol } AB_3$

$1.0 \text{ mol } B_2 \ \times \ \dfrac{2 \text{ mol } AB_3}{3 \text{ mol } B_2} \ = \ 0.67 \text{ mol } AB_3$

6.33   (a) Mixing of sodium and carbonate ions produces outcome (1). No insoluble product is formed, and sodium and carbonate ions remain in solution.

        (b) Mixing barium and chromate ions produces outcome (2). $BaCrO_4$ precipitate forms (one barium ion for each chromate ion), and the excess barium ions remain in solution.

        (c) Mixing silver and sulfite ions yields outcome (3). Ag_2SO_3 precipitate forms (two silver ions for each sulfite ion), and no Ag^+ or SO_3^{2-} ions remain in solution.

6.34   The observed product is a precipitate that contains two cations per anion. From the list of cations, Ag^+ is the only one that forms precipitates and has a 2:1 cation :anion ratio with the anions listed. The anion can be either CO_3^{2-} or CrO_4^{2-}, since both form precipitates with Ag^+. Thus, the possible products are Ag_2CO_3 and Ag_2CrO_4.

6.35   Note: to save space, ethylene oxide will be represented as EO, and ethylene glycol as EG.

$$9.0 \text{ g H}_2\text{O} \ \times \ \frac{1 \text{ mol H}_2\text{O}}{18.0 \text{ g H}_2\text{O}} \ \times \ \frac{1 \text{ mol EO}}{1 \text{ mol H}_2\text{O}} \ \times \ \frac{44.0 \text{ g EO}}{1 \text{ mol EO}} = 22 \text{ g ethylene oxide}$$

$$9.0 \text{ g H}_2\text{O} \ \times \ \frac{1 \text{ mol H}_2\text{O}}{18.0 \text{ g H}_2\text{O}} \ \times \ \frac{1 \text{ mol EG}}{1 \text{ mol H}_2\text{O}} \ \times \ \frac{62.0 \text{ g EG}}{1 \text{ mol EG}} = 31 \text{ g ethylene glycol}$$

Balancing Chemical Equations

6.36   A balanced equation is an equation in which the number of atoms of each kind is the same on both sides of the reaction arrow.

6.37   Changing the subscripts on a substance to balance an equation changes the identity of the substance and makes the equation meaningless.

6.38   (a) $SO_2(g) + H_2O(g) \longrightarrow H_2SO_3(aq)$

        (b) $2 K(s) + Br_2(l) \longrightarrow 2 KBr(s)$

        (c) $C_3H_8(g) + 5 O_2(g) \longrightarrow 3 CO_2(g) + 4 H_2O(g)$

6.39 $4 NH_3(g) + Cl_2(g) \longrightarrow N_2H_4(l) + 2 NH_4Cl(s)$

6.40   (a) $2 C_2H_6(g) + 7 O_2(g) \longrightarrow 4 CO_2(g) + 6 H_2O(l)$

        (b) balanced

        (c) $2 Mg(s) + O_2(g) \longrightarrow 2 MgO(s)$

        (d) $2 K(s) + 2 H_2O(l) \longrightarrow 2 KOH(aq) + H_2(g)$

6.41 (a) $Hg(NO_3)_2(aq) + 2\,LiI(aq) \longrightarrow 2\,LiNO_3(aq) + HgI_2(s)$

(b) $I_2(s) + 5\,Cl_2(g) \longrightarrow 2\,ICl_5(s)$

(c) $4\,Al(s) + 3\,O_2(g) \longrightarrow 2\,Al_2O_3(s)$

(d) $CuSO_4(aq) + 2\,AgNO_3(aq) \longrightarrow Ag_2SO_4(s) + Cu(NO_3)_2(aq)$

(e) $2\,Mn(NO_3)_3(aq) + 3\,Na_2S(aq) \longrightarrow Mn_2S_3(s) + 6\,NaNO_3(aq)$

(f) $4\,NO_2(g) + O_2(g) \longrightarrow 2\,N_2O_5(g)$

(g) $P_4O_{10}(s) + 6\,H_2O(l) \longrightarrow 4\,H_3PO_4(aq)$

6.42 $2\,NaHCO_3(aq) + H_2SO_4(aq) \longrightarrow 2\,CO_2(g) + Na_2SO_4(aq) + 2\,H_2O(l)$

6.43 (a) $2\,C_4H_{10}(g) + 13\,O_2(g) \longrightarrow 8\,CO_2(g) + 10\,H_2O(l)$

(b) $C_2H_6O(g) + 3\,O_2(g) \longrightarrow 2\,CO_2(g) + 3\,H_2O(l)$

(c) $2\,C_8H_{18}(g) + 25\,O_2(g) \longrightarrow 16\,CO_2(g) + 18\,H_2O(l)$

Molar Masses and Moles

6.44 One mole of a substance is an amount equal to its formula weight in grams. One mole of a molecular compound contains 6.022×10^{23} molecules.

6.45 Molecular weight is the sum of the atomic weights of the individual atoms in a molecule. Formula weight is the sum of the atomic weights of the individual atoms in a formula unit of any compound, whether molecular or ionic.
Molar mass is the mass in grams of 6.022×10^{23} molecules or formula units of any substance.

6.46

$$\frac{6.022 \times 10^{23} \text{ units } CaCl_2}{1 \text{ mol } CaCl_2} \times \frac{1\ Ca^{2+}\ \text{ion}}{1 \text{ unit } CaCl_2} = \frac{6.022 \times 10^{23}\ Ca^{2+}\ \text{ions}}{1 \text{ mol } CaCl_2}$$

$$\frac{6.022 \times 10^{23} \text{ units } CaCl_2}{1 \text{ mol } CaCl_2} \times \frac{2\ Cl^-\ \text{ions}}{1 \text{ unit } CaCl_2} = \frac{1.204 \times 10^{24}\ Cl^-\ \text{ions}}{1 \text{ mol } CaCl_2}$$

6.47 Each formula unit of K_2SO_4 contains 3 ions – two K^+ ions and one SO_4^{2-} ion. Thus, one mole of K_2SO_4 contains 3 moles of ions, and:

$$1.75 \text{ mol } K_2SO_4 \times \frac{3 \text{ mol ions}}{1 \text{ mol } K_2SO_4} = 5.25 \text{ mol ions}$$

6.48

$$16.2 \text{ g Ca} \times \frac{1 \text{ mol}}{40.1 \text{ g Ca}} \times \frac{6.022 \times 10^{23} \text{ atoms}}{1 \text{ mol}} = 2.43 \times 10^{23} \text{ atoms}$$

6.49

$$2.68 \times 10^{22} \text{ atoms} \ \times \ \frac{1 \text{ mol}}{6.022 \times 10^{23} \text{ atoms}} \ \times \ \frac{238.0 \text{ g}}{1 \text{ mol}} = 10.6 \text{ g uranium}$$

6.50 Molar mass of caffeine = 194 g

$$125 \text{ mg caffeine} \ \times \ \frac{1 \text{ g}}{10^3 \text{ mg}} \ \times \ \frac{1 \text{ mol caffeine}}{194 \text{ g caffeine}} = 6.44 \times 10^{-4} \text{ mol caffeine}$$

6.51 Molar mass of aspirin = 180 g

$$500 \text{ mg aspirin} \ \times \ \frac{1 \text{ g}}{10^3 \text{ mg}} \ \times \ \frac{1 \text{ mol aspirin}}{180 \text{ g aspirin}} = 2.78 \times 10^{-3} \text{ mol aspirin}$$

6.52 Molar mass of $C_{16}H_{13}ClN_2O$:
$(16 \times 12.0 \text{ g}) + (13 \times 1.0 \text{ g}) + (35.5 \text{ g}) + (2 \times 14.0 \text{ g}) + 16.0 \text{ g} = 284.5 \text{ g/ mol Valium}$

6.53, 6.54, 6.57

Compound	Molar Mass	Number of Moles in 5.00 g	Number of Grams in 0.050 mol
(a) C_6H_6	78.0 g	0.0641 mol	3.90 g
(b) $NaHCO_3$	84.0 g	0.0595 mol	4.20 g
(c) $CHCl_3$	119.5 g	0.0418 mol	5.98 g
(d) $C_{16}H_{18}N_2O_5S$	350.1 g	0.0143 mol	17.5 g

Note: Slightly different values for molar mass result when exact atomic weights are used.

6.55 Molar mass of $FeSO_4$ = 151.9 g

$$300 \text{ mg FeSO}_4 \ \times \ \frac{1 \text{ g}}{10^3 \text{ mg}} \ \times \ \frac{1 \text{ mol FeSO}_4}{151.9 \text{ g FeSO}_4} = 1.97 \times 10^{-3} \text{ mol FeSO}_4$$

6.56 Molar mass of aspirin = 180 g

$$0.0015 \text{ mol aspirin} \ \times \ \frac{180 \text{ g aspirin}}{1 \text{ mol aspirin}} = 0.27 \text{ g aspirin}$$

Mole and Mass Relationships from Chemical Equations

6.58 (a) $N_2(g) + O_2(g) \longrightarrow 2 NO(g)$

(b) 7.50 mol of N_2 are needed to react with 7.50 mol of O_2.

(c) $3.81 \text{ mol N}_2 \ \times \ \frac{2 \text{ mol NO}}{1 \text{ mol N}_2} = 7.62 \text{ mol NO}$

(d) $0.250 \text{ mol NO} \ \times \ \frac{1 \text{ mol O}_2}{2 \text{ mol NO}} = 0.125 \text{ mol O}_2$

6.59   (a) $C_4H_8O_2(l) + 2\,H_2(g) \longrightarrow 2\,C_2H_6O(l)$

   (b) 3.0 mol of ethyl alcohol are produced from 1.5 mol of ethyl acetate.

   (c) $1.5 \text{ mol } C_4H_8O_2 \times \dfrac{2 \text{ mol } C_2H_6O}{1 \text{ mol } C_4H_8O_2} \times \dfrac{46.0 \text{ g } C_2H_6O}{1 \text{ mol } C_2H_6O} = 138 \text{ g } C_2H_6O$

   (d) $12.0 \text{ g } C_4H_8O_2 \times \dfrac{1 \text{ mol } C_4H_8O_2}{88.0 \text{ g } C_4H_8O_2} \times \dfrac{2 \text{ mol } C_2H_6O}{1 \text{ mol } C_4H_8O_2} \times \dfrac{46.0 \text{ g } C_2H_6O}{1 \text{ mol } C_2H_6O}$
   $= 12.5 \text{ g } C_2H_6O$

   (e) $12.0 \text{ g } C_4H_8O_2 \times \dfrac{1 \text{ mol } C_4H_8O_2}{88.0 \text{ g } C_4H_8O_2} \times \dfrac{2 \text{ mol } H_2}{1 \text{ mol } C_4H_8O_2} \times \dfrac{2.0 \text{ g } H_2}{1 \text{ mol } H_2} = 0.55 \text{ g } H_2$

6.60   (a) $N_2(g) + 3\,H_2(g) \longrightarrow 2\,NH_3(g)$

   (b) $16.0 \text{ g } NH_3 \times \dfrac{1 \text{ mol } NH_3}{17.0 \text{ g } NH_3} \times \dfrac{1 \text{ mol } N_2}{2 \text{ mol } NH_3} = 0.471 \text{ mol } N_2$

   (c) $75.0 \text{ g } N_2 \times \dfrac{1 \text{ mol } N_2}{28.0 \text{ g } N_2} \times \dfrac{3 \text{ mol } H_2}{1 \text{ mol } N_2} \times \dfrac{2.0 \text{ g } H_2}{1 \text{ mol } H_2} = 16.1 \text{ g } H_2$

6.61   (a) $2\,Fe_2O_3(s) + 3\,C(s) \longrightarrow 4\,Fe(s) + 3\,CO_2(g)$

   (b) $525 \text{ g } Fe_2O_3 \times \dfrac{1 \text{ mol } Fe_2O_3}{159.6 \text{ g } Fe_2O_3} \times \dfrac{3 \text{ mol } C}{2 \text{ mol } Fe_2O_3} = 4.93 \text{ mol } C$

   (c) $4.93 \text{ mol } C \times \dfrac{12.0 \text{ g } C}{1 \text{ mol } C} = 59.2 \text{ g } C$

6.62   (a) $Fe_2O_3(s) + 3\,CO(g) \longrightarrow 2\,Fe(s) + 3\,CO_2(g)$

   (b) $3.02 \text{ g } Fe_2O_3 \times \dfrac{1 \text{ mol } Fe_2O_3}{159.6 \text{ g } Fe_2O_3} \times \dfrac{3 \text{ mol } CO}{1 \text{ mol } Fe_2O_3} \times \dfrac{28.0 \text{ g } CO}{1 \text{ mol } CO} = 1.59 \text{ g } CO$

   (c) $1.68 \text{ mol } Fe_2O_3 \times \dfrac{3 \text{ mol } CO}{1 \text{ mol } Fe_2O_3} \times \dfrac{28.0 \text{ g } CO}{1 \text{ mol } CO} = 141 \text{ g } CO$

6.63   (a) $2\,Mg(s) + O_2(g) \longrightarrow 2\,MgO(s)$

   (b) $25.0 \text{ g } Mg \times \dfrac{1 \text{ mol } Mg}{24.3 \text{ g } Mg} \times \dfrac{1 \text{ mol } O_2}{2 \text{ mol } Mg} \times \dfrac{32.0 \text{ g } O_2}{1 \text{ mol } O_2} = 16.5 \text{ g } O_2$

   41.5 g MgO will result from reaction of 25.0 g Mg and 16.5 g O_2.

   (c) $25.0 \text{ g } O_2 \times \dfrac{1 \text{ mol } O_2}{32.0 \text{ g } O_2} \times \dfrac{2 \text{ mol } Mg}{1 \text{ mol } O_2} \times \dfrac{24.3 \text{ g } Mg}{1 \text{ mol } Mg} = 38.0 \text{ g } Mg$

   63.0 g MgO will result from reaction of 25.0 g O_2 and 38.0 g Mg.

6.64 $TiO_2(s) \longrightarrow Ti(s) + O_2(g)$

$$95 \text{ kg Ti } \times \frac{1 \text{ mol Ti}}{47.9 \text{ g Ti}} \times \frac{1 \text{ mol TiO}_2}{1 \text{ mol Ti}} \times \frac{79.9 \text{ g TiO}_2}{1 \text{ mol TiO}_2} = 158 \text{ kg TiO}_2$$

6.65

$$105 \text{ kg Fe}_2O_3 \times \frac{1 \text{ mol Fe}_2O_3}{159.6 \text{ g Fe}_2O_3} \times \frac{2 \text{ mol Fe}}{1 \text{ mol Fe}_2O_3} \times \frac{55.8 \text{ g Fe}}{1 \text{ mol Fe}} = 73.4 \text{ kg Fe}$$

Percent Yield

6.66

(a) $10.0 \text{ g CO } \times \dfrac{1 \text{ mol CO}}{28.0 \text{ g CO}} \times \dfrac{1 \text{ mol CH}_3OH}{1 \text{ mol CO}} \times \dfrac{32.0 \text{ g CH}_3OH}{1 \text{ mol CH}_3OH} = 11.4 \text{ g CH}_3OH$

(b) $\dfrac{9.55 \text{ g}}{11.4 \text{ g}} \times 100 \% = 83.8\% \text{ yield}$

6.67

(a) $75.0 \text{ kg Fe}_2O_3 \times \dfrac{1 \text{ mol Fe}_2O_3}{159.6 \text{ g Fe}_2O_3} \times \dfrac{4 \text{ mol Fe}}{2 \text{ mol Fe}_2O_3} \times \dfrac{55.8 \text{ g Fe}}{1 \text{ mol Fe}} = 52.4 \text{ kg Fe}$

(b) $\dfrac{51.3 \text{ kg}}{52.4 \text{ kg}} \times 100 \% = 97.9\% \text{ yield of Fe}$

6.68 (a) $CH_4(g) + 2 Cl_2(g) \longrightarrow CH_2Cl_2(l) + 2 HCl(g)$

(b) $50.0 \text{ g CH}_4 \times \dfrac{1 \text{ mol CH}_4}{16.0 \text{ g CH}_4} \times \dfrac{2 \text{ mol Cl}_2}{1 \text{ mol CH}_4} \times \dfrac{71.0 \text{ g Cl}_2}{1 \text{ mol Cl}_2} = 444 \text{ g Cl}_2$

(c) If the reaction occurred in 100% yield:

$$50.0 \text{ g CH}_4 \times \frac{1 \text{ mol CH}_4}{16.0 \text{ g CH}_4} \times \frac{1 \text{ mol CH}_2Cl_2}{1 \text{ mol CH}_4} \times \frac{85.0 \text{ g CH}_2Cl_2}{1 \text{ mol CH}_2Cl_2} = 266 \text{ g CH}_2Cl_2$$

Since the reaction occurs in 76% yield:

$266 \text{ g } \times 0.76 = 202 \text{ g CH}_2Cl_2 \text{ are actually formed}$

6.69

(a) $55.8 \text{ g K}_2PtCl_4 \times \dfrac{1 \text{ mol K}_2PtCl_4}{415.3 \text{ g K}_2PtCl_4} \times \dfrac{2 \text{ mol NH}_3}{1 \text{ mol K}_2PtCl_4} \times \dfrac{17.0 \text{ g NH}_3}{1 \text{ mol NH}_3} = 4.57 \text{ g NH}_3$

(b) If the reaction occurred in 100% yield:

$$55.8 \text{ g K}_2PtCl_4 \times \frac{1 \text{ mol K}_2PtCl_4}{415.3 \text{ g K}_2PtCl_4} \times \frac{1 \text{ mol cisplatin}}{1 \text{ mol K}_2PtCl_4} \times \frac{300.1 \text{ g cisplatin}}{1 \text{ mol cisplatin}}$$

$= 40.3 \text{ g cisplatin}$

Since the reaction occurs in 95% yield, $40.3 \text{ g } \times 0.95 = 38 \text{ g cisplatin}$ are actually formed.

Types of Chemical Reactions

6.70

(a) $2\,H^+(aq) + 2\,F^-(aq) + Ca^{2+}(aq) + 2\,OH^-(aq) \rightarrow Ca^{2+}(aq) + 2\,F^-(aq) + 2\,H_2O(l)$

$H^+(aq) + OH^-(aq) \rightarrow H_2O(l)$

(b) $2\,H^+(aq) + 2\,NO_3^-(aq) + Mg^{2+}(aq) + 2\,OH^-(aq) \rightarrow 2\,NO_3^-(aq) + Mg^{2+}(aq) + 2\,H_2O(l)$

$H^+(aq) + OH^-(aq) \rightarrow H_2O(l)$

6.71

(a) $Ba^{2+}(aq) + 2\,NO_3^-(aq) + 2\,K^+(aq) + SO_4^{2-}(aq) \rightarrow BaSO_4(s) + 2\,K^+(aq) + 2\,NO_3^-(aq)$

$Ba^{2+}(aq) + SO_4^{2-}(aq) \rightarrow BaSO_4(s)$

(b) $Zn(s) + 2\,H^+(aq) + SO_4^{2-}(aq) \rightarrow Zn^{2+}(aq) + H_2(g) + SO_4^{2-}(aq)$

$Zn(s) + 2\,H^+(aq) \rightarrow Zn^{2+}(aq) + H_2(g)$

6.72 Use Section 6.9 as a guide.
All of the listed compounds are insoluble in water ($PbCl_2$ is soluble in hot water).

6.73 Use Section 6.9 as a guide.
Only $Ba(NO_3)_2$ is soluble in water.

6.74 A precipitation reaction occurs only in (b). A neutralization occurs with the reagents in (a).

(b) $FeCl_2(aq) + 2\,KOH(aq) \longrightarrow Fe(OH)_2(s) + 2\,KCl(aq)$

6.75 If the products consist of soluble ions, no reaction will occur. No reaction occurs in (b) and (c).

(a) $2\,NaBr(aq) + Hg_2(NO_3)_2(aq) \longrightarrow Hg_2Br_2(s) + 2\,NaNO_3(aq)$

(d) $(NH_4)_2CO_3(aq) + CaCl_2(aq) \longrightarrow CaCO_3(s) + 2\,NH_4Cl(aq)$

(e) $2\,KOH(aq) + MnBr_2(aq) \longrightarrow Mn(OH)_2(s) + 2\,KBr(aq)$

(f) $3\,Na_2S(aq) + 2\,Al(NO_3)_3(aq) \longrightarrow Al_2S_3(s) + 6\,NaNO_3(aq)$

6.76 In net ionic reactions, no spectator ions appear. Otherwise, the equations are balanced for number of atoms and charge, and coefficients are reduced to their lowest common denominators.

(a) $Mg(s) + Cu^{2+}(aq) \longrightarrow Mg^{2+}(aq) + Cu(s)$

(b) $2\,Cl^-(aq) + Pb^{2+}(aq) \longrightarrow PbCl_2(s)$

(c) $2\,Cr^{3+}(aq) + 3\,S^{2-}(aq) \longrightarrow Cr_2S_3(s)$

6.77 (a) $2\,Au^{3+}(aq) + 3\,Sn(s) \longrightarrow 3\,Sn^{2+}(aq) + 2\,Au(s)$

(b) $2\,I^-(aq) + Br_2(l) \longrightarrow 2\,Br^-(aq) + I_2(s)$

(c) $2\,Ag^+(aq) + Fe(s) \longrightarrow Fe^{2+}(aq) + 2\,Ag(s)$

Redox Reactions and Oxidation Numbers

6.78 In general, the best reducing agents are metals. The most reactive reducing agents are in groups 1A and 2A. The most reactive oxidizing agents are in groups 6A and 7A.

6.79 The most easily reduced elements are found in groups 6A and 7A. The most easily oxidized elements are in groups 1A and 2A.

6.80 Gains electrons: (a) oxidizing agent, (d) substance undergoing reduction
Loses electrons: (b) reducing agent, (c) substance undergoing oxidation

6.81 Oxidation number increases: (b) reducing agent, (c) substance undergoing oxidation
Oxidation number decreases: (a) oxidizing agent, (d) substance undergoing reduction

6.82

+4 -2	+6 -2	+4 -2 -1	0 +1 -1
(a) NO_2	(b) SO_3	(c) $COCl_2$	(d) CH_2Cl_2

6.83 (a) Co: +3 (b) Fe: +2 (c) U: +6 (d) Cu: +2 (e) Ti: +4 (f) Sn: +2

6.84 The reduced element gains electrons, and the oxidized element loses electrons.

	(a)	(b)	(c)
Oxidized	Si	Br	Sb
Reduced	Cl	Cl	Cl

6.85

	(a)	(b)	(c)	(d)
Oxidized	S	Na	Zn	Cl
Reduced	O	Cl	Cu	F

Applications

6.86 The most serious error in calculating Avogadro's number by spreading oil on water is the estimate of the size of the area the oil covered. Some approximations that Franklin made, but that can be determined with reasonable precision, are the volume of oil, the mass of the oil, its density and its molar mass. Other assumptions, involving the thickness of the oil layer and the arrangement of oil molecules on the surface of the water, are also sources of error.

6.87

$$\frac{0.067 \text{ g}}{1 \text{ L}} \times \frac{1 \text{ mol}}{190 \text{ g}} = \frac{3.5 \times 10^{-4} \text{ mol}}{1 \text{ L}}$$

3.5×10^{-4} mol of sodium urate dissolve in 1.00 L of water.

6.88 Zinc is the reducing agent in a dry-cell battery.

6.89 Light is passed through the negative image onto special paper coated with AgBr. The layer that is darkest has been exposed to the most light. The paper is developed with hydroquinone to amplify the image and fixed with sodium thiosulfate to remove the remaining AgBr, producing a positive image – the "negative of a negative."

General Questions and Problems

6.90

(a) $15.0 \text{ g Zn } \times \dfrac{1 \text{ mol Zn}}{65.4 \text{ g Zn}} \times \dfrac{1 \text{ mol H}_2}{1 \text{ mol Zn}} \times \dfrac{2.0 \text{ g H}_2}{1 \text{ mol H}_2} = 0.459 \text{ g H}_2$

(b) In this redox reaction, H^+ is reduced (oxidizing agent) and Zn is oxidized (reducing agent).

6.91

$80.0 \text{ kg H}_2\text{O } \times \dfrac{1 \text{ mol H}_2\text{O}}{18.0 \text{ g H}_2\text{O}} \times \dfrac{1 \text{ mol Li}_2\text{O}}{1 \text{ mol H}_2\text{O}} \times \dfrac{29.8 \text{ g Li}_2\text{O}}{1 \text{ mol Li}_2\text{O}} = 132 \text{ kg Li}_2\text{O}$

This is not a redox reaction because the oxidation numbers of reactant and product atoms remain the same.

6.92 (a) $2 \text{ Al}(s) + \text{Fe}_2\text{O}_3(s) \longrightarrow \text{Al}_2\text{O}_3(l) + 2 \text{ Fe}(l)$

(b) $2 \text{ NH}_4\text{NO}_3(s) \longrightarrow 2 \text{ N}_2(g) + \text{O}_2(g) + 4 \text{ H}_2\text{O}(g)$

6.93 Molar mass of batrachotoxin ($C_{31}H_{42}N_2O_6$) = 538 g/mol

$0.05 \text{ μg } \times \dfrac{1 \text{ g}}{10^6 \text{ μg}} \times \dfrac{1 \text{ mol}}{538 \text{ g}} \times \left[6.022 \times 10^{23} \dfrac{\text{molecules}}{\text{mol}} \right] = 6 \times 10^{13} \text{ molecules}$

6.94 $3 \text{ CuCl}_2(aq) + 2 \text{ Na}_3\text{PO}_4(aq) \longrightarrow \text{Cu}_3(\text{PO}_4)_2(s) + 6 \text{ NaCl}(aq)$
  A precipitate of $\text{Cu}_3(\text{PO}_4)_2$ forms

$3 \text{ Cu}^{2+}(aq) + 2 \text{ PO}_4{}^{3-}(aq) \longrightarrow \text{Cu}_3(\text{PO}_4)_2(s)$

6.95 (a) $C_{12}H_{22}O_{11}(s) \longrightarrow 12 \text{ C}(s) + 11 \text{ H}_2\text{O}(l)$

(b) $60.0 \text{ g sucrose } \times \dfrac{1 \text{ mol sucrose}}{342 \text{ g sucrose}} \times \dfrac{12 \text{ mol C}}{1 \text{ mol sucrose}} \times \dfrac{12.0 \text{ g C}}{1 \text{ mol C}} = 25.3 \text{ g carbon}$

(c) $6.50 \text{ g C } \times \dfrac{1 \text{ mol C}}{12.0 \text{ g C}} \times \dfrac{11 \text{ mol H}_2\text{O}}{12 \text{ mol C}} \times \dfrac{18.0 \text{ g H}_2\text{O}}{1 \text{ mol H}_2\text{O}} = 8.94 \text{ g H}_2\text{O}$

6.96 (a) $\text{Cu}(s) + 4 \text{ H}^+(aq) + 2 \text{ NO}_3{}^-(aq) \longrightarrow \text{Cu}^{2+}(aq) + 2 \text{ NO}_2(g) + 2 \text{ H}_2\text{O}(l)$

(b) $35.0 \text{ g HNO}_3 \times \dfrac{1 \text{ mol HNO}_3}{63.0 \text{ g HNO}_3} \times \dfrac{1 \text{ mol Cu}}{4 \text{ mol HNO}_3} \times \dfrac{63.5 \text{ g Cu}}{1 \text{ mol Cu}} = 8.82 \text{ g Cu}$

35.0 g HNO_3 is more than enough to dissolve 5.00 g Cu.

6.97

(a) $1.50 \text{ g C}_2\text{H}_6\text{O} \times \dfrac{1 \text{ mol C}_2\text{H}_6\text{O}}{46.0 \text{ g C}_2\text{H}_6\text{O}} \times \dfrac{2 \text{ mol K}_2\text{Cr}_2\text{O}_7}{3 \text{ mol C}_2\text{H}_6\text{O}} \times \dfrac{294.2 \text{ g K}_2\text{Cr}_2\text{O}_7}{1 \text{ mol K}_2\text{Cr}_2\text{O}_7}$

$= 6.40 \text{ g K}_2\text{Cr}_2\text{O}_7$

(b) $80.0 \text{ g C}_2\text{H}_6\text{O} \times \dfrac{1 \text{ mol C}_2\text{H}_6\text{O}}{46.0 \text{ g C}_2\text{H}_6\text{O}} \times \dfrac{3 \text{ mol C}_2\text{H}_4\text{O}_2}{3 \text{ mol C}_2\text{H}_6\text{O}} \times \dfrac{60.0 \text{ g C}_2\text{H}_4\text{O}_2}{1 \text{ mol C}_2\text{H}_4\text{O}_2}$

$= 104 \text{ g C}_2\text{H}_4\text{O}_2$

6.98

$100.0 \text{ lb C}_6\text{H}_{12}\text{O}_6 \times \dfrac{454 \text{ g}}{1 \text{ lb}} \times \dfrac{1 \text{ mol C}_6\text{H}_{12}\text{O}_6}{180.0 \text{ g C}_6\text{H}_{12}\text{O}_6} \times \dfrac{2 \text{ mol C}_2\text{H}_6\text{O}}{1 \text{ mol C}_6\text{H}_{12}\text{O}_6} \times \dfrac{46.0 \text{ g C}_2\text{H}_6\text{O}}{1 \text{ mol C}_2\text{H}_6\text{O}}$

$= 2.32 \times 10^4 \text{ g C}_2\text{H}_6\text{O}$

$2.32 \times 10^4 \text{ g ethanol} \times \dfrac{1 \text{ mL ethanol}}{0.789 \text{ g ethanol}} \times \dfrac{1 \text{ qt}}{946.4 \text{ mL}} = 31.1 \text{ qts ethanol}$

6.99 (a) $\text{Al(OH)}_3(aq) + 3 \text{ HNO}_3(aq) \longrightarrow \text{Al(NO}_3)_3(aq) + 3 \text{ H}_2\text{O}(l)$

(b) $3 \text{ AgNO}_3(aq) + \text{FeCl}_3(aq) \longrightarrow 3 \text{ AgCl}(s) + \text{Fe(NO}_3)_3(aq)$

(c) $(\text{NH}_4)_2\text{Cr}_2\text{O}_7(s) \longrightarrow \text{Cr}_2\text{O}_3(s) + 4 \text{ H}_2\text{O}(g) + \text{N}_2(g)$

(d) $\text{Mn}_2(\text{CO}_3)_3(s) \longrightarrow \text{Mn}_2\text{O}_3(s) + 3 \text{ CO}_2(g)$

Self-Test for Chapter 6

Multiple choice:

1. Which of the following salts is soluble in water?
    (a) FeSO_4 (b) BaSO_4 (c) CaSO_4 (d) PbSO_4

2. Which of the following compounds has sulfur in a +1 oxidation state?
    (a) S_2F_2 (b) H_2SO_4 (c) SO_2 (d) Na_2S

3. What mass of CaCO_3 has the same number of atoms as 21 g of NaF?
    (a) 10 g (b) 20 g (c) 50 g (d) 100 g

4. In the equation $\text{P}_2\text{O}_5 + 3 \text{ H}_2\text{O} \longrightarrow 2 \text{ H}_3\text{PO}_4$ the mole ratio of product to H_2O is:
    (a) 2:1 (b) 2:3 (c) 3:2 (d) 1:2

5. When the equation $\text{SiCl}_4 + \text{H}_2\text{O} \longrightarrow \text{SiO}_2 + \text{HCl}$ is balanced, the coefficients are:
    (a) 1,1,1,1 (b) 1,1,1,2 (c) 1,2,1,2 (d) 1,2,1,4

6. Which of the following is not a redox process?
    (a) Respiration (b) Corrosion (c) Neutralization (d) Combustion

7.   If you wanted to remove Ba^{2+} from solution, which reagent would you add?
       (a) CH_3CO_2H (b) NaOH   (c) H_2SO_4 (d) HCl

8.   In the reaction $2\ Ca + O_2 \longrightarrow 2\ CaO$, how many grams of CaO can be produced from 20 g
       of Ca? (a) 20 g   (b) 28 g   (c) 40 g   (d) 56 g

9.   When HCl is added to a solution, bubbles of gas appear. Which compound is probably
       present in the solution?
       (a) $SrCO_3$ (b) $Ca(OH)_2$ (c) AgBr   (d) K_2SO_4

10. $3\ NO_2 + H_2O \longrightarrow 2\ HNO_3 + NO$

       All the following statements about the above reaction are true except:
       (a) The starting material is both oxidized and reduced.
       (b) NO_2 in the atmosphere might contribute to acid rain.
       (c) At least 6 g of H_2O are needed to react completely with 46 g of NO_2.
       (d) 92 g of NO_2 produces 28 g of NO.

Complete the following sentences:

1.   The numbers placed in front of formulas to balance equations are called _____.

2.   A _____ is a solid that forms during a reaction.

3.   Ions that appear on both sides of the reaction arrow are _____ ions.

4.   The substances in a reaction can be solids, liquids, or gases, or they can be in _____

       solution.

5.   Grams and moles can be converted by using _____ _____ as a conversion factor.

6.   The amount of a substance produced in a reaction, divided by the amount that could

       theoretically be produced, is the _____ _____.

7.   In a chemical equation, _____ are shown on the left of the reaction arrow.

8.   The oxidation state of gold in $AuCl_3$ is _____.

9.   In the reaction $2\ Mg + O_2 \longrightarrow 2\ MgO$, Mg is the _____ agent.

10.   A reaction between an acid and a base is a _____ reaction.

Tell whether the following statements are true or false:

1. A mole of oxygen atoms has the same mass as a mole of nitrogen atoms.

2. The coefficients in chemical reactions show the relative numbers of moles of reactants and products.

3. Limestone ($CaCO_3$) can be dissolved by treatment with HNO_3.

4. In a redox equation, the oxidizing agent is oxidized and the reducing agent is reduced.

5. If all coefficients in a chemical equation are even numbers, the equation is not completely balanced.

6. Mole ratios are used to convert between moles and grams of a compound.

7. In the reaction between K and Cl_2, K is the oxidizing agent.

8. In the reaction $4\ Al + 3\ O_2 \longrightarrow 2\ Al_2O_3$, the mole ratio of product to Al is 2.

9. Most sodium salts are soluble in water.

10. The same compound can be both oxidized and reduced in a reaction.

Match each item on the left with its partner on the right:

1.	Zn	(a) converts moles Na to grams Na
2.	$C_3H_8O + O_2 \longrightarrow C_3H_6O + H_2O$	(b) molar mass of NaF
3.	42.0 amu	(c) redox reaction
4.	23.0 g sodium / 1 mol	(d) precipitation reaction
5.	$CoCO_3$	(e) salt soluble in water
6.	$S + O_2 \longrightarrow SO_2$	(f) unbalanced equation
7.	$HCl + NaOH \longrightarrow NaCl + H_2O$	(g) converts grams Na to moles Na
8.	42.0 g	(h) oxidized in a battery
9.	1 mol / 23.0 g sodium	(i) salt insoluble in water
10.	MnO_2	(j) neutralization reaction
11.	$AgNO_3 + NaCl \longrightarrow AgCl + NaNO_3$	(k) formula weight of NaF
12.	$CoCl_2$	(l) reduced in a battery

Chapter Outline

I. Energy (Sections 7.1–7.3).
  A. Heat changes during chemical reactions (Section 7.1).
    1. Bond dissociation energies measure the strength of covalent bonds.
      a. Bond breaking requires heat and is endothermic.
      b. Bond formation releases heat and is exothermic.
    2. The reverse of an endothermic process is exothermic, and the reverse of an exothermic process is endothermic.
    3. The Law of Conservation of Energy states that energy can neither be created nor destroyed during any physical or chemical change.
    4. The difference between the energy needed for breaking bonds and the energy released in forming bonds is the heat of reaction, also known as enthalpy (ΔH).
  B. Exothermic and endothermic reactions: ΔH (Section 7.2).
    1. In exothermic reactions, the bond dissociation energies of the products are greater than the bond dissociation energies of the reactants, and ΔH is negative.
    2. In endothermic reactions, the bond dissociation energies of the products are smaller than the bond dissociation energies of the reactants, and ΔH is positive.
    3. The amount of heat absorbed or released in the reverse of a reaction is equal to that absorbed in the forward reaction, but ΔH has the opposite sign.
  C. Free energy: ΔG (Section 7.3).
    1. Spontaneous processes.
      a. A spontaneous process proceeds without any external influence.
      b. A nonspontaneous process needs a constant external source of energy.
    2. Entropy (ΔS) measures the amount of disorder in a system.
      a. If disorder increases, ΔS is positive.
      b. If disorder decreases, ΔS is negative.
    3. The absorption of heat and the increase or decrease in disorder determine if a reaction will be spontaneous.
      a. $\Delta G = \Delta H - T\Delta S$.
      b. If ΔG is negative, the process is spontaneous, and the reaction is exergonic.
      c. If ΔG is positive, the process isn't spontaneous, and the reaction is endergonic.
    4. ΔG for the reverse of a reaction is equal in value to ΔG for the forward reaction, but the sign is changed.
    5. Some nonspontaneous processes become spontaneous when temperature increases.
II. Reaction rates (Sections 7.4–7.5).
  A. How reactions occur (Section 7.4).
    1. In addition to the value of ΔG, other factors determine if a reaction will occur.
      a. Reactants must collide in the correct orientation.
      b. The energy of collision must be great enough to cause bond breaking.
      c. Many reactions with a favorable free energy don't occur at room temperature, and heat must be added to get them started
    2. The energy changes during a reaction can be graphed on a reaction energy diagram.
    3. The amount of energy needed to produce favorable collisions is the activation energy E_{act}.
      a. E_{act} determines the reaction rate.
      b. The size of E_{act} is unrelated to the size of ΔH.

  B. Factors that affect reaction rate (Section 7.5).
      1. Increasing temperature increases reaction rate.
      2. Increasing the concentration of reactants increases reaction rate.
      3. Catalysts increase the reaction rate by lowering E_{act}.
III. Chemical equilibrium (Sections 7.6–7.8).
  A. Reversible reactions (Section 7.6).
      1. Some reactions proceed to virtual completion.
      2. Other reactions go to partial completion, at which point products begin to reform starting material.
        a. These reactions are reversible.
        b. The reaction from left to right is the forward reaction.
        c. The reaction from right to left is the reverse reaction.
      3. At some point the rate of the forward reaction equals the rate of the reverse reaction, and equilibrium is established.
      4. It is not necessary for the concentrations of products and reactants to be equal at equilibrium.
  B. Equilibrium (Section 7.7).
      1. Equilibrium equations.
        a. For the reaction a A + b B —> c C + d D,

$$K = \frac{[C]^c[D]^d}{[A]^a[B]^b}$$

        b. K = equilibrium constant.
        c. Expression on the right = equilibrium constant expression.
      2. The value of K determines the position of equilibrium.
        a. When $K \gg 1$, reaction goes to completion.
        b. When $K > 1$, the forward reaction is favored.
        c. When K is of intermediate value, significant amounts of reactants and products are present at equilibrium.
        d. When $K < 1$, the reverse reaction is favored.
        e. When $K \ll 1$, there is essentially no reaction.
  C. Effect of changing reaction conditions (Section 7.8).
      1. LeChâtelier's principle: When a stress is applied to a system, the equilibrium shifts to remove the stress.
      2. Effect of changing concentration.
        a. Increasing the concentration of reactants favors the forward reaction.
        b. Increasing the concentration of products favors the reverse reaction.
      3. Effect of changing temperature.
        a. Decreasing temperature favors an exothermic reaction.
        b. Increasing temperature favors an endothermic reaction.
      4. Effect of changing pressure.
        a. No effect unless one of the reactants or products is a gas.
        b. Increasing pressure shifts the equilibrium in the direction that produces fewer gas molecules.

Solutions to Chapter 7 Problems

7.1   (a) The reaction is endothermic because heat appears on the left side of the equation and is absorbed in the reaction.
(b) $\Delta H = +678$ kcal
(c) $C_6H_{12}O_6(aq) + 6 O_2(g) \longrightarrow 6 CO_2(g) + 6 H_2O(l) + 678$ kcal

7.2   (a) The reaction is endothermic because ΔH is positive.

(b) $\dfrac{801 \text{ kcal}}{4 \text{ mol Al}} \times 1.00 \text{ mol Al} = 200$ kcal required.

(c) $10.0 \text{ g Al} \times \dfrac{1 \text{ mol Al}}{27.0 \text{ g Al}} \times \dfrac{801 \text{ kcal}}{4 \text{ mol Al}} = 74.2$ kcal required

7.3

$145 \text{ g NO} \times \dfrac{1 \text{ mol}}{30.0 \text{ g NO}} \times \dfrac{43 \text{ kcal}}{2 \text{ mol NO}} = 104$ kcal absorbed

7.4   (a) Entropy increases.
(b) Entropy increases because disorder increases when liquids vaporize.
(c) Entropy decreases because one mole of product is formed for each two moles of reactant and because a gaseous reactant is converted into a solid product.

7.5   (a) Formation of lime from limestone doesn't occur at 25°C because ΔG is positive.
(b) Entropy increases because a gas is formed from a solid.
(c) The reaction is spontaneous at higher temperatures. In the expression $\Delta G = \Delta H - T\Delta S$, the term $T\Delta S$ becomes larger at high temperature and causes ΔG to become negative.

7.6 $\Delta G = \Delta H - T\Delta S :$ $\Delta H = +1.44$ kcal/mol $\Delta S = +5.26$ cal/(mol $\cdot$ K)
(a) If $T = 263$ K,

$T\Delta S = 263 \text{ K} \times \dfrac{5.26 \text{ cal}}{\text{mol K}} \times \dfrac{1 \text{ kcal}}{10^3 \text{ cal}} = \dfrac{1.38 \text{ kcal}}{\text{mol}}$

$\Delta G = 1.44$ kcal/mol $- 1.38$ kcal/mol $= +0.06$ kcal/mol
At 263 K, melting is not spontaneous because ΔG is positive.

(b) If $T = 273$ K,

$T\Delta S = 273 \text{ K} \times \dfrac{5.26 \text{ cal}}{\text{mol K}} \times \dfrac{1 \text{ kcal}}{10^3 \text{ cal}} = \dfrac{1.44 \text{ kcal}}{\text{mol}}$

$\Delta G = 1.44$ kcal/mol $- 1.44$ kcal/mol $= +0.00$ kcal/mol
At 273 K, $\Delta G = 0$, and melting and freezing are in equilibrium.

(c) If $T = 283$ K,

$T\Delta S = 283 \text{ K} \times \dfrac{5.26 \text{ cal}}{\text{mol K}} \times \dfrac{1 \text{ kcal}}{10^3 \text{ cal}} = \dfrac{1.49 \text{ kcal}}{\text{mol}}$

$\Delta G = 1.44$ kcal/mol $- 1.49$ kcal/mol $= -0.05$ kcal/mol
At 283 K, melting is spontaneous because ΔG is negative.

7.7 (a) The sign of ΔS is positive because disorder increases from reactant to products.
(b) In the expression $\Delta G = \Delta H - T\Delta S$, ΔH is a negative number. Because ΔS is positive, $(-T\Delta S)$ is negative at all temperatures. Thus, ΔG is negative at all temperatures, and the reaction is spontaneous at all temperatures.

7.8

In this reaction, E_{act} is large, the reaction is slow, and the free energy change is large and negative.

7.9

In this reaction, ΔG is small and positive. E_{act} can be small or large, but it is always larger than ΔG.

7.10 (a) If the temperature is increased, the reaction rate increases.
(b) Removal of the catalyst decreases the reaction rate.
(c) Halving the concentration of H_2 decreases the rate.

7.11

$$K = \frac{[\text{products}]}{[\text{reactants}]}$$

(a) $K = \dfrac{[NO_2]^2}{[N_2O_4]}$ (b) $K = \dfrac{[CH_3Cl][HCl]}{[CH_4][Cl_2]}$ (c) $K = \dfrac{[Br_2][F_2]^5}{[BrF_5]^2}$

Don't forget that the coefficients of the reactants and products appear as exponents in the equilibrium expression.

7.12 If K is greater than 1, the reaction favors products. If K is less than 1, the reaction favors reactants.
(a) Products are strongly favored.
(b) Reactants are strongly favored.
(c) Products are somewhat favored.

7.13 In the expression for the equilibrium constant, the concentration of the product HI is squared in the numerator. The concentrations of the reactants appear in the denominator. Substitute the given concentrations into the expression. The equilibrium favors products.

$$K = \frac{[\text{HI}]^2}{[\text{H}_2][\text{I}_2]} = \frac{[0.251]^2}{[0.0250][0.0869]} = 29.0$$

7.14 The reaction that forms CD has a larger equilibrium constant because it has a greater ratio of product to reactant than does the reaction that forms AB.

7.15 High pressure favors the production of SO_3 because increasing the pressure shifts the equilibrium in the direction that decreases the number of molecules in the gas phase. Low temperature favors the production of SO_3 because exothermic reactions are favored by lower temperatures.

7.16 (a) Increasing the temperature shifts the equilibrium to the left, favoring reactants.
(b) Increasing the pressure shifts the equilibrium to the right, favoring product.
(b) Removing CH_4 from the reaction vessel causes more CH_4 to be formed and shifts the equilibrium toward the right, favoring product.

Understanding Key Concepts

7.17 ΔH is positive because energy must be supplied in order to break the attractive forces between molecules of the crystal. ΔS is also positive because the molecules of gas are more disordered than the molecules of solid. ΔG is negative because it is stated in the problem that the reaction is spontaneous.

7.18 ΔH is negative because energy is released when a liquid condenses. ΔS is negative because disorder decreases when a gas condenses. ΔG is negative because it is stated in the problem that the reaction is spontaneous.

7.19 (a) $2 A_2 + B_2 \longrightarrow 2 A_2B$

(b) ΔG is negative because the reaction is spontaneous. ΔS is negative because the product mixture has fewer gas molecules and less disorder than the reactant mixture. ΔH must be negative in order for ΔG to be negative since $(-T \Delta S)$ is positive.

7.20 (a) The red curve represents the slower reaction, since more energy is needed to surmount the energy barrier leading to formation of products.
(b) The red curve represents a spontaneous reaction since the energy of its products is less than the energy of its reactants : ΔG is negative.

7.21 The red curve represents the catalyzed reaction, since a catalyst lowers the energy barrier of a reaction.

7.22

7.23 (a) ΔS is positive because the product has more disorder than the reactants.

(b) At low temperatures, the reaction is nonspontaneous because ΔH is positive and $T\Delta S$ is small. As the temperature rises, a certain temperature is reached at which $\Delta H = T\Delta S$. At this temperature, $\Delta G = 0$. Above this temperature, ΔG is negative and the reaction is spontaneous.

Enthalpy and Heat of Reaction

7.24 In an endothermic reaction, the total enthalpy of the products is greater than the total enthalpy of the reactants. In other words, the reactants have stronger bonds and are more stable, while the products have weaker bonds and are less stable. Energy must therefore be supplied for the reaction to take place.

7.25 In a chemical reaction, the difference in bond energies between products and reactants is known as the *heat of reaction* , or enthalpy change.

7.26 (a) ΔH is positive.

(b) $6.5 \text{ mol Br}_2 \ \times \ \dfrac{7.4 \text{ kcal}}{1 \text{ mol Br}_2} = 48 \text{ kcal needed}$

(c) $75 \text{ g Br}_2 \ \times \ \dfrac{1 \text{ mol Br}_2}{159.8 \text{ g Br}_2} \ \times \ \dfrac{7.4 \text{ kcal}}{1 \text{ mol Br}_2} = 3.5 \text{ kcal needed}$

7.27 (a) ΔH is negative.

(b) $3.4 \text{ mol H}_2\text{O} \ \times \ \dfrac{-1.44 \text{ kcal}}{1 \text{ mol H}_2\text{O}} = -4.9 \text{ kcal}$

(c) $25 \text{ g H}_2\text{O} \ \times \ \dfrac{1 \text{ mol H}_2\text{O}}{18 \text{ g H}_2\text{O}} \ \times \ \dfrac{-1.44 \text{ kcal}}{1 \text{ mol H}_2\text{O}} = -2.0 \text{ kcal}$

(d) $+1.44 \text{ kcal/mol}$

7.28 (a) $C_6H_{12}O_6 + 6 O_2 \longrightarrow 6 CO_2 + 6 H_2O$

(b) $\dfrac{-3.8 \text{ kcal}}{1 \text{ g glucose}} \times \dfrac{180 \text{ g glucose}}{1 \text{ mol glucose}} \times 1.50 \text{ mol glucose} = -1.0 \times 10^3 \text{ kcal}$

(c) The production of glucose from CO_2 and H_2O is an endothermic process.

$\dfrac{3.8 \text{ kcal}}{1 \text{ g glucose}} \times 15.0 \text{ g glucose} = 57 \text{ kcal needed to produce 15 g glucose}$

7.29 (a) $C_2H_5OH + 3 O_2 \longrightarrow 2 CO_2 + 3 H_2O + \text{heat}$

(b) ΔH is negative, because energy is released.

(c) $\dfrac{35.5 \text{ kcal}}{5.00 \text{ g } C_2H_5OH} \times \dfrac{46.0 \text{ g } C_2H_5OH}{1 \text{ mol } C_2H_5OH} = \dfrac{327 \text{ kcal}}{1 \text{ mol } C_2H_5OH} \text{ released}$

(d) $450.0 \text{ kcal} \times \dfrac{1 \text{ mol } C_2H_5OH}{327 \text{ kcal}} = 1.38 \text{ mol } C_2H_5OH$

$1.38 \text{ mol} \times \dfrac{46.0 \text{ g}}{1 \text{ mol}} = 63.5 \text{ g } C_2H_5OH$

(e) $10.0 \text{ g } C_2H_5OH \times \dfrac{35.5 \text{ kcal}}{5.00 \text{ g } C_2H_5OH} = 71.0 \text{ kcal released}$

(f) Calories needed = specific heat of H_2O x mass (g) x temperature change (°C)

Specific heat of water = 1.00 cal /(g · °C); mass of 500 mL H_2O = 500 g; Temperature change = 80.0°C

$\text{Calories} = \dfrac{1.00 \text{ cal}}{\text{g} \cdot °\text{C}} \times 500.0 \text{ g} \times 80.0°\text{C} = 4.00 \times 10^4 \text{ cal} = 40.0 \text{ kcal}$

$40.0 \text{ kcal} \times \dfrac{5.00 \text{ g } C_2H_5OH}{35.5 \text{ kcal}} = 5.63 \text{ g } C_2H_5OH$

Entropy and Free Energy

7.30 Increased disorder: (a)
Decreased disorder: (b) (c)

7.31 All three processes result in a decrease in disorder (increase in order).

7.32 A spontaneous process is one that, once started, proceeds without any external influence.

7.33 A reaction with a negative free energy change is spontaneous, and a reaction with a positive free energy change is nonspontaneous.

7.34 The two factors that influence the spontaneity of a reaction are (1) the release or absorption of heat, and (2) the increase or decrease in entropy.

7.35 An exothermic reaction releases heat (negative ΔH), whereas an exergonic reaction is spontaneous (negative ΔG).

7.36 The free energy change (ΔG) of a chemical reaction shows whether or not a reaction is spontaneous. If the sign of ΔG is negative, the reaction is spontaneous. Of the two factors that contribute to ΔG (ΔH and ΔS), ΔH is usually larger at low temperatures. Thus if a reaction is spontaneous (negative ΔG) it is usually exothermic (negative ΔH).

7.37 If an exothermic reaction is accompanied by a large decrease in entropy, the ($-T\Delta S$) term in the expression for ΔG becomes large and positive and outweighs the negative enthalpy term, resulting in a positive value for ΔG and indicating a nonspontaneous reaction.

7.38 (a) Dissolution of NaCl is endothermic since ΔH is positive.
(b Entropy increases because disorder increases.
(c) Since the dissolution of NaCl is spontaneous, ΔG for the reaction must be negative. Because we already know that ΔH is positive, it must be true that $T\Delta S$ is the major contributor to ΔG.

7.39 (a) Entropy decreases because two atoms of liquid and one molecule of gas react to yield two molecules of solid.
(b) We can't tell with the information given whether the process is spontaneous, because ΔG, not ΔH, determines spontaneity. To decide if a process is spontaneous, we must also know T and the value of ΔS.

7.40 (a) $H_2(g) + Br_2(l) \longrightarrow 2\,HBr(g)$
(b) Entropy increases because the number of gaseous product molecules is greater than the number of gaseous reactant molecules.
(c) The process is spontaneous at all temperatures because ΔH is negative and ΔS is positive.
(d) $\Delta G = \Delta H - T\Delta S$; $\Delta H = -17.4$ kcal/mol; $\Delta S = 27.2$ cal/(mol $\cdot$K); $T = 300$ K

$$T\Delta S = 300 \text{ K} \times \frac{27.2 \text{ cal}}{\text{mol K}} \times \frac{1 \text{ kcal}}{10^3 \text{ cal}} = \frac{8.16 \text{ kcal}}{\text{mol}}$$

$$\Delta G = -17.4 \text{ kcal/mol} - 8.16 \text{ kcal/mol} = -25.6 \text{ kcal/mol}$$

7.41 (a) ΔS is negative because two molecules of a gas combine to form one molecule of liquid.
(b) This reaction is spontaneous only up to a certain temperature, above which $T\Delta S$ is greater than ΔH and the reaction becomes nonspontaneous.

Rates of Chemical Reactions

7.42 The *activation energy* of a reaction is the amount of energy needed for reactants to surmount the energy barrier to reaction.

7.43 A reaction with $E_{act} = 5$ kcal is faster than one with $E_{act} = 10$ kcal because less energy is needed to surmount the energy barrier.

7.44

7.45

The free energy change is zero.

7.46 Increasing temperature increases reaction rate for two reasons:
1. Particles move faster and are more likely to collide.
2. Collisions occur with more energy.

7.47 Increasing concentration increases the reaction rate because the increased crowding of reactants causes more collisions.

7.48 A catalyst is a substance that increases reaction rate by lowering the activation energy barrier, yet remains unchanged when the reaction is completed.

7.49 A catalyst that reduces the energy of activation of a forward reaction by 5.0 kcal/mol (from 28.0 kcal/mol to 23.0 kcal/mol) also reduces the energy of activation of the reverse reaction by 5.0 kcal/mol. Lowering the energy of activation of the reverse reaction, however, will not cause it to take place if it is not spontaneous.

7.50 (a) The negative value of ΔG indicates that diamonds spontaneously turn into graphite at 25°C.
(b) Because this behavior is not observed, the activation energy of the above reaction must be extremely high and the reaction rate must be extremely slow.

7.51 (a) The reaction of hydrogen with carbon is not spontaneous at 25°C because ΔG is positive.
(b) It is not possible to find a catalyst for the reaction because it is not spontaneous.

Chemical Equilibria

7.52 In a reversible reaction, chemical equilibrium is a state in which the rates of the forward reaction and the reverse reaction are equal. The amounts of reactants and products need not be equal at equilibrium.

7.53 Catalysts lower the height of the activation energy barrier for both forward and reverse reactions by the same amount but don't change the equilibrium constant.

7.54

(a) $K = \dfrac{[CO_2]^2}{[CO]^2[O_2]}$ (b) $K = \dfrac{[C_2H_4Cl_2][HCl]^2}{[C_2H_6][Cl_2]^2}$

(c) $K = \dfrac{[H_3O^+][F^-]}{[HF][H_2O]}$ (d) $K = \dfrac{[O_3]^2}{[O_2]^3}$

7.55

(a) $K = \dfrac{[H_2S]^2}{[S_2][H_2]^2} = 2.8 \times 10^{-21}$ (b) $K = \dfrac{[CH_3OH]}{[CO][H_2]^2} = 10.5$

(c) $K = \dfrac{[BrCl]^2}{[Br_2][Cl_2]} = 58.0$ (d) $K = \dfrac{[I]^2}{[I_2]} = 6.8 \times 10^{-3}$

A reaction with K greater than 1 favors products.
A reaction with K less than 1 favors reactants.
   Favors reactants: (a) (d)
   Favors products: (b) (c)

7.56

$$K = \frac{[NO_2]^2}{[N_2O_4]} = \frac{(0.025 \text{ mol/L})^2}{(0.0869 \text{ mol/L})} = 7.2 \times 10^{-3}$$

7.57

$$K = \frac{[OF_2]^2}{[F_2]^2[O_2]} = \frac{(0.0633 \text{ mol/L})^2}{(0.0100 \text{ mol/L})^2 (0.200 \text{ mol/L})} = 2.00 \times 10^2$$

7.58

(a) $K = 7.2 \times 10^{-3} = \dfrac{(0.12 \text{ mol/L})^2}{[N_2O_4]}$; $[N_2O_4] = 2.0 \text{ mol/L}$

(b) $K = 7.2 \times 10^{-3} = \dfrac{[NO_2]^2}{(0.12 \text{ mol/L})}$; $[NO_2] = 0.029 \text{ mol/L}$

7.59

(a) $2.00 \times 10^2 = \dfrac{(0.220 \text{ mol/L})^2}{(0.0300 \text{ mol/L})^2 [O_2]}$

$[O_2] = \dfrac{(0.220 \text{ mol/L})^2}{(0.0300 \text{ mol/L})^2 \times 2.00 \times 10^2} = 0.269 \text{ mol/L}$

(b) $[OF_2]^2 = K \times [F_2]^2 \times [O_2] = 2.00 \times 10^2 \times (0.0800 \text{ mol/L})^2 \times 0.650 \text{ mol/L} = 0.832$

$[OF_2] = 0.912 \text{ mol/L}$

7.60 If the pressure is raised, relatively more reactants than products are found at equilibrium, because high pressure favors the reaction that produces fewer gas molecules.

7.61 If the pressure is lowered, a relatively greater concentration of reactants than products is found at equilibrium, because lower pressure favors the reaction that produces more gas molecules.

Le Châtelier's Principle

7.62 (a) The reaction is endothermic.
(b) Reactants are favored at equilibrium.
(c) (1) Increasing pressure favors formation of ozone, since increased pressure shifts the equilibrium in the direction of the reaction that produces fewer gas molecules.
(2) Increasing the O_2 concentration increases the amount of O_3 formed.
(3) Increasing the concentration of O_3 shifts the equilibrium to the left.
(4) A catalyst has no effect on the equilibrium.
(5) Increasing the temperature shifts the equilibrium to the right.

7.63 (a) This reaction is exothermic.
(b) Products are favored at equilibrium.
(c) (1) Increasing pressure has no effect on the equilibrium.
(2) Increasing the HCl concentration shifts the equilibrium to the left.
(3) Increasing the Cl_2 concentration increases the amount of HCl formed.
(4) Decreasing the H_2 concentration decreases the amount of HCl formed.
(5) A catalyst has no effect on the equilibrium.

7.64 According to LeChâtelier's principle, an increase in pressure shifts the equilibrium in the direction that decreases the number of molecules in the gas phase.
(a) The concentration of products decreases.
(b) The concentration of products remains the same.
(c) The concentration of products increases.

7.65 (a) The equilibrium shifts to favor reactants.
(b) The equilibrium shifts to favor products.
(c) The position of equilibrium remains the same.

7.66 $CO(g) + H_2O(g) \rightleftharpoons CO_2(g) + H_2(g)$ $\Delta H = -9.8$ kcal/mol

Because it has a negative value of ΔH, the reaction is exothermic, and the equilibrium favors products. Increasing the temperature shifts the equilibrium to favor reactants and decreases the amount of H_2.

7.67 $3\,O_2(g) \rightleftharpoons 2\,O_3(g)$ $\Delta H = +68$ kcal/mol

Increasing the temperature of the reaction increases the equilibrium constant.

7.68 $H_2(g) + I_2(g) \rightleftharpoons 2\,HI(g)$ $\Delta H = -2.2$ kcal/mol

(a) Adding I_2 to the reaction mix increases the equilibrium concentration of HI.
(b) Removing H_2 causes the equilibrium concentration of HI to decrease.
(c) Addition of a catalyst does not change the equilibrium concentration of HI.
(d) Increasing the temperature decreases the concentration of HI.

7.69 $Fe^{3+}(aq) + Cl^-(aq) \rightleftharpoons FeCl^{2+}(aq)$

(a) Addition of $Fe(NO_3)_3$ increases the equilibrium concentration of $FeCl^{2+}$.
(b) Removal of Cl^- by precipitation decreases the concentration of $FeCl^{2+}$.
(c) Increasing the temperature of the endothermic reaction increases the equilibrium concentration of $FeCl^{2+}$.
(d) Addition of a catalyst does not change the equilibrium concentration of $FeCl^{2+}$.

Applications

7.70   A gram of fat contains more energy (9 kcal/g) than a gram of carbohydrate (4 kcal/g).

7.71   Body temperature is regulated by the thyroid gland and by the hypothalamus region of the brain.

7.72   Dilation of the blood vessels cools the body by allowing more blood to flow close to the surface of the body.

7.73   Nitrogen fixation is the conversion of N_2 into chemically usable nitrogen compounds. In nature this is accomplished by microorganisms that live in the roots of legumes and by lightning.

General Questions and Problems

7.74 $N_2(g) + 3\,H_2(g) \longrightarrow 2\,NH_3(g)$ $\Delta H = -22$ kcal/mol

(a) The production of ammonia from its elements is an exothermic process.

(b) $\dfrac{-22 \text{ kcal}}{2 \text{ mol } NH_3} \times 0.500 \text{ mol } NH_3 = -5.5 \text{ kcal}$

7.75 (a) $Fe_3O_4(s) + 4 H_2(g) \longrightarrow 3 Fe(s) + 4 H_2O(g)$ $\Delta H = +36$ kcal/mol

(b) $75 \text{ g Fe} \times \dfrac{1 \text{ mol Fe}}{55.8 \text{ g Fe}} \times \dfrac{36 \text{ kcal}}{1 \text{ mol Fe}_3O_4} \times \dfrac{1 \text{ mol Fe}_3O_4}{3 \text{ mol Fe}} = 16 \text{ kcal required}$

(c) $75 \text{ g Fe} \times \dfrac{1 \text{ mol Fe}}{55.8 \text{ g Fe}} \times \dfrac{4 \text{ mol H}_2}{3 \text{ mol Fe}} \times \dfrac{2.0 \text{ g H}_2}{1 \text{ mol H}_2} = 3.6 \text{ g H}_2$

(d) Reactants are favored in this reaction.

7.76 (a) CO removes Hb from the bloodstream because the reaction of CO with Hb is more favored than the reaction of O_2 with Hb. Less Hb is available to react with O_2, and less HbO_2 is available to the tissues.

(b) Administering high doses of O_2 to a victim of CO poisoning shifts the equilibrium in the following reaction to the right.

$$Hb(CO)(aq) + O_2(aq) \rightleftharpoons HbO_2(aq) + CO(aq)$$

This shift results in displacement of CO from Hb(CO) and in formation of HbO_2 to replenish body tissues with O_2.

7.77

$1700 \text{ kcal} \times \dfrac{1 \text{ g}}{3.8 \text{ kcal}} = 450 \text{ g glucose}$

7.78

(a) $10.0 \text{ g H}_2O \times \dfrac{1 \text{ mol H}_2O}{18.0 \text{ g H}_2O} \times \dfrac{9.72 \text{ kcal}}{1 \text{ mol H}_2O} = 5.40 \text{ kcal needed}$

(b) 5.40 kcal are released.

7.79 (a) $4 NH_3(g) + 5 O_2(g) \rightleftharpoons 4 NO(g) + 6 H_2O(g) + \text{heat}$

(b) $K = \dfrac{[NO]^4 [H_2O]^6}{[NH_3]^4 [O_2]^5}$

(c) (1) Raising the pressure shifts the equilibrium to the left and favors reactants.
(2) Adding NO(g) shifts the equilibrium to the left and favors reactants.
(3) Decreasing NH_3 shifts the equilibrium to the left and favors reactants.
(4) Lowering the temperature shifts the equilibrium to the right and favors products.

7.80 (a) $2 CH_3OH(l) + 3 O_2(g) \longrightarrow 2 CO_2(g) + 4 H_2O(g)$

(b) $50.0 \text{ g CH}_3OH \times \dfrac{1 \text{ mol CH}_3OH}{32.0 \text{ g CH}_3OH} \times \dfrac{-174 \text{ kcal}}{1 \text{ mol CH}_3OH} = -272 \text{ kcal}$

7.81

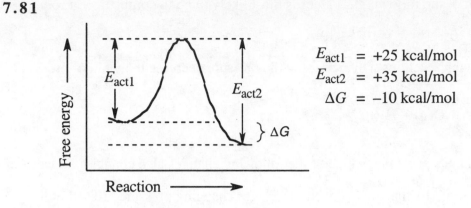

$$E_{act1} = +25 \text{ kcal/mol}$$
$$E_{act2} = +35 \text{ kcal/mol}$$
$$\Delta G = -10 \text{ kcal/mol}$$

(a) The forward process is exergonic.

(b) $\Delta G = -10$ kcal/mol

7.82

$$5.00 \text{ g} \times \frac{1 \text{ mol Al}}{27.0 \text{ g Al}} \times \frac{-336.6 \text{ kcal}}{2 \text{ mol Al}} = -31.2 \text{ kcal}$$

7.83

$$1.00 \text{ g} \times \frac{1 \text{ mol Na}}{23.0 \text{ g}} \times \frac{-88.0 \text{ kcal}}{2 \text{ mol Na}} = -1.91 \text{ kcal}$$

1.91 kcal of heat is evolved. The reaction is exothermic.

Self-Test for Chapter 7

Multiple choice:

1. In which of the following processes does entropy decrease?
   (a) $C_6H_{12}O_6(s) + 6\ O_2(g) \longrightarrow 6\ CO_2(g) + 6\ H_2O(l)$
   (b) $2\ Na(s) + 2\ H_2O(l) \longrightarrow 2\ NaOH(aq) + H_2(g)$
   (c) $2\ Mg(s) + O_2(g) \longrightarrow 2\ MgO(s)$
   (d) $Zn(s) + CuSO_4(aq) \longrightarrow Cu(s) + ZnSO_4(aq)$

2. The reaction that is most likely to proceed has:
   (a) negative ΔH, negative ΔS (b) negative ΔH, positive ΔS (c) positive ΔH, positive ΔS
   (d) positive ΔH, negative ΔS

3. Which of the conditions in Problem 2 indicates the reaction with the largest positive value of ΔG?

4. In the reaction $CH_3CO_2H + CH_3OH \rightleftharpoons CH_3CO_2CH_3 + H_2O$, the yield of $CH_3CO_2CH_3$ can be improved by :
   (a) distilling off the $CH_3CO_2CH_3$ (b) removing the water   (c) using more CH_3CO_2H and CH_3OH (d) all of the above

5. The equilibrium expression for the reaction $C_6H_6 + 3\ H_2 \longrightarrow C_6H_{12}$ is:

   (a) $\dfrac{[C_6H_{12}]}{[C_6H_6]\,[H_2]}$ (b) $\dfrac{[C_6H_{12}]}{[C_6H_6]\,[H_2]^3}$ (c) $\dfrac{[C_6H_{12}]}{[C_6H_6]\,[3\ H_2]}$ (d) $\dfrac{[C_6H_6]\,[H_2]^3}{[C_6H_{12}]}$

6. A reaction with which of the following K values is most likely to go to completion at room temperature?
   (a) $K = 10^5$ (b) $K = 10^2$ (c) $K = 10^{-1}$ (d) $K = 10^{-4}$

7. In which of the following reactions will increasing the pressure decrease the yield of product?
   (a) $2\ Mg(s) + O_2(g) \longrightarrow 2\ MgO(s)$
   (b) $H_2C=CH_2(g) + H_2(g) \longrightarrow CH_3CH_3(g)$
   (c) $C(s) + H_2O(g) \longrightarrow CO(g) + H_2(g)$
   (d) $3\ O_2(g) \longrightarrow 2\ O_3(g)$

8. According to LeChâtelier's principle, which of the following changes also changes the value of K?
   (a) changing temperature   (b) changing concentration   (c) changing pressure   (d) all of the above

9. All of the following statements are true about the reaction $3\ O_2(g) \longrightarrow 2\ O_3(g)$ (heat of formation = +34 kcal/mol at 25°C) except :
   (a) The reaction is endothermic.   (b) ΔS is negative.   (c) ΔG is positive.   (d) The rate of the reverse reaction increases with temperature.

10. In the reaction $Si + O_2 \longrightarrow SiO_2$ ($\Delta H = -218$ kcal/mol at 25°C), what is ΔH in kcal when 80 g of O_2 reacts with 70 g of Si?
    (a) 218 kcal   (b) –218 kcal   (c) –436 kcal   (d) –545 kcal

Complete the following sentences:

1. A reaction that has equal amounts of reactants and products at equilibrium has $K =$ ___.

2. The Law of _____ ___ _____ states that energy can be neither created nor destroyed.

3. Addition of a _____ increases the rate of a reaction.

4. A reaction that easily proceeds in either direction is _____.

5. A reaction that absorbs heat from the surroundings is an _____ reaction.

6. An _____ _____ _____ gives the relationship between the concentrations of products and reactants at equilibrium.

7. The rate of a reaction can be increased by increasing _____ or ____ or by adding a _____.

8. The reactions that continually take place in the body are known as _____.

9. ____ ___ is unrelated to reaction spontaneity.

10. For a chemical reaction to occur, reactant molecules must _____.

Match the entries on the left with their partners on the right:

1.   Enzyme

2.   Exergonic reaction

3. K

4.   Enthalpy

5.   Reaction energy diagram

6.   Free energy

7.   Exothermic reaction

8.   Endergonic reaction

9. E_{act}

10. Entropy

11. Reversible reaction

12. Endothermic reaction

(a) Shows energy relationships in a reaction

(b) A reaction that gives off heat

(c) Reduces the size of E_{act}

(d) Energy needed for a reaction to occur

(e) Measure of the amount of disorder in a reaction.

(f) Reaction that is not spontaneous

(g) Reaction that can go in either direction

(h) Reaction that absorbs heat

(i) Difference in energy of products and reactants

(j) Reaction that is spontaneous

(k) Determines if a reaction is spontaneous

(l) Measures the ratio of products to reactants

Tell whether the following statements are true or false:

1.   The caloric value of food tells how much energy is absorbed when food is burned in oxygen.

2.   In a chemical equilibrium, both product and reactant concentrations remain constant.

3.   According to LeChâtelier's Principle, changing pressure only affects equilibrium if gaseous reactants or products are involved.

4.   In an exothermic reaction, the bond dissociation energies of the products are greater than the bond dissociation energies of the reactants.

5.   A reaction with a large E_{act} will probably have a large heat of reaction.

6.   Raising the temperature of a reaction always increases the rate of reaction.

7.   A very unfavorable reaction can take place if the temperature is high enough.

8.   Catalysts increase the rate of a reaction by increasing the number of collisions between reactants.

9.   At chemical equilibrium, all chemical reaction stops.

10. At low temperatures, the spontaneity of a reaction is determined by ΔH.

Chapter Outline

I. Introduction to gases, liquids and solids (Section 8.1).
   A. Phases of matter are determined by the attractive forces between molecules.
      1. In gases, attractive forces are very weak.
      2. In liquids, attractive forces are strong.
      3. In solids, forces are so strong that atoms are held in place.
   B. During changes of phase, also known as changes of state, heat is either absorbed or released.
      1. Every change of state is characterized by a free-energy change, ΔG.
         a. ΔG consists of an enthalpy term and an entropy term.
         b. The enthalpy term is a measure of the heat absorbed or released during a phase change.
         c. The entropy change is a measure of the change in molecular disorder.
      2. At the temperature where a change of phase occurs, two states are in equilibrium.
      3. At the change from solid to liquid, two phases are at equilibrium at the melting point.
      4. At the change from liquid to gas, two phases are at equilibrium at the boiling point.
II. Gases (Sections 8.2–8.10).
   A. The kinetic-molecular theory explains the behavior of gases (Section 8.2).
      1. A gas consists of a great many molecules moving about with no attractive forces.
      2. The amount of space that molecules occupy is much smaller than the space between molecules.
      3. The energy of the molecules is related to Kelvin temperature.
      4. When molecules collide, their total kinetic energy is conserved.
      5. A gas that obeys all these behaviors is an ideal gas.
   B. Pressure (Sections 8.3).
      1. Pressure is defined as force per unit area.
      2. Units of pressure are mm Hg, Pascal (in the SI system), atmosphere and pounds per square inch.
      3. Gas pressure can be measured by using a barometer or a manometer.
   C. Gas laws (Sections 8.4–8.10).
      1. Boyle's law (for a fixed amount of gas at constant T) (Section 8.4):
         a. The pressure of a gas is inversely proportional to its volume.
         b. $P_1V_1 = P_2V_2$.
      2. Charles' law (for a fixed amount of gas at constant P) (Section 8.5):
         a. The volume of a gas is directly proportional to its temperature in K.
         b. $V_1/T_1 = V_2/T_2$.
      3. Gay-Lussac's law (for a fixed amount of gas at constant V) (Section 8.6):
         a. Pressure is directly proportional to temperature in K.
         b. $P_1/T_1 = P_2/T_2$.
      4. Combined gas law (Section 8.7).
         $P_1V_1/T_1 = P_2V_2/T_2$ for a fixed amount of gas.
      5. Avogadro's law (at constant T and P) (Section 8.8):
         a. The volume of a gas is directly proportional to its molar amount at constant T and P.
         b. $V_1/n_1 = V_2/n_2$.
         c. Standard temperature and pressure = 273.16 K and 1 atm.
         d. Standard molar volume of a gas = 22.4 L.

6. Ideal gas law (Section 8.9).

$PV = nRT$, where R is a gas constant.

7. Dalton's Law of Partial Pressure (Section 8.10).

a. Mixtures of gases behave the same as a pure gas.

b. The partial pressure of a gas in a mixture is the same as the gas would have if it were alone.

III. Intermolecular forces (Section 8.11).

A. Intermolecular forces are the forces that act between molecules.

B. In an ideal gas, intermolecular forces are unimportant.

C. Three types of intermolecular forces are important in liquids and solids.

1. Dipole–dipole forces occur when the positive end of a polar molecule is attracted to the negative end of a second molecule.

2. London forces.

a. Short-lived polarity in molecules causes a temporary attraction between molecules.

b. London forces increase with increasing molecular weight and vary with molecular shape.

3. Hydrogen bonding.

a. Hydrogen bonds occur between a hydrogen atom bonded to an electronegative atom and an unshared electron pair of a second electronegative atom.

b. In hydrogen bonds, the hydrogen atom is partially bonded to two different electronegative atoms.

c. Hydrogen bonds can be quite strong, and hydrogen bonding is responsible for elevated boiling points.

IV. Liquids and solids (Sections 8.12–8.15).

A. Liquids (Section 8.12–8.13).

1. Evaporation occurs when molecules near the surface of a liquid escape into the gaseous state.

When molecules are in the gaseous state, they obey gas laws.

2. The contribution of the partial pressure of the escaped gas to the total pressure is known as vapor pressure.

Vapor pressure rises with increasing temperature.

3. The normal boiling point of a liquid is at 760 mm Hg.

The boiling point rises or falls with atmospheric pressure.

4. Viscosity and surface tension are properties of liquids.

a. Viscosity is a liquid's resistance to flow.

b. Surface tension is the resistance of a liquid to spread out.

5. Water is a unique liquid (Section 8.13).

a. Water has very high specific heat, heat of vaporization and strong hydrogen bonding.

b. Solid water is less dense than liquid water.

B. Solids (Section 8.14).

1. A crystalline solid has atoms, molecules or ions rigidly held in an orderly arrangement.

Categories of crystalline solids include ionic solids, molecular solids, covalent network solids and metallic solids.

2. Particles in an amorphous solid do not have an orderly arrangement.

C. Changes of phase (Section 8.15).

1. The heat needed to completely melt a solid is the heat of fusion.

2. The heat needed to completely vaporize a liquid is the heat of vaporization.

Solutions to Chapter 8 Problems

8.1   (a) The change of state from liquid to gas is disfavored by ΔH (positive sign) but is favored by ΔS (large positive value).

(b) $\Delta G = \Delta H - T\Delta S : \Delta H = +9.72$ kcal/mol; $\Delta S = +26.1$ cal/(mol $\cdot$ K); $T = 373$ K

$$T\Delta S = 373 \text{ K} \times \frac{26.1 \text{ cal}}{\text{mol K}} \times \frac{1 \text{ kcal}}{10^3 \text{ cal}} = \frac{9.74 \text{ kcal}}{\text{mol}}$$

$\Delta G = 9.72$ kcal/mol $-$ 9.74 kcal/mol $= +0.02$ kcal/mol

(c) For the change from gas to liquid, $\Delta H = -9.72$ kcal/mol and $\Delta S = -26.1$ cal/(mol·K)

8.2   Use the appropriate conversion factor from Section 8.3

$$220 \text{ mm Hg} \times \frac{1 \text{ atm}}{760 \text{ mm Hg}} = 0.29 \text{ atm}$$

$$220 \text{ mm Hg} \times \frac{14.7 \text{ psi}}{760 \text{ mm Hg}} = 4.3 \text{ psi}$$

$$220 \text{ mm Hg} \times \frac{101,325 \text{ Pa}}{760 \text{ mm Hg}} = 29,000 \text{ Pa}$$

8.3   The pressure of the gas inside the manometer is greater than atmospheric pressure because the mercury level is higher in the open arm of the manometer than in the closed end. Since atmospheric pressure is 750 mm Hg and since the difference in mercury levels in the manometer arm is 250 mm Hg, the pressure of the gas inside the manometer is 750 mm + 250 mm = 1000 mm Hg.

8.4   If the variables in the problem are pressure and volume, Boyle's Law must be used.

Solution: $P_1 \times V_1 = P_2 \times V_2$

$$V_2 = \frac{P_1 \times V_1}{P_2} = \frac{(90 \text{ atm})(5.0 \text{ L})}{(1.0 \text{ atm})} = 450 \text{ L}$$

Ballpark Check: Since the pressure is reduced by almost 100 times, the volume must increase by almost 100 times, from 5 L to 500 L.

The ballpark solution and the detailed solution agree.

8.5   *Solution*: $P_1 \times V_1 = P_2 \times V_2$

$$P_2 = \frac{P_1 \times V_1}{V_2} = \frac{(5.0 \text{ atm}) (2.5 \text{ L})}{(10.0 \text{ L})} = 1.2 \text{ atm}$$

Ballpark Check: Since the volume increases by four times, the pressure must decrease by four times, from 5.0 atm to 1.25 atm.

At a volume of 0.20 L: $P_2 = \dfrac{P_1 \times V_1}{V_2} = \dfrac{(5.0 \text{ atm})(2.5 \text{ L})}{(0.20 \text{ L})} = 62 \text{ atm}$

8.6 Charles' Law is used to calculate volume or temperature changes when pressure and quantity remain constant.

Solution:

$$\frac{V_1}{T_1} = \frac{V_2}{T_2}$$

$$V_2 = \frac{V_1 \times T_2}{T_1} = \frac{(0.30\ L)(350\ K)}{273\ K} = 0.38\ L$$

Ballpark Check: Since the temperature increases by about 25%, the volume must also increase by about 25%, from 0.30 L to around 0.38 L.

At 500°C (773 K): $V_2 = \dfrac{V_1 \times T_2}{T_1} = \dfrac{(0.30\ L)(773\ K)}{273\ K} = 0.85\ L$

8.7 Use Gay-Lussac's Law when pressure and temperature vary, and volume and quantity are unchanged.

Solution:

$$\frac{P_1}{T_1} = \frac{P_2}{T_2}$$

$$P_2 = \frac{P_1 \times T_2}{T_1} = 30\ \text{psi} \times \frac{318\ K}{288\ K} = 33\ \text{psi}$$

Ballpark Check: Since the temperature increase is about 10%, the pressure increase is also expected to be approximately 10%.

8.8 In this problem, P, V, and T vary.

$$\frac{P_1 V_1}{T_1} = \frac{P_2 V_2}{T_2};$$ $P_1 = 745$ mm Hg; $T_1 = 295$ K; $V_1 = 250$ L

$P_2 = 570$ mm Hg; $T_2 = 209$ K; $V_2 = ?$

$$V_2 = \frac{P_1 V_1 T_2}{P_2 T_1} = \frac{(745\ \text{mm Hg})\,(250\ L)(209\ K)}{(570\ \text{mm Hg})(295\ L)} = 231\ L$$

8.9

$$\frac{P_1 V_1}{T_1} = \frac{P_2 V_2}{T_2};$$ $T_1 = 291$ K; $V_1 = 225$ L; $P_1 = 763$ mm Hg;

$T_2 = 218$ K; $V_2 = 1365$ L; $P_2 = ?$

$$P_2 = \frac{P_1 V_1 T_2}{V_2 T_1} = \frac{(763\ \text{mm Hg})\,(225\ L)(291\ K)}{(1365\ L)(218\ K)} = 168\ \text{mm Hg}$$

Ballpark Check: Although temperature varies from low to high altitude, the major change is the approximately fivefold increase in volume. The predicted pressure is about 1/5 the original pressure.

8.10   Use Avogadro's Law; the quantity on the left side of the equation is the standard molar volume of a gas, 22.4 L/mol.

$$\frac{V_1}{n_1} = \frac{V_2}{n_2}$$

$$n_2 = \frac{V_2 \times n_1}{V_1} = 1.00 \times 10^5 \text{ L CH}_4 \times \frac{1.0 \text{ mol}}{22.4 \text{ L}} = 4.46 \times 10^3 \text{ mol CH}_4$$

The same container could also hold 4.46×10^3 moles of CO_2.

$$4.46 \times 10^3 \text{ mol CH}_4 \times \frac{16.0 \text{ g CH}_4}{1 \text{ mol CH}_4} = 7.14 \times 10^4 \text{ g CH}_4$$

$$4.46 \times 10^3 \text{ mol CO}_2 \times \frac{44.0 \text{ g CO}_2}{1 \text{ mol CO}_2} = 1.96 \times 10^5 \text{ g CO}_2$$

Ballpark Check: Since one mole of a gas occupies 22.4 L at STP, a 100,000 L container holds 100,000/22.4 moles, or about 4500 moles. Thus, the ballpark solution and the exact solution agree.

8.11 $PV = nRT$; $P = nRT/V$

$$n = 3.2 \text{ g} \times \frac{1 \text{ mol}}{44.0 \text{ g}} = 0.073 \text{ mol} ; \quad R = 0.0821 \frac{\text{L·atm}}{\text{mol·K}}$$

$$T = 20°C = 293 \text{ K} ; \quad V = 350 \text{ mL} = 0.35 \text{ L}$$

$$P = \frac{0.073 \text{ mol} \times \dfrac{0.0821 \text{ L·atm}}{\text{mol·K}} \times 293 \text{ K}}{0.35 \text{ L}} = 5.0 \text{ atm}$$

8.12 $PV = nRT$; $n = PV/RT$

$$P = 150 \text{ atm}; \quad V = 180 \text{ L He}; \quad R = 0.0821 \frac{\text{L·atm}}{\text{mol·K}} ; \quad T = 25°C = 298 \text{ K}$$

$$n = \frac{150 \text{ atm} \times 180 \text{ L He}}{0.0821 \dfrac{\text{L·atm}}{\text{mol·K}} \times 298 \text{ K}} = 1.1 \times 10^3 \text{ mol He}$$

$$1.1 \times 10^3 \text{ mol He} \times \frac{4.0 \text{ g}}{1 \text{ mol He}} = 4.4 \times 10^3 \text{ g He}$$

8.13 We can use the ideal gas law to compare the volumes of two gases: Since the piston is moveable, $P = 1$ atm in all cases.

(a) The increase in temperature increases the volume to $450/300 = 3/2$ of the original volume, and the decrease in amount decreases the volume to $0.200/0.300 = 2/3$ of the original value. Since $3/2 \times 2/3 = 1$, the two changes exactly cancel, and the final volume is the same as the original volume.

$T_1 = 300$ K; $n_1 = 0.300$ mol; $T_2 = 450$ K; $n_2 = 0.200$ mol; $V_1/V_2 = ?$

$$\frac{V_1}{V_2} = \frac{n_1 T_1 P_2}{n_2 T_2 P_1} = \frac{n_1 T_1}{n_2 T_2}; \quad \frac{V_1}{V_2} = \frac{(0.300 \text{ mol})(300 \text{ K})}{((0.200 \text{ mol})((450 \text{ K})} = 1$$

(b) The decrease in temperature decreases the volume to $200/300 = 2/3$ of the original, and the increase in amount increases the volume to $0.400/0.300 = 4/3$ of the original volume. Since $2/3 \times 4/3 = 8/9$, the final volume is a bit less than the original volume.

$T_1 = 300$ K; $n_1 = 0.300$ mol; $T_2 = 200$ K; $n_2 = 0.400$ mol; $V_1/V_2 = ?$

$$\frac{V_1}{V_2} = \frac{(0.300 \text{ mol})(300 \text{ K})}{((0.400 \text{ mol})((200 \text{ K})} = \frac{9}{8}$$ The volume in (b) is 8/9 of the original volume.

$P = 1$ atm $\qquad$ (a) $\qquad\qquad$ (b)

$T = 300$ K $\qquad\quad$ $T = 450$ K $\qquad\qquad$ $T = 200$ K
$n = 0.300$ mol $\qquad$ $n = 0.200$ mol $\qquad$ $n = 0.400$ mol

8.14 0.98×9.5 atm $= 9.3$ atm He
0.020×9.5 atm $= 0.19$ atm O_2

The partial pressure of oxygen in diving gas (0.19 atm) is approximately equal to the partial pressure of oxygen in air (0.21 atm).

8.15

$$\frac{573 \text{ mm Hg}}{760 \text{ mm Hg}} \times 100\% = 75.4\% \text{ N}_2; \qquad \frac{100 \text{ mm Hg}}{760 \text{ mm Hg}} \times 100\% = 13.2\% \text{ O}_2$$

$$\frac{40 \text{ mm Hg}}{760 \text{ mm Hg}} \times 100\% = 5.3\% \text{ CO}_2; \qquad \frac{47 \text{ mm Hg}}{760 \text{ mm Hg}} \times 100\% = 6.2\% \text{ H}_2\text{O}$$

8.16 We know from the previous problem that the partial pressure of O_2 in the lungs at atmospheric pressure is 13.2%. Thus, at 685 mm Hg:

685 mm $\times 0.132 = 90.4$ mm Hg

8.17 Drawing (c) best represents the mixture. In (c), the particles act independently of each other, in accordance with kinetic-molecular theory, and the mixture is homogeneous.

8.18 Boiling points generally increase with increasing molecular (or atomic) weight because of London dispersion forces.

(a) Kr, Ar, Ne. This series is arranged in order of decreasing boiling point.
(b) Cl_2, Br_2, I_2. This series is arranged in order of increasing boiling point.

8.19 Methyl alcohol (a) and methylamine (c) are capable of hydrogen bonding because each contains a hydrogen atom bonded to an electronegative atom. Ethylene (b) does not form hydrogen bonds.

8.20 (a) *London forces* are the only intermolecular forces between nonpolar ethane molecules, and thus ethane has a low boiling point.
(b) The major intermolecular force between ethyl alcohol molecules is *hydrogen bonding*, which causes ethyl alcohol to be high boiling. Dipole–dipole interactions and London forces are also present but are weaker than hydrogen bonding.
(c) *Dipole–dipole* interactions are the principal forces between ethyl chloride molecules and cause the boiling point of ethyl chloride to be higher than that of ethane. London forces are also present.

8.21 To melt isopropyl alcohol:

$$1.50 \text{ mol} \times \frac{60.0 \text{ g}}{1 \text{ mol}} \times \frac{21.4 \text{ cal}}{1 \text{ g}} \times \frac{1 \text{ kcal}}{10^3 \text{ cal}} = 1.93 \text{ kcal}$$

To boil isopropyl alcohol:

$$1.50 \text{ mol} \times \frac{60.0 \text{ g}}{1 \text{ mol}} \times \frac{159 \text{ cal}}{1 \text{ g}} \times \frac{1 \text{ kcal}}{10^3 \text{ cal}} = 14.3 \text{ kcal}$$

Understanding Key Concepts

8.22

(a)   (b)   (c)

(a) According to Charles' Law, the volume of a gas at fixed pressure is directly proportional to its temperature. Since the temperature increases by 50% (from 300 K to 450 K), volume also increases by 50%.
(b) Boyle's Law states that the volume of a gas is inversely proportional to its pressure. Doubling the pressure halves the volume.
(c) For changes in both pressure and temperature, the Combined Gas Law states that *PV/T* is constant. Thus, reducing both the pressure and the temperature by one-third leaves the volume unchanged.

8.23   Drawing (c) represents the gas in a sealed container after the temperature has been lowered from 350 K to 150 K. The gas remains a gas and its volume is unchanged; only pressure is reduced.

8.24   Drawing (a) shows the sample of water as a solid, its state at 200 K. At 300 K, water is a liquid with a very low vapor pressure (as shown in Figure 8.20), represented by drawing (c).

8.25   At equilibrium, the gases are totally mixed.

8.26

8.27   The horizontal parts of the curve represent phase changes.
   (a) Melting point: 10°C.
   (b) Boiling point: 75°C.
   (c) Heat of fusion: 1 kcal/mol (the distance between the two points of the curve at the melting point).
   (d) Heat of vaporization: 7.5 kcal/mol (the distance between the two points of the curve at the boiling point).

8.28 Refer to Problem 8.13 for an approach to solving this problem. Note the quantities that change and those that remain constant; these differ in each part of the problem. Be sure to convert temperature to Kelvins.

(a) $\dfrac{V_2}{V_1} = \dfrac{n_2 T_2 P_1}{n_1 T_1 P_2} = \dfrac{T_2}{T_1}$; $\dfrac{V_2}{V_1} = \dfrac{(323 \text{ K})}{((298 \text{ K})} = 1.08$

(b) $\dfrac{V_2}{V_1} = \dfrac{n_2 T_2 P_1}{n_1 T_1 P_2} = \dfrac{T_2 P_1}{T_1 P_2}$; $\dfrac{V_2}{V_1} = \dfrac{(448 \text{ K})(0.92 \text{ atm})}{((298 \text{ K})(2.7 \text{ atm})} = 0.51$

(c) $\dfrac{V_2}{V_1} = \dfrac{n_2 T_2 P_1}{n_1 T_1 P_2} = \dfrac{n_2 P_1}{n_1 P_2}$; $\dfrac{V_2}{V_1} = \dfrac{(0.22 \text{ mol})(0.92 \text{ atm})}{(0.075 \text{ mol})(2.7 \text{ atm})} = 1.0$

(a)	(b)	(c)

$T = 298 \text{ K}$ $T = 323 \text{ K}$ $T = 448 \text{ K}$ $T = 298 \text{ K}$

$n = 0.075 \text{ mol}$ $n = 0.075 \text{ mol}$ $n = 0.075 \text{ mol}$ $n = 0.22 \text{ mol}$

$P = 0.92 \text{ atm}$ $P = 0.92 \text{ atm}$ $P = 2.7 \text{ atm}$ $P = 2.7 \text{ atm}$

8.29 The proportions of each gas in the container:
$P_{red} + P_{yellow} + P_{green} = 600 \text{ mm}$:
    red = 6/12 = 1/2;   yellow = 2/12 = 1/6;   green = 4/12 = 1/3
$P_{red} = 1/2 \times 600 \text{ mm Hg} = 300 \text{ mm Hg}$;
$P_{yellow} = 1/6 \times 600 \text{ mm Hg} = 100 \text{ mm Hg}$
$P_{green} = 1/3 \times 600 \text{ mm Hg} = 200 \text{ mm Hg}$

Gases and Pressure

8.30 One atmosphere is the amount of pressure needed to hold a column of mercury 760 mm high.

8.31 Four common units for measuring pressure: atmosphere(atm), mm Hg, pounds per square inch (psi), Pascal (Pa).
        1 atm = 760 mm Hg = 14.7 psi = 101,325 Pa

8.32 (1) A gas consists of many tiny particles moving about at random with no attractive forces between particles.
(2) The amount of space occupied by gas molecules is much smaller than the amount of space between molecules.
(3) The average kinetic energy of gas particles is proportional to Kelvin temperature.
(4) When molecules collide, they spring apart elastically, and their total energy is constant.

8.33 According to the kinetic-molecular theory of gases, gas pressure is due to collisions with the walls of the container. The more collisions, the higher the pressure.

8.34

(a) $1 \text{ atm} \times \dfrac{760 \text{ mm Hg}}{1 \text{ atm}} = 760 \text{ mm Hg}$

(b) $0.25 \text{ atm} \times \dfrac{760 \text{ mm Hg}}{1 \text{ atm}} = 190 \text{ mm Hg}$

(c) $7.5 \text{ atm} \times \dfrac{760 \text{ mm Hg}}{1 \text{ atm}} = 5.7 \times 10^3 \text{ mm Hg}$

(d) $28.0 \text{ in. Hg} \times \dfrac{25.4 \text{ mm}}{1 \text{ in.}} = 711 \text{ mm Hg}$

(e) $41.8 \text{ Pa} \times \dfrac{760 \text{ mm Hg}}{101,325 \text{ Pa}} = 0.314 \text{ mm Hg}$

8.35

(a) $440 \text{ mm Hg} \times \dfrac{1 \text{ atm}}{760 \text{ mm Hg}} = 0.58 \text{ atm}$

(b) $440 \text{ mm Hg} \times \dfrac{133.3224 \text{ Pa}}{1 \text{ mm Hg}} = 59,000 \text{ Pa}$

8.36 When the level in the arm connected to the container is 176 mm (17.6 cm) lower than the level open to the atmosphere, the pressure in the gas container is greater than atmospheric pressure.

$754.3 \text{ mm Hg} + 176 \text{ mm Hg} = 930 \text{ mm Hg}$

8.37 When the level in the arm connected to the container is 283 mm (28.3 cm) higher than the level open to the atmosphere, the pressure in the gas container is less than atmospheric pressure.

$283 \text{ mm Hg} \times \dfrac{1 \text{ atm}}{760 \text{ mm Hg}} = 0.372 \text{ atm}$ $1.021 \text{ atm} - 0.372 \text{ atm} = 0.649 \text{ atm}$

Boyle's Law

8.38 Boyle's law: Volume varies inversely with pressure at constant temperature and number of moles; that is, $P_1V_1 = P_2V_2$.

8.39 Boyle's law involves an inverse proportionality: Pressure and volume change in opposite directions.

8.40 $P_1V_1 = P_2V_2$; $P_1 = 65.0 \text{ mm Hg}$; $P_2 = 385 \text{ mm Hg}$; $V_1 = 600.0 \text{ mL} = 0.600 \text{ L}$; $V_2 = ?$

$V_2 = \dfrac{P_1V_1}{P_2} = \dfrac{65.0 \text{ mm Hg} \times 0.600 \text{ L}}{385 \text{ mm Hg}} = 0.101 \text{ L} = 101 \text{ mL}$

8.41 $P_1V_1 = P_2V_2$; $P_1 = 1.00$ atm; $P_2 = ?$; $V_1 = 3.50$ L; $V_2 = 2.00$ L

$$P_2 = \frac{P_1V_1}{V_2} = \frac{1.00 \text{ atm x } 3.50 \text{ L}}{2.00 \text{ L}} = 1.75 \text{ atm}$$

8.42 $P_1V_1 = P_2V_2$; $P_1 = 150$ atm; $P_2 = 1.00$ atm; $V_1 = 50.0$ L; $V_2 = ?$

$$V_2 = \frac{P_1V_1}{P_2} = \frac{150 \text{ atm x } 50.0 \text{ L}}{1.00 \text{ atm}} = 7500 \text{ L} = 7.5 \text{ x } 10^3 \text{ L}$$

8.43 $P_1V_1 = P_2V_2$; $P_1 = 14.7$ psi; $P_2 = ?$; $V_1 = 10.0$ cc; $V_2 = 2.00$ cc

$$P_2 = \frac{P_1V_1}{V_2} = \frac{14.7 \text{ psi x } 10.0 \text{ cc}}{2.00 \text{ cc}} = 73.5 \text{ psi}$$

Charles's Law

8.44 Charles's law: Volume varies directly with temperature at constant pressure and number of moles; that is, $V_1/T_1 = V_2/T_2$.

8.45 Charles's law involves a direct proportionality: Volume and temperature change in the same direction.

8.46

$$\frac{V_1}{T_1} = \frac{V_2}{T_2}; \qquad V_1 = 960 \text{ L}; \ V_2 = 1200 \text{ L}; \ T_1 = 18°C = 291 \text{ K}; \ T_2 = ?$$

$$T_2 = \frac{V_2T_1}{V_1} = \frac{1200 \text{ L x } 291 \text{ K}}{960 \text{ L}} = 364 \text{ K} = 91° \text{ C}$$

8.47

$$\frac{V_1}{T_1} = \frac{V_2}{T_2}; \qquad V_1 = 875 \text{ L}; \ V_2 = 955 \text{ L}; \ T_1 = ? \ ; \ T_2 = 56°C = 329 \text{ K}$$

$$T_1 = \frac{V_1T_2}{V_2} = \frac{875 \text{ L x } 329 \text{ K}}{955 \text{ L}} = 301 \text{ K} = 28 ° \text{ C}$$

8.48

$$\frac{V_1}{T_1} = \frac{V_2}{T_2}; \qquad V_1 = 125 \text{ mL}; \ V_2 = ?; \ T_1 = 25°C = 298 \text{ K}; \ T_2 = 37°C = 310 \text{ K}$$

$$V_2 = \frac{V_1T_2}{T_1} = \frac{125 \text{ mL x } 310 \text{ K}}{298 \text{ K}} = 130 \text{ mL}$$

8.49

$$\frac{V_1}{T_1} = \frac{V_2}{T_2}; \qquad V_1 = 43.0 \text{ L}; \ V_2 = ?; \ T_1 = 20°C = 293 \text{ K}; \ T_2 = -5°C = 268 \text{ K}$$

$$V_2 = \frac{V_1T_2}{T_1} = \frac{43.0 \text{ L x } 268 \text{ K}}{293 \text{ K}} = 39.3 \text{ L}$$

Gay-Lussac's Law

8.50 Gay-Lussac's law: Pressure varies directly with temperature at constant volume and number of moles; that is, $P_1/T_1 = P_2/T_2$.

8.51 Gay-Lussac's law involves a direct proportionality: Pressure and temperature change in the same direction.

8.52

$$\frac{P_1}{T_1} = \frac{P_2}{T_2}; \quad P_1 = 0.95 \text{ atm}; \ P_2 = ?; \ T_1 = 25°C = 298 \text{ K}; \ T_2 = 125°C = 398 \text{ K}$$

$$P_2 = \frac{P_1 T_2}{T_1} = \frac{0.95 \text{ atm} \times 398 \text{ K}}{298 \text{ K}} = 1.3 \text{ atm}$$

8.53

$$\frac{P_1}{T_1} = \frac{P_2}{T_2}; \quad P_1 = 3.75 \text{ atm}; \ P_2 = 16.6 \text{ atm}; \ T_1 = 25°C = 298 \text{ K}; \ T_2 = ?$$

$$T_2 = \frac{P_2 T_1}{P_1} = \frac{16.6 \text{ atm} \times 298 \text{ K}}{3.75 \text{ atm}} = 1320 \text{ K} = 1050°C$$

Combined Gas Law

8.54

$$\frac{P_1 V_1}{T_1} = \frac{P_2 V_2}{T_2}; \quad P_1 = 760 \text{ mm Hg}; \ V_1 = 2.84 \text{ L}; \ T_1 = 273 \text{ K}$$
$$P_2 = 520 \text{ mm Hg}; \ V_2 = 7.50 \text{ L}; \ T_2 = ?$$

$$T_2 = \frac{P_2 V_2 T_1}{P_1 V_1} = \frac{520 \text{ mm Hg} \times 7.50 \text{ L} \times 273 \text{ K}}{760 \text{ mm Hg} \times 2.84 \text{ L}} = 493 \text{ K} = 220° \text{ C}$$

8.55

$$\frac{P_1 V_1}{T_1} = \frac{P_2 V_2}{T_2}; \quad P_1 = 1.14 \text{ atm}; \ V_1 = 3.50 \text{ L}; \ T_1 = 22.0° \text{ C} = 295 \text{ K}$$
$$P_2 = 1.20 \text{ atm}; \ V_2 = ?; \ T_2 = 30.0°C = 303 \text{ K}$$

$$V_2 = \frac{P_1 V_1 T_2}{T_1 P_2} = \frac{1.14 \text{ atm} \times 3.50 \text{ L} \times 303 \text{ K}}{295 \text{ K} \times 1.20 \text{ atm}} = 3.42 \text{ L}$$

8.56

$$\frac{P_1 V_1}{T_1} = \frac{P_2 V_2}{T_2}; \quad P_1 = 749 \text{ mm Hg}; \ V_1 = 55.0 \text{ mL}; \ T_1 = 26° \text{ C} = 299 \text{ K}$$
$$P_2 = 760 \text{ mm Hg}; \ V_2 = ?; \ T_2 = 0°C = 273 \text{ K}$$

$$V_2 = \frac{P_1 V_1 T_2}{T_1 P_2} = \frac{749 \text{ mm Hg} \times 55.0 \text{ mL} \times 273 \text{ K}}{299 \text{ K} \times 760 \text{ mm Hg}} = 49.5 \text{ mL}$$

8.57

$$\frac{P_1V_1}{T_1} = \frac{P_2V_2}{T_2}; \qquad P_1 = 140 \text{ atm}; \ V_1 = 8.00 \text{ L}; \ T_1 = 20°\text{ C} = 293 \text{ K}$$

$$P_2 = 1.00 \text{ atm}; \ V_2 = ?; \ T_2 = 273 \text{ K}$$

$$V_2 = \frac{P_1V_1T_2}{T_1P_2} = \frac{140 \text{ atm } \times \ 8.00 \text{ L } \times \ 273 \text{ K}}{293 \text{ K } \times \ 1.00 \text{ atm}} = 1040 \text{ L} = 1.04 \times 10^3 \text{ L}$$

8.58 (a) For one mole of gas, the combined gas law states that P is proportional to T/V, or P $\propto$ T/V. Thus, if the temperature doubles and the volume is halved, the new pressure is four times greater than the original pressure:

$$\frac{P_1V_1}{T_1} = \frac{P_2V_2}{T_2}; \qquad V_2 = 0.5 \ V_1; \ T_2 = 2 \ T_1; \ P_2 = ?$$

$$P_2 = \frac{P_1V_1T_2}{T_1V_2} = \frac{P_1V_1 \ \times \ 2T_1}{T_1 \ \times \ 0.5V_1} = 4 \ P_1$$

(b) If the temperature is halved and the volume is doubled, the new pressure is one fourth the original pressure:

$$\frac{P_1V_1}{T_1} = \frac{P_2V_2}{T_2}; \qquad V_2 = 2 \ V_1; \ T_2 = 0.5 \ T_1; \ P_2 = ?$$

$$P_2 = \frac{P_1V_1T_2}{T_1V_2} = \frac{P_1V_1 \ \times \ 0.5T_1}{T_1 \ \times \ 2V_1} = 0.25 \ P_1$$

8.59 (a) For one mole of gas, the combined gas law states that V is proportional to T/P, or $V \propto$ T/P. Thus, if the pressure is halved and the temperature is doubled, the new volume is four times greater than the original volume.

$$\frac{P_1V_1}{T_1} = \frac{P_2V_2}{T_2}; \qquad P_2 = 0.5 \ P_1; \ T_2 = 2 \ T_1; \ V_2 = ?$$

$$V_2 = \frac{P_1V_1T_2}{T_1P_2} = \frac{P_1V_1 \ \times \ 2T_1}{T_1 \ \times \ 0.5 \ P_1} = 4 \ V_1$$

(b) If both the pressure and the temperature are doubled, the volume remains the same.

$$\frac{P_1V_1}{T_1} = \frac{P_2V_2}{T_2}; \qquad P_2 = 2 \ P_1; \ T_2 = 2 \ T_1; \ V_2 = ?$$

$$V_2 = \frac{P_1V_1T_2}{T_1P_2} = \frac{P_1V_1 \ \times \ 2T_1}{T_1 \ \times \ 2 \ P_1} = V_1$$

8.60

$$\frac{P_1V_1}{T_1} = \frac{P_2V_2}{T_2};$$

$$P_1 = 775 \text{ mm Hg}; \; V_1 = 590 \text{ mL}; \; T_1 = 352 \text{ K}$$

$$P_2 = 800.0 \text{ mm Hg}; \; V_2 = ?; \; T_2 = 298 \text{ K}$$

$$V_2 = \frac{P_1V_1T_2}{P_2T_1} = \frac{775 \text{ mm Hg} \times 590 \text{ mL} \times 298 \text{ K}}{800.0 \text{ mm Hg} \times 352 \text{ K}} = 484 \text{ mL}$$

8.61 In this problem, temperature is constant. First, we find the volume of gas at 1.25 atm and 25°C.

$$P_1V_1 = P_2V_2; \; P_1 = 1850 \text{ atm}; \; P_2 = 1.25 \text{ atm}; \; V_1 = 2.30 \text{ L}; \; V_2 = ?$$

$$V_2 = \frac{P_1V_1}{P_2} = \frac{1850 \text{ atm} \times 2.30 \text{ L}}{1.25 \text{ atm}} = 3400 \text{ L}$$

If the cylinder holds 3400 L of helium at 1.25 atm and 25°C, it can be used to fill 3400 L / 1.50 L = 2270 balloons.

Avogadro's Law and Standard Molar Volume

8.62 Avogadro's law states that equal volumes of gases at the same temperature and pressure contain equal numbers of molecules. Since the volume of space taken up by gas molecules is so much smaller than the amount of space between molecules, Avogadro's Law is true regardless of the chemical identity of the gas.

8.63 The conditions of STP are 760 mm Hg (1 atm) pressure and 273 K temperature.

8.64 A mole of gas at STP occupies 22.4 L.

8.65 The samples contain equal numbers of molecules. 1.0 L of O_2 weighs more than 1.0 L of H_2 because the molecular weight of O_2 is greater than the molecular weight of H_2, and equal numbers of moles of both are present.

8.66

$$0.20 \text{ g Cl}_2 \times \frac{1 \text{ mol Cl}_2}{71 \text{ g Cl}_2} \times \frac{22.4 \text{ L}}{1 \text{ mol Cl}_2} = 0.063 \text{ L} = 63 \text{ mL}$$

8.67

$$1.75 \text{ g HCN} \times \frac{1 \text{ mol}}{27.0 \text{ g HCN}} \times \frac{22.4 \text{ L}}{1 \text{ mol HCN}} = 1.45 \text{ L HCN at STP}$$

8.68

$$V = 4.0 \text{ m} \times 5.0 \text{ m} \times 2.5 \text{ m} = 50 \text{ m}^3; \; 50 \text{ m}^3 \times \frac{10^3 \text{ L}}{1 \text{ m}^3} = 5.0 \times 10^4 \text{ L}$$

$$\frac{1 \text{ mol}}{22.4 \text{ L}} \times 5.0 \times 10^4 \text{ L} = 2230 \text{ mol gas}$$

$$0.21 \times 2230 \text{ mol O}_2 = 470 \text{ mol O}_2$$

$$470 \text{ mol O}_2 \times \frac{32.0 \text{ g O}_2}{1 \text{ mol O}_2} = 15000 \text{g O}_2 = 15 \text{ kg O}_2$$

8.69 0.79×2230 mol $N_2 = 1760$ mol N_2

1760 mol N_2 x $\dfrac{28.0 \text{ g } N_2}{1 \text{ mol } N_2} = 49000$ g $N_2 = 49$ kg N_2

The Ideal Gas Law

8.70   The ideal gas law : $PV = nRT$

8.71   The combined gas law can be used to calculate changes in P, V and T when the amount of gas is fixed. The ideal gas law is valid for any number of moles and uses the ideal gas constant R to calculate any one of the variables P, V, T and n if the other three are known.

8.72 $PV = nRT$; $n = PV/RT$;

For Cl_2: $P = 1.0$ atm; $V = 2.0$ L; $R = 0.082 \dfrac{\text{L·atm}}{\text{mol·K}}$; $T = 273$ K

$$n = \dfrac{1.0 \text{ atm x } 2.0 \text{ L}}{0.082 \dfrac{\text{L·atm}}{\text{mol·K}} \text{ x } 273 \text{ K}} = 0.089 \text{ mol } Cl_2$$

0.089 mol Cl_2 x $\dfrac{71 \text{ g}}{1 \text{ mol } Cl_2} = 6.3$ g Cl_2

For CH_4: $P = 1.5$ atm; $V = 3.0$ L; $R = 0.082 \dfrac{\text{L·atm}}{\text{mol·K}}$; $T = 300$ K

$$n = \dfrac{1.5 \text{ atm x } 3.0 \text{ L}}{0.082 \dfrac{\text{L·atm}}{\text{mol·K}} \text{ x } 300 \text{ K}} = 0.18 \text{ mol } CH_4$$

0.18 mol CH_4 x $\dfrac{16.0 \text{ g}}{1 \text{ mol } CH_4} = 2.9$ g CH_4

There are more molecules in the CH_4 sample than in the Cl_2 sample. The Cl_2 sample, however, weighs more because the molar mass of Cl_2 is much greater than the molar mass of CH_4.

8.73   As in the preceding problem, use the relationship $n = PV/RT$.

For CO_2 : $n = \dfrac{500 \text{ mm Hg x } 2.0 \text{ L } CO_2}{62.4 \dfrac{\text{mm Hg·L}}{\text{mol·K}} \text{ x } 300 \text{ K}} = 0.053 \text{ mol } CO_2$

For N_2 : $n = \dfrac{760 \text{ mm Hg x } 1.5 \text{ L } N_2}{62.4 \dfrac{\text{mm Hg·L}}{\text{mol·K}} \text{ x } 330 \text{ K}} = 0.055 \text{ mol } N_2$

The CO_2 sample has slightly fewer molecules. Since the formula weight of CO_2 is much greater than the formula weight of N_2, however, the CO_2 sample weighs more (2.3 g) than the N_2 sample (1.5 g).

8.74

$$n = 15.0 \text{ g CO}_2 \text{ x } \frac{1 \text{ mol}}{44 \text{ g}} = 0.34 \text{ mol CO}_2; \quad T = 310 \text{ K}; \quad V = 0.30 \text{ L}$$

$$P = \frac{nRT}{V} = \frac{0.34 \text{ mol CO}_2 \text{ x } 62.4 \frac{\text{mm Hg·L}}{\text{mol·K}} \text{ x } 310 \text{ K}}{0.30 \text{ L}} = 2.2 \text{ x } 10^4 \text{ mm Hg}$$

8.75

$$PV = nRT; \quad n = 20.0 \text{ g N}_2 \text{ x } \frac{1 \text{ mol}}{28.0 \text{ g}} = 0.714 \text{ mol N}_2; \quad V = 4.00 \text{ L}; \quad P = 6.00 \text{ atm}$$

$$T = \frac{PV}{nR} = \frac{6.00 \text{ atm } \text{ x } 4.00 \text{ L}}{0.714 \text{ mol } \text{ x } 0.0821 \frac{\text{L·atm}}{\text{mol·K}}} = 409 \text{ K}$$

8.76

$$n = 18.0 \text{ g O}_2 \text{ x } \frac{1 \text{ mol}}{32.0 \text{ g}} = 0.56 \text{ mol O}_2; \quad T = 350 \text{ K}; \quad P = 550 \text{ mm Hg}$$

$$V = \frac{nRT}{P} = \frac{0.56 \text{ mol O}_2 \text{ x } 62.4 \frac{\text{mm Hg·L}}{\text{mol·K}} \text{ x } 350 \text{ K}}{550 \text{ mm Hg}} = 22 \text{ L O}_2$$

8.77

$$n = \frac{PV}{RT}; \quad P = 2.5 \text{ atm}; \quad V = 0.55 \text{ L}; \quad T = 347 \text{ K}$$

$$= \frac{2.5 \text{ atm } \text{ x } 0.55 \text{ L}}{0.082 \frac{\text{L·atm}}{\text{mol·K}} \text{ x } 347 \text{ K}} = 0.048 \text{ moles}$$

Dalton's Law and Partial Pressure

8.78 Partial pressure is the pressure contribution of one component of a mixture of gases to the total pressure.

8.79 Dalton's law of partial pressure says that the total pressure exerted by a gas mixture is the sum of the individual pressures of the components in the mixture.

8.80

$$440 \text{ mm Hg } \text{ x } \frac{1 \text{ atm}}{760 \text{ mm Hg}} \text{ x } \frac{160 \text{ mm Hg}}{1.0 \text{ atm}} = 93 \text{ mm Hg}$$

8.81 Each 100 g of gas contains 1.00 g CO_2 and 99.0 g O_2 , or:

$$1.00 \text{ g } CO_2 \text{ x } \frac{1 \text{ mol}}{44.0 \text{ g}} = 0.0227 \text{ mol } CO_2 \qquad 99.0 \text{ g } O_2 \text{ x } \frac{1 \text{ mol}}{32.0 \text{ g}} = 3.09 \text{ mol } O_2$$

Total moles: 3.09 mol + 0.02 mol = 3.11 mol

According to Dalton's law, the total pressure of a gas sample equals the sum of the partial pressures of the individual gases.

$$\text{For } O_2: \frac{3.09 \text{ mol } O_2}{3.11 \text{ mol gas}} \text{ x } 0.977 \text{ atm} = 0.971 \text{ atm}$$

$$\text{For } CO_2: \frac{0.0227 \text{ mol } CO_2}{3.11 \text{ mol gas}} \text{ x } 0.977 \text{ atm} = 0.0071 \text{ atm}$$

Liquids and Intermolecular Forces

8.82 The vapor pressure of a liquid is the partial pressure of the vapor above the liquid.

8.83 At a liquid's normal boiling point, its vapor pressure equals 1 atm pressure.

8.84 Increased pressure raises a liquid's boiling point; decreased pressure lowers a liquid's boiling point.

8.85 A liquid's heat of vaporization is the amount of heat needed to vaporize one gram of the liquid at its boiling point.

8.86 (a) All molecules exhibit London forces, which increase in strength with increasing molecular weight.
(b) Dipole-dipole interactions are important for molecules that have polar covalent bonds.
(c) Hydrogen bonding occurs between an unshared electron pair on an electronegative atom (O, N, or F) and a hydrogen atom bonded to a second electronegative atom (O, N, F).

8.87 Dipole–dipole interactions are most important in compounds that do not exhibit ionic bonding or hydrogen bonding and have polar covalent bonds. Thus, dipole–dipole interactions are most important only for HCN (b) and CH_3Cl (e). (CCl_4 has polar covalent bonds, but it is symmetrical.)

8.88 Ethanol is higher boiling than dimethyl ether because of hydrogen bonding. Since molecules of ethanol are strongly attracted to each other, the boiling point of ethanol is higher than that of dimethyl ether, whose molecules are held together by weaker dipole-dipole interactions.

8.89 London forces are the major attractive forces for Br_2 and I_2 molecules. Since London forces become stronger with increasing molecular weight, the melting point of I_2 is higher than the melting point of Br_2.

8.90

(a) $\dfrac{9.72 \text{ kcal}}{1 \text{ mol H}_2\text{O}}$ x 3.00 mol H$_2$O = 29.2 kcal of heat required

(b) $\dfrac{9.72 \text{ kcal}}{1 \text{ mol H}_2\text{O}}$ x $\dfrac{1 \text{ mol H}_2\text{O}}{18.0 \text{ g}}$ x 255 g = 138 kcal of heat is released

8.91

$\dfrac{8.25 \text{ kcal}}{1 \text{ mol C}_8\text{H}_{18}}$ x $\dfrac{1 \text{ mol C}_8\text{H}_{18}}{114.0 \text{ g}}$ x 100.0 g = 7.24 kcal of heat is required

Solids

8.92 The atoms in a crystalline solid are arranged in a regular, orderly network. The atoms in an amorphous solid have no regular arrangement.

8.93

Type of Solid	*Example*
Ionic solid	NaCl, MgBr$_2$
Molecular solid	Ice, sucrose
Covalent network solid	Diamond
Metallic solid	Cu, Fe

8.94

$\dfrac{45.9 \text{ cal}}{1 \text{ g}}$ x $\dfrac{1 \text{ kcal}}{1000 \text{ cal}}$ x $\dfrac{60.0 \text{ g}}{1 \text{ mol}}$ x 1.66 mol = 4.57 kcal

8.95

$\dfrac{630 \text{ cal}}{1 \text{ mol Na}}$ x $\dfrac{1 \text{ kcal}}{1000 \text{ cal}}$ x $\dfrac{1 \text{ mol Na}}{23.0 \text{ g Na}}$ x 245 g Na = 6.71 kcal

Applications

8.96 *Systolic pressure* (the higher number) is the maximum blood pressure developed in the artery just after contraction. *Diastolic pressure* (the lower number) is the minimum pressure that occurs at the end of the heartbeat cycle. A blood pressure reading of 180/110 is an indication of high blood pressure.

8.97 The three most important greenhouse gases are carbon dioxide, water vapor and methane.

8.98 Normally, a large portion of solar radiation is reflected back into space. Greenhouse gases such as CO$_2$ trap some of this radiation, which warms the atmosphere. The larger the amount of greenhouse gas, the greater the amount of radiation absorbed, and the greater the warming.

8.99 A biomaterial is a substance that has been created specifically for use in biological systems and that does not provoke an immune response.

8.100 The supercritical state of matter is a situation intermediate between solid and gas, in which there is some space between molecules yet they are too close together to be truly a gas.

8.101 Supercritical CO$_2$ is nontoxic and nonflammable and can be continuously recycled.

General Questions and Problems

8.102 As the temperature increases, the kinetic energy of gas molecules increases, and the force per unit area which they exert in colliding against the walls of a container increases, thus increasing pressure.

8.103 Two moles of hydrogen react with one mole of oxygen according to the balanced equation. Since equal volumes of gases have equal numbers of moles at STP, 2.5 L of O_2 reacts with 5.0 L of H_2.

8.104 3.0 L of H_2 and 1.5 L of O_2 react completely. At STP, one mole of H_2 occupies 22.4 L. Thus, 3.0 L of hydrogen = 3.0/22.4 or 0.13 mol. This is also the number of moles of H_2O formed.

$$n = 0.13 \text{ mol } H_2O \; ; \quad T = 373 \text{ K} \; ; \quad P = 1.0 \text{ atm}$$

$$V = \frac{nRT}{P} = \frac{0.13 \text{ mol } H_2O \; \text{x} \; 0.0821 \dfrac{\text{L·atm}}{\text{mol·K}} \; \text{x} \; 373 \text{ K}}{1.0 \text{ atm}} = 4.0 \text{ L } H_2O$$

8.105 $PV = nRT$; $P = 1.0$ atm; $V = 0.24$ L; $T = 310$ K

$$n = \frac{PV}{RT} = \frac{1.0 \text{ atm x } 0.24 \text{ L}}{0.0821 \dfrac{\text{L·atm}}{\text{mol·K}} \text{ x } 310 \text{ K}} = 0.0094 \text{ mol} = 9.4 \text{ mmol } CO_2$$

8.106

$$0.0094 \text{ mol } CO_2 \; \text{x} \; \frac{44.0 \text{ g } CO_2}{1 \text{ mol } CO_2} = 0.41 \text{ g } CO_2$$

$$\frac{0.41 \text{ g } CO_2}{1 \text{ min}} \; \text{x} \; \frac{60 \text{ min}}{1 \text{ hr}} \; \text{x} \; \frac{24 \text{ hr}}{1 \text{ day}} = \frac{590 \text{ g } CO_2}{\text{day}}$$

8.107 At STP, equal volumes of gases have an equal number of moles. However, O_2 has a greater molecular weight than H_2, and the vessel containing O_2 is heavier.

8.108

Gas	Molecular Weight	Density (g/L) at STP
(a) CH_4	16.0 amu	0.714
(b) CO_2	44.0 amu	1.96
(c) O_2	32.0 amu	1.43

8.109 $n = 1$ mol ; $T = 1$ K ; $P = 1 \text{ x } 10^{-14}$ mm Hg

$$V = \frac{nRT}{P} = \frac{1 \text{ mol x } 62.4 \dfrac{\text{mm Hg·L}}{\text{mol·K}} \text{ x } 1 \text{ K}}{1 \text{ x } 10^{-14} \text{ mm Hg}} = 6 \text{ x } 10^{15} \text{ L}$$

$$\text{Density} = \frac{6.022 \text{ x } 10^{23} \text{ atoms}}{6 \text{ x } 10^{15} \text{ L}} = \frac{1 \text{ x } 10^{8} \text{ atoms}}{\text{L}}$$

8.110

(a)

H—$\overset{\displaystyle\cdot\cdot}{\underset{\displaystyle\cdot\cdot}{O}}$—$\overset{\displaystyle H}{\underset{\displaystyle H}{C}}$—$\overset{\displaystyle H}{\underset{\displaystyle H}{C}}$—$\overset{\displaystyle\cdot\cdot}{\underset{\displaystyle\cdot\cdot}{O}}$—H

(b)

H—$\overset{\displaystyle H}{\underset{\displaystyle H}{C}}$—$\overset{\displaystyle H}{\underset{\displaystyle H}{C}}$—$\overset{\displaystyle\cdot\cdot}{\underset{\displaystyle\cdot\cdot}{Cl}}$:

Ethylene glycol   Chloromethane

(c) Ethylene glycol is higher boiling than chloroethane because it forms hydrogen bonds.

8.111 (a) For N_2: $P_1V_1 = P_2V_2$; $P_1 = 35.0$ atm; $P_2 = ?$; $V_1 = 25.0$ L; $V_2 = 15.0$ L

$$P_2 = \frac{P_1V_1}{V_2} = \frac{35.0 \text{ atm} \times 25.0 \text{ L}}{15.0 \text{ L}} = 58.3 \text{ atm}$$

For O_2: $P_1 = 15.0$ atm; $P_2 = ?$; $V_1 = 10.0$ L; $V_2 = 15.0$ L

$$P_2 = \frac{P_1V_1}{V_2} = \frac{15.0 \text{ atm} \times 10.0 \text{ L}}{15.0 \text{ L}} = 10.0 \text{ atm}$$

(b) Total pressure = 58.3 atm + 10.0 atm = 68.3 atm.

8.112 (a) Since the size of a Rankine degree is the same as a Fahrenheit degree, we can use the same conversion factor as we use for °F/°C conversions.

$$\frac{9°R}{5°C} \times 273.15°C = 492°R$$

(b) To calculate the gas constant R, use the ideal gas law at standard temperature and pressure.

$R = \frac{PV}{nT}$; $P = 1$ atm; $V = 22.4$ L; $n = 1$ mol; $T = 492°R$

$$R = \frac{1 \text{ atm} \times 22.4 \text{ L}}{1 \text{ mol} \times 492°R} = 0.0455 \frac{\text{L·atm}}{\text{mol·}°R}$$

8.113 (a) $2 C_8H_{18} + 25 O_2 \longrightarrow 16 CO_2 + 18 H_2O$

(b) $4.6 \times 10^{10} \text{ L } C_8H_{18} \times \frac{0.792 \text{ g}}{1 \text{ mL}} \times \frac{10^3 \text{ mL}}{1 \text{ L}} = 3.6 \times 10^{13} \text{ g } C_8H_{18}$

$= 3.6 \times 10^{10} \text{ kg } C_8H_{18}$

$3.6 \times 10^{13} \text{g } C_8H_{18} \times \frac{1 \text{ mol } C_8H_{18}}{114 \text{ g } C_8H_{18}} \times \frac{16 \text{ mol } CO_2}{2 \text{ mol } C_8H_{18}} \times \frac{44.0 \text{ g } CO_2}{1 \text{ mol } CO_2} = 1.1 \times 10^{14} \text{ g } CO_2$

$= 1.1 \times 10^{11} \text{ kg } CO_2$

(c) To find the volume of CO_2, use the ideal gas law at STP; n can be calculated from the mass of CO_2 that was found in part (b).

$$n = 1.1 \times 10^{14} \text{ g } CO_2 \times \frac{1 \text{ mol } CO_2}{44 \text{ g } CO_2} = 2.5 \times 10^{12} \text{ mol } CO_2$$

$$V = \frac{nRT}{P} = \frac{2.5 \times 10^{12} \text{ mol } CO_2 \times 0.0821 \frac{\text{L·atm}}{\text{mol·K}} \times 273 \text{ K}}{1.0 \text{ atm}} = 5.6 \times 10^{13} \text{ L } CO_2$$

Self-Test for Chapter 8

Multiple choice:

1. Which of the following units would you be least likely to use in a laboratory?
   (a) Pascal   (b) pounds per square inch   (c) mm Hg   (d) atmosphere

2. A fixed amount of a gas has its temperature and volume doubled. What happens to its pressure?
   (a) increases fourfold   (b) doubles   (c) stays the same   (d) is halved

3. In which of the gas laws is the amount of gas not fixed?
   (a) Boyle's law   (b) Charles' law   (c) Gay-Lussac's law   (d) Avogadro's law

4. Which of the following compounds does not exhibit hydrogen bonding?
   (a) CH_3OCH_3 (b) CH_3OH (c) HF   (d) CH_3NH_2

5. Which of the following compounds is the lowest melting?
   (a) NaI   (b) Au   (c) SiO_2 (d) sugar

6. Which term describes the change of state that occurs when a gas changes to a solid?
   (a) fusion   (b) condensation   (c) deposition   (d) sublimation

7. When does a gas obey ideal behavior?
   (a) at low density   (b) at high pressure   (c) at low temperature   (d) in a large container

8. If 22.0 g of CO_2 has a pressure of 1.00 atm at 300 K, what is its volume?
   (a) 22.4 L   (b) 12.3 L   (c) 11.2 L   (d) 9.5 L

9. What volume does the amount of gas in the previous problem occupy at STP?
   (a) 22.4 L   (b) 12.3 L   (c) 11.2 L   (d) 9.5 L

10. What is the density of CO_2 gas in g/L at STP if one mole of gas has a volume of 22.4 L?
    (a) 44.0 g/L   (b) 11.0 g/L   (c) 6.4 g/L   (d) 1.96 g/L

Complete the following sentences:

1. In Boyle's law, the _____ of a gas is inversely proportional to its _____.

2. A liquid has _____ volume and _____ shape.

3. _____ law states that the total pressure of a gas mixture is the sum of the individual pressure of the components in the mixture.

4. A pressure of 760 mm Hg and a temperature of 273 K are known as _____.

5. _____ law says that equal volumes of gases at the same temperature contain equal numbers of molecules.

6. In a closed container, liquid and vapor are at _____.

7. Units for measuring pressure include _____, _____, _____, and _____.

8. The _____ __ _____ is the heat necessary to melt one gram of a solid at its melting point.

9. In Charles' law, _____ and _____ are kept constant.

10. Gas particles move in straight lines, with energy proportional to _____.

11. The transformation of a substance from one phase to another is known as a _____ ___ _____.

12. A liquid that evaporates readily is said to be _____.

Tell whether the following statements are true or false:

1. Molecules of ethyl alcohol exhibit hydrogen bonding.

2. All gases are similar in their physical behavior.

3. Molecules of CH_3Cl experience both dipole dipole interactions and London forces.

4. Doubling the pressure of a gas at constant temperature doubles the volume.

5. $R = 0.082$ L atm/(mol·K) is a value for the gas constant.

6. Atoms in solids have an orderly arrangement.

7. Standard temperature and pressure are 760 mm Hg and 273°C.

8. All substances become solids if the temperature is low enough.

9. The atmospheric pressure in Death Valley (282 ft below sea level) is lower than the atmospheric pressure at sea level.

10. The more liquid there is in a closed container, the higher the vapor pressure.

11. Surface tension is a liquid's resistance to flow.

Match the entries on the left with their partners on the right

1. $P_1V_1 = P_2V_2$ (a) Avogadro's law

2.   Dipole–dipole attraction   (b) Gas constant

3. $P_{total} = P_{gas\ 1} + P_{gas\ 2} + ...$ (c) Force per unit area

4.   760 mm Hg at 273 K   (d) Charles' law

5.   Hydrogen bonding   (e) Occurs between molecules of CH_3Br

6. $V_1/n_1 = V_2/n_2$ (f) STP

7.   0.007500 mm Hg   (g) Boyle's law

8.   London forces   (h) Occurs between molecules of CH_3OH

9.   62.3 mm Hg L / mol K   (i) Ideal gas law

10. $V_1/T_1 = V_2/T_2$ (j) Pascal

11. Pressure   (k) Dalton's law of partial pressure

12. $PV = nRT$ (l) Occurs between molecules of N_2

Chapter 9 – Solutions

Chapter Outline

I. Characteristics of solutions (Sections 9.1–9.6).
   A. Mixtures and solutions (Section 9.1).
      1. Mixtures are either heterogeneous or homogeneous.
         a. Heterogeneous mixtures have non-uniform mixing.
         b. Homogeneous mixtures have uniform mixing.
      2. Homogeneous mixtures can be classified by particle size.
         a. In solutions, particles range in size from 0.1–2 nm.
         b. In colloids, particles range in size from 2–1000 nm.
      3. When a solid is dissolved in a liquid, the liquid is the solvent and the solid is the solute.
   B. The solution process (Sections 9.2–9.3).
      1. Solubility depends on the strength of attraction between solute particles and solvent relative to the attractions in the pure substances.
      2. In predicting solubility, polar solvents dissolve polar substances, and nonpolar solvents dissolve nonpolar substances.
      3. Solution can be either an exothermic or an endothermic process.
      4. Some ionic compounds attract water to form solid hydrates (Section 9.3).
   C. Solubility (Sections 9.4–9.6).
      1. Solubility is a dynamic process (Section 9.4).
         a. When no more of an added solute will dissolve, the solution is said to be saturated.
         b. In a saturated solution, an equilibrium is established between dissolving and crystallizing.
         c. Two liquids are miscible if they are mutually soluble in all proportions.
      2. The solubility of a substance is the maximum amount of the substance that will dissolve in a solvent.
      3. Effect of temperature on solubility (Section 9.5).
         a. The effect of temperature on the solubility of a solid solute is unpredictable.
         b. A gas is always less soluble as temperature increases.
         c. A solid that is more soluble at high temperature than at low may form a supersaturated solution.
      4. Effect of pressure on solubility (Section 9.6).
         a. Increased pressure makes gas molecules more soluble in a liquid.
         b. Henry's law: $P_{gas} = kC$.
           The solubility of a gas in a liquid is proportional to its partial pressure over the liquid at constant T.
         c. When the partial pressure of a gas changes:

$$\frac{C_1}{P_1} = \frac{C_2}{P_2} = k \text{ (at constant T)}$$

II. Quantitative relationships in solutions (Sections 9.7–9.10).
   A. Concentration (Section 9.7).
      1. Molarity $= \dfrac{\text{moles of solute}}{\text{volume of solution (L)}}$.
         Molarity can be used as a conversion factor.
      2. weight/volume % concentration [(w/v)%] $= \dfrac{\text{grams of solute}}{\text{mL of solution}} \times 100\%$.

3. volume/volume % concentration $[(v/v)\%] = \dfrac{\text{volume of solute (mL)}}{\text{volume of solution (mL)}} \times 100\%$.

4. parts per million (ppm) $= \dfrac{\text{mass of solute (g)}}{\text{mass of solution (g)}} \times 10^6$.

$= \dfrac{\text{volume of solute (mL)}}{\text{volume of solution (mL)}} \times 10^6$.

B. Dilution (Section 9.8).
1. During dilution, the number of moles of solute remains constant, while volume changes.
2. $M_1 \times V_1 = M_2 \times V_2$.
3. V_1/V_2 is known as a dilution factor.

C. Equivalents and milliequivalents (Sections 9.9–9.10).
1. Electrolytes (Section 9.9).
    a. Substances that dissociate completely are strong electrolytes.
    b. Substances that dissociate partially are weak electrolytes.
    c. Molecular substances that don't produce ions are nonelectrolytes.
2. The concentration of electrolytes is expressed in equivalents (Section 9.10).
    a. 1 equivalent of an ion $= \dfrac{\text{molar mass of the ion}}{\text{number of charges on the ion}}$
    b. Milliequivalents are useful when measuring ion concentrations in body fluids.

III. Properties of solutions (Sections 9.11–9.13).
A. Effects of particles in solution - colligative properties (Section 9.11).
1. Lowering of vapor pressure.
2. Boiling point elevation.
3. Freezing point depression.
4. These effects don't depend on the identity of the particles.

B. Osmosis (Section 9.12–9.13).
1. When two solutions of different concentrations are separated by a semipermeable membrane, water passes through to the more concentrated side. This is known as osmosis.
2. Osmotic pressure can be applied to establish an equilibrium between the rates of forward and reverse passage of water across the membrane.
3. The osmotic pressure of a solution depends only on the number of particles in solution.
4. Osmolarity = molarity x number of particles per formula unit.
5. Two solutions that are isotonic have the same osmolarity.
    a. In cells, a hypotonic solution causes hemolysis.
    b. A hypertonic solution causes crenation.
6. Dialysis is a process similar to osmosis except that the pores in the membrane allow small solute molecules to pass (Section 9.13).
    a. Hemodialysis is used to cleanse the blood of people whose kidneys malfunction.
    b. Colloidal particles are too large to pass through semipermeable membranes.

Solutions to Chapter 9 Problems

9.1 Orange juice is heterogeneous, and all of the other mixtures are homogeneous, although hand lotion might be heterogeneous in some cases. Apple juice and tea are solutions because they are nonfilterable and transparent to light. Hand lotion is a colloid.

9.2 Remember the rule "like dissolves like."
(a) CCl_4 and H_2O don't form solutions because CCl_4 is nonpolar and H_2O is polar.
(b) Gasoline and $MgSO_4$ don't form solutions because $MgSO_4$ is ionic and gasoline is nonpolar.
(c)(d) These two pairs of substances form solutions because they are chemically similar.

9.3 Glauber's salt: $Na_2SO_4 \cdot 10H_2O$

9.4 Molar mass of Glauber's salt: 322 g/mol. 322 g of Glauber's salt provides 1.00 mol of sodium sulfate.

9.5 The solubility of KBr at 50°C is approximately 80 g/100 mL.

9.6

$$\frac{C_1}{P_1} = \frac{C_2}{P_2}; P_1 = 760 \text{ mm Hg}; C_1 = 0.169 \text{ g/100 mL}; P_2 = 2.5 \times 10^4 \text{ mm Hg}; C_2 = ?$$

$$C_2 = \frac{C_1 P_2}{P_1} = \frac{\left(\frac{0.169 \text{ g}}{100 \text{ mL}}\right) \times 2.5 \times 10^4 \text{ mm Hg}}{760 \text{ mm Hg}} = 5.6 \text{ g } CO_2/100 \text{ mL}$$

9.7

$$\frac{C_1}{P_1} = \frac{C_2}{P_2}; P_1 = 1.00 \text{ atm}; C_1 = 0.169 \text{ g/100 mL}; P_2 = 4.0 \times 10^{-4} \text{ atm}; C_2 = ?$$

$$C_2 = \frac{C_1 P_2}{P_1} = \frac{\left(\frac{0.169 \text{ g}}{100 \text{ mL}}\right) \times 4.0 \times 10^{-4} \text{ atm}}{1.00 \text{ atm}} = 6.8 \times 10^{-5} \text{ g } CO_2/100 \text{ mL}$$

9.8

$$50.0 \text{ g} \times \frac{1 \text{ mol}}{337 \text{ g}} = 0.148 \text{ mol}; \quad \frac{0.148 \text{ mol}}{0.160 \text{ L}} = 0.925 \text{ M}$$

9.9

$$\# \text{moles} = \text{molarity(M)} \times \text{volume} = \frac{\text{mol}}{\text{L}} \times \text{L}$$

(a) $M = \dfrac{0.25 \text{ mol } NaNO_3}{1 \text{ L}}$; $V = 125 \text{ ml} = 0.125 \text{ L}$

$$\# \text{moles} = \frac{0.25 \text{ mol}}{1 \text{ L}} \times 0.125 \text{ L} = 0.031 \text{ mol } NaNO_3$$

(b) $M = \dfrac{1.5 \text{ mol } HNO_3}{1 \text{ L}}$; $V = 450 \text{ ml} = 0.45 \text{ L}$

$$\# \text{moles} = \frac{1.5 \text{ mol}}{1 \text{ L}} \times 0.45 \text{ L} = 0.68 \text{ mol } HNO_3$$

9.10   First, find the number of moles of cholesterol in 250 mL of blood:

$$250 \text{ mL } \times \frac{0.0050 \text{ mol cholesterol}}{1000 \text{ mL}} = 0.001\ 25 \text{ mol cholesterol}$$

Next, find the molar mass of cholesterol:

$$(27 \times 12.0 \text{ g/mol C}) + (46 \times 1.0 \text{ g/mol H}) + (16.0 \text{ g/mol O}) = 386.0 \text{ g/mol}$$

Now, convert moles into grams:

$$0.001\ 25 \text{ mol cholesterol } \times \frac{386.0 \text{ g}}{1 \text{ mol}} = 0.48 \text{ g cholesterol}$$

9.11   Molar mass of $CaCO_3$ = 100.0 g

$$0.075 \text{ L } \times \frac{0.10 \text{ mol HCl}}{1 \text{ L}} \times \frac{1 \text{ mol CaCO}_3}{2 \text{ mol HCl}} \times \frac{100.0 \text{ g CaCO}_3}{1 \text{ mol CaCO}_3} = 0.38 \text{ g CaCO}_3$$

9.12   1 dL = 100 mL

$$\frac{8.6 \text{ mg}}{100 \text{ mL}} \times \frac{1 \text{ g}}{1000 \text{ mg}} \times 100\% = 0.0086\% \text{ (w/v) Ca}^{2+}$$

Remember: [(w/v)%] specifies that the weight of solute be expressed in grams.

9.13

$$\frac{23 \text{ g KI}}{350 \text{ mL}} \times 100\% = 6.6\% \text{ (w/v) KI}$$

9.14   (a) A 12% (w/v) solution contains 12 g of solute per 100 mL of solution. Thus, 12 g of glucose are needed.

(b) A 2% (w/v) solution contains 2 g of solute per 100 mL of solution.

$$75 \text{ mL } \times \frac{2.0 \text{ g KCl}}{100 \text{ mL}} = 1.5 \text{ g KCl}$$

9.15   A 7.5% (v/v) solution contains 7.5 mL of solute per 100 mL of solution.

$$500 \text{ mL solution } \times \frac{7.5 \text{ mL acetic acid}}{100 \text{ mL solution}} = 38 \text{ mL acetic acid}$$

To prepare the desired solution, measure 38 mL of acetic acid into a 500.0 mL volumetric flask and add water to the 500.0 mL mark.

9.16   (a) 22 mL of ethyl alcohol are needed.

(b) $150 \text{ mL solution } \times \dfrac{12 \text{ mL acetic acid}}{100 \text{ mL solution}} = 18 \text{ mL acetic acid}$

9.17

$$\frac{32 \text{ mg NaF}}{20 \text{ kg solution}} \times \frac{1 \text{ kg}}{10^6 \text{ mg}} \times 10^6 = 1.6 \text{ ppm}$$

9.18 For lead:

$$\frac{0.015 \text{ mg Pb}}{1 \text{ kg solution}} \times \frac{1 \text{ kg}}{10^6 \text{ mg}} \times 10^6 = 0.015 \text{ ppm}$$

$$\frac{0.015 \text{ mg Pb}}{1 \text{ kg solution}} \times \frac{1 \text{ kg}}{10^3 \text{ g}} \times 100 \text{ g} = 0.0015 \text{ mg Pb}$$

For copper:

$$\frac{1.3 \text{ mg Cu}}{1 \text{ kg solution}} \times \frac{1 \text{ kg}}{10^6 \text{ mg}} \times 10^6 = 1.3 \text{ ppm}$$

$$\frac{1.3 \text{ mg Cu}}{1 \text{ kg solution}} \times \frac{1 \text{ kg}}{10^3 \text{ g}} \times 100 \text{ g} = 0.13 \text{ mg Cu}$$

9.19 $M_1 = 12.0 \text{ M}$; $V_1 = 100.0 \text{ mL}$; $V_2 = 500.0 \text{ mL}$; $M_2 = ?$

$$M_2 = M_1 \times \frac{V_1}{V_2} = 12.0 \text{ M} \times \frac{100.0 \text{ mL}}{500.0 \text{ mL}} = 2.40 \text{ M}$$

Ballpark check: Since there is a fivefold dilution, the final molarity is 1/5 of the initial molarity

9.20 $V_2 = 500.0 \text{ mL}$; $M_2 = 1.25 \text{ M}$; $M_1 = 16.0 \text{ M}$; $V_1 = ?$

$$V_1 = V_2 \times \frac{M_2}{M_1} = 500.0 \text{ mL} \times \frac{1.25 \text{ M}}{16.0 \text{ M}} = 39.1 \text{ mL}$$

Ballpark check: Since the final molarity is about 1/12 the initial molarity, the initial volume is about 1/12 the final volume, or about 40 mL.

9.21 – 9.22
One equivalent = molar mass of ion (g) ÷ # of charges on ion

Ion	Molar Mass	Charge	Equivalent Weight	Milliequivalent Weight
(a) K^+	39.1 g	+1	39.1 g	39.1 mg, or 3.91×10^{-2} g
(b) Br^-	79.9 g	−1	79.9 g	79.9 mg, or 7.99×10^{-2} g
(c) Mg^{2+}	24.3 g	+2	12.2 g	12.2 mg, or 1.22×10^{-2} g
(d) SO_4^{2-}	96.0 g	−2	48.0 g	48.0 mg, or 4.80×10^{-2} g

9.23 One equivalent of Mg^{2+} = 12.2 g [Problem 9.21 (c)].

$$\frac{g \text{ Mg}^{2+}}{1 \text{ L}} = \frac{12 \text{ g Mg}^{2+}}{1 \text{ Eq}} \times \frac{1 \text{ Eq}}{1000 \text{ mEq}} \times \frac{3.0 \text{ mEq}}{1 \text{ L}} = \frac{0.036 \text{ g Mg}^{2+}}{1 \text{ L}}$$

$$\frac{0.036 \text{ g Mg}^{2+}}{L} \times \frac{1000 \text{ mg}}{1 \text{ g}} \times \frac{1 \text{ L}}{1000 \text{ mL}} \times 250 \text{ mL} = 9.0 \text{ mg Mg}^{2+}$$

9.24 0.75 mol of KBr yields 1.5 mol solute particles, which raise the boiling point of 1.0 kg H_2O by 1.5 x 0.51°C = 0.76°C.

Boiling point = 100°C + 0.76°C = 100.76°C

9.25 If HF were a strong electrolyte it would dissociate completely, and a solution of 1.0 mol HF would yield 2.0 mol particles, which would elevate the boiling point of water by 2.0 x 0.51°C = 1.02°C. Since the observed boiling point elevation is only 0.5°C, HF must be a weak electrolyte that is only slightly dissociated.

9.26 (a) The red curve represents the pure solvent, because the solvent boils at a lower temperature than the solution.
(b) A liquid boils when its vapor pressure equals atmospheric pressure. The solvent boils at 62°C, and the solution boils at 69°C.
(c) One mole of solute raises the boiling point approximately 3.5°C, and the observed boiling point elevation is approximately 7°C. Thus, the concentration of the solute is about 2 M.

9.27 Glucose is not an electrolyte. Thus 1.0 mol glucose lowers the freezing point of 1.0 kg H_2O by 1.9°C.

Freezing point = 0°C – 1.9°C = –1.9°C

9.28 A freezing point depression of 1.86°C is produced by 1 mol of ions in 1 kg of water. Thus, a freezing point depression of 2.8°C must be produced by 2.8 ÷ 1.86 = 1.5 mol of ions. Since 0.5 mol of the ionic substance produces the freezing point depression expected for 1.5 mol ions, the substance gives 3 ions when it dissolves.

9.29 Osmolarity = molarity x number of particles

(a) For 0.35 M KBr, osmolarity = 0.35 M x 2 = 0.70 osmol, since KBr yields two particles (K^+ and Br^-) in solution.

(b) For 0.15 M glucose, osmolarity = 0.15 M x 1 = 0.15 osmol, since glucose yields only one particle in solution. For K_2SO_4, osmolarity = 0.05 M x 3 = 0.15 osmol, since K_2SO_4 provides 3 particles per mole in solution. Total osmolarity = 0.30 osmol.

9.30 For the oral rehydration solution, osmolarity is equal to the sum of the osmolarities of the individual components. For each of the ionic components, the number of millimoles = the number of mEq, since each ion has one charge.Thus,

90 mM Na^+ + 20 mM K^+ + 110 mM Cl^- = 220 mM ions = 0.22 M ions

For glucose:

$$\frac{2.0 \text{ g glucose}}{100 \text{ mL}} \times \frac{1000 \text{ mL}}{1 \text{ L}} \times \frac{1 \text{ mol}}{180 \text{ g glucose}} = 0.11 \text{ M glucose}$$

Osmolarity = molarity x number of particles. In this problem, all components yield 1 particle in solution.
Osmolarity = 0.22 M + 0.11 M = 0.33 osmol

Understanding Key Concepts

9.31

before equilibrium   at equilibrium

The membrane is permeable to the unshaded spheres but impermeable to the shaded spheres. Solvent (unshaded spheres) passes through the membrane until equilibrium is reached.

9.32 The boiling point of water is elevated by 0.5°C for every mole of dissolved particles. 1 mol HCl dissolves to form 2 mol particles, which elevate the boiling point of water by 1°C. Acetic acid exists in solution almost completely as CH_3COOH, and 1 mol acetic acid dissolves to form 1 mol particles, which elevate the boiling point of water by only 0.5°.

9.33 The same reasoning used in the previous problem applies here. The freezing point of water is depressed by 1.9°C for every mole of dissolved particles. 1 mol HBr dissociates to form 2 mol ions, which lower the freezing point of water by 3.7°C, but 1 mol HF is only slightly dissociated and lowers the freezing point by 1.9°C.

9.34 The lower line on the graph (green) represents the solubility of a gas as a function of temperature. The solubility of a solid may increase or decrease with increasing temperature, but the solubility of a gas *always* decreases when temperature is raised.

9.35

(a)   (b)   (c)

When a beaker of glucose solution (shaded) and a beaker of pure water (unshaded) stand for several days, the liquid levels appear as those pictured in (a). The dissolved glucose particles lower the vapor pressure of water and slow evaporation.

9.36 Drawing (d) represents the solution that results when 50.0 mL of (a) is withdrawn and diluted by a factor of 4.

9.37 At a given temperature, the vapor pressure of the solution is lower than that of the pure solvent because the dissolved particles in the solution slow evaporation of its solvent. The green curve represents the vapor pressure curve of the solvent, and the red curve represents the vapor pressure of a solution.

Solutions and Solubility

9.38   In a homogeneous mixture (such as tea), mixing is uniform throughout because the particle size is small. In a heterogeneous mixture (such as chicken soup), mixing is nonuniform because particle size is larger.

9.39   A solution is transparent to light; a colloid usually appears murky or opaque.

9.40   The polarity of water enables it to dissolve many ionic solids.

9.41   Water doesn't dissolve motor oil because oil is nonpolar and water is polar.

9.42   Rubbing alcohol (b) and black coffee (d) are true solutions.

9.43   All the pairs are miscible.

9.44

$$C_2 = \frac{C_1 P_2}{P_1}; \quad C_1 = 51.8 \text{ g/100 mL}; \quad P_1 = 760.0 \text{ mm Hg}; \quad P_2 = 250.0 \text{ mm Hg}$$

$$= \frac{(51.8 \text{ g/100 mL}) \times 250.0 \text{ mm Hg}}{760.0 \text{ mm Hg}} = 17.0 \text{ g/100 mL}$$

9.45

$$C_2 = \frac{C_1 P_2}{P_1}; \quad C_1 = 0.44 \text{ g/100 mL}; \quad P_1 = 159 \text{ mm Hg}; \quad P_2 = 760 \text{ mm Hg}$$

$$= \frac{(0.44 \text{ g/100 mL}) \times 760 \text{ mm Hg}}{159 \text{ mm Hg}} = 2.1 \text{ g/100 mL}$$

Concentration and Dilution of Solutions

9.46   Depending on the solubility of the solute in the solvent, a saturated solution may be either dilute or concentrated. If a solute is only slightly soluble in a solvent, a saturated solution will be dilute. If the solute is very soluble in the solvent, a saturated solution will be concentrated. For a highly soluble solute, even a highly concentrated solution may be unsaturated.

9.47   Weight/volume percent concentration [(w/v)%] is defined as the number of grams of solute per 100 mL of solution.

9.48   Molarity (M) is defined as the number of moles of solute per liter of solution.

9.49   Volume/volume percent concentration [(v/v)%] is defined as the volume of solute in 100 mL of solution

9.50

$$\frac{5.0 \text{ mL ethyl alcohol}}{100.0 \text{ mL solution}} \times 500.0 \text{ mL solution} = 25.0 \text{ mL ethyl alcohol}$$

Add water to 25.0 mL of ethyl alcohol to make a final volume of 500.0 mL.

9.51

$$500.0 \text{ mL solution} \times \frac{0.50 \text{ g B(OH)}_3}{100 \text{ mL solution}} = 2.5 \text{ g B(OH)}_3$$

Dissolve 2.5 g B(OH)$_3$ in water to a final volume of 500.0 mL.

9.52

$$250 \text{ mL solution} \times \frac{0.10 \text{ mol NaCl}}{1000 \text{ mL solution}} = 0.025 \text{ mol NaCl}$$

$$0.025 \text{ mol NaCl} \times \frac{58.5 \text{ g}}{1 \text{ mol}} = 1.5 \text{ g NaCl}$$

Dissolve 1.5 g NaCl in water to a final volume of 250 mL.

9.53

$$1000 \text{ mL solution} \times \frac{7.5 \text{ g KBr}}{100 \text{ mL solution}} = 75 \text{ g KBr}$$

Dissolve 75 g KBr in water and dilute to 1.0 L.

9.54

(a) $\dfrac{5.0 \text{ g KCl}}{75 \text{ mL}} \times 100 \text{ mL} = 6.7 \text{ g KCl} \; ; \dfrac{6.7 \text{ g KCl}}{100 \text{ mL}} \times 100\% = 6.7\% \text{ (w/v) KCl}$

(b) $\dfrac{15 \text{ g sucrose}}{350 \text{ mL}} \times 100 \text{ mL} = 4.3 \text{ g sucrose} \; ; \dfrac{4.3 \text{ g}}{100 \text{ mL}} \times 100\% = 4.3\% \text{ (w/v) sucrose}$

9.55

$$\frac{90 \text{ mg glucose}}{100 \text{ mL}} \times \frac{1 \text{ g}}{1000 \text{ mg}} = \frac{0.090 \text{ g glucose}}{100 \text{ mL}} \; ; \; 0.090\% \text{ (w/v) glucose}$$

9.56

(a) $50.0 \text{ mL} \times \dfrac{8.0 \text{ g KCl}}{100 \text{ mL}} = 4.0 \text{ g KCl}$

(b) $200.0 \text{ mL} \times \dfrac{7.5 \text{ g acetic acid}}{100 \text{ mL}} = 15 \text{ g acetic acid}$

9.57

(a) For 0.50 M KCl : $\dfrac{0.50 \text{ mol KCl}}{1 \text{ L}} \times \dfrac{74.6 \text{ g}}{1 \text{ mol}} = \dfrac{37.3 \text{ g KCl}}{1 \text{ L}} = \dfrac{3.73 \text{ g KCl}}{100 \text{ mL}}$

For 5% (w/v) KCl : $\dfrac{5.0 \text{ g KCl}}{100 \text{ mL}}$

The 5% (w/v) solution is more concentrated.

(b) 2.5% (w/v) $NaHSO_4 = \dfrac{2.5 \text{ g } NaHSO_4}{100 \text{ mL solution}}$

$$\dfrac{0.025 \text{ mol } NaHSO_4}{1 \text{ L}} \times \dfrac{120 \text{ g}}{1 \text{ mol}} = \dfrac{3.0 \text{ g } NaHSO_4}{1 \text{ L}} = \dfrac{0.30 \text{ g } NaHSO_4}{100 \text{ mL}}$$

The 2.5% (w/v) solution is more concentrated.

9.58

$23 \text{ g KOH} \times \dfrac{100 \text{ mL}}{10.0 \text{ g KOH}} = 230 \text{ mL of a 10.0\% (w/v) solution}$

$23 \text{ g KOH} \times \dfrac{1 \text{ mol}}{56.1 \text{ g KOH}} = 0.41 \text{ mol KOH}$

$0.41 \text{ mol KOH} \times \dfrac{1000 \text{ mL}}{0.25 \text{ mol KOH}} = 1600 \text{ mL of 0.25 M solution}$

9.59

$\dfrac{90 \text{ mg glucose}}{100 \text{ mL}} \times \dfrac{1000 \text{ mL}}{1 \text{ L}} \times 5.0 \text{ L} = 4500 \text{ mg glucose} = 4.5 \text{ g glucose}$

9.60

$\dfrac{10 \text{ mg KCN}}{1 \text{ kg body weight}} \times \dfrac{1 \text{ kg}}{10^6 \text{ mg}} \times 10^6 = 10 \text{ ppm}$

9.61

$\dfrac{0.050 \text{ mg As}}{1 \text{ kg } H_2O} \times \dfrac{1 \text{ kg}}{10^6 \text{ mg}} \times 10^6 = 0.050 \text{ ppm}$

$\dfrac{0.050 \text{ mg As}}{1 \text{ kg } H_2O} \times \dfrac{1 \text{ kg}}{10^6 \text{ mg}} \times 10^9 = 50 \text{ ppb}$

9.62

(a) $12.5 \text{ g } NaHCO_3 \times \dfrac{1 \text{ mol}}{84.0 \text{ g}} = 0.149 \text{ mol } NaHCO_3 \; ; \; \dfrac{0.149 \text{ mol}}{0.350 \text{ L}} = 0.426 \text{ M}$

(b) $45.0 \text{ g } H_2SO_4 \times \dfrac{1 \text{ mol}}{98.0 \text{ g}} = 0.459 \text{ mol } H_2SO_4 \; ; \; \dfrac{0.459 \text{ mol}}{0.300 \text{ L}} = 1.53 \text{ M}$

(c) $30.0 \text{ g NaCl} \times \dfrac{1 \text{ mol}}{58.5 \text{ g}} = 0.512 \text{ mol NaCl}; \; \dfrac{0.512 \text{ mol}}{0.500 \text{ L}} = 1.03 \text{ M}$

9.63

(a) $0.200 \text{ L} \times \dfrac{0.30 \text{ mol acetic acid}}{1 \text{ L}} = 0.060 \text{ mol acetic acid}$

(b) $1.50 \text{ L} \times \dfrac{0.25 \text{ mol NaOH}}{1 \text{ L}} = 0.38 \text{ mol NaOH}$

(c) $0.750 \text{ L} \times \dfrac{2.5 \text{ mol } HNO_3}{1 \text{ L}} = 1.9 \text{ mol } HNO_3$

9.64

$$0.0040 \text{ mol HCl} \times \frac{1000 \text{ mL}}{0.75 \text{ mol}} = 5.3 \text{ mL HCl}$$

9.65

$$1.5 \text{ mg} \times \frac{1 \text{ g}}{1000 \text{ mg}} \times \frac{100 \text{ mL}}{0.40 \text{ g}} = 0.38 \text{ mL}$$

9.66 First, calculate the number of moles of H_2SO_4 spilled:

$$0.450 \text{ L} \times \frac{0.50 \text{ mol } H_2SO_4}{1 \text{ L}} = 0.22 \text{ mol } H_2SO_4$$

According to the equation given in the problem, each mole of H_2SO_4 reacts with two moles of $NaHCO_3$. Thus, the 0.22 mol of H_2SO_4 spilled needs to be neutralized with 0.44 mol of $NaHCO_3$.

$$0.44 \text{ mol } NaHCO_3 \times \frac{84 \text{ g}}{1 \text{ mol}} = 37 \text{ g } NaHCO_3$$

9.67

$$0.450 \text{ g AgBr} \times \frac{1 \text{ mol AgBr}}{187.8 \text{ g}} = 2.40 \times 10^{-3} \text{ mol AgBr}$$

According to the equation given, one mole of AgBr reacts with 2 moles of $Na_2S_2O_3$. Thus, 2.40×10^{-3} mol AgBr reacts with 4.80×10^{-3} mol $Na_2S_2O_3$. To calculate the volume of 0.0200 M $Na_2S_2O_3$:

$$4.80 \times 10^{-3} \text{mol} \times \frac{1000 \text{ mL}}{0.0200 \text{ mol}} = 240 \text{ mL of } 0.0200 \text{ M } Na_2S_2O_3$$

9.68

$$20.0\% \text{ (v/v) means : } \frac{20.0 \text{ mL concentrate}}{100.0 \text{ mL juice}}$$

$$\text{Thus, } 100.0 \text{ mL concentrate} \times \frac{100.0 \text{ mL juice}}{20.0 \text{ mL concentrate}} = 500.0 \text{ mL juice}$$

Since the final volume of the diluted juice is 500.0 mL, you would have to add 400.0 mL water to the original 100.0 mL of concentrate.

9.69

$$V_2 = V_1 \times \frac{M_1}{M_2}; \; V_1 = 100.0 \text{ mL}; \; M_1 = 0.500 \text{ M}; \; M_2 = 0.150 \text{ M}$$

$$= 100.0 \text{ mL} \times \frac{0.500 \text{ M}}{0.150 \text{ M}} = 333 \text{ mL of } 0.150 \text{ M NaOH solution}$$

100.0 mL of 0.500 M NaOH is diluted with 233 mL water to give 333 mL of 0.150 M NaOH solution.

9.70

$$V_2 = V_1 \times \frac{M_1}{M_2}; \quad V_1 = 25.0 \text{ mL}; \quad M_1 = 12.0 \text{ M}; \quad M_2 = 0.500 \text{ M}$$

$$= 25.0 \text{ mL} \times \frac{12.0 \text{ M}}{0.500 \text{ M}} = 600 \text{ mL of } 0.500 \text{ M HCl solution}$$

9.71

$$V_1 = V_2 \times \frac{M_2}{M_1}; \quad V_2 = 750.0 \text{ mL}; \quad M_1 = 0.100 \text{ M}; \quad M_2 = 0.0500 \text{ M}$$

$$= 750.0 \text{ mL} \times \frac{0.0500 \text{ M}}{0.100 \text{ M}} = 375 \text{ mL of } 0.100 \text{ M NaHCO}_3$$

Electrolytes

9.72   An electrolyte is a substance that conducts electricity when dissolved in water.

9.73   Sodium chloride is an example of a strong electrolyte. Glucose is an example of a nonelectrolyte.

9.74   If the concentration of Ca^{2+} is 3.0 mEq/L, there are 3.0 mmol of charges due to calcium per liter of blood. Since calcium has a charge of +2, there are 1.5 mmol of calcium per liter of blood.

9.75   The total anion concentration in the solution must equal the total cation concentration in order to conserve charge. Thus:

[Cations] = [Anions] = 5.0 mEq/L Na^+ + 12.0 mEq/L Ca^{2+} + 2.0 mEq/L K^+ = 19 mEq/L

9.76

$$10\% \text{ (w/v)} = \frac{10 \text{ g KCl}}{100 \text{ mL}} \quad ; \quad 30 \text{ mL} \times \frac{10 \text{ g KCl}}{100 \text{ mL}} = 3.0 \text{ g KCl}$$

The molar mass of KCl is 74.6 g/mol. Thus:

$$3.0 \text{ g KCl} \times \frac{1 \text{ mol}}{74.6 \text{ g}} = 0.040 \text{ mol KCl}$$

Since one equivalent equals one mole when an ion has only one charge, there are 0.040 Eq, or 40 mEq, of K^+ in a 30 mL dose.

9.77   Because SO_4^{2-} has a charge of –2, each mole of SO_4^{2-} contains two equivalents. Thus, a concentration of 0.025 M SO_4^{2-} equals 0.050 Eq/L or 50 mEq/L.

9.78   Use the value 100 mEq/L for the concentration of Cl^- in blood:
For Cl^- ion, 100 mEq = 100 mmol = 0.100 mol

$$\frac{0.100 \text{ mol Cl}^-}{1 \text{ L}} \times 0.100 \text{ L} = 0.0100 \text{ mol Cl}^- \text{ in 100.0 mL blood}$$

$$0.0100 \text{ mol Cl}^- \times \frac{35.5 \text{ g}}{1 \text{ mol}} = 0.355 \text{ g Cl}^- \text{ in 100.0 mL blood}$$

9.79 For Mg^{2+}, with a molar mass of 24.3 g and a charge of +2, the mass of one equivalent is 24.3 g/2 = 12.2 g, and the mass of 1 milliequivalent is 12.2 mg.

$$\frac{3 \text{ mEq } Mg^{2+}}{1 \text{ L}} \times \frac{12 \text{ mg } Mg^{2+}}{1 \text{ mEq } Mg^{2+}} \times \frac{1 \text{ L}}{1000 \text{ mL}} \times 100.0 \text{ mL} = 4 \text{ mg } Mg^{2+}$$

Properties of Solutions

9.80 0.20 mol NaOH contains 0.40 mol solute particles, and 0.20 mol $Ba(OH)_2$ contains 0.60 mol solute particles. Since $Ba(OH)_2$ produces more solute particles, it produces greater freezing point lowering of 2.0 kg of water.

9.81 When 0.300 mol KCl dissolves, it produces 0.600 mol particles; when 0.500 mol glucose dissolves, it produces 0.500 mol particles. The solution with more dissolved particles (0.300 mol KCl) has the higher boiling point.

9.82 Methanol has a molar mass of 32.0 g and provides one mole of solute particles per mole of methanol.

$$10.0° \text{ C} \times \frac{1 \text{ mol}}{1.86° \text{ C} \times 1 \text{ kg}} \times 5.00 \text{ kg} = 26.9 \text{ mol methanol}$$

$$26.9 \text{ mol} \times \frac{32.0 \text{ g}}{1 \text{ mol}} = 861 \text{ g of methanol needed}$$

9.83 Ethylene glycol provides one mole of solute particles per mole. The boiling point elevation:

$$\frac{350 \text{ g ethylene glycol}}{1.5 \text{ kg } H_2O} \times \frac{1 \text{ mol}}{62.1 \text{ g}} \times \frac{0.51°\text{C} \times 1 \text{ kg}}{1 \text{ mol}} = 1.9°\text{C}$$

The boiling point of the resulting solution is 100°C + 1.9°C = 101.9°C.

Osmosis

9.84 The inside of a red blood cell contains dissolved substances and therefore has a higher osmolarity than pure water. Water thus passes through the cell membrane to dilute the cell contents until pressure builds up and the cell eventually bursts.

9.85 If a 0.15 M NaCl solution is isotonic with blood, then the NaCl solution has the same osmolarity as blood. If distilled water is hypotonic with blood, then the water has a lower osmolarity than blood.

9.86

Solution	Molarity	# of Particles	Osmolarity
(a) 0.25 M KBr	0.25 M	2	0.50 osmol
0.20 M Na_2SO_4	0.20 M	3	0.60 osmol (greater)
(b) 0.30 M NaOH	0.30 M	2	0.60 osmol
3% (w/v) NaOH	0.75 M	2	1.5 osmol (greater)

9.87 The solution with the higher osmolarity will give rise to the greater osmotic pressure at equilibrium.

For NaCl: $\dfrac{5.0 \text{ g}}{0.350 \text{ L}}$ x $\dfrac{1 \text{ mol}}{58.5 \text{ g}}$ x 2 particles = 0.49 osmol

For glucose: $\dfrac{35.0 \text{ g}}{0.400 \text{ L}}$ x $\dfrac{1 \text{ mol}}{180 \text{ g}}$ x 1 particle = 0.49 osmol

Both solutions will give rise to the same osmotic pressure.

Applications

9.88 At high altitude, P_{O2} is low, and not enough oxygen is available to cause 100% saturation of hemoglobin. In order to deliver enough oxygen to body tissues, the body compensates by manufacturing more hemoglobin, which drives the hemoglobin equilibrium to the right.

9.89 The major electrolytes in sweat are sodium ion (30–40 mEq/L), potassium ion (5–10 mEq/L), small amounts of metals such as magnesium, and chloride to balance charge (35–50 mEq/L).

9.90 In addition to fluid replacement, sports drinks provide electrolytes to replenish those lost during exercise, they furnish soluble complex carbohydrates for slow-release energy, and they may contain vitamins to protect cells from damage.

9.91 An enteric coating on a medication is a polymeric material that isn't digested by stomach acid but passes into the intestine, where it dissolves in the more basic intestinal environment and releases the medication.

General Questions and Problems

9.92 Molar mass of uric acid ($C_5H_4N_4O_3$) = 168 g.

(a) (w/v)%: $\dfrac{0.067 \text{ g}}{1 \text{ L}} = \dfrac{0.0067 \text{ g}}{100 \text{ mL}}$; $\dfrac{0.0067 \text{ g}}{100 \text{ mL}}$ x 100% = 0.0067% (w/v)

(b) ppm: One L of water weighs 1 kg. Thus:

$\dfrac{0.067 \text{ g}}{1 \text{ L}} = \dfrac{0.067 \text{ g}}{1 \text{ kg}}$ x $\dfrac{1 \text{ kg}}{1000 \text{ g}}$; $\dfrac{0.067 \text{ g}}{1000 \text{ g}}$ x 10^6 = 67 ppm

(c) $\dfrac{0.067 \text{ g}}{1 \text{ L}}$ x $\dfrac{1 \text{ mol}}{168 \text{ g}}$ = 0.000 40 M = 4.0×10^{-4} M

9.93

5.0% (w/v) = $\dfrac{5.0 \text{ g CaCl}_2}{100 \text{ mL}}$; $\dfrac{5.0 \text{ g CaCl}_2}{100 \text{ mL}}$ x 5.0 mL = 0.25 g $CaCl_2$

0.25 g $CaCl_2$ x $\dfrac{1 \text{ mol}}{111 \text{ g}}$ = 0.0023 mol $CaCl_2$ = 0.0023 mol Ca^{2+}

0.0023 mol Ca^{2+} x $\dfrac{2 \text{ Eq}}{1 \text{ mol}}$ = 0.0046 Eq Ca^{2+} = 4.6 mEq Ca^{2+}

9.94 $M_1 = 16\ M$, $\quad M_2 = 0.20\ M$, $\quad V_2 = 750\ mL$

$$V_1 = V_2 \times \frac{M_2}{M_1} = 750\ mL \times \frac{0.20\ M}{16\ M} = 9.4\ mL\ HNO_3$$

9.95

$$5.50\ g\ KOH \times \frac{1\ mol}{56.1\ g} = 0.0980\ mol\ KOH$$

According to the balanced equation, one mole of KOH reacts with one mole of HNO_3. Thus, 0.0980 mol of KOH reacts with 0.0980 mol of HNO_3.

$$0.0980\ mol\ HNO_3 \times \frac{1\ L}{16\ mol} = 0.0061\ L\ HNO_3 = 6.1\ mL\ HNO_3$$

9.96 $M_1 = 12.0\ M$, $\quad V_1 = 25\ mL$, $\quad V_2 = 525\ mL$; $\quad M_2 = ?$

$$M_2 = M_1 \times \frac{V_1}{V_2} = 12.0\ M \times \frac{25\ mL}{525\ mL} = 0.57\ M$$

9.97

(a) $13.0\ mL \times \dfrac{0.0100\ mol}{1000\ mL} = 1.30 \times 10^{-4}\ mol\ I_2$

According to the equation, one mole of I_2 reacts with one mole of $C_6H_8O_6$. Thus, the 25.0 mL sample contains $1.30 \times 10^{-4}\ mol\ C_6H_8O_6$.

$$\frac{1.30 \times 10^{-4}\ mol}{25.0\ mL} \times \frac{1000\ mL}{1\ L} = 0.005\ 20\ M = 5.20\ mM$$

(b) Molar mass of $C_6H_8O_6 = 176\ g$.

$$\frac{176\ g}{1\ mol} \times \frac{0.005\ 20\ mol}{1\ L} \times \frac{1000\ mg}{1\ g} = \frac{915\ mg\ ascorbic\ acid}{1\ L}$$

$$60\ mg \times \frac{1\ L}{915\ mg\ ascorbic\ acid} \times \frac{1000\ mL}{1\ L} = 66\ mL\ juice$$

9.98 – 9.99

Component	Weight	Molar Mass	Molarity	Osmolarity
(a) NaCl	8.6 g	58.5 g	0.147 M	0.294 osmol
(b) KCl	0.30 g	74.6 g	0.0040 M	0.0080 osmol
(c) $CaCl_2$	0.33 g	111 g	0.0030 M	0.0090 osmol
			Total:	0.31 osmol

Ringer's solution (0.31 osmol) is essentially isotonic with blood plasma (0.30 osmol).

9.100

$$0.080\%\ (v/v) = \frac{0.080\ mL}{100\ mL} = \frac{0.80\ mL}{1\ L};\ \frac{0.80\ mL}{1\ L} \times 5.0\ L = 4.0\ mL\ alcohol$$

9.101

(a)

(b) $\dfrac{51.8 \text{ g}}{1 \text{ L}} \times \dfrac{1 \text{ mol}}{17.0 \text{ g}} = 3.05 \text{ mol/L}$

9.102 (a) $CoCl_2 + 6 H_2O \rightleftharpoons CoCl_2 \cdot 6H_2O$

(b) Molar mass of $CoCl_2 \cdot 6H_2O = 238$ g

$2.50 \text{ g } CoCl_2 \times \dfrac{1 \text{ mol } CoCl_2 \cdot 6 H_2O}{238 \text{ g}} \times \dfrac{6 \text{ mol } H_2O}{1 \text{ mol } CoCl_2 \cdot 6 H_2O} \times \dfrac{18.0 \text{ g } H_2O}{1 \text{ mol } H_2O} = 1.13 \text{ g } H_2O$

9.103 $BaCl_2(aq) + Na_2SO_4(aq) \longrightarrow BaSO_4(s) + 2 NaCl(aq)$

According to the balanced equation, one mole of $BaCl_2$ reacts with one mole of Na_2SO_4.

\# moles $Na_2SO_4 = \dfrac{0.200 \text{ mol}}{1 \text{ L}} \times 0.0350 \text{ L} = 0.007\ 00 \text{ mol} = $ # moles $BaCl_2$

$0.007\ 00 \text{ mol } BaCl_2 \times \dfrac{1 \text{ L}}{0.150 \text{ mol}} = 0.0467 \text{ L} = 46.7 \text{ mL } BaCl_2$

$0.007\ 00 \text{ mol} \times \dfrac{233.3 \text{ g}}{1 \text{ mol}} = 1.63 \text{ g } BaSO_4$

9.104 0.100 mol trichloroacetic acid (TCA) dissolved in 100 0 g water is equivalent to 1.00 mol TCA dissolved in 1000 g water. A freezing point depression of 1.86°C is produced by 1 mol of ions, so a freezing point depression of 2.53°C must be produced by 2.53 ÷ 1.86 = 1.36 mol of ions. Since 1.00 mol TCA behaves as 1.36 mol solute, TCA is 36% dissociated.

Self-Test for Chapter 9

Multiple choice:

1. 50 mL of a 1.0 M NaOH solution is diluted to 1.0 L. What is the dilution factor?
    (a) 1/50   (b) 1/20   (c) 1/10   (d) 1/2

2. Which of the following will not speed up the rate of solution of a solid?
    (a) stirring   (b) heating   (c) grinding the solid into powder   (d) increasing pressure on the solution

3. To make up 500 mL of a 5% (v/v) solution of methanol (CH_3OH ; molar mass = 32 g) in water:
   (a) dilute 25 mL of CH_3OH with water to a volume of 500 mL
   (b) dilute 5 mL of CH_3OH with water to a volume of 500 mL
   (c) add 32 g of CH_3OH to 500 g of water
   (d) add 25 mL of CH_3OH to 500 mL of water

4. Which solution has the greatest osmolarity?
   (a) 0.2 M $CaCl_2$ (b) 0.3 M Na_3PO_4 (c) 0.5 M NaCl   (d) 0.8 M glucose

5. Which of the following is a colloid?
   (a) wine   (b) maple syrup   (c) milkshake   (d) salad oil

6. How many mL of a 12.0 M HCl solution are needed to make 1.0 L of 0.10 M HCl?
   (a) 120 mL   (b) 83 mL   (c) 50 mL   (d) 8.3 mL

7. Which of the following properties do not depend on the number of particles in solution?
   (a) boiling point elevation   (b) osmotic pressure   (c) heat of solution   (d) freezing point depression

8. How many grams of NaOH are needed to make 300 mL of a 0.3 M solution?
   (a) 40 g   (b) 12 g   (c) 3.6 g   (d) 1.0 g

9. How many moles of glucose are present in 250 mL of a 0.25 M solution?
   (a) 0.0625 mol   (b) 0.1 mol   (c) 0.25 mol   (d) 1.0 mol

10. How many mL of a 0.20 M solution of NaF contain 2.1 g of NaF?
    (a) 500 mL   (b) 250 mL   (c) 100 mL   (d) 50 mL

Complete the following sentences:

1. Two liquids soluble in each other are said to be _____.

2. An _____ is the amount of an ion in grams that contains Avogadro's number of charges.

3. A weight/volume solution can be made up in a piece of glassware called a _____ _____.

4. According to Henry's law, the _____ of a gas varies with its _____ _____.

5. Two solutions that have the same osmolarity are _____.

6. Compounds that attract water from the atmosphere are called _____.

7. The formula used for calculating dilutions is _____.

8. Milk is an example of a _____.

9. _____ and _____ _____ _____ can pass through a dialysis membrane.

10. A solution that has reached its solubility limit is said to be _____.

11. An example of a nonelectrolyte is _____.

12. A solution that is hypotonic with respect to blood has a _____ osmolarity than blood plasma.

Tell whether the following statements are true or false:

1. A solute is the liquid used to dissolve a substance.

2. It is possible to have a solution of a solid in a solid.

3. In making a volume/volume percent solution, one liquid is added to 100 mL of the other liquid.

4. All ionic compounds are soluble in water.

5. A solution of 0.10 M Na_3PO_4 has a greater osmolarity than a solution of 0.15 M NaCl.

6. Weight/weight percent is a useful way to express concentration.

7. In carrying out a dilution, the number of moles of solute remains constant.

8. The solubility of most substances increases with temperature.

9. A colloid differs from a solution in its ability to transmit light.

10. A blood cell undergoes crenation when placed in distilled water.

11. Particles dissolved in water lower the boiling point of water.

12. The amount of gas dissolved in a liquid increases with increasing pressure.

Match the entries on the left with their partners on the right.

1. Osmotic membrane   (a) Muddy water

2. V_1/V_2 (b) Molarity x number of particles

3. Solution   (c) Conducts electricity in water

4. Equivalent   (d) Vinegar

5. Suspension   (e) Crystalline compound that holds water

6. Dialysis membrane   (f) Dilution factor

7. Osmolarity   (g) Butter

8. Hypotonic   (h) Permeable only to water

9. Colloid   (i) A solution of lower osmolarity than another

10. Crenation   (j) Formula weight / number of charges

11. Hydrate   (k) Permeable to water and small molecules

12. Electrolyte   (l) Happens to cell in hypertonic solution

Chapter 10 – Acids and Bases

Chapter Outline

I. Introduction to acids and bases (Sections 10.1–10.5).
   A. Definition of acids and bases (Sections 10.1, 10.3).
      1. Arrhenius definition (Section 10.1).
         a. Acids donate H^+ ions in solution.
         b. Bases donate OH^- ions in solution.
         c. Acid + base —> salt + H_2O.
      2. Brønsted–Lowry definition (Section 10.3).
         a. A Brønsted–Lowry acid is a proton donor (an H_3O^+ donor).
            Some acids can donate more than one proton.
         b. A Brønsted–Lowry base is a proton acceptor.
            The base may be negatively charged or neutral.
         c. An acid–base reaction is one in which a proton is transferred.
         d. Products of acid–base reactions are also acids and bases.
            In the reaction $HA + B: —> A^- + BH^+$
            i. HA and A^- are an acid–conjugate base pair.
            ii. B: and BH^+ are a base–conjugate acid pair.
   B. Many common substances are acids or bases (Section 10.2).
   C. Water as acid and a base (Section 10.4).
      1. Water can act both as an acid and a base.
      2. Substances that can act as both acids and bases are amphoteric.
   D. Common acid–base reactions (Section 10.5).
      1. Acid + hydroxide ion —> water + salt
      2. Acid + carbonate or bicarbonate —> water + salt + CO_2
      3. Acid + ammonia —> ammonium salt
II. Acid/base strength (Sections 10.6–10.11).
   A. Strong/weak acids and bases (Section 10.6).
      1. Strong acids and bases are 100% dissociated in water.
      2. Weak acids and bases are less than 100% dissociated in solution.
      3. The stronger the acid, the weaker the conjugate base.
         The weaker the acid, the stronger the conjugate base.
      4. An acid–base proton transfer always favors formation of the weaker acid.
   B. Acid dissociation constants (Section 10.7).
      1. K_a is a measure of the degree to which an acid HA dissociates to H_3O^+ and A^-.
      2. K_a values for weak acids are much less than 1.
      3. Donation of each successive H^+ ion from a polyprotic acid becomes successively more difficult.
      4. Most organic acids have K_a near 10^{-5}.
   C Dissociation of H_2O (Section 10.8).
      1. $K_w = [H_3O^+][OH^-] = 1.00 \times 10^{-14}$ at 25°C.
      2. This relationship is true for any aqueous solution.
      3. Thus, we can calculate $[H_3O^+]$ or $[OH^-]$ for any aqueous solution.

    D. Measuring acidity (Sections 10.9–10.11).
        1. pH (Sections 10.9–10.10).
           a. A pH of < 7 indicates acidity; a pH of > 7 indicates basicity.
           b. pH is the negative logarithm of $[H_3O^+]$.
           c. The pH scale is logarithmic.
           d. pH can be computed with a calculator.
        2. In the laboratory, pH can be measured with indicators or a pH meter (Section 10.11).
III. Buffers (Sections 10.12–10.13).
    A. Characteristics of buffers (Section 10.12).
        1. A buffer is the solution of a weak acid and its salt (or a weak base and its salt) at similar concentration.
        2. When a small amount of acid or base is added to a buffered solution, pH changes very little.
        3. The effective pH range of a buffer solution is determined by the K_a of the acid or base.
           a. A buffer solution works best when [HA] is close in value to $[A^-]$.
           b. A buffer solution works best when [HA] and $[A^-]$ are approximately ten times greater than the amount of acid or base added.
    B. Buffers in the body (Section 10.13).
        1. The carbonate/bicarbonate buffer system is the major regulator of the pH of body fluids.
           a. An increase of $[CO_2]$ makes blood more acidic.
           b. A decrease in $[CO_2]$ makes blood less acidic.
           c. The acidity of blood is regulated by:
               i. A reservoir of excess HCO_3^- that keeps pH fluctuations small.
               ii Change of breathing rate.
               iii. The kidneys.
           d. This regulation prevents alkalosis (pH greater than 7.45) and acidosis (pH lower than 7.35).
        2. The phosphate system and proteins are two other buffer systems in the body.
IV. Equivalents of acids and bases (Sections 10.14–10.15).
    A. Normality (Section 10.14).
        1. An equivalent of acid or base $= \dfrac{\text{molar mass}}{\text{\# of } H^+ \text{ or } OH^- \text{ produced}}$.
        2. One equivalent of acid neutralizes one equivalent of base.
        3. Normality $= \dfrac{\text{equivalents of acid or base}}{\text{liters of solution}}$.
        4. Normality = (molarity of acid or base) x (# of H^+ or OH^- produced).
    B. Titration (Section 10.15).
        1. Titration is used to determine the acid or base concentration of a solution.
        2. In titration, a known volume of a solution of unknown acid or base concentration completely reacts with a solution of known concentration.
        3. The volume of solution of known concentration is measured, and the concentration of the unknown is calculated.
V. Acidity and basicity of salt solutions (Section 10.16).
    A. The salt of a strong base and a strong acid is neutral in solution.
    B. The salt of a strong base and a weak acid is basic in solution.
    C. The salt of a weak base and a strong acid is acidic in solution.
    D. The pH of the salt of a weak base and a weak acid can be predicted only if K_a values are known.

Solutions to Chapter 10 Problems

10.1 HCO_2H (a) and H_2S (b) are Brønsted–Lowry acids because they have protons to donate.

10.2 SO_3^{2-} (a) and F^- (c) are Brønsted–Lowry bases because they can be proton acceptors.

10.3 (a) The conjugate acid of HS^- is H_2S.
(b) The conjugate acid of PO_4^{3-} is HPO_4^{2-}.
(c) The conjugate base of H_2CO_3 is HCO_3^-.
(d) The conjugate base of NH_4^+ is NH_3.

10.4

10.5 Water acts as an acid when it reacts to form OH^-; water acts as a base when it reacts to form H_3O^+.

Water as an acid: (b) $F^-(aq) + H_2O(l) \rightleftharpoons HF(aq) + OH^-(aq)$

Water as a base: (a) $H_3PO_4(aq) + H_2O(l) \rightleftharpoons H_2PO_4^-(aq) + H_3O^+(aq)$

(c) $NH_4^+(aq) + H_2O(l) \rightleftharpoons H_3O^+(aq) + NH_3(aq)$

10.6 $3\,HCl(aq) + Al(OH)_3(aq) \longrightarrow 3\,H_2O(l) + AlCl_3(aq)$

$2\,HCl(aq) + Mg(OH)_2(aq) \longrightarrow 2\,H_2O(l) + MgCl_2(aq)$

10.7 (a) $2\,KHCO_3(aq) + H_2SO_4(aq) \longrightarrow 2\,H_2O(l) + 2\,CO_2(g) + K_2SO_4(aq)$

(b) $MgCO_3(aq) + 2\,HNO_3(aq) \longrightarrow H_2O(l) + CO_2(g) + Mg(NO_3)_2(aq)$

10.8 $H_2SO_4(aq) + 2\,NH_3(aq) \longrightarrow (NH_4)_2SO_4(aq)$

10.9

$$
\begin{array}{ccc}
 & H \quad H \quad H & \\
 & |\quad\;\; |\quad\;\; | & \\
H-C-C-N: & + \; HCl \rightleftharpoons & H-C-C-N^+-H \;\; Cl^- \\
 & |\quad\;\; |\quad\;\; | &
\end{array}
$$

10.10 In Table 10.1, the stronger acid is listed *higher* in the table than the weaker acid.

Stronger acids: (a) NH_4^+ (b) H_2SO_4 (c) H_2CO_3

10.11 In Table 10.1, the stronger base is listed *lower* in the table than the weaker base.

Stronger bases: (a) F^- (b) OH^-

10.12 $HPO_4^{2-}(aq) + OH^-(aq) \rightleftharpoons PO_4^{3-}(aq) + H_2O(l)$
      acid   base   conjugate base   conjugate acid

From Table 10.1, we see that OH^- is a stronger base than PO_4^{3-} and that HPO_4^{2-} is a stronger acid than H_2O. Thus, the forward direction of the equilibrium is favored.

$HPO_4^{2-}(aq) + OH^-(aq) \rightleftharpoons PO_4^{3-}(aq) + H_2O(l)$
stronger acid   stronger base   weaker base   weaker acid

10.13 Remember that an electrostatic potential map shows the most electron-rich area of the molecule as red and the least electron-rich area as blue. In alanine, the $-NH_3^+$ group is the most electron-poor, and thus its hydrogens are the most acidic.

10.14 Citric acid is stronger because it has a larger value for K_a, indicating a larger $[H_3O^+]$.

10.15 (a) Beer is slightly acidic. Since $10^{-14} = [H_3O^+][OH^-]$,

$$[OH^-] = \frac{K_w}{[H_3O^+]} = \frac{1.0 \times 10^{-14}}{3.2 \times 10^{-5}} = 3.1 \times 10^{-10} \text{ M}$$

(b) Ammonia is basic.

$$[OH^-] = \frac{K_w}{[H_3O^+]} = \frac{1.0 \times 10^{-14}}{3.1 \times 10^{-12}} = 3.2 \times 10^{-3} \text{ M}$$

10.16 A solution with pH = 5 has a greater $[H_3O^+]$ because its pH is a smaller number, indicating a greater concentration of $[H_3O^+]$. The solution with pH = 9 has a greater $[OH^-]$.

10.17 (a) If $[H_3O^+] = 1 \times 10^{-5}$ M, then pH = 5.

(b) If $[OH^-] = 1 \times 10^{-9}$ M, then

$$[H_3O^+] = \frac{1 \times 10^{-14}}{1 \times 10^{-9}} = 1 \times 10^{-5} \text{ M} ; \text{pH} = 5$$

10.18 (a) For pH = 13, $[H_3O^+] = 1 \times 10^{-13}$ M
(b) For pH = 3, $[H_3O^+] = 1 \times 10^{-3}$ M
(c) For pH = 8, $[H_3O^+] = 1 \times 10^{-8}$ M

The solution of pH = 3 is most acidic, and the solution of pH = 13 is most basic.

10.19 $\text{pH} = -\log[H_3O^+]$; $[H_3O^+] = 1 \times 10^{-4}$; $\log[H_3O^+] = -4$; $-\log[H_3O^+] = -(-4) = 4$

The pH of a 1×10^{-4}M solution of HNO_3 is 4.

10.20

Solution	pH	Acidic/Basic	$[H_3O^+]$
(a) Saliva	6.5	acidic	3×10^{-7} M
(b) Pancreatic juice	7.9	basic	1×10^{-8} M
(c) Orange juice	3.7	acidic	2×10^{-4} M
(d) Wine	3.5	acidic	3×10^{-4} M

Least acidic ⟶ Pancreatic juice   Saliva   Orange juice   Wine   Most acidic

10.21 Use a calculator to determine pH.

(a) $[H_3O^+] = 5.3 \times 10^{-9}$ mol/L: pH = 8.28
(b) $[H_3O^+] = 8.9 \times 10^{-6}$ mol/L: pH = 5.05

10.22 $[H_3O^+] = 2.5 \times 10^{-3}$, since HCl is a strong acid. As in the previous problem, use the EE key and the log key on your calculator, and take the negative value of the log.
$[H_3O^+] = 2.5 \times 10^{-3}$; pH $= -\log(2.5 \times 10^{-3}) = -(-2.60) = 2.60$

10.23 Refer to Worked Examples 10.11 and 10.12 in the text.
When 0.020 mol of HNO_3 is added, the HF concentration increases from 0.100 M to 0.120 M, and the F^- decreases from 0.100 M to 0.080 M because of the reaction:

$$F^-(aq) + HNO_3(aq) \longrightarrow HF(aq) + NO_3^-(aq)$$

$$[H_3O^+] = K_a \frac{[HA]}{[A^-]} = (3.5 \times 10^{-4})\frac{[0.120]}{[0.080]} = 5.2 \times 10^{-4} \text{ M}$$

$$pH = -\log(5.2 \times 10^{-4}) = 3.28$$

10.24

$$[H_3O^+] = K_a \frac{[HA]}{[A^-]} = (1.8 \times 10^{-4})\frac{[0.050]}{[0.060]} = 1.5 \times 10^{-4} \text{ M}$$

$$pH = -\log(1.5 \times 10^{-4}) = 3.82$$

10.25 If a small amount of extra base is added to a mixture of HCl and NaCl, the base is neutralized to form H_2O, and the pH of the solution changes slightly. If extra acid is added, however, it can't be neutralized because Cl^- is not basic. Thus, the HCl – NaCl system is a poor buffer. As we have seen in Problem 10.23 and Worked Example 10.12, however, a small amount of added acid or added base changes the pH of the HF / NaF buffer system only slightly. Thus, the system of the weak acid HF and its conjugate base F^- is an effective buffer.

10.26–10.27

Sample	Mass	Molar Mass	# of ions*	Equivalent Mass	# of Eq	Normality of 300.0 mL
(a) HNO_3	5.0 g	63.0 g	1	63.0 g	0.079	0.26 N
(b) $Ca(OH)_2$	12.5 g	74.1 g	2	37.0 g	0.338	1.13 N
(c) H_3PO_4	4.5 g	98.0 g	3	32.7 g	0.14	0.47 N

*The "number of ions" refers to the number of H^+ or OH^- ions produced for each mole of acid or base in solution

10.28 First, write the balanced equation for the neutralization reaction:

$$HCl(aq) + NaOH(aq) \longrightarrow H_2O(l) + NaCl(aq)$$

We see from this equation that one mole of base is needed to neutralize each mole of acid.

$$\text{Moles HCl} = 58.4 \text{ mL} \times \frac{0.250 \text{ mol NaOH}}{1 \text{ L}} \times \frac{1 \text{ L}}{1000 \text{ mL}} \times \frac{1 \text{ mol HCl}}{1 \text{ mol NaOH}}$$

$$= 0.0146 \text{ mol HCl}$$

$$\frac{0.0146 \text{ mol HCl}}{20.0 \text{ mL}} \times \frac{1000 \text{ mL}}{1 \text{ L}} = 0.730 \text{ M HCl}$$

10.29 $2 NaOH(aq) + H_2SO_4(aq) \longrightarrow 2 H_2O(l) + Na_2SO_4(aq)$

Notice that two moles of base are needed to neutralize one mole of acid.

$$\text{Moles NaOH} = 50.0 \text{ mL} \times \frac{0.200 \text{ mol } H_2SO_4}{1 \text{ L}} \times \frac{1 \text{ L}}{1000 \text{ mL}} \times \frac{2 \text{ mol NaOH}}{1 \text{ mol } H_2SO_4}$$

$$= 0.0200 \text{ mol NaOH}$$

$$0.0200 \text{ mol NaOH} \times \frac{1 \text{ L}}{0.150 \text{ mol}} = 0.133 \text{ L NaOH} = 133 \text{ mL NaOH}$$

10.30 $2 KOH(aq) + H_2SO_4(aq) \longrightarrow 2 H_2O(l) + Na_2SO_4(aq)$

$$\text{Moles KOH} = 16.1 \text{ mL} \times \frac{0.150 \text{ mol } H_2SO_4}{1 \text{ L}} \times \frac{1 \text{ L}}{1000 \text{ mL}} \times \frac{2 \text{ mol KOH}}{1 \text{ mol } H_2SO_4}$$

$$= 0.004 \, 83 \text{ mol KOH}$$

$$\frac{0.004 \, 83 \text{ mol}}{0.0215 \text{ L}} = 0.225 \text{ M KOH}$$

10.31 The salt of a weak acid and a strong base produces a basic solution, the salt of a strong acid and a weak base produces an acidic solution, and the salt of a strong acid and a strong base is neutral.

Salt	Cation is from:	Anion is from:	Solution is:
(a) K_2SO_4	strong base (KOH)	strong acid(H_2SO_4)	neutral
(b) Na_2HPO_4	strong base (NaOH)	weak acid ($H_2PO_4^-$)	basic
(c) MgF_2	strong base ($Mg(OH)_2$)	weak acid (HF)	basic
(d) NH_4Br	weak base (NH_3)	strong acid (HBr)	acidic

Understanding Key Concepts

10.32

(a)

(b)

10.33 (a) The reaction of HF with OH^- is represented by outcome (2). One OH^- reacts with each HF to produce 3 F^- anions, and 9 OH^- anions are left over.
   (b) The reaction of H_2SO_3 with OH^- is represented by outcome (3). Two OH^- ions react with each H_2SO_3 molecule to produce 3 SO_3^{2-} anions, and 6 OH^- anions are left over.
   (c) The reaction of H_3PO_4 with OH^- is represented by outcome (1). Three OH^- anions react with each H_3PO_4 molecule to produce 3 PO_4^{3-} anions, and 3 OH^- anions are left over.

10.34 In both molecules, the most acidic hydrogen (deepest blue) is bonded to oxygen. Acetic acid is more acidic because its hydrogen is more positively polarized and less tightly held.

10.35 (a) The acid in the first picture (1) is the weakest because it is the least dissociated.
   (b) The acid in the second picture (2) is the strongest acid because all molecules of the acid are dissociated
   (c) The acid in the first picture (1) has the smallest value of K_a because it is the weakest acid.

10.36 (a) Picture (3) represents a weak diprotic acid, which has dissociated slightly to form the HA^- anion.
   (b) Picture (1) represents an impossible situation. H_2A dissociates stepwise to form HA^-. Only when virtually all H_2A has dissociated to form HA^- is A^{2-} formed by dissociation of HA^-.

10.37 The titration reaction uses up 2/3 of the 1.0 M solution in the buret. Since the solution in the buret is 1.0 M, the solution in the flask must be 0.67 M.

Acids and Bases

10.38 In water, HBr dissociates almost completely. Water acts as a base to accept a proton, and a solution of H_3O^+ and Br^- results.

10.39 In water, CH_3CO_2H dissociates only to the extent of about 1%. Water acts as a base, yielding a solution of CH_3CO_2H, along with smaller amounts of H_3O^+ and $CH_3CO_2^-$.

10.40 In water, KOH dissociates completely to yield K^+ and OH^- ions.

10.41 In water, NH_3 remains largely unreacted, but a small amount acts as a base and accepts a proton from water to yield NH_4^+ and OH^- ions.

10.42 A monoprotic acid, such as HCl, has only one proton to donate, whereas a diprotic acid, such as H_2SO_4, has two protons to donate.

10.43 H^+ represents a proton, but the species H^+ is too reactive to exist in solution. Instead, the proton reacts with water to form H_3O^+.

10.44 Strong acids: (a) $HClO_4$ (e) HI

10.45 Weak bases: (a) NH_3 (c) HPO_4^{2-} (e) CN^-

Brønsted–Lowry Acids and Bases

10.46 Brønsted–Lowry acids: (a) HCN (d) H_2CO_3 (f) $CH_3NH_3^+$
Brønsted–Lowry bases: (b) $CH_3CO_2^-$
Neither: (c) $AlCl_3$ (e) Mg^{2+}

10.47 Base and conjugate acid are pairs, as are acid and conjugate base.

(a) $CO_3^{2-}(aq) + HCl(aq) \longrightarrow HCO_3^-(aq) + Cl^-(aq)$
    base   acid   conjugate acid   conjugate base

(b) $H_3PO_4(aq) + NH_3(aq) \longrightarrow H_2PO_4^-(aq) + NH_4^+(aq)$
    acid   base   conjugate base   conjugate acid

(c) $NH_4^+(aq) + CN^-(aq) \rightleftharpoons NH_3(aq) + HCN(aq)$
    acid   base   conjugate base   conjugate acid

(d) $HBr(aq) + OH^-(aq) \longrightarrow H_2O(l) + Br^-(aq)$
    acid   base   conjugate acid   conjugate base

(e) $H_2PO_4^-(aq) + N_2H_4(aq) \rightleftharpoons HPO_4^{2-}(aq) + N_2H_5^+(aq)$
    acid   base   conjugate base   conjugate acid

10.48

Base	(a) $CH_2ClCO_2^-$	(b) C_5H_5N	(c) SeO_4^{2-}	(d) $(CH_3)_3N$
Conjugate acid	CH_2ClCO_2H	$C_5H_5NH^+$	$HSeO_4^-$	$(CH_3)_3NH^+$

10.49

Acid	(a) HCN	(b) $(CH_3)_2NH_2^+$	(c) H_3PO_4	(d) $HSeO_3^-$
Conjugate base	CN^-	$(CH_3)_2NH$	$H_2PO_4^-$	SeO_3^{2-}

10.50 $HCO_3^-(aq) + HCl(aq) \longrightarrow H_2O(l) + CO_2(g) + Cl^-(aq)$

$HCO_3^-(aq) + NaOH(aq) \longrightarrow H_2O(l) + Na^+(aq) + CO_3^{2-}(aq)$

$H_2PO_4^-(aq) + HCl(aq) \longrightarrow H_3PO_4(aq) + Cl^-(aq)$

$H_2PO_4^-(aq) + NaOH(aq) \longrightarrow HPO_4^{2-}(aq) + H_2O(l) + Na^+(aq)$

10.51 The stronger acid and weaker base are conjugate pairs, as are the stronger base and weaker acid. The reaction to form weaker base and weaker acid is favored.

(a) $HCl(aq) + PO_4^{3-}(aq) \rightleftharpoons HPO_4^{2-}(aq) + Cl^-(aq)$
     stronger acid stronger base   weaker acid   weaker base

(b) $CN^-(aq) + HSO_4^-(aq) \rightleftharpoons HCN(aq) + SO_4^{2-}(aq)$
     stronger base   stronger acid   weaker acid   weaker base

(c) $HClO_4(aq) + NO_2^-(aq) \rightleftharpoons HNO_2(aq) + ClO_4^-(aq)$
     stronger acid   stronger base   weaker acid   weaker base

(d) $HF(aq) + CH_3O^-(aq) \rightleftharpoons CH_3OH(aq) + F^-(aq)$
     stronger acid   stronger base   weaker acid   weaker base

10.52 $2 HCl(aq) + CaCO_3(s) \longrightarrow H_2O(l) + CO_2(g) + CaCl_2(aq)$

10.53 (a) $LiOH(aq) + HNO_3(aq) \longrightarrow H_2O(l) + LiNO_3(aq)$

(b) $BaCO_3(aq) + 2 HI(aq) \longrightarrow H_2O(l) + CO_2(g) + BaI_2(aq)$

(c) $H_3PO_4(aq) + 3 KOH(aq) \longrightarrow 3 H_2O(l) + K_3PO_4(aq)$

(d) $Ca(HCO_3)_2(aq) + 2 HCl(aq) \longrightarrow 2 H_2O(l) + 2 CO_2(g) + CaCl_2(aq)$

(e) $Ba(OH)_2(aq) + H_2SO_4(aq) \longrightarrow 2 H_2O(l) + BaSO_4(s)$

Acid and Base Strength: K_a and pH

10.54 For the reaction: $HA(aq) + H_2O(l) \rightleftharpoons H_3O^+(l) + A^-(aq)$

$$K = \frac{[H_3O^+][A^-]}{[HA][H_2O]}$$

Since $[H_2O]$ is constant, we define a new constant:

$$K_a = K[H_2O] = \frac{[H_3O^+][A^-]}{[HA]}$$

10.55

$$[H_3O^+] = \frac{K_a[HA]}{[A^-]}$$

10.56 K_w is the product of the molar concentrations of H_3O^+ and OH^- in any aqueous solution and is numerically equal to 1.0×10^{-14} at 25°C.

$$K_a = \frac{[H_3O^+][OH^-]}{[H_2O]}; \quad K_a[H_2O] = K_w = [H_3O^+][OH^-]$$

10.57 pH is defined as the negative logarithm of the molar H_3O^+ concentration. For example, if $[H_3O^+] = 1.0 \times 10^{-3}$ M, then pH = 3.

10.58 $NH_4^+(aq) + H_2O(l) \rightleftharpoons NH_3(g) + H_3O^+(aq)$

$$K_a = \frac{[H_3O^+][NH_3]}{[NH_4^+]}$$

10.59 $H_3PO_4(aq) + H_2O(l) \rightleftharpoons H_2PO_4^-(aq) + H_3O^+(aq)$

$$K_a = \frac{[H_2PO_4^-][H_3O^+]}{[H_3PO_4]}$$

$H_2PO_4^-(aq) + H_2O(l) \rightleftharpoons HPO_4^{2-}(aq) + H_3O^+(aq)$

$$K_a = \frac{[HPO_4^{2-}][H_3O^+]}{[H_2PO_4^-]}$$

$HPO_4^{2-}(aq) + H_2O(l) \rightleftharpoons PO_4^{3-}(aq) + H_3O^+(aq)$

$$K_a = \frac{[PO_4^{3-}][H_3O^+]}{[HPO_4^{2-}]}$$

10.60 (a) HF is slightly stronger.   (b) HSO_4^- is a stronger acid.
(c) $H_2PO_4^-$ is a stronger acid.   (d) CH_3CO_2H is slightly stronger.

10.61 The stronger base appears lower in the "Base" column of Table 10.1.
(a) OH^- (b) NO_2^- (c) OH^- (d) CN^- (e) HPO_4^{2-}

10.62 Urine (pH = 7.9) is weakly basic, since solutions with pH greater than 7.0 are basic.

10.63 Because the pH of a 0.10 M HCN solution is lower than 7.0, the solution is acidic. If HCN were a strong acid, the pH of the 0.10 M solution would be 1. Thus, HCN is a weak acid.

10.64 The concentration of HCl in gastric juice is approximately 1×10^{-2} M.

10.65 For spinal fluid, $[H_3O^+] = 4 \times 10^{-8}$ M

10.66 $[H_3O^+] = 10^{-pH}$. Since, in this problem, $[H_3O^+] = 0.10\ M = 1.0 \times 10^{-1}\ M$, the pH = 1.00.

10.67

$$K_w = [H_3O^+][OH^-] = 10^{-14}; \quad [H_3O^+] = \frac{K_w}{[OH^-]} = \frac{10^{-14}}{10^{-1}} = 10^{-13}$$

$$[H_3O^+] = 10^{-pH}; \text{pH} = 13$$

10.68 , 10.71

	$[H_3O^+]$	pH	$[OH^-]$
(a) Egg white	$2.5 \times 10^{-8}\ M$	7.60	4×10^{-7}
(b) Apple cider	$5.0 \times 10^{-4}\ M$	3.30	2.0×10^{-11}
(c) Ammonia	$2.3 \times 10^{-12}\ M$	11.64	4.3×10^{-3}

Ammonia is least acidic and apple cider is most acidic.

10.69 (a) pH = 4; $[H_3O^+] = 1 \times 10^{-4}\ M$ (b) pH = 11; $[H_3O^+] = 1 \times 10^{-11}\ M$
(c) pH = 0; $[H_3O^+] = 1\ M$ (d) pH = 1.38; $[H_3O^+] = 4.2 \times 10^{-2}\ M$
(e) pH = 7.96; $[H_3O^+] = 1.1 \times 10^{-8}\ M$

10.70 (a) $[OH^-] = 1 \times 10^{-10}\ M$ (b) $[OH^-] = 1 \times 10^{-3}\ M$
(c) $[OH^-] = 1 \times 10^{-14}\ M$ (d) $[OH^-] = 2.4 \times 10^{-13}\ M$
(e) $[OH^-] = 9.1 \times 10^{-7}\ M$

10.71 See 10.68

Buffers

10.72 A buffer is composed of a weak acid and its conjugate base. Any added H_3O^+ can react with the conjugate base and be neutralized, and any added OH^- can react with the acid. In either case, the ratio of acid to conjugate base changes only slightly, and the pH of a buffered solution remains nearly constant.

10.73 $CH_3CO_2H + CH_3CO_2^-\ Na^+$ is a better buffer than $HNO_3 + NaNO_3$ because acetic acid is a weak acid and acetate ion is its conjugate base. Nitric acid is a strong acid, and nitrate ion is nonbasic. Thus, the nitric acid/sodium nitrate mixture is not a buffer and can't control pH.

10.74 $CH_3CO_2^-\ Na^+(aq) + HNO_3(aq) \longrightarrow CH_3CO_2H(aq) + NaNO_3(aq)$.
The added acid is neutralized by sodium acetate.

$CH_3CO_2H(aq) + OH^-(aq) \longrightarrow CH_3CO_2^-(aq) + H_2O(l)$
The added base is neutralized by acetic acid.

10.75 The carbon dioxide/bicarbonate relationship is shown by the following equation:

$$CO_2(aq) + H_2O(l) \rightleftharpoons H_2CO_3(aq) \rightleftharpoons HCO_3^-(aq) + H_3O^+(aq)$$

The rearranged equilibrium expression for this relationship is given by:

$$[H_3O^+] = K_a \frac{[CO_2]}{[HCO_3^-]}$$

(a) When a person breathes heavily, large amounts of CO_2 are removed from the bloodstream. According to Le Châtelier's Principle, removal of CO_2 shifts the above equilibrium to the left. The reaction below predominates.

$$HCO_3^-(aq) + H_3O^+(aq) \longrightarrow H_2CO_3(aq) \longrightarrow CO_2(aq) + H_2O(l)$$

When $[CO_2]$ decreases, $[H_3O^+]$ decreases, and pH rises.
(b) If a person has difficulty breathing, $[CO_2]$ in the bloodstream increases. The reaction shown below predominates, $[H_3O^+]$ increases, and pH is lowered.

$$CO_2(aq) + H_2O(l) \longrightarrow H_2CO_3(aq) \longrightarrow HCO_3^-(aq) + H_3O^+(aq)$$

10.76

$$[H_3O^+] = \frac{K_a[HA]}{[A^-]} \; ; \; K_a = 4.9 \times 10^{-10}, [HCN] = 0.200 \text{ M}, [CN^-] = 0.150 \text{ M}$$

$$[H_3O^+] = \frac{4.9 \times 10^{-10}[0.200 \text{ M}]}{[0.150 \text{ M}]} = 6.5 \times 10^{-10} \text{ M}; \text{ pH} = 9.19$$

10.77 Use the formula in the previous problem. Adding 0.020 mol HCl to 1.00 L of the above solution changes the value of [HCN] to 0.220 M and the value of [CN⁻] to 0.130 M.

$$[H_3O^+] = \frac{4.9 \times 10^{-10}[0.220 \text{ M}]}{[0.130 \text{ M}]} = 8.3 \times 10^{-10} \text{ M}; \text{ pH} = 9.08$$

If 0.020 mol NaOH is added to 1.00 L of the HCN/NaCN buffer system, the concentrations change to [HCN] = 0.180 M and [CN⁻] = 0.170 M.

$$[H_3O^+] = \frac{4.9 \times 10^{-10}[0.180 \text{ M}]}{[0.170 \text{ M}]} = 5.2 \times 10^{-10} \text{ M}; \text{ pH} = 9.28$$

Concentrations of Acid and Base Solutions

10.78 An equivalent of an acid or base is its formula weight in grams divided by the number of H_3O^+ or OH^- ions it produces.

10.79 The normality of an acid or base solution is a measure of concentration expressed in number of equivalents per liter of solution.

10.80 The number of equivalents is equal to the number of moles times the number of H^+ or OH^- ions produced. In this problem, we first find the number of moles of each acid and then multiply by the number of H^+ ions produced.

For HNO_3 : $0.500 \text{ L} \times \dfrac{0.50 \text{ mol H}^+}{1 \text{ L}} \times \dfrac{1 \text{ Eq}}{1 \text{ mol}} = 0.25 \text{ Eq H}^+$

For H_3PO_4 : $0.500 \text{ L} \times \dfrac{0.50 \text{ mol H}^+}{1 \text{ L}} \times \dfrac{3 \text{ Eq}}{1 \text{ mol}} = 0.75 \text{ Eq H}^+$

10.81 Since one equivalent of any base neutralizes one equivalent of any acid, 0.035 equivalents of NaOH neutralize 0.035 equivalents of H_3PO_4.

10.82 Since a 0.0050 N solution of any acid has 0.0050 equivalents per liter, 25 mL of a 0.0050 N KOH solution is needed to neutralize 25 mL of either 0.0050 N H_2SO_4 or 0.0050 N HCl.

10.83

$$PV = nRT \text{ or } V = \frac{nRT}{P}; \; T = 273 \text{ K}; \; P = 1 \text{ atm}; \; R = \frac{0.0821 \text{ L·atm}}{\text{mol·K}}$$

For HCN, molarity equals normality. Thus:

$$n = 0.250 \text{ L } \times \frac{0.10 \text{ mol}}{1 \text{ L}} = 0.025 \text{ mol HCN}$$

$$V = \frac{0.025 \text{ mol } \times \dfrac{0.0821 \text{ L·atm}}{\text{mol·K}} \times 273 \text{ K}}{1 \text{ atm}} = 0.56 \text{ L HCN}$$

10.84 (a) 0.25 mol $Mg(OH)_2$ x 2 Eq/mol = 0.50 Eq $Mg(OH)_2$

(b) Molar mass of $Mg(OH)_2$ = 58.3 g ;   1 Eq $Mg(OH)_2$ = 29.6 g

$$2.5 \text{ g } Mg(OH)_2 \times \frac{1 \text{ Eq}}{29.6 \text{ g}} = 0.084 \text{ Eq } Mg(OH)_2$$

(c) Molar mass of CH_3CO_2H = 60.0 g ;   1 Eq CH_3CO_2H = 60.0 g

$$15 \text{ g } CH_3CO_2H \times \frac{1 \text{ Eq}}{60 \text{ g}} = 0.25 \text{ Eq } CH_3CO_2H$$

10.85

Molar mass of $C_6H_5O_7H_3$ = 192.0 g; 1 Eq $C_6H_5O_7H_3$ = $\dfrac{192.0 \text{ g}}{1 \text{ mol}} \times \dfrac{1 \text{ mol}}{3 \text{ Eq}}$ = 64.0 g

$$\frac{64.0 \text{ g}}{1 \text{ Eq}} \times \frac{1 \text{ Eq}}{1000 \text{ mEq}} \times 152 \text{ mEq} = 9.73 \text{ g}$$

10.86 Molar mass of $Ca(OH)_2$ = 74.1 g; 1 Eq $Ca(OH)_2$ = 37.0 g

$$\frac{5.0 \text{ g}}{0.400 \text{ L}} \times \frac{1 \text{ mol}}{74.1 \text{ g}} = 0.17 \text{ M}; \quad \frac{0.17 \text{ mol}}{1 \text{ L}} \times \frac{2 \text{ Eq}}{1 \text{ mol}} = \frac{0.34 \text{ Eq}}{1 \text{ L}} = 0.34 \text{ N}$$

10.87 Molar mass of $C_6H_5O_7H_3$ = 192 g; 1 Eq $C_6H_5O_7H_3$ = 64.0 g

$$\frac{25 \text{ g}}{0.750 \text{ L}} \times \frac{1 \text{ mol}}{192 \text{ g}} = 0.17 \text{ M}; \quad \frac{0.17 \text{ mol}}{1 \text{ L}} \times \frac{3 \text{ Eq}}{1 \text{ mol}} = \frac{0.51 \text{ Eq}}{1 \text{ L}} = 0.51 \text{ N}$$

10.88 $2\,KOH(aq) + H_2SO_4(aq) \longrightarrow 2\,H_2O(l) + K_2SO_4(aq)$

$$0.0150\text{ L H}_2SO_4 \times \frac{0.0250\text{ mol H}_2SO_4}{1\text{ L H}_2SO_4} \times \frac{2\text{ mol KOH}}{1\text{ mol H}_2SO_4} = 0.00075\text{ mol KOH}$$

$$\frac{0.00075\text{ mol NaOH}}{0.010\text{ L NaOH}} = 0.075\text{ M}$$

10.89 $V_1 \times N_1 = V_2 \times N_2;\ V_1 = 35.0\text{ mL};\ N_1 = 0.100\text{ N};\ V_2 = 21.5\text{ mL}$

$$N_2 = \frac{V_1 \times N_1}{V_2} = \frac{35.0\text{ mL} \times 0.100\text{ N}}{21.5\text{ mL}} = 0.163\text{ N}$$

Applications

10.90 (a) $NaAl(OH)_2CO_3(aq) + 4\,HCl(aq) \longrightarrow$
$$CO_2(g) + 3\,H_2O(l) + NaCl(aq) + AlCl_3(aq)$$

(b) Molar mass of $NaAl(OH)_2CO_3(aq) = 144$ g/mol

$$\frac{0.0955\text{ mol HCl}}{1\text{ L}} \times 0.0150\text{ L} = 0.001\ 43\text{ mol HCl}$$

$$0.001\ 43\text{ mol HCl} \times \frac{1\text{ mol antacid}}{4\text{ mol HCl}} \times \frac{144\text{ g}}{1\text{ mol antacid}} = 0.0515\text{ g} = 51.5\text{ mg}$$

10.91 Gastric juice is the most acidic body fluid, and pancreatic juice is the most basic.

10.92 pH of acid rain = 5.6; $[H_3O^+] = 2 \times 10^{-6}$ M

10.93 (a) $[H_3O^+] = .03$ M

(b) $25\text{ L} \times \dfrac{0.03\text{ mol}}{1\text{ L}} \times \dfrac{63\text{ g}}{1\text{ mol}} = 47$ g, or approximately 50 g HNO_3

General Questions and Problems

10.94 Citric acid reacts with sodium bicarbonate to release CO_2 bubbles:

$$C_6H_5O_7H_3(aq) + 3\,NaHCO_3(aq) \longrightarrow C_6H_5O_7Na_3(aq) + 3\,H_2O(l) + 3\,CO_2(g)$$

Sodium bicarbonate is the antacid.

10.95 $2\,NaOH(aq) + H_2SO_4(aq) \longrightarrow 2\,H_2O(l) + Na_2SO_4(aq)$

$$0.040\text{ L H}_2SO_4 \times \frac{0.10\text{ mol H}_2SO_4}{1\text{ L H}_2SO_4} \times \frac{2\text{ mol NaOH}}{1\text{ mol H}_2SO_4} = 0.0080\text{ mol NaOH}$$

$$0.0080\text{ mol NaOH} \times \frac{1000\text{ mL NaOH}}{0.50\text{ mol NaOH}} = 16\text{ mL NaOH}$$

10.96 Both 50 mL of a 0.20 N HCl solution and 50 mL of a 0.20 acetic acid solution contain the same number of moles of acid – 0.010 moles. Because HCl is a strong acid, it is almost completely dissociated in water, and the H_3O^+ concentration approaches 0.20 M. Acetic acid, however, is a weak acid that is only slightly dissociated, and the H_3O^+ concentration is much lower – around 0.002 M. Since the HCl solution has a higher H_3O^+ concentration, it has a lower pH.

10.97 If aspirin were a strong acid, the $[H_3O^+]$ of a 0.010 M solution would be nearly 0.010 M, or 10^{-2} M, and the pH of the solution would be around 2. Since the observed pH is 3.3, aspirin must be a weak acid.

10.98 $2\,HCl(aq)\ +\ Ca(OH)_2(aq)\ \longrightarrow\ 2\,H_2O(l)\ +\ CaCl_2(aq)$

$$0.140\ \text{L HCl}\ \times\ \frac{0.150\ \text{mol HCl}}{1\ \text{L HCl}}\ \times\ \frac{1\ \text{mol Ca(OH)}_2}{2\ \text{mol HCl}}\ =\ 0.0105\ \text{mol Ca(OH)}_2$$

$$\frac{0.0105\ \text{mol Ca(OH)}_2}{0.0300\ \text{L Ca(OH)}_2}\ =\ 0.35\ \text{M Ca(OH)}_2$$

10.99 Both (a), NaF and HF, and (c), NH_4Cl and NH_3 are effective buffer systems. The NaF / HF system is a solution of a weak acid and the salt of its anion. The NH_4Cl / NH_3 system is a solution of a weak base and the salt of its cation. Neither (b) nor (d) are buffer systems because $HClO_4$ and HBr are both strong acids.

10.100

(a) $\underset{\text{acid}}{NH_4^+(aq)}\ +\ \underset{\text{base}}{OH^-(aq)}\ \longrightarrow\ \underset{\text{conjugate base}}{NH_3(g)}\ +\ \underset{\text{conjugate acid}}{H_2O(l)}$

(b) $PV = nRT$; $P = 755$ mm Hg; $V = 2.86$ L; $T = 333$ K; $R = \dfrac{62.3\ \text{mm Hg·L}}{\text{mol·K}}$

$$n\ =\ \frac{PV}{RT}\ =\ \frac{755\ \text{mm}\ \times\ 2.86\ \text{L}}{\dfrac{62.3\ \text{mm Hg·L}}{\text{mol·K}}\ \times\ 333\ \text{K}}\ =\ 0.104\ \text{mol NH}_3$$

$$0.104\ \text{mol}\ \times\ \frac{53.5\ \text{g}}{1\ \text{mol}}\ =\ 5.56\ \text{g NH}_4\text{Cl}$$

10.101 $M_1 \times V_1 = M_2 \times V_2$; $V_1 = 0.025$ L; $M_1 = 0.40$ M; $V_2 = 2.00$ L

$$M_2\ =\ \frac{M_1 \times V_1}{V_2}\ =\ \frac{0.40\ \text{M}\ \times\ 0.025\ \text{L}}{2.00\ \text{L}}\ =\ 0.0050\ \text{M}\ =\ 5.0 \times 10^{-3}\ \text{M OH}^-$$

$$[H_3O^+]\ =\ \frac{10^{-14}}{[OH^-]}\ =\ \frac{10^{-14}}{5.0 \times 10^{-3}}\ =\ 2.0 \times 10^{-12};\ \text{pH}\ =\ 11.70$$

10.102

(a) $Na_2O(aq) + H_2O(l) \longrightarrow 2\ NaOH(aq)$

(b) $1.55\ g\ Na_2O \times \dfrac{1\ mol\ Na_2O}{62.0\ g\ Na_2O} \times \dfrac{2\ mol\ NaOH}{1\ mol\ Na_2O} = 0.0500\ mol\ NaOH$

$\dfrac{0.0500\ mol\ NaOH}{500.0\ mL} \times \dfrac{1000\ mL}{1\ L} = 0.100\ M\ NaOH;\ pH = 13.00$

(c) $0.0500\ mol\ NaOH \times \dfrac{1\ mol\ HCl}{1\ mol\ NaOH} \times \dfrac{1\ L}{0.0100\ mol\ HCl} = 5.00\ L\ HCl$

Self-Test for Chapter 10

Multiple choice:

1. What volume of 0.10 M H_2SO_4 will neutralize 30 mL of 0.05 M $Ca(OH)_2$?
    (a) 30 mL   (b) 15 mL   (c) 10 mL   (d) 6.0 mL

2. Which of the following salts is acidic in solution?
    (a) NH_4Br (b) NaBr   (c) NH_4CN (d) NaCN

3. KCN is the salt of a:
    (a) strong acid and strong base   (b) strong acid and weak base   (c) weak acid and strong base
    (d) weak acid and weak base

4. A solution has a pH of 9. What is the value of $[OH^-]$?
    (a) 5   (b) 10^{-9} (c) 9   (d) 10^{-5}

5. Which of the following is a diprotic acid?
    (a) CH_3CO_2H (b) $Ba(OH)_2$ (c) H_2SO_3 (d) H_3PO_4

6. Look at Table 10.2 and decide which base is a weaker base than F^-:
    (a) $H_2PO_4^-$ (b) HCO_3^- (c) CN^- (d) NH_3

7. Which of the following substances turns phenolphthalein red?
    (a) urine   (b) milk of magnesia   (c) blood   (d) coffee

8. Which of the following bases is an Arrhenius base?
    (a) NaOH   (b) $Ca_3(PO_4)_2$ (c) NH_3 (d) LiF

9. In the reaction $Mg(OH)_2(aq) + 2\ HBr(aq) \longrightarrow 2\ H_2O(l) + MgBr_2(aq)$ what is the conjugate acid of $Mg(OH)_2$?
    (a) HBr   (b) H_2O (c) $MgBr_2$ (d) can't tell

10. How many water molecules are produced in the neutralization reaction of $H_3PO_4 + Mg(OH)_2$?
    (a) 2   (b) 3   (c) 4   (d) 6

Complete the following sentences:

1. One _____ of an acid reacts with one _____ of a base.

2. Phenolphthalein turns _____ in basic solution.

3. H_2CO_3 is a _____ acid.

4. The anion of a weak acid is a _____ base.

5. _____ is the splitting apart of an acid into a proton and an anion.

6. An Arrhenius base yields _____ when dissolved in water.

7. _____ is the reaction of an acid with a base.

8. _____ is the measure of a solution's acidity.

9. To completely neutralize 10.0 mL of 1.0 M H_3PO_4, you need _____ mL of 1.0 M NaOH.

10. CH_3CO_2H and $CH_3CO_2^-$ are known as a _____ acid–base pair.

11. The buffer system of blood is the _____ / _____ system.

12. Substances that can act as either acids or bases are _____.

Tell whether the following statements are true or false:

1. 30.0 mL of 0.10 M H_2SO_4 is neutralized by 30.0 mL of 0.10 M NaOH.

2. A change of one pH unit is a tenfold change in $[H_3O^+]$.

3. H_2SO_4 / HSO_4^- is a good buffer system.

4. All bases are negatively charged.

5. Bicarbonate ion neutralizes more acid than carbonate ion.

6. If the pH of a solution is 7.0, $[OH^-] = 10^{-7}$.

7. Water can act as both an acid and a base.

8. According to the Brønsted definition, an acid is a substance that dissolves in water to give H_3O^+ ions.

9. Ammonia reacts with an acid to yield ammonium hydroxide.

10. Whether an acid or a base is strong or weak depends on its percent dissociation in water.

11. The reaction $H_2O + H_2PO_4^- \longrightarrow H_3O^+ + HPO_4^{2-}$ proceeds in the direction written.

12. One equivalent of $Ca(OH)_2$ equals 37 g.

Match the entries on the left with their partners on the right:

1.   Strong acid   (a) $[H_3O^+]\,[OH^-]$

2.   1 M HCl   (b) Cl^-

3. $[H_3O^+] = 10^{-8}$ (c) pH = 6

4.   Alkalosis   (d) HCl

5. K_w (e) 1 N acid

6.   Weak base   (f) CH_3CO_2H

7.   Strong base   (g) $[OH^-] = 10^{-6}$

8.   Salt   (h) Blood pH lower than 7.35

9. $[H_3O^+] = 10^{-6}$ (i) $CH_3CO_2^-$

10. Weak acid   (j) Na_2SO_4

11. 1 M H_3PO_4 (k) 3 N acid

12. Acidosis   (l) Blood pH higher than 7.35

Chapter Outline

I. Introduction to radioactivity (Sections 11.1–11.3)
    A Nuclear reactions (Section 11.1).
        1. A nuclear reaction occurs when a nuclide spontaneously changes to a different nuclide.
        2. Nuclear reactions differ from chemical reactions in several ways.
           a. Nuclear reactions produce different elements.
           b. Different isotopes have the same behavior in chemical reactions but different behavior in nuclear reactions.
           c. The rate of a nuclear reaction is unaffected by a change in temperature.
           d. A nuclear reaction is the same whether an atom is in a compound or is elemental.
           e. The energy change in a nuclear reaction is immense.
    B. The discovery and nature of radioactivity (Section 11.2).
        1. Radioactivity was discovered by Becquerel and the Curies.
        2. Three types of radiation may be emitted:
           a. α radiation: He^{2+} nuclei with low penetrating power.
           b. β radiation: electrons (e^-) with medium penetrating power.
           c γ radiation: high energy light waves with very high penetrating power.
    C. Stable and unstable isotopes (Section 11.3).
        1. All elements have radioactive isotopes.
        2. Most radioisotopes are made in particle accelerators: these are known as artificial radioisotopes.
        3. Radioisotopes have the same chemical properties as their nonradioactive isotopes.
II. Nuclear decay (Sections 11.4–11.7).
    A. Nuclear emissions (Section 11.4)
        1. Alpha emission.
             After α emission, the atomic number of the resulting isotope decreases by 2, and the mass number decreases by 4.
        2. Beta emission.
           a. In β emission, a neutron decomposes to a proton and an electron.
           b. The electron is emitted, and the proton is retained.
           c. The atomic number of the resulting isotope increases by 1, and the mass number is unchanged.
        3. Gamma (γ) emission.
             Gamma (γ) emission usually accompanies α or β emission and doesn't affect either mass number or atomic number.
        4. Positron emission.
           a. Positron emission occurs when a proton is converted to a neutron and an ejected positron (positive electron).
           b. The mass number of the nucleus is unchanged, but the atomic number decreases by 1
        5. Electron capture (EC).
           a. EC occurs when a nucleus captures an electron from the surrounding electron cloud, converting a proton into a neutron.
           b. The mass number of the nucleus is unchanged, but the atomic number decreases by 1

B. Half-life (Section 11.5).
   1. Half-life is the amount of time it takes for half of a sample of a radioisotope to decay.
   2. Half-life doesn't depend on the amount of sample or on temperature.
   3. Each half-life sees the decay of half of what remains of the sample.
C. Radioactive decay series (Section 11.6).
      Some heavy radioisotopes undergo a series of disintegrations until a nonradioactive product is reached.
D. Ionizing radiation (Section 11.7).
   1. Ionizing radiation is any high-energy radiation that can create reactive ions when it collides with a chemical compound.
   2. Ionizing radiation converts molecules into highly reactive ions.
   3. Ionizing radiation can injure the body.
      a. Gamma and X radiation are more harmful when radiation comes from outside the body.
      b. Alpha and β radiation are more dangerous when emitted from within the body.
   4. The intensity of radiation decreases with the square of the distance from the source.
III. Detecting radiation (Sections 11.8–11.9).
   A. Devices for detecting radiation (Section 11.8).
      1. Photographic film badges.
      2. Geiger counter.
      3. Scintillation counter.
   B. Units of radiation (Section 11.9).
      1. The *curie* measures the number of disintegrations per second.
      2. The *roentgen* measures the intensity of radiation.
      3. The *rad* measures the energy absorbed per gram tissue.
      4. The *rem* and the *sievert* measure tissue damage.
IV. Artificial transmutation (Section 11.10).
   A. Artificial transmutation occurs when nuclei are bombarded with high energy particles.
   B. After bombardment, a new nucleus is produced.
   C. The transuranium elements were all produced via artificial transmutation.
V. Nuclear fission and nuclear fusion (Section 11.11).
   A. Nuclear fission.
      1. Nuclear fission occurs when a heavy nucleus fragments after bombardment by a small particle, such as a neutron.
      2. Many different fission products can result from one bombardment.
      3. In some cases, bombardment with one neutron can cause production of more than one neutron, in addition to fragmentation.
         a. This is called a chain reaction.
         b. If the bombarded sample weighs more than a critical mass, a nuclear explosion can result.
         c. A controlled fission reaction can be used to produce energy.
   B. Nuclear fusion.
      1. If two light nuclei are made to collide, a nuclear fusion reaction occurs that produces a combined nucleus plus energy.
      2. Nuclear fusion reactions occur in stars.

Solutions to Chapter 11 Problems

11.1 For α emission, subtract 2 from the atomic number of radon and 4 from the mass number:

$$^{222}_{86}Rn \rightarrow \, ^{4}_{2}He + \, ^{218}_{84}?$$

Then, look in the periodic table for the element with atomic number 84:

$$^{222}_{86}Rn \rightarrow \, ^{4}_{2}He + \, ^{218}_{84}Po$$

11.2 Add 4 to the mass number of radon-222 to calculate the isotope of radium:

$$^{226}_{88}Ra \rightarrow \, ^{4}_{2}He + \, ^{222}_{86}Rn$$

11.3

$$^{14}_{6}C \rightarrow \, ^{0}_{-1}e + \, ?$$

The mass number of the product element stays the same, but the atomic number increases by 1, to 7. Looking in the periodic table, we find that ^{14}N is the element formed:

$$^{14}_{6}C \rightarrow \, ^{0}_{-1}e + \, ^{14}_{7}N$$

11.4

(a) $^{3}_{1}H \rightarrow \, ^{0}_{-1}e + \, ^{3}_{2}He$ (b) $^{210}_{82}Pb \rightarrow \, ^{0}_{-1}e + \, ^{210}_{83}Bi$ (c) $^{20}_{9}F \rightarrow \, ^{0}_{-1}e + \, ^{20}_{10}Ne$

11.5 For positron emission, the atomic number decreases by 1, but the mass number stays the same.

(a) $^{38}_{20}Ca \rightarrow \, ^{0}_{1}e + \, ^{38}_{19}K$ (b) $^{118}_{54}Xe \rightarrow \, ^{0}_{1}e + \, ^{118}_{53}I$ (c) $^{79}_{37}Rb \rightarrow \, ^{0}_{1}e + \, ^{79}_{36}Kr$

11.6 As in positron emission, the atomic number decreases by one and the mass number stays unchanged in electron capture.

(a) $^{62}_{30}Zn + \, ^{0}_{-1}e \rightarrow \, ^{62}_{29}Cu$ (b) $^{110}_{50}Sn + \, ^{0}_{-1}e \rightarrow \, ^{110}_{49}In$ (c) $^{81}_{36}Kr + \, ^{0}_{-1}e \rightarrow \, ^{81}_{35}Br$

11.7 Table 11.2 shows the changes brought about by various radioactive decay patterns. Only β emission produces a change of +1 to the atomic number and a decrease in the number of neutrons. The original element was indium ($Z = 49$), and tin ($Z = 50$) is the decay product.

$$^{120}_{49}In \rightarrow \, ^{0}_{-1}e + \, ^{120}_{50}Sn$$

11.8 $17,000 \div 5730 = 2.97$, or approximately 3 half-lives.

The percentage of $^{14}_{6}C$ is $(1/2) \times (1/2) \times (1/2) \times 100\% = 12.5\%$ of the original sample.

11.9 Find the point on the graph that represents 50% of the sample remaining. Locate the time that corresponds to this point; this is the half-life – 3 days.

11.10

$$\frac{I_1}{I_2} = \frac{d_2^2}{d_1^2} : I_1 = 250 \text{ units}; I_2 = 25 \text{ units}; d_1^2 = (4.0 \text{ m})^2 = 16 \text{ m}^2; d_2^2 = ?$$

$$d_2^2 = \frac{d_1^2 \times I_1}{I_2} = \frac{16 \text{ m}^2 \times 250 \text{ units}}{25 \text{ units}} = 160 \text{ m}^2$$

$$d_2 = 13 \text{ m}$$

11.11

$$\frac{5 \text{ mrem}}{270 \text{ mrem}} \times 100\% = 1.9\%$$

The annual dose of radiation for most people will increase by approximately 2%.

11.12

$$\frac{175 \, \mu \text{Ci}}{\text{dose}} \times \frac{1 \text{ mL}}{44 \, \mu \text{Ci}} = \frac{4.0 \text{ mL}}{\text{dose}}$$

11.13

$$^{241}_{95}\text{Am} \rightarrow \, ^4_2\text{He} + \, ^{237}_{93}\text{Np}$$

11.14

$$^{241}_{95}\text{Am} + \, ^4_2\text{He} \rightarrow 2 \, ^1_0\text{n} + \, ^{243}_{97}\text{Bk}$$

11.15

$$^{40}_{18}\text{Ar} + \, ^1_1\text{H} \rightarrow \, ^1_0\text{n} + \, ^{40}_{19}\text{K}$$

11.16

$$^{235}_{92}\text{U} + \, ^1_0\text{n} \rightarrow 2 \, ^1_0\text{n} + \, ^{137}_{52}\text{Te} + \, ^{97}_{40}\text{Zr}$$

Understanding Key Concepts

11.17 After one half-life, the sample would consist of eight $^{28}_{13}\text{Al}$ atoms and eight $^{28}_{12}\text{Mg}$ atoms. After two half-lives, the remaining eight $^{28}_{12}\text{Mg}$ atoms would have decayed to four $^{28}_{13}\text{Al}$ atoms, producing the outcome shown in the picture.

11.18

● Aluminum-28

○ Magnesum-28

11.19 The illustrated isotope, with six protons and eight neutrons, is $^{14}_6\text{C}$.

11.20 The shorter arrows represent β emission because they show the decomposition of a neutron with an accompanying 1 unit increase in atomic number.
The longer arrows represent α emission because they indicate a decay that results in the loss of two protons and two neutrons (α particle).

11.21

$$^{241}_{94}Pu \rightarrow ^{241}_{95}Am \rightarrow ^{237}_{93}Np \rightarrow ^{233}_{91}Pa \rightarrow ^{233}_{92}U$$

11.22 The isotope can decay by either positron emission or electron capture since the atomic number decreases by 1 but the mass number remains the same.

$$^{148}_{69}Tm \rightarrow ^{0}_{1}e + ^{148}_{68}Er \quad or \quad ^{148}_{69}Tm + ^{0}_{-1}e \rightarrow ^{148}_{68}Er$$

11.23 The half-life is approximately 3.5 years.

Radioactivity

11.24 A substance is said to be radioactive if it emits radiation by decay of an unstable nucleus.

11.25

Radiation	Particle Produced	Atomic Number	Mass Number	Penetrating Power
α emission	$^{4}_{2}He$	decreases by 2	decreases by 4	low
β emission	$^{0}_{-1}e$	increases by 1	unchanged	medium
γ emission	none	unchanged	unchanged	high
positron emission	$^{0}_{1}e$	decreases by 1	unchanged	
electron capture	$^{0}_{-1}e$ (captured, not emitted)	decreases by 1	unchanged	

11.26

Nuclear Reaction	*Chemical Reaction*
involves change in an atom's nucleus	involves change in an atom's outer shell electrons
usually produces a different element	never produces a different element
different isotopes have different behavior in a nuclear reaction	different isotopes have the same behavior in a chemical reaction
rate is unaffected by a change in temperature or by a catalyst	rate changes with a change in temperature or by using a catalyst
rate is the same, whether the atom is in a compound or uncombined	
energy change is millions of times larger for a nuclear reaction	

11.27 Transmutation is the change of one element into another brought about by nuclear decay.

11.28 The symbol for an α particle is $^{4}_{2}He$.

11.29 The symbol for a β particle is $^{0}_{-1}e$.

11.30 Gamma radiation has the highest penetrating power, and α radiation has the lowest penetrating power.

11.31 When ionizing radiation strikes a molecule, a high-energy reactive ion with an odd number of electrons is produced. This reactive ion immediately reacts with other chemical compounds, creating other reactive fragments that can cause further reactions.

11.32 Ionizing radiation causes cell damage by breaking bonds in DNA. The resulting damage may lead to mutation, cancer, or cell death.

11.33 Background radiation may arise from naturally occurring radioactive isotopes or from cosmic rays.

11.34 A neutron in the nucleus decomposes to a proton and an electron, which is emitted as a β particle.

11.35 An α particle is a helium nucleus, $_{2}^{4}\text{He}$; a helium atom is a helium nucleus plus two electrons.

Nuclear Decay and Transmutation

11.36 A nuclear equation is balanced if the number of nucleons is the same on both sides and if the sums of the charges on the nuclei and any elementary particles is the same on both sides.

11.37 A transuranium element is an element with an atomic number greater than 92. It is produced by bombardment of a lighter element with high-energy particles.

11.38 For an atom emitting an α particle, the atomic number decreases by two, and the mass number decreases by four.
For an atom emitting a β particle, the atomic number increases by one, and the mass number is unchanged.

11.39 For an atom emitting a γ ray, both atomic number and mass number are unchanged.
For an atom emitting a positron, the atomic number decreases by one, and the mass number is unchanged

11.40 In nuclear fission, bombardment of a nucleus causes fragmentation in many different ways to yield a large number of smaller fragments. Normal radioactive decay of a nucleus produces an atom with a similar mass and yields a predictable product.

11.41 Bombardment of a $_{92}^{235}\text{U}$ nucleus with one neutron produces three neutrons, which, on collision with three more $_{92}^{235}\text{U}$ nuclei yield nine neutrons, and so on. Because the reaction is self-sustaining, it is known as a chain reaction.

11.42

(a) $_{16}^{35}\text{S} \rightarrow _{-1}^{0}\text{e} + _{17}^{35}\text{Cl}$

(b) $_{10}^{24}\text{Ne} \rightarrow _{-1}^{0}\text{e} + _{11}^{24}\text{Na}$

(c) $_{38}^{90}\text{Sr} \rightarrow _{-1}^{0}\text{e} + _{39}^{90}\text{Y}$

11.43

(a) $^{190}_{78}Pt \rightarrow ^4_2He + ^{186}_{76}Os$ (b) $^{208}_{87}Fr \rightarrow ^4_2He + ^{204}_{85}At$

(c) $^{245}_{96}Cm \rightarrow ^4_2He + ^{241}_{94}Pu$

11.44

(a) $^{140}_{55}Cs \rightarrow ^0_{-1}e + ^{140}_{56}Ba$ (b) $^{246}_{96}Cm \rightarrow ^4_2He + ^{242}_{94}Pu$

11.45

(a) $^{109}_{47}Ag + ^4_2He \rightarrow ^{113}_{49}In$ (b) $^{10}_5B + ^4_2He \rightarrow ^{13}_7N + ^1_0n$

11.46

(a) $^{235}_{92}U + ^1_0n \rightarrow ^{160}_{62}Sm + ^{72}_{30}Zn + 4^1_0n$

(b) $^{235}_{92}U + ^1_0n \rightarrow ^{87}_{35}Br + ^{146}_{57}La + 3^1_0n$

11.47

(a) $^{126}_{50}Sn \rightarrow ^0_{-1}e + ^{126}_{51}Sb$ (b) $^{210}_{88}Ra \rightarrow ^4_2He + ^{206}_{86}Rn$

(c) $^{76}_{36}Kr + ^0_{-1}e \rightarrow ^{76}_{35}Br$

11.48

$^{198}_{80}Hg + ^1_0n \rightarrow ^{198}_{79}Au + ^1_1H$

A proton is produced in addition to gold-198.

11.49

$^{209}_{83}Bi + ^{58}_{26}Fe \rightarrow ^{266}_{109}Mt + ^1_0n$ A neutron is also produced.

Half-Life

11.50 If strontium-90 has a half-life of 28.8 years, half of a given quantity of strontium-90 will have decayed after 28.8 years.

11.51 1/2 x 1/2 x 100% = 25%. 25% of the original radioactivity remains in a sample after 2 half-lives.

11.52 365 ÷ 120 = 3.04, or approximately 3 half-lives.

$$0.050 \text{ g} \times \frac{1}{2} \times \frac{1}{2} \times \frac{1}{2} = 0.0062 \text{ g}$$

Approximately 0.006 grams of $^{75}_{34}Se$ will remain after a year.

11.53 After seven half-lives, 99% of any sample will have decayed. Since the half-life of $^{75}_{34}Se$ is approximately 0.33 year, 99% of the sample will have disintegrated in 7 x 0.33 = 2.3 years.

11.54 If the half-life of mercury–97 is 64.1 hrs.,
6 days = 144 h ; 144/64.1 = 2.3, or approximately 2 half-lives
27 days = 648 h ; 648/64.1 = approximately 10 half-lives
5.0 ng x 1/2 x 1/2 = approx. 1 ng of mercury-197 remains after 6 days.
5.0 ng x $(1/2)^{10}$ = approx. 5 x 10^{-3} ng of mercury-197 remains after 27 days.

11.55

(a) $^{198}_{79}Au \rightarrow {}^{0}_{-1}e + {}^{198}_{80}Hg$

(b) $\dfrac{3.75 \text{ mCi}}{30.0 \text{ mCi}}$ = 0.125 = 3.00 half lives ; 3.00 x 2.695 days = 8.09 days

(c) $\dfrac{1.0 \text{ mCi}}{1 \text{ kg}}$ x 70.0 kg = 70 mCi

Measuring Radioactivity

11.56 The inside walls of a Geiger counter tube are negatively charged, and a wire in the center is positively charged. Radiation ionizes argon gas inside the tube, which creates a conducting path for current between the wall and the wire. The current is detected, and the Geiger counter makes a clicking sound.

11.57 A film badge is protected from light exposure, but exposure to other radiation causes the film to get cloudy. Photographic development of the film and comparison with a standard allows the amount of exposure to be calculated.

11.58 Rems indicate the amount of tissue damage from any type of radiation, and allow comparisons between equivalent doses of different types of radiation to be made.

11.59 According to Table 11.6, any amount of radiation above 25 rems produces detectable effects in humans.

11.60 (1) curie   (c) Number of disintegrations per second
(2) rem   (b) Amount of tissue damage
(3) rad   (d) Amount of radiation per gram of tissue
(4) roentgen   (a) Ionizing intensity of radiation

11.61

68 kg x $\dfrac{180 \text{ μCi}}{1 \text{ kg}}$ x $\dfrac{1 \text{ mCi}}{10^3 \text{ μCi}}$ x $\dfrac{1 \text{ mL}}{5.0 \text{ mCi}}$ = 2.4 mL

11.62

$$\frac{I_1}{I_2} = \frac{d_2^2}{d_1^2}; \quad I_1 = 300.0 \text{ rem}; \quad I_2 = 25 \text{ rem}; \quad d_1^2 = (2.0 \text{ m})^2 = 4.0 \text{ m}^2; \quad d_2^2 = ?$$

$$d_2^2 = \frac{d_1^2 \times I_1}{I_2} = \frac{4.0 \text{ m}^2 \times 300.0 \text{ rem}}{25 \text{ rem}} = 48 \text{ m}^2$$

$$d_2 = 6.9 \text{ m}$$

11.63

$$\frac{I_1}{I_2} = \frac{d_2^2}{d_1^2}; \quad I_1 = 650 \text{ rem}; \quad d_1^2 = 1.0 \text{ m}^2; \quad d_2^2 = (50.0 \text{ m})^2 = 2500 \text{ m}^2; \quad I_2 = ?$$

$$I_2 = \frac{d_1^2 \times I_1}{d_2^2} = \frac{1.0 \text{ m}^2 \times 650 \text{ rem}}{(50 \text{ m})^2} = 0.26 \text{ rem}$$

Applications

11.64 Radiation therapy is used in cancer treatment because ionizing radiation selectively destroys rapidly dividing cells, such as cancer cells.

11.65 (1) *In vivo procedures* take place inside the body and assess the functioning of organs or body systems.
(2) *Therapeutic procedures* are used to kill diseased tissue.
(3) *Body imaging* techniques, which include radiopharmaceutical imaging, CAT scans and PET, show body structure and function.

11.66 The purpose of food irradiation is to kill harmful microorganisms by exposing food to ionizing radiation, which destroys the genetic material of the microorganisms.

11.67 Gamma rays from cobalt-60 are used to treat food.

11.68 The body-imaging techniques, CT and PET, are noninvasive and yield a large array of images that can be processed by computer to produce a three-dimensional image of an organ.

11.69 Only living organisms can incorporate atmospheric $^{14}CO_2$. In organisms that are still alive, the ratio of $^{14}C/^{12}C$ is constant, but after death the ratio of $^{14}C/^{12}C$ decreases. By measuring the ratio, it is possible to determine the age of the sample.

11.70 The leather is too new. The age of the leather sample is so much smaller than the half-life of $^{14}CO_2$ that the ratio of ^{14}C to ^{12}C is almost the same as the atmospheric ratio.

11.71 It takes three half-lives for radiation to decay to one-eighth of its original value.
3 x 5715 years = 17,100 years old

General Questions and Problems

11.72 Nuclear reactions occur spontaneously, and no substance can "react with" radioactive emissions to neutralize them.

11.73 A film badge is more useful for measuring radiation exposure over a period of time. Scintillation counters and Geiger counters are more useful for measuring a current source of radiation.

11.74

(a) $^{99}_{42}\text{Mo} \rightarrow ^{0}_{-1}\text{e} + ^{99}_{43}\text{Tc}$ ^{99}Mo decays to Tc-99m by β emission.

(b) $^{98}_{42}\text{Mo} + ^{1}_{0}\text{n} \rightarrow ^{99}_{42}\text{Mo}$

11.75 24 h $\div$ 6.01 = approx 4 half-lives. 15 μCi x $(1/2)^4$ = 0.94 μCi

11.76

(a) $^{238}_{94}\text{Pu} \rightarrow ^{4}_{2}\text{He} + ^{234}_{92}\text{U}$

(b) The metal case serves as a shield to protect the wearer from α radiation.

11.77 The apron protects from radiation parts of the body that are not being X-rayed.

11.78 Embryos and fetuses are particularly susceptible to the effects of radiation because their cells divide frequently.

11.79 Nuclear fusion produces few radioactive by-products, and the deuterium fuel used is abundant and inexpensive. Drawbacks include providing high enough temperatures and holding materials long enough for nuclei to react.

11.80

(a) $^{162}_{75}\text{Re} \rightarrow ^{4}_{2}\text{He} + ^{158}_{73}\text{Ta}$ (b) $^{188}_{74}\text{W} \rightarrow ^{0}_{-1}\text{e} + ^{188}_{75}\text{Re}$

11.81

(a) $^{253}_{99}\text{Es} + ^{4}_{2}\text{He} \rightarrow ^{256}_{101}\text{Md} + ^{1}_{0}\text{n}$ (b) $^{250}_{98}\text{Cf} + ^{11}_{5}\text{B} \rightarrow ^{257}_{103}\text{Lr} + 4\,^{1}_{0}\text{n}$

11.82

$^{238}_{92}\text{U} + ^{1}_{0}\text{n} \rightarrow 2\,^{0}_{-1}\text{e} + ^{239}_{94}\text{Pu}$

11.83

$^{10}_{5}\text{B} + ^{1}_{0}\text{n} \rightarrow ^{7}_{3}\text{Li} + ^{4}_{2}\text{He}$

11.84

$$^{232}_{90}\text{Th} \rightarrow \ ^{208}_{82}\text{Pb} + 6 \ ^4_2\text{He} + 4 \ ^0_{-1}\text{e}$$

The 24 amu loss in mass in going from $^{232}_{90}\text{Th}$ to $^{208}_{82}\text{Pb}$ is due to the emission of 6 α particles, which also account for the reduction in atomic number from 90 to 78. The emission of 4 β particles increases the atomic number from 78 to 82 and yields $^{208}_{82}\text{Pb}$.

11.85 Alpha particles are used for the bombardment.

$$^{238}_{92}\text{U} + 3 \ ^4_2\text{He} \rightarrow \ ^{246}_{98}\text{Cf} + 4 \ ^1_0\text{n}$$

Self-Test For Chapter 11

Multiple choice:

1. Bombardment of a uranium-235 atom with a neutron produces three neutrons, which can go on to bombard 3 more U-235 atoms. How many neutrons are produced after the fourth cycle?
   (a) 12 (b) 36 (c) 81 (d) 108

2. The product of the α emission of $^{146}_{62}\text{Sm}$ is:
   (a) $^{146}_{63}\text{Eu}$ (b) $^{144}_{61}\text{Pm}$ (c) $^{144}_{60}\text{Nd}$ (d) $^{142}_{60}\text{Nd}$

3. A half-inch thick piece of plastic blocks 50% of radiation. How much radiation passes through a one inch thick piece of plastic?
   (a) 50% (b) 25% (c) 12% (d) 0%

4. The *curie* measures:
   (a) amount of radioactivity (b) ionizing intensity of radiation (c) amount of radiation absorbed (d) tissue damage

5. A sample of a radionuclide has a half-life of 40 days. How much radioactivity remains after 160 days?
   (a) 25% (b) 12.5% (c) 6.25% (d) 0%

6. How many disintegrations per second does one microcurie of a sample emit?
   (a) 3.7×10^{10} (b) 3.7×10^7 (c) 3.7×10^6 (d) 3.7×10^4

7. If a person standing 100 cm from a radiation source approaches to within 10 cm of the source, how much does the intensity of the radiation change?
   (a) increases by a hundredfold (b) increases tenfold (c) stays the same (d) decreases tenfold

8. Artificial transmutation was probably used to produce which one of the following radionuclides?
   (a) $^{238}_{92}\text{U}$ (b) $^{210}_{82}\text{Pb}$ (c) $^{60}_{27}\text{Co}$ (d) $^{239}_{94}\text{Pu}$

9. Which of the following radioisotopes is not medically useful?
   (a) $^{131}_{53}\text{I}$ (b) $^{14}_{6}\text{C}$ (c) $^{11}_{24}\text{Na}$ (d) $^{60}_{27}\text{Co}$

10. In an experiment by the Curies, aluminum-27 was bombarded with α particles. If each aluminum-27 atom captured one α particle and emitted one neutron, what other atom was produced?

(a) $^{29}_{13}Al$ (b) $^{28}_{14}Si$ (c) $^{30}_{15}P$ (d) $^{31}_{15}P$

Complete the following sentences:

1.   The change of one element to another is called _____.

2.   _____ _____ causes the most tissue damage.

3.   A chemical compound tagged with a radioactive atom can be used as a _____.

4.   All people are exposed to _____ radiation.

5.   A nuclear equation is balanced when the number of _____ is the same on both sides of the equation.

6.   The age of a sample can be determined by measuring the amount of _____ it contains.

7.   The _____ is a unit for measuring the number of radioactive disintegrations per second.

8.   In _____ _____, an atom is split apart by neutron bombardment to give small fragments.

9.   People who work around radiation sources wear _____ _____ for detection of radiation.

10.   PET and CT are techniques for _____ _____.

11.   Very light elements release large amounts of energy when they undergo _____ _____.

12.   The _____ _____ is the size of a radioactive sample that is needed for a nuclear reaction to be self-sustaining

Tell whether the following statements are true or false:

1.   If a sample has a half-life of 12 days, it will have decayed completely in 24 days.

2.   X-rays are considered to be ionizing radiation.

3.   The ratio of carbon-14 to carbon-12 in the atmosphere is constant.

4.   Pierre and Marie Curie discovered radioactivity.

5.   A β particle travels at nearly the speed of light.

6.   An α particle travels at nearly the speed of light.

7.   The product of β emission has an atomic number one amu smaller than the starting material.

8.   A nuclear power plant can undergo a nuclear explosion in an accident.

9.   The rad is the unit most commonly used in medicine to measure radiation dosage.

10. Radiation causes injury by ionizing molecules.

11. Most of the known radioisotopes are naturally occurring.

12. Many isotopes undergo nuclear fission.

Match the entries on the left with their partners on the right:

1.   Rutherford   (a) Alpha particle

2. $^{245}_{96}$Cm   (b) Used in cancer therapy

3. $t_{1/2}$ (c) Discovered radioactivity

4. $^{0}_{-1}$e   (d) Neutron

5.   Becquerel   (e) Used for archeological dating

6. $^{90}_{38}$Sr   (f) Discovered α,β particles

7. $^{1}_{0}$n   (g) Natural radioactive element that undergoes fission

8.   P. and M. Curie   (h) Discovered radium

9. $^{60}_{27}$Co   (i) Transuranium element

10. $^{4}_{2}$He   (j) Component of radioactive waste

11. $^{14}_{6}$C   (k) Beta particle

12. $^{235}_{92}$U   (l) Half-life

Chapter 12 – Introduction to Organic Chemistry: Alkanes

Chapter Outline

I. Introduction to Organic Chemistry (Sections 12.1–12.5).
  A. The nature of organic molecules (Section 12.1).
    1. Carbon always forms four bonds.
    2. Almost all of the bonds in organic molecules are covalent.
      a. These bonds are polar covalent bonds when carbon forms a bond to an element on the far left of the periodic table.
      b. Carbon can form multiple bonds by sharing more than two electrons.
    3. Organic molecules have specific three-dimensional shapes.
    4. In addition to hydrogen, oxygen and nitrogen are often present in organic molecules.
    5. Organic molecules are low-melting and boiling, relative to inorganic compounds.
    6. Organic molecules are usually insoluble in water and don't conduct electricity.
  B. Functional groups (Section 12.2).
    1. A functional group is an atom or group of atoms that has a characteristic reactivity.
    2. The chemistry of organic molecules is determined by functional groups.
    3. Functional groups fall into three categories.
      a. Hydrocarbons.
      b. Compounds with C–X single bonds, where X is electronegative.
      c. Compounds with C=O double bonds.
  C. Structures of organic molecules: alkane isomers (Sections 12.3–12.4).
    1. When hydrocarbons contain more than three carbons, there is more than one way to arrange the carbon atoms.
      a. Some alkanes are straight-chain.
      b. Other alkanes are branched.
    2. Compounds with the same formula but different orders of connecting the carbon atoms are called constitutional isomers.
        Constitutional isomers have different structures and different properties.
    3. Drawing structures (Section 12.4).
      a. Condensed structures are simpler to draw than structural formulas.
      b. In condensed structures, C–H and C–C single bonds are implied, rather than drawn.
      c. Vertical bonds are often shown for clarity.
      d. Occasionally, parentheses are used to show a row of –CH_2– groups.
  D. The shapes of organic molecules (Section 12.5).
    1. The groups around a C–C bond are free to assume an infinite number of conformations.
    2. Molecules adopt the least crowded conformation.
    3. Two structures with identical connections between atoms are identical, no matter how they are drawn.
II. Alkanes (Sections 12.6–12.8).
  A. Naming alkanes (Section 12.6).
    1. Straight-chain alkanes.
      a. Count the carbons.
      b. Find the root name.
      c. Add -ane to the root name.

2. Alkyl groups.
   a. Remove a hydrogen from an alkane and replace -ane with -yl.
   b. More than one alkyl group can be formed from some alkanes.
      i. Isopropyl and propyl are the two groups that can be formed from propane.
      ii. Four groups can be formed from butane.
      iii. Alkyl groups can be substituents on a straight chain.
3. Substitution patterns.
   a. Primary carbon: $R-CH_3$.
   b. Secondary carbon: $R-CH_2-R'$.
   c. Tertiary carbon:

$$R-\overset{\overset{\displaystyle R'}{|}}{C}H-R$$

   d. Quaternary carbon:

$$R-\overset{\overset{\displaystyle R'}{|}}{\underset{\underset{\displaystyle R''}{|}}{C}}-R'$$

4. Naming branched-chain alkanes.
   a. Name the main chain by finding the longest continuous chain of carbons and naming it.
   b. Number the carbons in the main chain, starting from the end nearer the first branch point.
   c. Identify and number each branching substituent according to its point of attachment to the main chain.
   d. Write the name as a single word.
B. Properties of alkanes (Section 12.7).
   1. The boiling points and melting points of alkanes increase with the number of carbons.
   2. Alkanes are insoluble in water but are soluble in nonpolar organic solvents.
   3. Alkanes are colorless and odorless.
   4. Alkanes are flammable.
   5. Alkanes with four or fewer carbons are gases, those from C_5 to C_{15} are liquids, and those with more than 15 carbons are solids.
C. Reactivity of alkanes (Section 12.8).
   1. Alkanes are very unreactive.
   2. Reactions that alkanes undergo:
      a. Combustion: alkane + $O_2 \longrightarrow CO_2 + H_2O$
      b. Halogenation: alkane + $X_2 \longrightarrow$ halogenated alkane + HCl
III. Cycloalkanes (Sections 12.9–12.10).
   A. Properties of cycloalkanes (Section 12.9).
      1. Cycloalkanes contain rings of carbon atoms.
      2. Cyclopropane and cyclobutane are more reactive than other cycloalkanes.
      3. Cyclohexane exists in a chair-like conformation.
      4. Cycloalkanes have properties similar to those of acyclic alkanes.
      5. Free rotation is not possible around the carbon–carbon bonds of a cycloalkane ring.
   B. Drawing and naming cycloalkanes (Section 12.10).
      1. Drawing cycloalkanes.
         The cycloalkane ring is represented as a polygon.
      2. Naming cycloalkanes.
         a. Use the cycloalkane as the parent.
         b. Number the substituents.
            i. Start numbering at the group that has alphabetical priority.
            ii. Proceed around the ring to give to the second group the lowest possible number.

Solutions to Chapter 12 Problems

12.1

(a)

alcohol

carboxylic acid

Lactic acid

(b)

C–C double bond   ester

Methyl methacrylate

(c)

aromatic ring   amine   carboxylic acid

Phenylalanine

12.2

(a)

an aldehyde

(b)

a carboxylic acid

12.3

C_7H_{16} Heptane

12.4   There are eight branched-chain heptanes:

12.5

(a)

CH₃CH₂CH₂CH₂CH₃

Pentane

(b)

$$CH_3$$
$$CH_3CHCH_2CH_3$$

2-Methylbutane

(c)

$$CH_3$$
$$CH_3CCH_3$$
$$CH_3$$

2,2-Dimethylpropane

12.6 All three structures have the same molecular formula (C_7H_{16}). Structures (a) and (c) are identical.

12.7 To solve this problem in a systematic way, use the following method:

(a) Draw the isomer of C_6H_{14} having no branches:

CH₃CH₂CH₂CH₂CH₂CH₃

(b) Draw the C_5H_{12} isomer having no branches, and replace one of the $-CH_2-$ hydrogens with a $-CH_3$. There are two different isomers:

(c) Draw the C_4H_{10} isomer having no branches, and replace two of the $-CH_2-$ hydrogens with $-CH_3$ groups. There are two different isomers:

12.8

(a)

2,6-Dimethyloctane

(b)

3,3-Diethylheptane

12.9 To answer this problem, draw the straight-chain hydrocarbon corresponding to the parent name, and replace –H's with the groups indicated.

(a)

$$\begin{array}{c} CH_3 \\ | \\ CH_3CH_2CH_2CHCH_2CH_3 \end{array}$$

3-Methylhexane

(b)

$$\begin{array}{c} CH_3 \\ | \\ CH_3CH_2CH_2CH_2CHCHCH_2CH_3 \\ | \\ CH_3 \end{array}$$

3,4-Dimethyloctane

(c)

$$\begin{array}{c} CH_3 \quad CH_3 \\ | \qquad | \\ CH_3CHCH_2CCH_3 \\ | \\ CH_3 \end{array}$$

2,2,4-Trimethylpentane

12.10

(a)

(b)

Where p = primary, s = secondary, t = tertiary, and q = quaternary

12.11 There are many answers to this question. For example:

(a)

$$CH_3$$
$$|$$
$$CH_3CHCH_3$$
$$t$$

2-Methylpropane

(b)

$$CH_3 \quad CH_3$$
$$| \qquad |$$
$$CH_3CHCH_2CH_2CCH_3$$
$$t \qquad\quad |q$$
$$CH_3$$

2,2,5-Trimethylhexane

12.12

(a)

2,2-Dimethylpentane

(b)

2,3,3-Trimethylpentane

12.13

$$2\ CH_3CH_3 + 7\ O_2 \longrightarrow 4\ CO_2 + 6\ H_2O$$

12.14

$$CH_3CH_2CH_3 + Cl_2 \longrightarrow CH_3CH_2CH_2Cl + \underset{Cl}{CH_3\overset{\textstyle |}{C}HCH_3} + \underset{\underset{Cl}{|}}{\overset{\overset{Cl}{|}}{CH_3CCH_3}}$$

$$+\ CH_3CH_2\overset{\overset{Cl}{|}}{C}HCl_2 + CH_3\overset{\overset{Cl}{|}}{C}HCH_2Cl + \overset{\overset{Cl}{|}}{C}H_2CH_2\overset{\overset{Cl}{|}}{C}H_2$$

Six different mono- and disubstitution products can be formed from the reaction of propane with chlorine.

12.15

(a)

1-Ethyl-4-methylcyclohexane

The parent ring is a cyclohexane The two substituents are an ethyl group and a methyl group. The ethyl group receives the smaller number because it has alphabetical priority

(b)

1-Ethyl-3-isopropylcyclopentane

The parent ring is a cyclopentane. The two substituents are an ethyl group and an isopropyl group The ethyl group receives the smaller number because it has alphabetical priority.

12.16

(a)

1,1-Diethylcyclohexane

(b)

1,3,5-Trimethylcycloheptane

12.17

Propylcyclohexane

Understanding Key Concepts

12.18

(a)

$$CH_3CCH_2CH_3$$ with CH_3 above and CH_3 below

(b)

$$CH_3CHCHCH_3$$ with CH_3 above and OH below

12.19 In a line drawing, a carbon is assumed to be at the intersection of lines.

(a)

(b)

12.20

(a) C–C double bond, ketone, ether

(b) amine, carboxylic acid, C–C double bond

12.21

(a)

$$CH_3CH_2CHCHCH_3$$

with CH_3 substituents

2,3-Dimethylpentane

(b)

$$CH_3CHCH_2CH_2CHCH_3$$

with CH_3 substituents

2,5-Dimethylhexane

12.22

(a)

1,1-Dimethylcyclopentane

(b)

Isopropylcyclobutane

12.23 In one of the isomers (b), the methyl groups are on the same side of the ring, and in the other isomer (a), they are on opposite sides.

(a) opposite sides

(b) same side

Organic Molecules and Functional Groups

12.24 If you look at the periodic table you will see that carbon belongs to group 4A, whose elements can form four bonds. Because carbon is in the middle of the periodic table, these bonds are covalent, and because it is in period 2, these bonds are strong.Consequently, carbon is unique in that it can form four strong bonds to other elements and to other carbon atoms, making possible a great many different compounds.

12.25 Functional groups are groups of atoms within a molecule that have a characteristic chemical behavior. They are important because most of the chemistry of organic compounds is determined by functional groups. The reactivity of a functional group is similar in all compounds in which it occurs.

12.26 Most organic compounds don't dissolve in water because they are nonpolar. They don't conduct electricity because they are covalent, not ionic.

12.27 There are several ways you might tell water and hexane apart. One way is to put a small amount of each sample in a test tube. The two liquids don't mix, and the less dense hexane remains on top. Alternatively, you might add a small amount of NaCl to each liquid. The salt dissolves in water but not in hexane.

12.28 A polar covalent bond is a covalent bond in which electrons are shared unequally, being more attracted to one atom than the other. For example, the electrons in the C–Br bond of bromomethane are attracted more strongly to the electronegative bromine than to carbon.

12.29 There are many possible answers to this question, and to the next question. For example:

(a)

CH_3CH_2OH

Ethanol

(b)

CH_3NH_2

Methylamine

(c)

$$CH_3\overset{\overset{\text{O}}{\|}}{C}-OH$$

Acetic acid

(d)

$CH_3CH_2OCH_2CH_3$

Diethyl ether

12.30

(a)

alcohol

Menthol

(b)

carboxylic acid

aromatic ring

ester

Aspirin

12.31

(a)

alcohol

C–C double bonds

Vitamin A

(b)

aromatic ring

alcohol

ketone

Estrone

12.32 There are many possible answers to each of these questions. For example:

(a)

$$CH_3CH_2CH_2\overset{\overset{\displaystyle O}{\|}}{C}CH_3$$

ketone

(b)

$$CH_3CH_2CH_2\overset{\overset{\displaystyle O}{\|}}{C}-OCH_2CH_3$$

ester

(c)

$$H_2N-CH_2\overset{\overset{\displaystyle O}{\|}}{C}-OH$$

aminc
carboxylic acid

12.33

(a)

$$CH_3CH_2CH_2\overset{\overset{\displaystyle O}{\|}}{C}-NH_2$$

amide

(b)

aldehyde

(c)

aromatic ether

Alkanes and Isomers

12.34 For two compounds to be isomers, they must have the same molecular formula but different structures.

12.35 Compounds with the formulas C_5H_{10} and C_4H_{10} are not isomers because they don't have the same molecular formulas.

12.36 A primary carbon is bonded to one other carbon; a secondary carbon is bonded to two other carbons; a tertiary carbon is bonded to three other carbons; and a quaternary carbon is bonded to four other carbons.

12.37 A compound can't have a quintary carbon because carbon forms only four bonds, not five.

12.38 There are many possible answers to this question. For example:

(a)

$$CH_3\overset{t}{C}H\overset{\overset{\displaystyle CH_3}{|}}{\underset{\underset{\displaystyle CH_3}{|}}{C}}HCH_3$$

2,3-Dimethylbutane

(b)

Cyclohexane

12.39

(a)

2,2-Dimethylpropane

(b)

2-Isopropyl-1,4-dimethylcyclohexane

12.40

12.41 There are several possible answers to this question. For example:

(a)   (b)   (c)   (d)

CH₃CH₂NH₂   ☐ or CH₃CH=CHCH₃   CH₃C—H   H—C—OH

12.42

(a)

CH₃CH₂CH₂CH₂OH   CH₃CH₂CHCH₃   CH₃CHCH₂OH   CH₃CCH₃

(b)

CH₃CH₂CH₂NH₂   CH₃CHCH₃   CH₃CH₂NCH₃   CH₃NCH₃

(c)

CH₃CH₂CH₂CCH₃   CH₃CH₂CCH₂CH₃   CH₃CHCCH₃

12.43

(a)

CH₃CH₂CH₂CH₂C—H   CH₃CH₂CHC—H   CH₃CHCH₂C—H   CH₃C—C—H

(b)

CH₃CH₂C—OCH₃   CH₃C—OCH₂CH₃   HC—OCH₂CH₂CH₃   HC—OCHCH₃

(c)

CH₃CH₂CH₂C—OH   CH₃CHC—OH

Remember that the C=O group of an aldehyde is found only at the end of a chain, and the C=O group of a ketone must occur in the middle.

12.44

(a)

$CH_3CH_2CH_3$ and $CH_3\overset{\underset{|}{CH_3}}{CH_2}$ are identical.

(b)

$CH_3\overset{\underset{|}{H}}{-N-}CH_3$ and $CH_3CH_2\overset{\underset{|}{H}}{-N-}H$ are isomers.

(c)

$CH_3CH_2CH_2-O-CH_3$ and $CH_3CH_2CH_2-\overset{\overset{O}{\|}}{C}-CH_3$ are unrelated.

(d)

$CH_3-\overset{\overset{O}{\|}}{C}-CH_2CH_2\overset{\underset{|}{CH_3}}{CH}CH_3$ and $CH_3CH_2-\overset{\overset{O}{\|}}{C}-CH_2CH_2CH_2CH_3$ are isomers.

(e)

$CH_3CH=CHCH_2CH_2-O-H$ and $CH_3CH_2\overset{\underset{|}{CH_3}}{CH}-\overset{\overset{O}{\|}}{C}-H$ are isomers.

12.45

(a)

The first two structures are identical; the third is an isomer.

(b)

$CH_3\overset{\underset{|}{CH_3}}{\underset{\underset{Br}{|}}{CH}}CHCH_3$ $CH_3\overset{\underset{|}{CH_3}}{\underset{\underset{Br}{|}}{CH}}CHCH_3$ $\overset{\underset{|}{CH_3}}{\underset{\underset{Br}{|}}{CH_2}}CHCH_2CH_3$

The first two structures are identical; the third is an isomer.

12.46 All three structures have a carbon atom with five bonds.

(a)

$CH_3=CHCH_2CH_2OH$

5 bonds

(b)

$CH_3CH_2CH=\overset{\overset{O}{\|}}{C}CH_3$

5 bonds

(c)

$CH_2CH_2CH_2C\equiv\overset{\underset{|}{CH_3}}{C}CH_3$

3 bonds   5 bonds

12.47

a. The carbon lettered "a" has five bonds.
b. The chlorine–carbon bond should be a single bond.

Naming Alkanes

12.48

(a)

CH₂CH₃
|
CH₃CH₂CH₂CH₂CHCHCH₂CH₃
|
CH₃

4-Ethyl-3-methyloctane

(b)

CH₃CHCH₃
|
CH₃CH₂CH₂CHCH₂CHCH₃
|
CH₂CH₃

5-Isopropyl-3-methyloctane

(c)

CH₃   CH₃
| |
CH₃CCH₂CH₂CH₂CHCH₃
|
CH₃

2,2,6-Trimethylheptane

(d)

CH₂CH₂CH₂CH₃
|
CH₃CH₂CH₂CCH₃
|
CH₃CHCH₃

4-Isopropyl-4-methyloctane

(e)

CH₃ CH₃
| |
CH₃CCH₂CCH₃
| |
CH₃ CH₃

2,2,4,4-Tetramethylpentane

(f)

CH₃CH₂ CH₃
| |
CH₃CH₂CCH₂CH
| |
CH₃CH₂ CH₃

4,4-Diethyl-2-methylhexane

(g)

CH₃
|
CH₃(CH₂)₇C—CH₃
|
CH₃

2,2-Dimethyldecane

12.49

CH₃CH₂CH₂CH₂CH₂CH₃

Hexane

CH₃
|
CH₃CH₂CH₂CHCH₃

2-Methylpentane

CH₃
|
CH₃CH₂CHCH₂CH₃

3-Methylpentane

CH₃
|
CH₃CH₂CCH₃
|
CH₃

2,2-Dimethylbutane

CH₃
|
CH₃CHCHCH₃
|
CH₃

2,3-Dimethylbutane

12.50

(a)

$$CH_3CH_2CH_2\overset{\overset{\displaystyle CH_2CH_3}{|}}{CH}CH_2CH_3$$

3-Ethylhexane

(b)

$$CH_3CH_2\overset{\overset{\displaystyle H_3C}{|}}{CH}\overset{\overset{\displaystyle CH_3}{|}}{\underset{\underset{\displaystyle CH_3}{|}}{C}}CH_3$$

2,2,3-Trimethylpentane

(c)

$$CH_3CH_2CH_2\overset{\overset{\displaystyle H_3C}{|}}{CH}\overset{\overset{\displaystyle CH_2CH_3}{|}}{\underset{\underset{\displaystyle CH_3}{|}}{C}}CH_2CH_3$$

3-Ethyl-3,4-dimethylheptane

(d)

$$CH_3CH_2CH_2\overset{\overset{\displaystyle CH_3CHCH_3}{|}}{CH}CH_2CH_2\overset{\overset{\displaystyle CH_3}{|}}{CH}CH_3$$

5-Isopropyl-2-methyloctane

(e)

$$CH_3CH_2CH_2\overset{\overset{\displaystyle CH_3}{|}}{\underset{\underset{\displaystyle CH_3}{|}}{C}}CH_2\overset{\overset{\displaystyle CH_2CH_2CH_3}{|}}{CH}CH_2\overset{\overset{\displaystyle CH_3}{|}}{\underset{\underset{\displaystyle CH_3}{|}}{C}}CH_3$$

2,2,6,6-Tetramethyl-4-propylnonane

(f)

1,1-Dimethylcyclopentane

12.51

(a)

Cyclooctane

(b)

1,2,3,4-Tetramethylcyclobutane

(c)

4-Ethyl-1,1-dimethylcyclohexane

(d)

Ethylcycloheptane

(e)

1,3,5-Triethylcyclohexane

(f)

1,2,4,5-Tetramethylcyclooctane

12.52

(a)

1-Isopropyl-1-methylcyclopentane

(b)

1,1,3,3-Tetramethylcyclopentane

(c)

CH₃CH₂CH₂—⬡

Propylcyclohexane

(d)

4-Butyl-1,1-dimethylcyclohexane

12.53

(a)

CH₂CH₃

Ethylcyclooctane

(b)

1,2-Diethyl-3-methylcyclopropane

(c)

CH₃

CH₃CH₂CH₂   CH₂CH₃

2-Ethyl-1-methyl-3-propylcyclopentane

12.54   *Structure*   *Error*

(a)

CH₃
|
CH₃CCH₂CH₂CH₃
|
CH₃

2,2-Dimethylpentane

The prefix "di-" must appear when
two substituents are the same.

(b)

CH₂CH₃
|
CH₃CHCH₂CHCH₂CH₃
|
CH₃

3,5-Dimethylheptane

You must choose the longest
carbon chain as the parent name.

(c)

CH₃
|
CH₃CHCH₂— ◇

This compound is an alkyl-substituted cycloalkane.

sec-Butylcyclobutane

12.55   *Structure*   *Error*

(a)

CH₂CH₃
|
CH₃CH₂CHCH₃

3-Methylpentane

The longest carbon chain is a pentane and should be used as the root name.

(b)

CH₃CHCH₃
|
CH₃CH₂CH₂CCH₃
|
CH₃

2,3,3–Trimethylhexane

The longest carbon chain is a hexane and should be used as the root name.

(c)

2-Ethyl-1,1-dimethylcyclopentane

The substituents should be given the lowest possible numbers. The prefix "di-" should be used when two substituents are the same.

(d)

CH₃   CH₂CH₃
| |
CH₃CCH₂CCH₂CH₃
| |
CH₃   CH₃

4-Ethyl-2,2,4-trimethylhexane

Numbering must start from the end nearer the first substituent.

(e)

4-Ethyl-1,2-dimethylcyclohexane

Substituents must be cited in alphabetical order (prefixes are not used for alphabetizing).

(f)

CH₂CH₃
|
CH₃CHCH₂CHCH₃
|
CH₂CH₃

3,5-Dimethylheptane

The longest carbon chain is a heptane and should be used as the root name.

(g)

$$CH_3CH_2CH_2\underset{\underset{CH_3CH_2}{|}}{\overset{\overset{CH_3CH_2}{|}}{C}} - \underset{\underset{CH_3}{|}}{\overset{\overset{CH_3}{|}}{C}} - \underset{\underset{CH_3}{|}}{\overset{\overset{CH_3}{|}}{C}}CH_2CH_2CH_2CH_3$$

4,4-Diethyl-5,5,6,6-tetramethyldecane

The prefixes "tetra-" and "di-" must be included in the name. Substituents must be cited in alphabetical order. Numbering must start from the end nearer to the first substituent.

12.56

$CH_3CH_2CH_2CH_2CH_2CH_2CH_3$
Heptane

$$CH_3CH_2CH_2CH_2\underset{\underset{CH_3}{|}}{CH}CH_3$$
2-Methylhexane

$$CH_3CH_2CH_2\underset{\underset{CH_3}{|}}{CH}CH_2CH_3$$
3-Methylhexane

$$CH_3CH_2CH_2\underset{\underset{CH_3}{|}}{\overset{\overset{CH_3}{|}}{C}}CH_3$$
2,2-Dimethylpentane

$$CH_3CH_2\underset{\underset{CH_3}{|}}{\overset{\overset{H_3C}{|}}{CH}}\overset{\overset{CH_3}{|}}{CH}CH_3$$
2,3-Dimethylpentane

$$CH_3\underset{\underset{CH_3}{|}}{\overset{\overset{CH_3}{|}}{CH}}CH_2\overset{\overset{CH_3}{|}}{CH}CH_3$$
2,4-Dimethylpentane

$$CH_3CH_2\underset{\underset{CH_3}{|}}{\overset{\overset{CH_3}{|}}{C}}CH_2CH_3$$
3,3-Dimethylpentane

$$CH_3CH_2\underset{\underset{CH_2CH_3}{|}}{CH}CH_2CH_3$$
3-Ethylpentane

$$CH_3\overset{\overset{CH_3}{|}}{CH} - \underset{\underset{CH_3}{|}}{\overset{\overset{CH_3}{|}}{C}}CH_3$$
2,2,3-Trimethylbutane

12.57

1,2-Dimethylcyclopropane   1,1-Dimethylcyclopropane   Ethylcyclopropane

Methylcyclobutane   Cyclopentane

Reactions of Alkanes

12.58

$$CH_3CH_2CH_3 + 5 O_2 \longrightarrow 3 CO_2 + 4 H_2O$$

12.59

$$2 C_8H_{18} + 25 O_2 \longrightarrow 16 CO_2 + 18 H_2O$$

12.60

12.61

Applications

12.62 A synthetically produced version of a compound and a "natural" compound have the same properties because their chemical structures are identical.

12.63 It is important to know the shape of a molecule because minor differences in shape can cause differences in chemical behavior and physiological activity.

12.64 Natural gas consists of $C_1 - C_4$ hydrocarbons and is a gas at room temperature. Petroleum consists of other alkanes, some of which are very high boiling.

12.65 Branched-chain hydrocarbons burn more efficiently than straight-chain alkanes in an internal combustion engine.

General Questions and Problems

12.66–12.67

(a)

(b)

amide   ester

carboxylic acid

amine

Aspartame

← aromatic ring

p = primary
s = secondary
t = tertiary
q = quaternary

12.68 Because carbon forms only four bonds, the largest number of hydrogens that can be bonded to three carbons is eight.

C_3H_8

12.69 Since "like dissolves like," lipstick, which is composed primarily of hydrocarbons, is more soluble in the hydrocarbon petroleum jelly than in water.

12.70

(a)   Br

monobromination product

+ Br_2 → light →   (b)   Br   Br +   Br   Br

+   Br   Br   +   Br   Br

Br

dibromination products

12.71 Pentane has a higher boiling point than neopentane because London forces, which must be overcome in boiling, are greater for linear than for more spherical or nonlinear compounds of the same formula weight.

12.72 Other structures are also possible.s

(a)

(b)

$CH_3CH_2CH_2CH\!\!=\!\!CHCH_2Br$

(c)

(d)

$CH_3CH\!\!=\!\!CHCH\!\!=\!\!CH_2$

Self-Test for Chapter 12

Multiple choice:

1. Which of the following functional groups doesn't contain a carbon–oxygen double bond?
   (a) ether   (b) aldehyde   (c) ketone   (d) ester

2. In which of the following alkanes are carbons not tetrahedral?
   (a) ethane   (b) propane   (c) cyclopropane   (d) cyclohexane

3. How many products can result from chlorination of ethane? (Include products with more than one chlorine.)
   (a) 2   (b) 4   (c) 6   (d) 9

4. How many branched-chain isomers of C_6H_{14} are there?
   (a) 2   (b) 3   (c) 4   (d) 5

5. Which of the following condensed structures doesn't represent a cycloalkane?
   (a) C_3H_6 (b) C_4H_{10} (c) C_5H_{10} (d) C_6H_{12}

6.

$$CH_3CH_2\overset{\overset{\displaystyle CH_3}{|}}{C}CH_2\overset{\overset{\displaystyle CH_3}{|}}{C}HCH_3$$
$$\underset{CH_2CH_3}{|}$$

   The correct name for the above structure is:
   (a) 3-ethyl-3,5-dimethylhexane   (b) 3-methyl-3-*sec*-butylpentane
   (c) 2,4-dimethyl-4-ethylhexane   (d) 4-ethyl-2,4-dimethylhexane

7. How many secondary carbons are in the structure shown in Problem 6?
   (a) 1   (b) 2   (c) 3   (d) 4

8. Which of the following structures is incorrectly drawn?

9. How many moles of O_2 are necessary for the complete combustion of one mole of C_6H_{12}?
   (a) 4   (b) 6   (c) 9   (d) 10

10. Which alkyl group has a quaternary carbon?
    (a) *tert*-butyl   (b) isobutyl   (c) *sec*-butyl   (d) butyl

Complete the following sentences:

1. C_{20} to C_{36} alkanes are known as _____.

2.   Alkynes are compounds that contain _____ bonds.

3.   Alcohols and ethers are functional groups that contain _____.

4.   Mixtures of hydrocarbons can be separated by _____.

5.   A _____ _____ is a shorthand way of drawing a chemical structure.

6.   A _____carbon is bonded to four other carbons.

7.   Organic compounds generally have _____ melting points than inorganic compounds.

8.   Cycloalkanes are compounds that contain carbon atoms joined together in a _____.

9.   Organic molecules are named by the _____ system.

10.   Compounds with the same formula but different structures are called _____.

11.   _____ is the reaction of an alkane with oxygen.

12.   A straight-chain alkane is _____ boiling than a branched-chain alkane.

Tell whether the following statements are true or false:

1.   Cyclohexane and hexane are isomers.

2.   A molecule with the formula C_5H_{12} can have the root name pentane, butane, or propane.

3.   A cyclohexane ring is flat.

4. The correct name of the following alkane is 1,3-dimethylpentane.

$$CH_3CH_2CHCH_2CH_2$$

with CH_3 and CH_3 branches

5. The compound 2,3-dimethylbutane has only primary and tertiary carbons.

6. Acyclic alkanes and cycloalkanes have similar chemical reactivity.

7. The C–Cl bond in CH_3Cl is ionic.

8. The compound 1,4-dimethylcyclohexane is correctly named.

9. Alkanes with one to four carbons exist as gases at room temperature.

10. Compounds with many functional groups are more reactive than compounds with few functional groups.

11. 2-Methylpentane and 3-methylpentane have nearly identical boiling points.

12. At room temperature, an alkane exists in a single conformation.

Match the entries on the left with their partners on the right:

1. $RCH=O$ (a) Contains polar covalent bonds

2. C_5H_{12} (b) Butyl group

3. $CH_3CH(CH_3)_2$ (c) Ketone

4. $CH_3CH_2CH_2CH_3$ (d) Natural gas

5. $CH_3CH_2CH_2-$ (e) Formula of methylcyclobutane

6. $R_2C=O$ (f) Branched-chain alkane

7. CH_2Cl_2 (g) An alkene

8. $C_{30}H_{62}$ (h) Propyl group

9. C_5H_{10} (i) Aldehyde

10. $CH_3CH_2CH_2CH_2-$ (j) Formula of 2-methylbutane

11. $CH_3CH=CH_2$ (k) A solid

12. CH_4 (l) Straight-chain alkane

Chapter Outline

I. Alkenes and alkynes (Sections 13.1–13.7).
  A. Introduction (Section 13.1).
    1. Alkenes are compounds that have double bonds (–C=C–).
    2. Alkynes are compounds that have triple bonds (–C≡C–).
  B. Naming alkenes and alkynes (Section 13.2).
    1. Find the longest chain containing the double or triple bond and name the parent
       compound by adding -ene or -yne to the root.
    2. Number the carbons in the main chain, beginning at the end nearer the multiple bond.
      a. If the bond is an equal distance from each end, begin numbering at the end nearer
         the first branch point.
      b. Cyclic alkenes are named cycloalkenes, and the double-bond carbons are carbons 1
         and 2.
    3. Write out the full name.
      a. Number the substituents, and list them alphabetically.
      b. Indicate the position of the multiple bond by giving it the number of the first carbon
         in the bond.
      c. If more than one bond is present, use the endings -diene, -triene,-tetraene.
  C. Cis–trans isomerism in alkenes (Section 13.3).
    1. Atoms attached to a double bond lie in a plane.
    2. If each end of the bond is bonded to two different groups, isomerism can result.
      a. When the larger groups are on the same side of the bond, the isomer is cis.
      b. When the larger groups are on opposite sides of the bond, the isomer is trans.
  D. Properties of alkenes and alkynes (Section 13.4).
    1. Nonpolar, insoluble in water, flammable.
    2. Alkane-like in physical properties.
    3. Alkenes show cis–trans isomerism.
    4. Both alkenes and alkynes react at the multiple bond to form addition products.
  E. Organic reactions (Sections 13.5 – 13.7).
    1. Types of organic reactions (Section 13.5).
      a. Addition reactions occur when two reactants add to form a single product.
      b. Elimination reactions occur when a reactant splits into two products.
      c. Substitution reactions occur when two reactants exchange parts.
      d. Rearrangement reactions occur when a single reactant undergoes a rearrangement of
         bonds to yield an isomeric product.
    2. Reaction of alkenes and alkynes (Sections 13.6 – 13.7).
      a. Addition reactions (Section 13.6).
        i. Alkene + H_2 —> alkane
          Alkyne + 2 H_2 —> alkane
        ii. Alkene + X_2 —> dihaloalkane (X = halogen).
        iii. Alkene + HX —> alkyl halide
          Direction of addition: X is bonded to the more substituted carbon
          (Markovnikov's rule).
        iv. Alkene + H_2O —> alcohol
          Addition also follows Markovnikov's rule.
      b. Mechanism of addition reactions, using HBr addition as an example (Section 13.7)
        i. H^+ adds to the alkene to form a carbocation.
        ii. Br^- adds to the carbocation to form the product.

F. Alkene polymers (Section 13.8).
  1. Simple alkenes of the type $H_2C=CHZ$ (monomer) can add to each other in long chains.
  2. The reaction is started by an initiator, which adds to an alkene to form a reactive intermediate.
  3. The reactive intermediate starts the growth of the chain.
  4. The product is a chain-growth polymer.
  5. Varying –Z varies the properties of the polymer.
  6. Properties of polymers also depend on chain length and degree of branching.
II. Aromatic compounds (Sections 13.9–13.11).
  A. Structure of benzene (Section 13.9).
    1. Benzene is a flat, six-membered ring containing three double bonds.
      a. All carbons in benzene are equivalent.
      b. The structure of benzene is an average of the two conventional structures.
      c. This phenomenon is known as resonance.
    2. Despite having double bonds, benzene is less reactive than alkenes.
    3. Aromatic compounds are nonpolar, water-insoluble, volatile and flammable.
    4. Some aromatic compounds are toxic and carcinogenic.
  B. Naming aromatic compounds (Section 13.10).
    1. Use "benzene" as the parent name.
    2. For monosubstituted benzenes, the name of the substituent is followed by -benzene (no number needed).
    3. For disubstituted benzenes:
      a. Ortho-disubstituted benzenes have substituents in the 1,2 positions of the ring.
      b. Meta-disubstituted benzenes have substituents in the 1,3 positions of the ring.
      c. Para-disubstituted benzenes have substituents in the 1,4 positions of the ring.
    4. Many aromatic compounds have trivial names.
  C. Reactions of aromatic compounds (Section 13.11).
    Aromatic compounds undergo substitution reactions.

    a. Aromatic ring + HNO_3 $\xrightarrow{H_2SO_4}$ Nitroaromatic ring

    b. Aromatic ring + X_2 $\xrightarrow{FeX_3}$ Haloaromatic ring

    c. Aromatic ring + SO_3 $\xrightarrow{H_2SO_4}$ Aromatic sulfonic acid

Solutions to Chapter 13 Problems

13.1

(a)   2-methyl ⟶ CH_3

$$CH_3CH_2CH_2CH=CHCHCH_3$$
$$\;7\;\;\;6\;\;\;5\;\;\;4\;\;\;\;\;3\;\;2\;\;1$$

2-Methyl-3-heptene

(b)

$$\;\;6\;\;\;\;5\;\;\;\;\;4\;\;\;\;\;3\;\;\;\;2\;\;\;\;1$$
$$H_2C=CHCH_2CH_2C=CH_2$$
2-methyl ⟶ CH_3

2-Methyl-1,5-hexadiene

13.2

(a)

CH₃CH₂CH₂CH₂CHCH=CH₂
with CH₃ branch

3-Methyl-1-heptene

(b)

H₃C—C—C≡C—CH₃
with CH₃ above and CH₃ below

4,4-Dimethyl-2-pentyne

(c)

CH₃CH₂CH₂CH=C—CH₃
with CH₃ branch

2-Methyl-2-hexene

(d)

CH₃CH₂CH=C—C—CH₃
with CH₃CH₂ and CH₃ above, CH₃ below

3-Ethyl-2,2-dimethyl-3-hexene

13.3

(a)

2,3-Dimethyl-1-pentene

(b)

2,3-Dimethyl-2-hexene

13.4   (a) Attached to C3: –H, –CH₂CH₃
Attached to C4: –H, –CH₂CH₂CH₃

Since each of the double-bond carbons has two different groups attached to it, 3-heptene exists as cis–trans isomers:

CH₃CH₂CH₂   CH₂CH₃
　　　C=C
　　H　　　H

cis-3-Heptene

CH₃CH₂CH₂   H
　　　C=C
　　H　　　CH₂CH₃

trans-3-Heptene

(b) Attached to C2: –CH₃, –CH₃
Attached to C3: –H, –CH₂CH₂CH₃

Since the two groups attached to C2 are identical, 2-methyl-2-hexene does not exist as cis–trans isomers:

CH₃CH₂CH₂   CH₃
　　　C=C
　　H　　　CH₃

2-Methyl-2-hexene

(c) Attached to C2: –H, –CH₃
   Attached to C3: –H, –CH₂CH(CH₃)₂

Since each carbon has two different groups attached to it, 5-methyl-2-hexene exists as cis–trans isomers:

cis-5-Methyl-2-hexene   trans-5-Methyl-2-hexene

13.5

cis-3,4-Dimethyl-3-hexene   trans-3,4-Dimethyl-3-hexane

13.6

(a)   (b)

cis-4 Methyl-2-hexene   trans-5,6-Dimethyl-3-heptene

13.7

(a)   CH₃Br + NaOH ⟶ CH₃OH + NaBr

This reaction is a substitution because two reagents exchange parts to give two different products.

(b)   H₂C=CH₂ + HCl ⟶ CH₃CH₂Cl

This reaction is an addition because two reactants combine to give one product.

(c)   CH₃CH₂Br ⟶ H₂C=CH₂ + HBr

In this elimination reaction, two products are formed from one reactant.

13.8

(a) $CH_3CH_2CH{=}CH_2$ + H_2 $\xrightarrow{Pd}$ $CH_3CH_2CH_2CH_3$

(b) $\underset{\underset{H}{\big|}}{\overset{\overset{H_3C}{\big|}}{C}}{=}\underset{\underset{H}{\big|}}{\overset{\overset{CH_3}{\big|}}{C}}$ + H_2 $\xrightarrow{Pd}$ $CH_3CH_2CH_2CH_3$

(c) $\underset{\underset{H}{\big|}}{\overset{\overset{H_3C}{\big|}}{C}}{=}\underset{\underset{CH_3}{\big|}}{\overset{\overset{H}{\big|}}{C}}$ + H_2 $\xrightarrow{Pd}$ $CH_3CH_2CH_2CH_3$

(d)   ⬡=CH_2 + H_2 $\xrightarrow{Pd}$ ⬡—CH_3

13.9

(a) $CH_3\overset{\overset{CH_3}{\big|}}{C}{=}CH_2$ + Br_2 $\longrightarrow$ $CH_3\underset{\underset{Br}{\big|}}{\overset{\overset{CH_3}{\big|}}{C}}{-}CH_2Br$

(b) $CH_3CH_2CH_2CH{=}CH_2$ + Cl_2 $\longrightarrow$ $CH_3CH_2CH_2\underset{\underset{Cl}{\big|}}{CH}{-}CH_2Cl$

(c) $CH_3CH_2CH{=}\overset{\overset{CH_3}{\big|}}{C}CH_2\underset{\underset{CH_3}{\big|}}{CH}CH_3$ + Cl_2 $\longrightarrow$ $CH_3CH_2\underset{\underset{Cl}{\big|}}{CH}{-}\underset{\underset{Cl}{\big|}}{\overset{\overset{CH_3}{\big|}}{C}}CH_2\underset{\underset{CH_3}{\big|}}{CH}CH_3$

13.10

(a)   ⬡ + HBr $\longrightarrow$ ⬡^{Br}

(b) $CH_3CH_2CH_2CH_2CH{=}CH_2$ + HCl $\longrightarrow$ $CH_3CH_2CH_2CH_2\underset{\underset{Cl}{\big|}}{CH}CH_3$

Chlorine bonds to the carbon that has fewer hydrogens.

(c) $CH_3\overset{\overset{CH_3}{\big|}}{CH}CH{=}CH_2$ + HCl $\longrightarrow$ $CH_3\overset{\overset{CH_3}{\big|}}{CH}\underset{\underset{Cl}{\big|}}{CH}CH_3$

13.11

(a)

CH₃CH₂C=CHCH₃   +   HCl   ⟶   CH₃CH₂CCH₂CH₃ (with CH₂CH₃ and Cl substituents)

3-Ethyl-2-pentene   3-Chloro-3-ethylpentane

(b)

CH₃CHC=CH₂ (with H₃C and CH₃ substituents)   +   HBr

2,3-Dimethyl-1-butene

or

H₃C,H₃C\C=C/CH₃,CH₃   +   HBr

2,3-Dimethyl-2-butene

⟶ CH₃CHCCH₃ (with H₃C, CH₃, and Br substituents)

13.12

H₃C\C=C/C...CH₃ (with CH₃, H, CH₃, H, H substituents)   +   HBr   ⟶   H₃C—C—C—C—CH₃ (with H, H, H₃C, Br, H, CH₃, H, H substituents)

13.13

(a)

(cyclohexane ring)=CH₂   +   H₂O   ⟶   (cyclohexane ring with CH₃ and OH)

(b)

(cyclohexene ring with CH₃)   +   H₂O   ⟶   (cyclohexane ring with CH₃ and OH)

13.14

CH₃CH₂C=CHCH₃ (with CH₃ substituent)
3-Methyl-2-pentene

or

CH₃CH₂CCH₂CH₃ (with CH₂ substituent)
2-Ethyl-1-butene

  +   H₂O   ⟶   CH₃CH₂CCH₂CH₃ (with CH₃ and OH substituents)

13.15

2-Methylpropene   carbocation   2-Chloro-2-
                       intermediate   methylpropane

13.16 To draw a vinyl polymer: (1) Orient the monomer unit so that the $CH_2=$ end is on the left. (2) Draw the functional group(s) at the other end of the molecule pointing up (or up and down). (3) Break the double bond, and draw a single bond extending from each carbon. (4) Connect a monomer unit to each of the new bonds.

13.17 Reverse the steps in the previous problem to identify the monomer unit of a polymer. (1) Break the bond between the carbon containing the functional group(s) and the $-CH_2-$ group to its right. (2) draw a double bond between the two carbons that once formed the carbon chain of the polymer.

(a)

13.18

o-Bromochlorobenzene   Butylbenzene   *o*-Bromotoluene

13.19

(a)

o-Dibromobenzene

(b)

p-Nitrotoluene

(c)

m-Diethylbenzene

(d)

m-Isopropylphenol

13.20

(a)

o Isopropylbenzaldehyde

(b)

p-Bromoaniline

13.21

(a)

H_3C— —CH_3 + Br_2 $\xrightarrow{Fe}$ H_3C— —CH_3 (Br)

(b)

H_3C— —CH_3 + HNO_3 $\xrightarrow{H_2SO_4}$ H_3C— —CH_3 (NO_2)

(c)

H_3C— —CH_3 + SO_3 $\xrightarrow{H_2SO_4}$ H_3C— —CH_3 (SO_3H)

13.22

ortho   meta   para

Understanding Key Concepts

13.23

(a)

2,5-Dimethyl-2-heptene

(b)

3.3-Dimethylcyclopentene

13.24

(a)

HC≡CCH₂CCH₂CH₃ with CH₃ groups

4,4-Dimethyl-1-hexyne

(b)

CH₃CHCH₂C≡CCH₂CHCH₃ with CH₃ groups

2,7-Dimethyl-4-octyne

13.25

(a)

(b)

m-Isopropylphenol

o-Bromobenzoic acid

13.26

(a)

(b)

13.27

(a)

4,4-Dimethyl-1-hexyne

3,3-Dimethylhexane

(b)

2,7-Dimethyl-4-octyne

2,7-Dimethyloctane

13.28

13.29

2-Methyl-1-pentene

or

2-Methyl-2-pentene

Naming Alkenes, Alkynes and Aromatic Compounds

13.30 Alkenes, alkynes, and aromatic compounds are said to be unsaturated because they have carbon–carbon multiple bonds to which hydrogen can be added.

13.31 The term "aromatic" in chemistry refers to compounds that have a six-membered ring containing three double bonds. The association with aroma is of historical origin but no longer has any meaning.

13.32

Family:	Alkene	Alkyne	Aromatic Compound
Name Ending:	*-ene*	*-yne*	*-benzene*

13.33 (a) The name of a 1,3-disubstituted benzene includes the prefix *meta-* (*m-*).
(b) The name of a 1,4-disubstituted benzene includes the prefix *para-* (*p-*).

13.34 There are many possible answers to this question. For example:

(a)

$CH_3CH_2CH_2CH{=}CH_2$

1-Pentene

(b)

$CH_3CH_2C{\equiv}CH$

1-Butyne

(c)

—CH_2CH_3

Ethylbenzene

13.35

(a)

CH₃CH₂CH₂ \
      C=CH₂ \
CH₃CH₂CH₂

(b)

13.36

(a)

$CH_3CH_2CH_2CH=CH_2$

1-Pentene

(b)

$\overset{\displaystyle CH_3}{\underset{\displaystyle |}{CH_3CHCH_2C}} \equiv CCH_3$

5-Methyl-2-hexyne

(c)

2,3-Dimethyl-2-butene

(d)

$\underset{\displaystyle CH_2CH_3}{\overset{\displaystyle CH_3}{CH_3CH=C-C=CH_2}}$

2-Ethyl-3-methyl-1,3-pentadiene

(e)

4-Ethyl-3,5-dimethylcyclohexene

(f)

3,3-Diethylcyclobutene

13.37

(a)

Isopropylbenzene

(b)

p-Bromonitrobenzene

(c)

m-Dinitrobenzene

13.38

(a)

cis-2-Hexene

(b)

$CH_3CH_2CH=CHCHCH_3$ with CH_3

2-Methyl-3-hexene

(c)

$H_2C=CHC=CH_2$ with CH_3

2-Methyl-1,3-butadiene

(d)

trans-3-Heptane

(e)

m-Bromotoluene

(f)

o-Ethylphenol

(g)

CH₃CH₂CH₂ — CH₂CH₂CH₃

m-Dipropylbenzene

13.39

(a)

Aniline

(b)

Phenol

(c)

o-Xylene

(d)

Toluene

(e)

Benzoic acid

(f)

p-Nitrophenol

(g)

o-Chloroaniline

(h)

CH₃CH₂CH₂CHCH=CHCCH₂CH₃

3,3-Diethyl-6-methyl-4-nonene

13.40

CH₃CH₂CH₂C≡CH

1-Pentyne

CH₃CH₂C≡CCH₃

2-Pentyne

CH₃CHC≡CH

3-Methyl-1-butyne

13.41

o-Bromotoluene

m-Bromotoluene

p-Bromotoluene

Bromomethylbenzene

13.42

$CH_3CH_2CH_2CH{=}CH_2$

1-Pentene

$CH_3CH_2CH{=}CHCH_3$

2-Pentene

$\overset{\displaystyle CH_3}{\underset{\displaystyle |}{CH_3CH_2C}}{=}CH_2$

2-Methyl-1-butene

$\overset{\displaystyle CH_3}{\underset{\displaystyle |}{CH_3CHCH}}{=}CH_2$

3-Methyl-1-butene

$\overset{\displaystyle CH_3}{\underset{\displaystyle |}{CH_3CH}}{=}CCH_3$

2-Methyl-2-butene

13.43

$CH_3CH_2CH{=}C{=}CH_2$

1,2-Pentadiene

$CH_3CH{=}CHCH{=}CH_2$

1,3-Pentadiene

$H_2C{=}CHCH_2CH{=}CH_2$

1,4-Pentadiene

$\overset{\displaystyle CH_3}{\underset{\displaystyle |}{H_2C}}{=}CHC{=}CH_2$

2-Methyl-1,3-butadiene

$\overset{\displaystyle CH_3}{\underset{\displaystyle |}{CH_3C}}{=}C{=}CH_2$

3-Methyl-1,2-butadiene

$CH_3CH{=}C{=}CHCH_3$

2,3-Pentadiene

Alkene Cis–Trans Isomers

13.44 For an alkene to show cis–trans isomerism, each carbon of the double bond must be bonded to two different groups.

13.45 Alkynes don't show cis–trans isomerism because a triple bond is linear and only one group is bonded to each alkyne carbon.

13.46 Only 2-pentene exists as cis–trans isomers:

cis-2-Pentene   *trans*-2-Pentene

13.47 1,3–Pentadiene is the only diene that can show cis–trans isomerism.

cis-1,3-Pentadiene   *trans*-1,3-Pentadiene

13.48

(a)

CH₃CH₂CH₂   CH₂CH₃

C=C

H   H

cis-3-Heptene

(b)

CH₃

CH₃CH   CH₃

C=C

H   H

cis-4-Methyl-2-pentene

(c)

CH₃

H   CHCH₃

C=C

CH₃CH   H

CH₃

trans-2,5-Dimethyl-3-hexene

13.49

(a)

Cl   Cl

C=C

H   CH₃

Cl   CH₃

C=C

H   Cl

(b)

CH₃CH₂CH₂   OCH₃

C=C

H   CH₃

CH₃CH₂CH₂   CH₃

C=C

H   OCH₃

13.50 (a) These compounds are identical:

H₃C   Br

C=C   *and*

H   Br

Br   H

C=C

Br   CH₃

(b) These compounds are also identical:

CH₃CH₂   Cl

C=C   *and*

Cl   H

H   Cl

C=C

Cl   CH₂CH₃

13.51

(a)

H₃C   H

C=C

CH₃CH   CH₃

CH₃

(b)

H   Br

C=C

Br   CCH₃

O

Kinds of Reactions

13.52 In a substitution reaction, two reactants exchange parts to give two new products. In an addition reaction, two reactants add together to form a single product, with no atoms left over.

13.53

$$CH_3CH{=}CHCH_3 \; + \; H_2 \quad \xrightarrow[\text{catalyst}]{\text{Pd}} \quad CH_3CH_2CH_2CH_3$$

13.54 The conversion of 2-methyl-2-pentene to 1-hexene would be a rearrangement because it is the conversion of a single reactant into a single product by the reorganization of bonds.

13.55 The conversion of bromocyclohexane to cyclohexene would be an elimination reaction because a single reactant splits to give two products (cyclohexene and HBr).

13.56

(a)

This reaction is a substitution because two reactants exchange parts to give two new products.

(b)

This is also a substitution reaction.

13.57

(a)

$$\underset{\text{substitution reaction}}{CH_3\overset{\displaystyle CH_3}{\underset{|}{C}}HCH_2CH_2CH_2Br} \; + \; NaCN \; \longrightarrow \; CH_3\overset{\displaystyle CH_3}{\underset{|}{C}}HCH_2CH_2CH_2C{\equiv}N \; + \; NaBr$$

(b)

$$\underset{\text{addition reaction}}{2 \; CH_3{-}\overset{\displaystyle O}{\overset{\|}{C}}{-}H} \quad \xrightarrow{\text{NaOH}} \quad CH_3{-}\overset{\displaystyle O{-}H}{\underset{\displaystyle H}{\overset{|}{\underset{|}{C}}}}{-}CH_2{-}\overset{\displaystyle O}{\overset{\|}{C}}{-}H$$

Reactions of Alkenes and Alkynes

13.58

13.59

13.60

(a)

(b)

$$CH_3CH=CH_2 \xrightarrow[\text{Pd catalyst}]{H_2} CH_3CH_2CH_3$$

(c)

$CH_3CH=CHCH_3$

or

$H_2C=CHCH_2CH_3$

$\xrightarrow{HBr}$

$CH_3\underset{\underset{Br}{|}}{C}HCH_2CH_3$

(d)

(e)

13.61

13.62

13.63

Addition of HBr to 4-methyl-1-pentyne can form either of the two bromoalkenes pictured above. The second product is actually formed because its intermediate carbocation is the one predicted by Markovnikov's rule.

13.64

13.65

$H_2C{=}CCl_2$ $\xrightarrow{\text{polymerization}}$

Reactions of Aromatic Compounds

13.66 Under conditions where an alkene would react with all four reagents, benzene reacts only with Br$_2$ (b) to give the product shown below.

13.67

13.68

13.69

Applications

13.70 The rod cells are responsible for vision in dim light, and the cone cells are responsible for vision in bright light and for color vision.

13.71 When light strikes rhodopsin, the cis double bond between C11 and C12 is isomerized to a trans double bond. The resulting isomerization brings about a change in molecular geometry that causes a nerve impulse to be sent to the brain, where it is perceived as vision. The trans isomer is then changed back to the cis isomer.

13.72 A polycyclic aromatic compound is a compound that has two or more benzene-like rings joined together to share a common bond.

13.73 The body attempts to excrete benz[*a*]pyrene by converting it into a water-soluble diol epoxide, which can react with cellular DNA and lead to mutations or cancer.

13.74 Since naphthalenc is white, it must absorb color in the ultraviolet range.

13.75 Tetrabromofluorescein is colored because it contains many alternating single and double bonds. Since tetrabromofluorescein is purple, it must absorb yellow light. (Yellow is the complement of purple.)

General Questions and Problems

13.76 A trans double bond is too strained to exist in a small ring like cyclohexene, but a large ring is more flexible and can include a trans double bond:

The double bond must be cis in this six-membered ring.

The double bond can be trans in this ten-membered ring.

13.77

Salicylic acid

13.78

  polymerization

13.79   *Structure*   *Error*

(a)

$CH_3CH=CHCH_2CHCH_3$

5-Methyl-2-hexene

Numbering should start from the end nearer the double bond.

(b) CH_3
$CH_3CC\equiv CCH_2CH_3$
         CH_3

2,2-Dimethyl-3-hexyne

Numbering should start from the end nearer the first substituent.

(c)

2-Methyl-1-hexene

The longest chain should be used
as the base name.

(d)

m-Dibromobenzene
(1,3-Dibromobenzene)

Substituents should receive the lowest
possible numbers. It is better to name
this compound as a *m*-disubstituted
benzene

(e)

3,4-Dimethylcyclohexene

The double bond receives the lowest
number. (For cyclic alkenes, the
double bond receives no number but is
understood to be between carbons 1 and 2.)

(f)

CH₃
|
H₂C=CHC=CHCH₃

3-Methyl-1,3-pentadiene

The double bonds should receive the
lowest possible numbers.

13.80 None of the reagents that add to alkenes react with alkanes such as cyclohexane. Thus, you
can mix a reagent such as Br₂ with a sample from each bottle. The mixture of cyclohexene
and Br₂ turns from reddish-brown to colorless, but the mixture of cyclohexane and Br₂
remains colored.

13.81 The same reasoning used in Problem 13.80 applies here. Benzene is much less reactive
than alkenes. Thus, treatment of a sample from each bottle with an alkene addition reagent
such as Br₂ gives a rapid reaction with cyclohexene but no reaction with benzene.

13.82

     p-Dichlorobenzene

13.83

     Menthene

13.84

13.85

(a)

(b)

(c)

(d)

(e)

(f)

Cinnamaldehyde

3-Phenylpropanal

13.86

The products are formed in equal amounts because each end of the double bond has the same number of hydrogens and the two intermediate carbocations are formed in approximately equal amounts.

13.87 In contrast to benzene, naphthalene is a solid at room temperature because it has a greater molecular weight and its London forces are greater.

13.88

(a)

Ocimene   (3,7-Dimethyl-1,3,6-octatriene)

(b)

Ocimene $\xrightarrow{\text{xs HBr}}$ CH$_3$CCH$_2$CH$_2$CH$_2$C—CHCH$_3$

13.89

3,4,4-Trimethyl-2-pentene

or

2-Ethyl-3,3-dimethyl-1-butene

13.90 Compound (b) does not exhibit cis–trans isomerism.

(a)

(c)

Self-Test for Chapter 13

Multiple choice:

1. Which of the following polymers is a hydrocarbon?
   (a) Teflon   (b) poly(vinyl chloride)   (c) Lucite   (d) polystyrene

2. $$CH_3CH=CHCHCH_3$$ with CH_2CH_3 substituent

   $$\begin{array}{c} CH_2CH_3 \\ | \\ CH_3CH{=}CHCHCH_3 \end{array}$$

   The name of this compound is:
   (a) 3-methyl-4-hexene   (b) 4-methyl-2-hexene   (c) 2-ethyl-3-pentene   (d) 3-ethyl-2-pentene

3. Which of the following statements about the reaction of benzene with Br_2 is true?
   (a) The reaction is catalyzed by iron.   (b) The reaction is an addition reaction.   (c) Two different products are formed.   (d) When bromine is added to benzene, the bromine color disappears.

4. Reaction of a hydrocarbon with 2 H_2 gives a product with the formula C_6H_{12}. Which of the following is the original hydrocarbon?
   (a) benzene   (b) 3-methyl-1,3-pentadiene   (c) 1,4-cyclohexadiene   (d) 2-hexyne

5. Which of the following molecules shows cis–trans isomerism?
   (a) 2-hexene   (b) 2-hexyne   (c) 2-methyl-2-pentene   (d) 2-ethyl-1-hexene

6. Which of the following statements about carbocations is true?
   (a) A carbocation has seven electrons in its outer shell.   (b) Two different carbocations can be formed in the reaction of HBr with 3-hexene.   (c) A carbocation is an intermediate in the reaction of HBr with an alkene.   (d) Carbocations are stable ions.

7. How many isomers with the formula C_5H_8 can be drawn? (Don't include isomers with rings or cis–trans isomers.)
   (a) 5   (b) 7   (c) 9   (d) 11

8. Which of the following is probably not a monomer in a polymerization reaction?
   (a) $H_2C{=}CHCN$ (b) $H_2C{=}CHCH_3$ (c) $CH_3CH{=}C(CH_3)_2$ (d) $H_2C{=}CCl_2$

9. If toluene reacted with one mole of Cl_2, and each of the products of the reaction reacted with one mole of Cl_2, how many different products could be formed? (Not all of these can be formed in the laboratory.)
   (a) 3   (b) 4   (c) 5   (d) 6

10. Which of the following alkenes is not a starting material for 3-bromo-3-methylhexane?
    (a) 2-ethyl-1-pentene   (b) 3-methyl-2-hexene   (c) 3-methyl-3-hexene   (d) 4-methyl-2-hexene

Complete the following sentences:

1. The name of $CH_3CH_2CH_2CH_2C{\equiv}CCH_3$ is _____.

2. Addition of hydrogen to an alkene or alkyne is known as _____.

3. A benzene ring with substituents at the 1 and 4 positions is said to be _____ disubstituted.

4. In the addition of HX to an alkene, the H becomes attached to the carbon that already has ____ H's, and the X becomes attached to the carbon that has _____ H's.

5. Ethanol can be produced by the _____ of ethylene.

6. In the nitration of benzene, H_2SO_4 is used as a _____.

7. The intermediate formed during the addition of HBr to an alkene is called a _____.

8. Compounds with double or triple bonds are said to be _____.

9. _____ is another name for methylbenzene.

10. The reaction of Br_2 with benzene is an example of a _____ reaction.

11. _____ _____ _____ are aromatic compounds consisting of two or more rings joined together by a common bond.

12. Simple alkenes are made by _____ _____ of natural gas and petroleum.

Tell whether the following statements are true or false:

1. Cis–trans isomers have identical physical properties.

2. Addition of one equivalent of H_2 to an alkyne yields an alkene.

3. Aromatic compounds are less reactive than alkenes.

4. The product of addition of HBr to 1-butene is 1-bromobutane.

5. The reaction of HBr with an alkene is known as halogenation.

6. A compound with the formula C_4H_6 can be either an alkyne or an alkene.

7. 1-Methylcyclohexene can exhibit cis–trans isomerism.

8. Mixing an alkene with water causes the hydration of the double bond.

9. Addition of HBr to an alkene is a two-step reaction.

10. Benzene and 1-butene react with Br_2 under the same reaction conditions.

11. Only aromatic compounds with more than one ring are carcinogenic.

12. Two different compounds result from the reaction of HBr with 2-pentene.

Match the entries on the left with their partners on the right:

1. HNO_3, H_2SO_4 (a) Does not have cis–trans isomers

2. H_2O, H_2SO_4 (b) Used to hydrogenate an alkene

3. $CH_3C\equiv CH$ (c) Polycyclic aromatic hydrocarbon

4. Hydroxybenzene   (d) Addition reaction

5. H_2, Pd   (e) Used to nitrate aromatic compounds

6. $(CH_3)_2CH^+$ (f) Substitution reaction

7. Propene + Br_2 (g) Exhibits cis–trans isomerism

8. Naphthalene   (h) Teflon monomer

9. 2-Methylpropene   (i) Alkyne

10. Benzene + Br_2 (j) Phenol

11. 2-Butene   (k) Used to hydrate an alkene

12. $CF_2=CF_2$ (l) Carbocation

Chapter Outline

I. Compounds containing oxygen (Sections 14.1–14.9).
   A. Introduction (Section 14.1).
      1. In all of these compounds, oxygen forms a single bond to either carbon or hydrogen.
      2. Alcohols (R–OH), phenols (Ar–OH) and ethers (R–O–R) are examples of these compounds.
         a. Many alcohols resemble water in their physical properties.
         b. Alcohols (and phenols) can form hydrogen bonds, which raise their boiling points.
   B. Alcohols (Sections 14.2–14.5).
      1. Common alcohols are methanol, ethanol, isopropanol, ethylene glycol and glycerol (Section 14.2).
      2. Naming alcohols (Section 14.3).
         a. Find the longest chain containing the hydroxyl group, and name the chain by replacing the -e ending of the corresponding alkane with -ol.
         b. Number the carbon atoms in the main chain, beginning at the end nearer the –OH group.
         c. Write the name.
            i.   Place the number of the –OH group immediately before the parent compound name.
            ii. Number all other substituents according to their positions and list them alphabetically.
         d. Diols are often known as glycols.
         e. Alcohols can be classified according to the number of substituents bonded to the –OH carbon.
            i.   If there is one substituent (RCH_2OH), the alcohol is primary.
            ii. If there are two substituents (R_2CHOH), the alcohol is secondary.
            iii. If there are three substituents (R_3COH), the alcohol is tertiary.
      3. Properties of alcohols (Section 14.4).
         a. Hydrogen bonding makes alcohols higher boiling than other compounds of similar mass.
         b. Hydrogen bonding also makes smaller alcohols miscible with water, as well as with organic solvents.
            i.   Alcohols of higher mass aren't soluble.
            ii. Diols (glycols) are even more soluble than alcohols of similar mass.
         c. Alcohols are weak acids.
      4. Reactions of alcohols (Section 14.5).
         a. Dehydration: alcohol $\xrightarrow{\text{H}_2\text{SO}_4}$ alkene + H_2O
            If more than one product is possible, the product with the more substituted double bond will be favored.
         b. Oxidation:
            i.   Primary alcohol $\xrightarrow{\text{[O]}}$ aldehyde $\xrightarrow{\text{[O]}}$ carboxylic acid
            ii. Secondary alcohol $\xrightarrow{\text{[O]}}$ ketone
            iii. Tertiary alcohol $\xrightarrow{\text{[O]}}$ no reaction

    C. Phenols (Sections 14.6–14.7).
       1. Properties of phenols (Section 14.6).
          a. Phenols are named by replacing -benzene with -phenol.
          b. The properties of phenols are influenced by hydrogen bonding.
             i. Many phenols are water-soluble.
             ii. Phenols are higher boiling than alkylbenzenes.
          c. Phenols are commonly used as disinfectants.
       2. Acidity of alcohols and phenols (Section 14.7).
          a. Alcohols and phenols are weak acids.
             i. Methanol and ethanol are as acidic as water.
             ii. Dissociation of alcohols in water, or reaction of alcohols with sodium metal, produces an alkoxide anion ($^-$OR).
          b. Phenols are more acidic than water.
             i. K_a of phenol is 1.0×10^{-10}.
             ii. Phenols are soluble in dilute aqueous NaOH.
  D. Ethers (Section 14.8).
       1. Names and properties of ethers.
          a. Ethers have two organic groups bonded to the same oxygen.
          b. Ethers are named by identifying the two groups and adding the word *ether*.
             i. Some cyclic ethers have common names (ethylene oxide, 1,4-dioxane).
             ii. An –OR group is an alkoxy group.
          c. Properties of ethers.
             i. Ethers are low-boiling and don't form hydrogen bonds.
             ii. Ethers are unreactive.
             iii. Ethers are good solvents for organic compounds.
             iv. Ethers are volatile and flammable.
             v. Ethers are only slightly soluble in water.
             vi. Ethers form explosive peroxides on standing.
       2. Some common ethers.
          a. Diethyl ether is commonly used as a solvent but was formerly an anesthetic.
          b. Ether groups occur in many essential oils.
II. Thiols and disulfides (Section 14.9).
  A. Thiols.
       1. Thiols are the sulfur analogs of alcohols (R–SH).
       2. Naming thiols is similar to naming alcohols, except that the suffix –thiol is added to the parent name.
       3. Thiols are important biologically because they occur in proteins.
       4. Thiols stink!
  B. Disulfides.
       1. Reaction of a thiol with a mild oxidizing agent produces a disulfide (RS–SR).
       2. The reverse reaction occurs when a disulfide is treated with a reducing agent.
III. Halogen-containing compounds (Section 14.10).
  A. Haloalkanes are named by considering the halogen as a substituent on a parent alkane.
  B. A few haloalkanes are named by naming the alkyl group and then naming the halide.
  C. Haloalkanes don't occur frequently in nature but are widely used in industry and agriculture.

Solutions to Chapter 14 Problems

14.1

(a)

CH₃CH₂CHCH₃
       |
       OH

an alcohol

(b)

⬡—OH

an alcohol

(c)

⬡—OH

a phenol

(d)

⬡—CH₂OH

an alcohol

(e)

⬡—OCH₃

an ether

(f)

CH₃CHOCH₂CH₃
    |
    CH₃

an ether

14.2

:Ö—H   (R→Ö—H

hydroxide ion   hydroxyl group

A hydroxide ion has three lone electron pairs and a negative charge. A hydroxyl group is an –OH group that is part of an organic molecule.

14.3

(a)

　　OH
　　|
CH₃CH₂CCH₂CH₃
　　|
　　CH₃

3-Methyl-3-pentanol
tertiary alcohol

(b)

⬡—OH

Cyclohexanol
secondary alcohol

(c)

　　　　　　OH　　CH₃
　　　　　　|　　　|
CH₃CH₂CH₂CHCH₂CHCH₃

2-Methyl-4-heptanol
secondary alcohol

(d)

　　OH
　　|
CH₃CH₂CHCH₃

2-Butanol
secondary alcohol

(e)

ClCH₂CH₂CH₂OH

3-Chloro-1-propanol
primary alcohol

14.4

(a)

　　OH
　　|
CH₃CH₂CHCH₂CH₃

3-Pentanol
secondary alcohol

(b)

　　　　CH₂OH
　　　　|
CH₃CH₂CHCH₂CH₂CH₃

2-Ethyl-1-pentanol
primary alcohol

(c)

$$CH_2OH$$
$$CH_3CH_2CHCH_2CH_2CH_2Br$$

5-Bromo-2-ethyl-1-pentanol
primary alcohol

(d)

H_3C —OH
H_3C

4,4-Dimethylcyclohexanol
secondary alcohol

14.5   See Problems 14.3 and 14.4.

14.6 $CH_3CH_2CH_2OH$ has the highest boiling point because it's the only compound listed that can form hydrogen bonds.

14.7

(a)

$$CH_3(CH_2)_{10}CH_2OH$$

The hydrocarbon part makes this alcohol water-insoluble.

(b)

$$\overset{OH}{CH_3CH_2CHCH_3}$$

Water-soluble.

(c)

$$CH_3CH_2OCH_3$$

An ether – slightly water-soluble.

14.8

(a)

H   OH
CH_3CH — CH_2 $\xrightarrow{H_2SO_4}$ CH_3CH = CH_2 + H_2O

(b)

H   OH
⬡ $\xrightarrow{H_2SO_4}$ ⬡   + H_2O

(c)

H   OH   H CH₃
CH_2 — CH — $CHCHCH_3$ $\xrightarrow{H_2SO_4}$ H_2C = $CHCH_2\overset{CH_3}{CHCH_3}$ + CH_3CH = $CH\overset{CH_3}{CHCH_3}$ + H_2O
                                                minor   major

14.9

(a)

H   OH
$CH_3\overset{H_3C}{\underset{H_3C}{C}}$ — $\overset{CH_3}{\underset{CH_3}{C}}CH_3$ $\xrightarrow{H_2SO_4}$ $\overset{H_3C}{\underset{H_3C}{C}}$ = $\overset{CH_3}{\underset{CH_3}{C}}$ + H_2O

(b)

$$CH_3CH_2CH-CH_2 \xrightarrow{H_2SO_4} CH_3CH_2CH=CH_2 + H_2O$$

or

$$CH_3CH-CH-CH_2 \xrightarrow{H_2SO_4} CH_3CH_2CH=CH_2 + CH_3CH=CHCH_3 + H_2O$$
minor   major

14.10

$$\xrightarrow{H_2SO_4}$$ major + H_2O

14.11

(a)

$$CH_3CH_2CH_2 = CH_3CH_2C-H \xrightarrow{[O]} CH_3CH_2C-H \xrightarrow{[O]} CH_3CH_2C-OH$$

(b)

$$CH_3CHCH_2CH_2CH_3 = CH_3C-H \xrightarrow{[O]} CH_3CCH_2CH_2CH_3$$
CH_2CH_2CH_3

(c)

$$CHCH_3 = C-H \xrightarrow{[O]} CCH_3$$
CH_3

14.12

(a)

$$CH_3CHCH_3 \xrightarrow{[O]} CH_3CCH_3$$

(b)

$$-OH \xrightarrow{[O]} O$$

(c)

$$CH_3CHCH_2CH_2OH \xrightarrow{[O]} CH_3CHCH_2C-H \xrightarrow{[O]} CH_3CHCH_2C-OH$$

14.13

(a)

$$H_2C=\underset{H_3C}{C}-CH_2\underset{CH_3}{CH}CH_2OH \xrightarrow{[O]} H_2C=\underset{H_3C}{C}-CH_2\underset{CH_3}{CH}C\underset{OH}{\overset{O}{\|}}$$

(b)

$$Br-C_6H_4-CH_2CH_2OH \xrightarrow{[O]} Br-C_6H_4-CH_2C\underset{H}{\overset{O}{\|}}$$

14.14

(a)

m-Bromophenol

(b)

CH_3CH_2- p-Ethylphenol

14.15

(a)

p-Chlorophenol

(b)

m-Methylphenol (*m*-Cresol)

14.16

(a)

$CH_3OCH_2CH_2CH_3$

Methyl propyl ether

(b)

$CH_3\underset{CH_3}{CH}O\underset{CH_3}{CH}CH_3$

Diisopropyl ether

(c)

Methyl phenyl ether
or
Methoxybenzene
(Anisole)

14.17

(a)

$$2\ CH_3CH_2CH_2SH \xrightarrow{[O]} CH_3CH_2CH_2S-SCH_2CH_2CH_3\ +\ H_2O$$

(b)

$$2\ CH_3\underset{CH_3}{CH}CH_2CH_2SH \xrightarrow{[O]} CH_3\underset{CH_3}{CH}CH_2CH_2S-SCH_2CH_2\underset{CH_3}{CH}CH_3\ +\ H_2O$$

14.18

(a)

1-Chloro-1-ethylcyclopentane

(b)

3-Bromo-5-methylheptane

Understanding Key Concepts

14.19

(a)

5-Methyl-3-hexanol

(b)

m-Methoxytoluene

(c)

3-Methylcyclohexanol

14.20

14.21

14.22

14.23

(a)

(b)

(c)

Alcohols, Ethers and Phenols

14.24 *Alcohols* have an –OH group bonded to an alkane-like carbon atom.
Ethers have an oxygen atom bonded to two carbon atoms.
Phenols have an –OH group bonded to a carbon of an aromatic ring.

      an alcohol   an ether   a phenol

14.25 A primary alcohol has one carbon substituent bonded to the OH-bearing carbon; a secondary alcohol has two carbon substituents bonded to the OH-bearing carbon; a tertiary alcohol has three carbon substituents bonded to the OH-bearing carbon.

     primary alcohol   secondary alcohol   tertiary alcohol

14.26 Alcohols contain –OH groups, which can form hydrogen bonds to each other. Since extra energy (heat) must be supplied to break these hydrogen bonds, alcohols are higher boiling than ethers, which can't hydrogen bond.

14.27 Phenol is a stronger acid than ethanol.

14.28

Prednisone

14.29

phenol

ether

Vitamin E

14.30, 14.34

(a)

2-Ethyl-1-pentanol
primary alcohol

(b)

3-Methyl-1-butanol
primary alcohol

(c)

1,2,4-Butanetriol
*primary alcohol
secondary alcohol

(d)

2-Phenyl-2-propanol
tertiary alcohol

(e)

2-Methylcyclopentanol
secondary alcohol

(f)

2-Ethyl-2-methyl-1-butanol
primary alcohol

14.31

(a)

o-Ethylphenol

(b)

Isopropyl methyl ether

(c)

Methyl p-nitrophenyl ether
or
p-Nitroanisole

(d)

Cyclopentyl methyl ether
or
Methoxycyclopentane

(e)

o-Butylphenol

(f)

Dipropyl ether

14.32

(a)

CH₃   OH
| |
CH₃CHCH₂CCH₃
      |
      CH₃

2,4-Dimethyl-2-pentanol

(b)

2,2-Dimethylcyclohexanol

(c)

CH₂CH₃
|
CH₃CH₂CCH₂CH₂CH₂CH₂OH
|
CH₂CH₃

5,5-Diethyl-1-heptanol

(d)

OH
|
CH₃CH₂CH₂CCH₂CH₃
|
CH₂CH₃

3-Ethyl-3-hexanol

(e)

2,3,7-Trimethylcyclooctanol

(f)

CH₂CH₃
|
HOCH₂CH₂CH₂CCH₂CH₂OH
|
CH₂CH₃

3,3-Diethyl-1,6-hexanediol

14.33

(a)

Ethyl phenyl ether

(b)

o-Dihydroxybenzene (catechol)

(c)

p-Bromophenyl *tert*-butyl ether

(d)

p-Nitrophenol

(e)

CH₃CH₂O   OCH₂CH₃
| |
CH₃CHCHCHCH₃
        |
        CH₃

2,4-Diethoxy-3-methylpentane

(f)

OCH₃
|
CH₃CHCHCH=CH₂
|
CH₃

4-Methoxy-3-methyl-1-pentene

14.34 See Problem 14.30

14.35

CH₂OH ⟵ primary alcohol

OH ⟵ tertiary alcohol

Prednisone

14.36	Compound	Boiling Point	Reason
Hexanol	Highest	Forms hydrogen bonds
Dipropyl ether	Middle	Polar, but doesn't form hydrogen bonds
Hexane	Lowest	Nonpolar

14.37 Glucose, with five hydroxyl groups, can form more hydrogen bonds with water and thus is more soluble than 1-hexanol, which has only one hydroxyl group.

Reactions of Alcohols

14.38 A ketone is formed on oxidation of a secondary alcohol:

A secondary alcohol   A ketone

14.39 Tertiary alcohols are not oxidized because they have no –H bonded to the OH-bearing carbon, and thus can't form a C=O double bond.

No hydrogen bonded to this carbon

A tertiary alcohol

14.40 Either an aldehyde or a carboxylic acid can be formed by oxidation of a primary alcohol:

a primary alcohol   an aldehyde   a carboxylic acid

14.41 An alkoxide anion is formed on reaction of an alcohol with Na metal.

$$2 \ H-OR + 2 \ Na \longrightarrow 2 \ Na^{+} \ {}^{-}OR + H_2$$

alcohol   sodium
alkoxide

14.42 Phenols are more acidic than alcohols and are converted into their sodium salts on reaction with NaOH. Thus, phenols dissolve in aqueous NaOH but alcohols do not.

14.43 The simplest way to distinguish the two alcohols is to try to oxidize them. The tertiary alcohol is unreactive toward oxidizing agents, but the secondary alcohol can be converted to a ketone.

14.44

(a)

or

(b)

$$\underset{\underset{\displaystyle CH_3CH_2CHCH_2OH}{|}}{CH_2CH_3} \xrightarrow{H_2SO_4} \underset{\underset{\displaystyle CH_3CH_2C=CH_2}{|}}{CH_2CH_3} + H_2O$$

or

$$\underset{\underset{\displaystyle CH_3}{|}}{\overset{\overset{\displaystyle OH}{|}}{CH_3CH_2CCH_2CH_3}} \xrightarrow{H_2SO_4} \underset{\underset{\text{minor}}{\underset{\displaystyle CH_3CH_2C=CH_2}{|}}}{CH_2CH_3} + \underset{\underset{\text{major}}{\underset{\displaystyle CH_3CH_2C=CHCH_3}{|}}}{CH_3} + H_2O$$

(c)

$$\underset{\underset{\displaystyle CH_3CH_2CH_2CHCH_2CH_3}{|}}{\overset{\overset{\displaystyle OH}{|}}{}} \xrightarrow{H_2SO_4} CH_3CH_2CH_2CH=CHCH_3 + CH_3CH_2CH=CHCH_2CH_3$$
$$+ H_2O$$

(d)

$$\underset{\underset{\displaystyle CH_3}{|}}{\overset{\overset{\displaystyle OH}{|}}{CH_3CCH_2CH_2CH_3}} \xrightarrow{H_2SO_4} \underset{\underset{\text{major}}{\underset{\displaystyle CH_3}{|}}}{CH_3C=CHCH_2CH_3} + \underset{\underset{\text{minor}}{\underset{\displaystyle CH_3}{|}}}{H_2C=CCH_2CH_2CH_3} + H_2O$$

or

$$\underset{\underset{\displaystyle CH_3}{|}}{\overset{\overset{\displaystyle OH}{|}}{CH_3CHCHCH_2CH_3}} \xrightarrow{H_2SO_4} \underset{\underset{\text{major}}{\underset{\displaystyle CH_3}{|}}}{CH_3C=CHCH_2CH_3} + \underset{\underset{\text{minor}}{\underset{\displaystyle CH_3}{|}}}{CH_3CHCH=CHCH_3} + H_2O$$

(e)

$$HOCH_2CH_2CH_2CH_2OH \xrightarrow{\text{xs } H_2SO_4} H_2C=CHCH=CH_2 + 2\ H_2O$$

or

$$\underset{\underset{\displaystyle CH_3CHCH_2CH_2OH}{|}}{\overset{\overset{\displaystyle OH}{|}}{}} \xrightarrow{\text{xs } H_2SO_4} H_2C=CHCH=CH_2 + 2\ H_2O$$

or

$$\underset{\underset{\displaystyle OH}{|}}{\overset{\overset{\displaystyle OH}{|}}{CH_3CHCHCH_3}} \xrightarrow{\text{xs } H_2SO_4} H_2C=CHCH=CH_2 + 2\ H_2O$$

(f)

or

14.45

(a)

major   minor

(b)

minor   major

(c)

major   minor

(d)

(e)

14.46

(a)

(b)

$$CH_3CHCH_2OH \xrightarrow{[O]} CH_3CHC-H \xrightarrow{[O]} CH_3CHC-OH$$

(c)

$$CH_3CH_2CCH_2CH_3 \xrightarrow{[O]} NR$$

(d)

(e)

$$CH_3CH_2CHCCH_3 \xrightarrow{[O]} NR$$

(f)

$$\xrightarrow{[O]}$$

14.47

(a)

$$\xrightarrow{[O]}$$

(b)

$$\xrightarrow{[O]} \xrightarrow{[O]}$$

(c)

$$CH_3CH_2CHCH_2CHCH_2CH_3 \xrightarrow{[O]} CH_3CH_2CHCH_2CCH_2CH_3$$

Thiols and Disulfides

14.48 The most noticeable characteristic of thiols is their vile stench.

14.49 A thiol is the sulfur analog of an alcohol.

R—S—H   R—O—H
a thiol   an alcohol

14.50

14.51

14.52 Propanol is high-boiling because its –OH groups can form hydrogen bonds. The –SH groups of ethanethiol don't form hydrogen bonds, and thus ethanethiol has a lower boiling point, as does chloroethane, which also doesn't form hydrogen bonds.

14.53 The explanation in the previous problem applies here. Propanol is very soluble in water because it can hydrogen-bond with water. Chloroethane and ethanethiol don't form hydrogen bonds with water and are thus only slightly soluble in water.

Applications

14.54 Ethanol is a depressant. Its effects on the central nervous system are like those of anesthetics and other central nervous system depressants.

14.55 At a blood alcohol concentration of 100–300 mg/dL, speech becomes slurred. At a blood alcohol concentration above 600 mg/dL, death may result.

14.56 The liver is vulnerable to damage from alcohol because it is the principal site of alcohol metabolism, and toxic products of alcohol metabolism accumulate there.

14.57 In the "breathalyzer test," a person breathes into a tube containing $K_2Cr_2O_7$ (yellow-orange). If alcohol is present in the breath, it is oxidized by $K_2Cr_2O_7$, which is reduced to a Cr (III) compound (blue-green). The color change can be measured accurately enough to indicate blood alcohol concentration.

14.58 A free radical is a reactive intermediate that contains an unpaired electron.

14.59 Vitamin E appears to be a phenolic antioxidant.

14.60 Diethyl ether was used as the first general anesthetic.

14.61 Minimum alveolar concentration (MAC) is defined as the concentration of anesthetic in inhaled air that results in anesthesia in 50% of patients.

14.62 The ozone layer acts as a shield to protect the earth from intense solar radiation.

14.63 Chlorofluorocarbons contribute to the destruction of ozone, and thus laws are being enacted to restrict the release of CFCs into the atmosphere.

General Questions and Problems

14.64 Alcohol isomers of $C_4H_{10}O$:

CH$_3$CH$_2$CH$_2$CH$_2$OH   CH$_3$CH$_2$CHCH$_3$ CH$_3$CHCH$_2$OH   CH$_3$CCH$_3$

1-Butanol   2-Butanol   2-Methyl-1-propanol   2-Methyl-2-propanol

Ether isomers of $C_4H_{10}O$:

CH$_3$CH$_2$OCH$_2$CH$_3$ CH$_3$OCH$_2$CH$_2$CH$_3$ CH$_3$OCHCH$_3$

Diethyl ether   Methyl propyl ether   Isopropyl methyl ether

14.65

Thyronine

$\xrightarrow{4\ I_2}$

Thyroxine

Thyroxine results from the aromatic substitution reaction of thyronine and I_2.

14.66   CH$_3$(CH$_2$)$_8$CH$_3$ CH$_3$(CH$_2$)$_7$CH$_2$OH

Decane – a hydrocarbon   1-Nonanol – an alcohol

Insoluble in water because   Insoluble because its hydrocarbon,
it is nonpolar   water-insoluble part, is much larger than
                                its polar hydroxyl group.

14.67

14.68 An antiseptic kills microorganisms on living tissue; a disinfectant is toxic and is used only to kill microorganisms on surfaces.

14.69

(a)

$$\underset{\text{OH}}{\text{CH}_3\text{CHCH}_3}$$

Isopropanol
(rubbing alcohol)

(b)

CH_3OH

Methanol
(wood alcohol)

(c)

CH_3CH_2OH

Ethanol
(grain alcohol)

(d)

$HOCH_2CH_2OH$

Ethylene glycol
(antifreeze)

14.70

(a)

m-Dichlorobenzene

(b)

$$\underset{\text{Br}}{\text{BrCH}}=\text{CCH}_2\text{CH}_3$$

1,2-Dibromo-1-butene

(c)

m-Propylphenol

(d)

1,1-Dibromocyclopentane

(e)

$$CH_3\underset{CH_3}{\overset{Cl}{C}}CH_2\underset{CH_2CH_3}{\overset{OH}{C}}CH_3$$

5-Chloro-3,5-dimethyl-3-hexanol

(f)

$$CH_3CH_2\overset{OH}{CH}CH\underset{CH_3}{CH_2}\overset{OH}{CH}CH_3$$

4-Methyl-2,5-heptanediol

(g)

$$CH_3C\equiv C\overset{Br}{CH}CH_2\underset{CH_3}{\overset{CH_3}{C}}CH_3$$

4-Bromo-6,6-dimethyl-2-heptyne

(h)

1-Bromo-2-chlorocyclopropane

14.71

(a)

$$CH_3C(CH_3)=CHCH_3 + HBr \longrightarrow CH_3C(CH_3)(Br)CH_2CH_3$$

(b)

$$CH_3CH_2CH_2C(CH_3)(CH_3)-CH(OH)CH_3 \xrightarrow{[O]} CH_3CH_2CH_2C(CH_3)(CH_3)-C(=O)CH_3$$

(c)

$$CH_3CH_2CH_2C(CH_3)(CH_3)-CH(OH)CH_3 \xrightarrow{H_2SO_4} CH_3CH_2CH_2C(CH_3)(CH_3)-CH=CH_2$$

(d)

$$H_3C-C(OH)(CH_3)-C(CH_3)=C(CH_3)-CH_3 \xrightarrow{Br_2} H_3C-C(OH)(CH_3)-C(Br)(CH_3)-C(Br)(CH_3)-CH_3$$

(e)

$$2\ H_3C-C(CH_3)(CH_3)-SH \xrightarrow{[O]} H_3C-C(CH_3)(CH_3)-S-S-C(CH_3)(CH_3)-CH_3$$

(f)

$$CH_3CH_2CH=C(CH_3)CH_3 \xrightarrow[H_2SO_4]{H_2O} CH_3CH_2CH_2C(OH)(CH_3)CH_3$$

(g)

$$C_6H_5-CH_2CH(OH)CH_3 \xrightarrow{[O]} C_6H_5-CH_2C(=O)CH_3$$

14.72

$$CH_3C(CH_3)=CHCH_2CH_2C(CH_3)=CHCH_2OH \xrightarrow{[O]} CH_3C(CH_3)=CHCH_2CH_2C(CH_3)=CHC(=O)-H$$

3,7-Dimethyl-2,6-octadiene-1-ol   Citral

14.73

$$CH_3CH_2OH \xrightarrow{[O]} CH_3\overset{\overset{\displaystyle O}{\|}}{C}-OH$$

Ethanol   Acetic acid

14.74

$$CH_3CH_2OH \; + \; 3\,O_2 \longrightarrow 2\,CO_2 \; + \; 3\,H_2O$$

14.75

$$CH_3CH_2CH_2OH \underset{\xleftarrow{\hspace{1cm}}}{\overset{H_2SO_4}{\rightleftharpoons}} CH_3CH{=}CH_2 \; + \; H_2O$$

The conversion of an alcohol, such as propanol, to the related alkene is an equilibrium process in which sulfuric acid serves as a catalyst for both the forward and the reverse reaction.

Self-Test for Chapter 14

Multiple choice:

1. Which of the following alcohols yields an aldehyde on oxidation?
    (a) 2-Hexanol   (b) 2-Methyl-2-hexanol   (c) 2-Methyl-1-hexanol   (d) *p*–Chlorophenol

2. Which of the following compounds is least acidic?
    (a) *p*-Chlorophenol   (b) 2-Butanol   (c) HCl   (d) Acetic acid

3. How many alcohols of the formula $C_4H_{10}O$ are primary alcohols?
    (a) 1   (b) 2   (c) 3   (d) 4

4. Which of the following is known as wood alcohol?
    (a) CH_3OH (b) CH_3CH_2OH (c) $CH_3CH_2CH_2OH$ (d) $HOCH_2CH_2OH$

5.
    $$\underset{CH_3\overset{\displaystyle |}{C}HCH_2\overset{\displaystyle |}{C}HCH_2CH_3}{\overset{\displaystyle HO \qquad CH_2CH_2CH_3}{}}$$

    What is the name of the above compound?
    (a) 4-Propyl-2-hexanol   (b) 4-Ethyl-6-heptanol   (c) 4-Ethylheptanol   (d) 4-Ethyl-2-heptanol

6. Which of the following is not a property of alcohols?
    (a) weakly acidic   (b) flammable   (c) react with acids   (d) low-boiling

7. Which of the following is not a product of dehydration of 2,3-dimethyl-3-pentanol?
    (a) 2,3-Dimethyl-1-pentene   (b) 2,3-Dimethyl-2-pentene   (c) 3,4-Dimethyl-2-pentene
    (d) 2-Ethyl-3-methyl-1-butene

8. Which of the following is a cyclic ether?
    (a) Enflurane   (b) Ethylene oxide   (c) Methoxybenzene (anisole)   (d) Methyl cyclohexyl ether

9. An alcohol of the formula $C_5H_{12}O$ forms a carboxylic acid on oxidation yet can't be dehydrated by acid. What is its name?
    (a) 1-Pentanol   (b) 2-Methyl-2-butanol   (c) 2,2-Dimethyl-1-propanol   (d) 2-Methyl-1-butanol

10. Which reagent doesn't react with alcohols?
    (a) Na   (b) H_2SO_4 (c) $KMnO_4$ (d) NaOH

Complete the following statements:

1. The common name for methanol is _____.

2. Dialcohols are often called _____.

3. Aromatic compounds called _____ react with NaOH to give salts.

4. The dehydration of an alcohol yields an _____.

5. Compounds called _____ are noted for their foul odors.

6. _____ can be used to oxidize an alcohol.

7. Ethers are _____ boiling than alcohols of similar molecular weight.

8. _____ is a phenol used as a food additive.

9. The major product of alcohol dehydration has the _____ number of alkyl groups attached to the double bond carbons.

10. A _____ _____ is a reactive intermediate containing an unpaired electron.

11. On prolonged contact with air, an ether forms a _____.

12. _____ is another name for a chlorofluorocarbon.

Tell whether the following statements are true or false:

1. Phenols can form hydrogen bonds.

2. An aldehyde can be formed by oxidation of a secondary alcohol.

3. Two different alkenes result from dehydration of 2-pentanol.

4. Another name for phenol is carbonic acid.

5. Phenols are more acidic than alcohols.

6. Another name for a thiol is a mercaptan.

7. Phenol, isopropyl alcohol, and chloroethane are all antiseptics.

8. Oxidation is the removal of two hydrogen ions.

9. Several halogenated alkanes are used as anesthetics.

10. Under careful reaction conditions, a primary alcohol is oxidized to an aldehyde.

11. Isopropyl alcohol is more toxic than methyl alcohol.

12. Hydrogen bonding accounts for both boiling-point elevation and water solubility.

Match the entries on the left with their partners on the right:

1. CCl_3F (a) Peroxide

2. $(CH_3)_2CHS–SCH(CH_3)_2$ (b) Thiol

3. $CH_3CH(OH)CH_2CH_2CH_3$ (c) Phenol

4. $CH_3CH_2OCH_3$ (d) Alcohol that is not water soluble

5. CH_3OH (e) Tertiary alcohol

6. CH_3SH (f) Forms two alkenes on dehydration

7. $(CH_3)_3C–OH$ (g) Disulfide

8. $CH_3CH_2OOCH_3$ (h) Ether

9. $(CH_3)_3CCOCH_3$ (i) Glycol

10. $CH_3(CH_2)_{10}CH_2OH$ (j) Chlorofluorocarbon

11. $CH_3CH(OH)CH_2OH$ (k) Oxidation product of 3,3-dimethyl-2-butanol

12. C_6H_5OH (l) Formed from CO and H_2

Chapter Outline

I. General characteristics of amines (Sections 15.1–15.3).
  A. Classification of amines (Section 15.1).
    1. Amines are classified by the degree of substitution at nitrogen.
      a. Primary amines have the structure RNH_2.
      b. Secondary amines have the structure R_2NH.
      c. Tertiary amines have the structure R_3N.
      d. Quaternary ammonium salts have the structure $R_4N^+ X^-$.
    2. The groups bonded to nitrogen may be alkyl or aryl groups and may also contain functional groups.
  B. Naming amines.
    1. Primary amines are named by identifying the alkyl group attached to nitrogen and adding the suffix *-amine*.
    2. Secondary and tertiary amines.
      a. If the groups are identical, the prefix *di-* or *tri-* is added to the name that would be given if the amine were primary.
      b. If the groups are different, the compound is named as an *N*-substituted derivative of a primary amine.
    3. The simplest aromatic amine is aniline.
    4. When the amino group is a substituent, the prefix *amino-* is used.
  C. Properties of amines (Section 15.2).
    1. Amines are basic.
    2. Primary and secondary amines form hydrogen bonds to each other.
    3. Amines can form hydrogen bonds with water.
    4. Simple amines are water-soluble.
    5. Amines have unpleasant odors.
    6. Amines are an important class of biomolecules.
  D. Heterocyclic amines (Section 15.3).
    1. In some nitrogen-containing compounds, nitrogen is part of a ring.
    2. Heterocyclic compounds may be aromatic or nonaromatic.
II. Reactions of amines (Sections 15.4–15.5).
  A. Acid–base reactions of amines (Section 15.4).
    1. Aqueous amines are weak bases that can accept a proton to form ammonium ions. Nonaromatic amines are stronger bases than aromatic amines.
    2. Amines can react with acids to form ammonium salts.
      a. Ammonium cations of alkylamines are named by replacing the ending *-amine* by the ending *-ammonium*.
      b. For cations of heterocyclic amines, *-e* is replaced by *-ium*.
    3. Ammonium salts react with hydroxide ion to yield an amine plus water.
    4. In the body, many amines are present as ammonium ions.
  B. Amine salts (Section 15.5).
    1. Amine salts are composed of an ammonium ion (the cation) and an anion.
    2. Most amine salts are much more soluble in water than the amines from which they were derived.
    3. Sometimes, amine salts are written as amine·HX.
    4. An amine can be regenerated from an amine salt by reaction with base.
    5. Amine salts can be formed by reaction of an amine with an alkyl halide.

6. If four alkyl groups are bonded to nitrogen, the compound is a quaternary ammonium salt. Quaternary ammonium salts are usually neither acidic or basic.
III. Alkaloids: amines in plants (Section 15.6).
1. Many alkaloids are toxic and physiologically active.
2. Familiar alkaloids are coniine, atropine, solanine and morphine.

Solutions to Chapter 15 Problems

15.1

(a)

$CH_3CH_2CH_2NH_2$

primary amine

(b)

$CH_3CH_2NHCH_2CH_3$

secondary amine

(c)

$$CH_3\overset{\overset{\displaystyle CH_3}{|}}{\underset{\underset{\displaystyle CH_3}{|}}{C}}-NH_2$$

primary amine

(d)

N—H

secondary amine

(e)

N—CH_3

tertiary amine

15.2

(a)

$CH_3CH_2CH_2NH_2$

Propylamine

(b)

$$H-\overset{\overset{\displaystyle CH_3}{|}}{N}-CH_3$$

Dimethylamine

(c)

—NHCH_2CH_2CH_2CH_2CH_3

N-Pentylaniline

15.3

(a)

$CH_3CH_2CH_2CH_2NH_2$

Butylamine

(b)

$$CH_3CH_2\overset{\overset{\displaystyle H}{|}}{N}CH_3$$

N-Methylethylamine

(c)

$$-\overset{\overset{\displaystyle CH_3}{|}}{N}CH_3$$

N,N-Dimethylaniline

(d)

$$CH_3CH_2\overset{\overset{\displaystyle NH_2}{|}}{C}HCH_2OH$$

2-Aminobutanol

15.4

$$H_3C-\overset{\overset{\displaystyle CH_3}{|}}{\underset{\underset{\displaystyle CH_3}{|}}{\overset{+}{N}}}-CH_3$$

Tetramethylammonium ion

The atoms of tetramethylammonium ion form sixteen bonds (12 C–H bonds and 4 C–N bonds) that contain 32 valence electrons. Four neutral carbon atoms, twelve hydrogen atoms, and one nitrogen atom have a total of 33 valence electrons. Since the ion has one electron fewer than the neutral atoms, the ion has a +1 charge.

15.5

CH₃CH₂CH₂CH₂NHCH₂CH₃

N-Ethylbutylamine

15.6

Lowest Boiling ⟶ *Highest Boiling*

$$\underset{(a)}{CH_3NCH_2CH_3} < \underset{(c)}{CH_3CH_2CH_2CH_2NH_2} < \underset{(b)}{CH_3CH_2CH_2CH_2OH}$$

with CH₃ on the N of (a)

Alcohol (b), is highest boiling because –OH bonds of alcohols are more polar and form stronger hydrogen bonds than –NH bonds of amines. Amine (a) is lowest boiling because molecules of (a), a tertiary amine, don't form hydrogen bonds to each other.

15.7 In Section 8.11, we learned that a hydrogen bond forms between an electron lone pair of an electronegative atom and a hydrogen bonded to a second electronegative atom. To draw the structures: (1) draw the amine, including the lone pair electrons; (2) form hydrogen bonds between (i) the amine lone pair and a hydrogen atom of water and (ii) the amine hydrogens bonded to –N and an electron lone pair of water. In (b), only hydrogen bonds of type (i) can form.

(a) (b)

[structures showing water molecules hydrogen-bonded to amines]

15.8

(a)

CH₃NH₂	CH₃CH₂NH₂	CH₃NHCH₃	CH₃NCH₃
Methylamine	Ethylamine	Dimethylamine	CH₃
			Trimethylamine

Amines that are gases at room temperature.

(b)   (c)

[pyridine structure]   [aniline structure]

Pyridine   Aniline

A heterocyclic amine   A compound with an amine group
                            on an aromatic ring

15.9

(a)

(b)

Piperidine
$C_5H_{11}N$

Purine
$C_5H_4N_4$

15.10 In a heterocyclic compound containing nitrogen, nitrogen must form part of the ring. Thus, compounds (a) and (d) are heterocyclic nitrogen compounds.

(a)

—CH₃CH₂NH₂ → CH₃CH₂NH₂

heterocyclic nitrogen
compound

(b)

—NH₂

(c)

HO— —CH₂CHCO₂⁻
           |
          NH₃⁺

(d)

HO

CH₂CH₂NH₃⁺

heterocyclic nitrogen
compound

15.11

$$CH_3\overset{H}{\underset{CH_3}{N}}: \;+\; H_2O \;\rightleftharpoons\; CH_3\overset{H}{\underset{CH_3}{\overset{+}{N}}}-H \;+\; OH^-$$

base   acid   acid   base

15.12–15.13

(a)

$$CH_3CH_2\underset{CH_3}{\overset{|}{C}H}NH_2 \;+\; HBr(aq) \;\longrightarrow\; CH_3CH_2\underset{CH_3}{\overset{|}{C}H}NH_3^+ \,Br^-(aq)$$

sec-Butylamine   *sec*-Butylammonium bromide

(b)

Aniline   Anilinium chloride

(c)

$CH_3CH_2NH_2$ + $CH_3COOH(aq)$ $\longrightarrow$ $CH_3CH_2NH_3^+ CH_3COO^-(aq)$

Ethylamine   Ethylammonium acetate

(d)

$CH_3NH_3^+ Cl^-(aq)$ + $NaOH(aq)$ $\longrightarrow$ CH_3NH_2 + $H_2O(l)$ + $NaCl(aq)$

Methylammonium chloride   Methylamine

15.14 Review Section 15.4 to choose the stronger base.

(a) Ethylamine is a stronger base than ammonia.
(b) Triethylamine (non-aromatic amine) is a stronger base than pyridine (aromatic amine).

15.15

(a)

Epinephrine   ammonium ion
amine

(b)

Amphetamine   ammonium ion
amine

15.16 – 15.17

(a)   (b)

$$CH_3CH_2CH_2CH_2CH_2CH_2\overset{\overset{\displaystyle CH_3}{|}}{\underset{\underset{\displaystyle CH_3}{|}}{N}}H^+ Cl^-$$

$CH_3CH_2NH_3^+ Br^-$

Hexyldimethylammonium chloride   Ethylammonium bromide
or N,N-Dimethylhexylammonium chloride
salt of a tertiary amine   salt of a primary amine

15.18

$$CH_3CH_2CH_2CH_2NH_3{}^+ \ Cl^-(aq) + NaOH \ (aq) \longrightarrow CH_3CH_2CH_2CH_2NH_2 + H_2O \ (l) + NaCl \ (aq)$$

15.19 Benadryl has the general antihistamine structure illustrated below. Attached to the central skeleton ($-Z-CH_2CH_2N-$) of Benadryl are two methyl groups bonded to nitrogen (R = $-CH_3$) and two phenyl groups (R' = R" = C_6H_5-) bonded to Z (Z = $-CHO-$).

Benadryl   general antihistamine structure

15.20

Benzylammonium chloride

Understanding Key Concepts

15.21 (a)

p = primary
s = secondary
t = tertiary

(b) The primary and secondary amine groups can participate in hydrogen bonding with nitrogens on other molecules of the above compound. The tertiary amine group can form hydrogen bonds with the primary and secondary amine groups but not with other tertiary amine groups. All amine groups can take part in hydrogen bonding with water.

15.22

Arginine

(a) The amine groups labeled "p" and "s" can participate in hydrogen bonding because each has an unshared electron pair. Hydrogens on the $-NH_3{}^+$ group and the $=NH_2{}^+$ group can form hydrogen bonds with the electron pairs of other amino groups.

(b) Arginine is likely to be water-soluble because it is ionic and because it can form hydrogen bonds with water.

15.23

15.24

An O–H bond of water is broken, and a N–H bond is formed in the reaction to form OH⁻, an ammonium ion and an amine. The electrons remain with their original atoms.

15.25

Most basic ——————→ *Least basic*

15.26

(a)

(b)

(c)

$(CH_3)_4N^+$ + OH^- ⟶ no reaction

(d)

Amines and Ammonium Salts

15.27

(a)

$CH_3CH_2CH_2NH_2$
Propylamine

(b)

$CH_3CH_2NCH_2CH_3$
Diethylamine

(c)

$CH_3CH_2CH_2NCH_3$
N-Methylpropylamine

15.28

(a)

$CH_3CH_2CH_2CH_2NCH_3$
N-Methylbutylamine

(b)

—NCH_2CH_3
N-Ethylcyclopentylamine

(c)

$CH_2CH_2CH_3$
m-Propylaniline

15.29

(a)

$CH_3CH_2CH_2CH_2NH_2$
Butylamine
primary amine

(b)

CH_3CHCH_3
Isopropylamine
primary amine

15.30

(a)

N-Methylcyclobutylamine
secondary amine

(b)

N-Cyclopentyl-*N*-methylaniline
tertiary amine

15.31 Water is a weaker base because the equilibrium reaction shown below takes place:

$$NH_3 + H_2O \rightleftharpoons NH_4^+ + OH^-$$

If water were a stronger base, this equilibrium (not observed) would occur:

$$NH_3 + H_2O \rightleftharpoons NH_2^- + H_3O^+$$

15.32 Diethylamine is a stronger base than diethyl ether because amines are more basic than ethers.

15.33

(a)

$$CH_3NH_3^+ Cl^-$$

Methyammonium chloride
(salt of a primary amine)

(b)

N-Methylanilinium bromide
(salt of a secondary amine)

(c)

$$\underset{\overset{|}{CH_3CH_2CH_2}}{CH_3CH_2CH_2CH_2NH_2^+} Br^-$$

N-Propylbutylammonium bromide
(salt of a secondary amine)

15.34

(a)

N-Methylcyclopentylammonium nitrate
(salt of a secondary amine)

(b)

Anilinium chloride
(salt of a primary amine)

(c)

$$\underset{\overset{|}{CH_2CH_3}}{\overset{\overset{CH_3CHCH_3}{|}}{CH_3CH_2CH_2CH_2CH_2CH_2NH^+}} Cl^-$$

N-Ethyl-*N*-isopropylhexylammonium chloride
(salt of a tertiary amine)

15.35

L–Dopa

15.36

Cocaine

15.37

Cocaine hydrochloride

15.38

Quinine hydrochloride

The nonaromatic nitrogen is protonated first because it is more basic.

Reactions of Amines

15.39

(a)

(b)

(c)

15.40

(a)

(b)

(c)

15.41 The ammonium salt pictured does not react with acids or bases because it is neither acidic nor basic.

15.42 Choline doesn't react with HCl because its nitrogen atom isn't basic.

Applications

15.43 Either water or alcohol is a satisfactory solvent for extraction of caffeine from ground coffee beans without extracting adenine. Caffeine is fairly soluble in both solvents, whereas adenine is only slightly soluble. Chloroform is the most effective solvent for extraction (because adenine is insoluble in chloroform), but it is not used in food processing because of concerns about its toxicity.

15.44 Functions that have been attributed to NO include: (1) lowering of blood pressure; (2) memory enhancement; (3) relief of angina pain, (4) destruction of parasites, and (5) promotion of wound healing.

15.45 Morphine sulfate and thorazine hydrochloride are more readily absorbed because they are administered as ammonium salts.

15.46

Promazine   Promazine hydrochloride

The nitrogen that is not part of a ring is protonated because it is more basic.

15.47 Intermediates in the citric acid cycle are citrate, isocitrate, α-ketoglutarate, succinyl-SCoA, succinate, fumarate, malate, and oxaloacetate. These intermediates are listed as anions because at physiological pH they exist in the anionic form, rather than as organic acids.

15.48 (a) Toxicologists work in three major areas. Clinical toxicologists are involved with the treatment of people harmed by toxic agents. Forensic toxicologists deal with the effects of toxic agents as they apply to criminal cases. Environmental toxicologists study the environmental impact of toxic substances.
(b) When working with a new toxin, a researcher needs to know the structure of the toxin, its mode of action at the molecular level, and a mechanism to reverse its effects.

General Questions and Problems

15.49 (a) Acetic acid has the highest boiling point of the compounds listed because it is more polar and undergoes more extensive hydrogen bonding than the other compounds listed.

(b)(c)(d) Butane is the lowest boiling, least soluble in water, and least reactive of the compounds listed because it is an alkane.

15.50 Decylamine is much less soluble in water than ethylamine because of its large hydrocarbon region, which is water-insoluble.

15.51 (a) Six secondary amines of the formula $C_5H_{13}N$ can be drawn.

(b) Many tertiary amines of the formula $C_6H_{13}N$ can be drawn. Here are several of them:

15.52

PABA

15.53

Sodium sulfanilamide

(a) Both PABA and sulfanilamide have *p*-amino-substituted aromatic rings.
(b) The sodium salt form of the drug is used because it is more soluble.

15.54

15.55 Trimethylamine is a stronger base than pyridine. Thus, the reaction of trimethylamine with pyridinium chloride proceeds in the following direction:

15.56

Amines	Alcohols
(a) foul smelling	pleasant smelling
(b) basic	not basic
(c) lower boiling, due to weaker hydrogen bonds, but higher boiling than ethers or alkyl halides	higher boiling, due to strong hydrogen bonds

15.57 Alkaloids are often bitter or poisonous.

15.58

15.59

(e) $(CH_3)_3N + H_2O \rightleftharpoons (CH_3)_3NH^+ + OH^-$

(f) $(CH_3)_3N + HCl \longrightarrow (CH_3)_3NH^+ Cl^-$

(g) $(CH_3)_3NH^+ + OH^- \longrightarrow (CH_3)_3N + H_2O$

15.60 Molecules of hexylamine can hydrogen-bond to each other. Heat must be supplied to break these hydrogen bonds, and thus the boiling point of hexylamine is higher than that of triethylamine, a tertiary amine whose molecules don't hydrogen-bond to each other.

15.61 The amine group is responsible for the odor of fish. The citric acid in lemon juice reacts with amines to form ammonium salts, which are odorless and are no longer volatile.

15.62

Psilocin   Indole

Psilocin is related to indole.

15.63 Aniline is not a heterocycle because its nitrogen atom is not part of a ring.

15.64 Pyridine is soluble in water because the ring nitrogen can form hydrogen bonds with water. No hydrogen bonding is possible for benzene.

15.65 15.39 (a) *N*-Ethylcyclohexylamine (b) Anilinium ion (c) *N*-Methylethylamine
15.40 (a) *N,N*-Dimethyl-*p*-methylanilinium bromide (b) Isopropylamine (c) Pyridine

Self-Test for Chapter 15

Multiple choice:

1. Which of the following amines is heterocyclic?
    (a) Aniline (b) Cyclohexylamine (c) Pyridine (d) Amphetamine

2. Which of the following amines is a secondary amine?
    (a) *N*-Methylaniline (b) Histamine (c) Triethylamine (d) Codeine

3. The name of the compound shown below is:
    (a) Ethylcyclopentylamine (b) Cyclopentylethylamine (c) *N*-Cyclopentylethylamine
    (d) *N*-Ethylcyclopentylamine

4. An amine and its ammonium salt differ in all respects except:
    (a) charge (b) solubility (c) carbon skeleton (d) basicity

5. Which of the following amines has the highest boiling point?
    (a) Triethylamine (b) Hexylamine (c) Tetramethylammonium chloride (d) Dipropylamine

6. Which of the following is an alkaloid?
    (a) Atropine (b) Amphetamine (c) Pyrimidine (d) Aniline

7. How many isomers of the formula $C_4H_{11}N$ are secondary amines?
   (a) 2   (b) 3   (c) 4   (d) 5

8. All of the following amines have a heterocyclic ring except:
   (a) Nicotine   (b) Caffeine   (c) Morphine   (d) Aniline

9. Propylamine and trimethylamine differ in all respects except:
   (a) formula weight   (b) boiling point   (c) solubility in water   (d) melting point

10. Which of the following is a quaternary ammonium salt?
    (a) Anilinium chloride   (b) Triethylpropylammonium chloride   (c) Pyridinium chloride
    (d) Trimethylammonium chloride

Complete the following sentences:

1. When the $-NH_2$ group is a substituent, _____ is used as a prefix.

2. Tetramethylammonium bromide is a _____ amine salt.

3. _____ contains nitrogen heterocyclic rings derived from either purine or pyrimidine.

4. _____ is the science devoted to poisons.

5. A _____ has a nitrogen atom contained in a ring.

6. ____ are a class of amines derived from plants.

7. Simple amines are water-soluble because of _____ _____.

8. Most amines can be made water-soluble by conversion to _____ salts.

9. Nitric oxide is a molecule that is a ____ _____ because it has an unpaired electron.

10. Ammonia is less basic than _____ _____.

Tell whether the following statements are true or false:

1. Amine groups in biomolecules are usually protonated in body fluids.

2. Ammonium salts are water-soluble.

3. Tertiary amines are higher boiling than primary or secondary amines.

4. Morphine and codeine are alkaloids.

5. Quaternary ammonium salts are acidic.

6. Caffeine is a heterocyclic amine.

7. Heroin is a naturally occurring alkaloid.

8.   The physical properties of low-molecular-weight amines and ammonia are similar.

9.   NO is responsible for elevating blood pressure.

10. The correct name for $CH_3CH_2CH_2CH_2NHCH_3$ is methylbutylamine.

Match the item in the left column with its partner on the right:

1.   Trimethylamine   (a) Amino acid

2.   Atropine   (b) Vitamin

3.   Piperidine   (c) Primary aromatic amine

4.   Tetramethylammonium chloride   (d) Tertiary amine

5.   Alanine   (e) Aromatic heterocycle

6.   Dimethylamine   (f) Neurotransmitter

7.   Pyridoxine   (g) Primary amine

8.   Putrescine   (h) Nonaromatic heterocycle

9.   Serotonin   (i) Quaternary ammonium salt

10. Methylamine   (j) Secondary amine

11. Pyridine   (k) Diamine

12. Aniline   (l) Alkaloid

Chapter 16 – Aldehydes and Ketones

Chapter Outline

I. Characteristics of aldehydes and ketones (Sections 16.1–16.4).
  A. The carbonyl group (Section 16.1).
    1. Carbonyl groups are polarized, with carbon having a partial positive charge and oxygen having a partial negative charge.
    2. Carbonyl groups are planar, with a 120° bond angle.
    3. Carbonyl compounds can be divided into two groups:
      a. In aldehydes and ketones, the carbonyl carbon is bonded to atoms that don't attract electrons strongly.
      b. In carboxylic acids, esters, anhydrides and amides, the carbonyl carbon is bonded to nitrogen or oxygen.
  B. Naming aldehydes and ketones (Section 16.2).
    1. Aldehydes are named by replacing the suffix of the parent compound with -al.
      a. For substituted aldehydes, the carbon chain is numbered with the aldehyde carbon as carbon 1.
      b. Aldehydes with common names are formaldehyde, acetaldehyde and benzaldehyde.
    2. Ketones are named by replacing the suffix of the parent compound with -one.
      a. Numbering starts at the end nearer the carbonyl carbon.
      b. Ketones with common names include acetone and acetophenone.
      c. Sometimes, ketones are named by naming the two alkyl groups, followed by the word *ketone*.
  C. Properties of aldehydes and ketones (Section 16.3).
    1. Aldehydes and ketones are polar.
    2. Aldehydes and ketones don't hydrogen-bond with each other.
    3. Aldehydes and ketones are soluble in organic solvents.
    4. Simple aldehydes and ketones are water-soluble because they can hydrogen-bond with water.
    5. Aldehydes and ketones have distinctive odors.
    6. Aldehydes and ketones are flammable.
  D. Common aldehydes and ketones (Section 16.4).
    1. Formaldehyde.
      a. Formaldehyde is an irritating component of smog.
      b. Formaldehyde is used as a disinfectant and as a preservative.
      c. Formaldehyde-containing polymers are used in building materials.
    2. Acetaldehyde.
    3. Acetone.
      a. Acetone is a commonly used organic solvent.
      b. Acetone is a product of fat metabolism.
II. Reactions of aldehydes and ketones (Sections 16.5–16.7).
  A. Oxidation (Section 16.5).
    1. Aldehydes can be oxidized to carboxylic acids.
      a. Tollens' reagent converts aldehydes to carboxylic acids and leaves a shiny silver residue on the flask.
      b. Benedict's reagent leaves a brick-red precipitate.
    2. Ketones don't react with most oxidizing agents.

B. Reduction (Section 16.6).
  1. Reducing agents reduce aldehydes to primary alcohols and ketones to secondary alcohols in a two-step reaction.
    a. Hydride ion adds to the carbonyl carbon.
    b. Hydrogen ion adds to the carbonyl oxygen.
  2. In the body, the coenzyme NADH is the reducing agent.
C. Formation of hemiacetals and acetals (Section 16.7).
  1. Hemiacetals.
    a. An alcohol can add to an aldehyde or ketone to form a hemiacetal.
      i. The negatively polarized alcohol oxygen adds to the positively polarized carbonyl carbon.
      ii. The reaction is reversible: Hemiacetals easily revert to an aldehyde or ketone.
    b. Although hemiacetals are often too unstable to isolate, the hemiacetals of sugars are stable.
  2. Acetals.
    a. Hemiacetals can react with a second molecule of an alcohol to form an acetal.
    b. Acetals are stable and can be isolated.
  3. Acetal hydrolysis.
    Aqueous acid reacts with acetals to regenerate the original aldehyde or ketone, plus alcohol.

Solutions to Chapter 16 Problems

16.1

(a) Aspirin — ester, carboxylic acid

(b) Testosterone — ketone

(c) Vanillin — aldehyde

(d) $C_4H_9COCH_3$ — ketone

(e) C_4H_9CHO — aldehyde

(f) $C_4H_9COOCH_3$ — ester

16.2

16.3

(a)

CH₃CH₂CH₂CH₂CH₂C—H

Hexanal

(b)

—CCH₃

Methyl phenyl ketone

(c)

CH₃ O
CH₃CH₂CHCH₂CCH₃

4-Methyl-2-hexanone

(d)

O
CH₃CHCH₂CCH₃
CH₃

Isobutyl methyl ketone

16.4

(a)

O
CH₃CH₂CH₂CH₂CH

Pentanal

(b)

O
CH₃CH₂CCH₂CH₃

3-Pentanone
(Diethyl ketone)

(c)

CH₃ O
CH₃CH₂CHCH₂CH₂CH

4-Methylhexanal

(d)

O
CH₃CH₂CH₂CCH₂CH₂CH₃

4-Heptanone
(Dipropyl ketone)

16.5

(a)

CH₃ O
CH₃CHCH₂CH₂CH

C₆H₁₂O

4-Methylpentanal
an aldehyde

(b)

CH₃ O
CH₃CHCH₂CCH₂CH₃

C₇H₁₄O

5-Methyl-3-hexanone
a ketone

16.6 The illustrated ketone, 3-pentanone, is a polar, flammable liquid with a boiling point close to 100°C.

16.7 Alcohols are higher boiling than aldehydes and ketones of similar molecular weight because hydrogen bonding takes place between alcohol molecules, raising their boiling points. Aldehydes and ketones, however, are higher boiling than alkanes of similar molecular weight because aldehydes and ketones are polar and show dipole-dipole interactions, which elevate their boiling points relative to the boiling points of alkanes.

16.8

(a)

CH_2OH ← alcohol

ketone → $C=O$

$HO-C-H$

alcohol

CH_2OH ← alcohol

(b)

CH_2OH ← alcohol

$HO-C-H$

alcohol

$H-C=O$ ← aldehyde

(c)

$-CH_2CHO$

aldehyde

(d)

$H_2NCH_2CH_2COCH_3$

amine   ketone

16.9

(a)

$CH_3CHCH_2CH_2CH_2CH$ (with CH_3 and O) $\xrightarrow{\text{Tollens' reagent}}$ $CH_3CHCH_2CH_2CH_2CO^-$ (with CH_3 and O) $+ NH_4^+ + Ag(s)$

(b)

$CH_3CH_2CH_2C-CH$ (with H_3C, O, H_3C) $\xrightarrow{\text{Tollens' reagent}}$ $CH_3CH_2CH_2C-CO^-$ (with H_3C, O, H_3C) $+ NH_4^+ + Ag(s)$

(c)

$CH_3CH_2CCHCH_3$ (with O and CH_3) $\xrightarrow{\text{Tollens' reagent}}$ NR

16.10 First, draw the aldehyde or ketone so that the C=O group is vertical. Next, break the double bond, and add one hydrogen to the carbon and one to the oxygen. Finally, redraw the product as a condensed structure.

(a)

CH_3CH-C (with CH_3, O, H) $\xrightarrow[\text{agent}]{\text{reducing}}$ $CH_3CH-C-H$ (with CH_3, $O-H$, H) $=$ CH_3CH-CH_2OH (with CH_3)

(b)

Cl—(benzene ring)—C (with O, H) $\xrightarrow[\text{agent}]{\text{reducing}}$ Cl—(benzene ring)—$C-H$ (with $O-H$, H) $=$ Cl—(benzene ring)—CH_2OH

(c)

(cyclopentanone)$=O$ $\xrightarrow[\text{agent}]{\text{reducing}}$ (cyclopentane with OH, H)

16.11

(a)

(b)

O
||
HCCH₂CH₂CHCH₃ → HOCH₂CH₂CH₂CHCH₃
| |
CH₃   CH₃

reducing agent

(c)

O
||
CH₃CH₂CH₂CHCH → CH₃CH₂CH₂CHCH₂OH
| |
CH₃   CH₃

reducing agent

16.12 To identify a hemiacetal, look for a carbon with single bonds to two different oxygens. If one group bonded to the carbon is –OH and the other is –OR (R = organic group), the compound is a hemiacetal.

(a)

OH ← bond to –OH
|
C—OCH₃
|
H ← bond to –OCH₃

This compound is a hemiacetal.

(b)

OH   OH
| |
CH₃CH—CHCH₃

This compound is not a hemiacetal.

(c)

OH

OCH₃

This compound is not a hemiacetal.

16.13

(a)
Redraw CH₃CH₂CH₂CHO as:

O—
|
CH₃CH₂CH₂C— + CH₃CH₂OH
|
H

acid
⇌
catalyst

OH
|
CH₃CH₂CH₂C—OCH₂CH₃
|
H

hemiacetal

The hemiacetal is formed by adding –H to oxygen and –OCH₂CH₃ to carbon.

(b)

Redraw $CH_3CH_2CCH_2CH(CH_3)_2$ as:

The equilibrium favors starting material.

16.14 Replace the –H bonded to oxygen with the alkyl part of the alcohol reagent to arrive at the structure of the acetal

(a)

(b)

16.15 Follow the instructions for Worked Example 16.5. If one carbon is bonded to two –OR groups, the compound is an acetal.

(a)   (b)   (c)   (d)

acetal   hemiacetal   neither acetal   acetal
                                        nor hemiacetal

16.16 If the carbon that bears the –OH or –OR groups also has a –H *and* an –R group bonded to it, the original compound was an aldehyde. If the carbon has two –R groups bonded to it, the original compound was a ketone. Thus, hemiacetal (b) and acetal (d) were formed from aldehydes, and acetal (a) was formed from a ketone.

16.17 Find the two –OR groups that form the acetal. Remove them and replace them with =O to form the original aldehyde or ketone. Add –H to the –OR groups to form the original alcohol.

Understanding Key Concepts

16.18 (a) The hydride ion is added to the carbonyl carbon. The carbon end of the polar C=O bond has a partial positive charge, and thus reaction with negatively charged reagents occurs at carbon.
(b) The top arrow (reaction to the right) represents reduction, and the bottom arrow (reaction to the left) represents oxidation.

16.19 Aldehydes can be oxidized to carboxylic acids, but ketones cannot. Two tests that can distinguish aldehydes from ketones take advantage of selective aldehyde oxidation. Tollens' reagent produces a deposit of silver when it is mixed with an aldehyde, but no reaction takes place with a ketone. Benedict's reagent yields a red copper oxide precipitate when it reacts with an aldehyde, but no reaction occurs with a ketone.

16.20 In a solution of an aldehyde in water, hydrogen bonds form between the oxygen atoms of the aldehyde and the hydrogen atoms of water. Molecules of aldehyde don't hydrogen-bond with each other, and the hydrogen atoms bonded to the aldehyde carbon don't take part in hydrogen bonding.

16.21 (a) Under acidic conditions, an alcohol adds to the carbonyl group of an aldehyde to form a hemiacetal. Although some hemiacetals are stable, most hemiacetals are either reconverted to aldehydes or further react with a second molecule of the alcohol to form acetals. The yield of acetal can be improved if the water byproduct is removed from the reaction mixture, driving the equilibrium to the right.

(b)

---- bonds broken

— bonds formed

16.22 In solution, glucose exists primarily in the cyclic hemiacetal form shown below because it is more stable in this form.

16.23 One equivalent of an alcohol adds to the carbonyl group of an aldehyde or ketone to form a hemiacetal. Two equivalents of alcohol add to the carbonyl group to yield an acetal.

Aldehydes and Ketones

16.24

(a)   (b)   (c)   (d)

16.25 There are many possible answers to this question.

(a)   (b)   (c)   (d)

16.26

(a)

$$CH_3CH_2\overset{\overset{\displaystyle H}{|}}{C}=O$$

aldehyde

(b)

$$O=\overset{\overset{\displaystyle NH_2}{|}}{C}CH_2CH_2\overset{\overset{\displaystyle CH_3}{|}}{CH}CH_3$$

amide

(c)

$$CH_3CH_2-O-CH=CH_2$$

no carbonyl group

(d)

$$CH_3CH_2\overset{\overset{\displaystyle OCH_3}{|}}{\underset{\underset{\displaystyle OCH_3}{|}}{C}}-OCH_3$$

no carbonyl group

(e)

$$\overset{\overset{\displaystyle H_3C}{|}}{CH_3CH}\overset{\overset{\displaystyle O}{||}}{C}OH$$

carboxylic acid

(f)

$$CH_3\overset{\overset{\displaystyle O}{||}}{C}CH_2CH_2OH$$

ketone

Structure (a) is an aldehyde, and structure (f) is a ketone.

16.27

(a)

$$CH_3CH_2\overset{\overset{\displaystyle O}{||}}{CH}$$

aldehyde

(b)

$$(CH_3)_2\overset{\overset{\displaystyle OH}{|}}{C}CH_2CH_2CH_3$$

no carbonyl group

(c)

$$H_3C-\langle\text{benzene}\rangle-\overset{\overset{\displaystyle O}{||}}{C}NH_2$$

amide

(d)

$$CH_3\overset{\overset{\displaystyle OH}{|}}{CH}CH_2\overset{\overset{\displaystyle OCH_3}{|}}{CH}CH_3$$

no carbonyl group

(e)

$$CH_3CH_2\overset{\overset{\displaystyle O}{||}}{C}CH_2CH_3$$

ketone

(f)

$$CH_3\overset{\overset{\displaystyle O}{||}}{C}OCH_3$$

ester

Structure (a) is an aldehyde, and structure (e) is a ketone.

16.28

(a)

$$CH_3CH_2CH_2CH_2CH_2CH_2\overset{\overset{\displaystyle O}{||}}{CH}$$

Heptanal

(b)

$$CH_3\overset{\overset{\displaystyle CH_3}{|}}{\underset{\underset{\displaystyle CH_3}{|}}{C}}CH_2CH_2\overset{\overset{\displaystyle O}{||}}{CH}$$

4,4-Dimethylpentanal

(c)

$$\langle\text{benzene, Cl}\rangle-\overset{\overset{\displaystyle O}{||}}{CH}$$

o-Chlorobenzaldehyde

(d)

$$CH_3CH_2CH_2CH_2\overset{\overset{\displaystyle O}{||}}{C}CH_2CH_3$$

3-Heptanone

(e)

$$CH_3\overset{\overset{\displaystyle}{\underset{\underset{\displaystyle CH_3}{|}}{CH}}}\overset{\overset{\displaystyle O}{||}}{C}\overset{\overset{\displaystyle}{\underset{\underset{\displaystyle CH_3}{|}}{CH}}}CH_3$$

2,4-Dimethyl-3-pentanone

(f)

$$O_2N-\langle\text{benzene}\rangle-\overset{\overset{\displaystyle O}{||}}{C}CH_3$$

m-Nitroacetophenone

16.29

(a)

CH₃CHCHC—CH with CH₃, CH₃, O, HO, CH₃ groups

3-Hydroxy-2,2,4-trimethylpentanal

(b)

CH₃CH₂CHCH₂CH—CH with CH₂CH₃, O, CH₃CHCH₃ groups

4-Ethyl-2-isopropylhexanal

(c)

Br—⟨ring⟩—CH with O

p-Bromobenzaldehyde

(d)

⟨cyclohexane ring⟩=O

Cyclohexanone

(e)

CH₃CH₂CCCl₃ with O

1,1,1-Trichloro-2-butanone

(f)

CH₃CH₂CH₂CCHCH₃ with O and CH₃

2-Methyl-3-hexanone

16.30

(a)

CH₃CH₂CHCHO with CH₃

2-Methylbutanal

(b)

CH₃CH₂CH₂CHCH₃ with CHO

2-Methylpentanal

(c)

(CH₃)₃CCHO

2,2-Dimethylpropanal

(d)

CH₃CH₂CCH₃ with O

2-Butanone

(e)

CH₃CCH₂CH₂CHCH₃ with O and CH₃

5-Methyl-2-hexanone

16.31

(a)

⟨benzene ring with CH₃ and CHO⟩

m-Methylbenzaldehyde

(b)

CH₃CH₂CCH₂CH with CH₃, O, CH₂CH₃

3-Ethyl-3-methylpentanal

(c)

CH₃CCH₂CH with Br, O, Br

3,3-Dibromobutanal

(d)

(CH₃)₃CCC(CH₃)₃ with O

2,2,4,4-Tetramethyl-3-pentanone

(e)

⟨cyclopentane ring with CH(CH₃)₂ and =O⟩

2-Isopropylcyclopentanone

16.32 (a) (b)The names 1-butanone and 4-butanone are incorrect because a ketone group can't occur at the end of a carbon chain.
(c) Numbering must start at the end of the carbon chain that is closer to the ketone functional group. Correct name: 2-Butanone.

16.33 (a) The name cyclohexanal is incorrect because an aldehyde carbon can't be part of a ring.
(b) The name 2-butanal is incorrect because an aldehyde group must be at the end of a chain, not in the middle.
(c) The name 1-pentanone is incorrect because a ketone group can't occur at the end of a carbon chain.

Reactions of Aldehydes and Ketones

16.34 A *hemiacetal* is produced when an aldehyde reacts with an alcohol in a 1:1 ratio. No second product is formed.

16.35 An *acetal* is produced when an aldehyde reacts with an alcohol in a 1:2 ratio in the presence of an acid catalyst: Water is a second product.

16.36 Remember that only aldehydes react with Tollens' reagent. Ketones are not oxidized.

16.37

| | *Compound* | *Tollens' Product* | *Reduction Product* |

(a)

benzaldehyde (C₆H₅CHO) → benzoic acid (C₆H₅COOH) → benzyl alcohol (C₆H₅CH₂OH)

(b)

$CH_3CH_2CCH_3$ (O) → no reaction → $CH_3CH_2CHCH_3$ (OH)

(c)

Cl_2CHCH (O) → Cl_2CHCOH (O) → Cl_2CHCH_2OH

16.38

| | *Carboxylic acid* | *Aldehyde* | *Primary alcohol* |

(a)

H_3C-⟨benzene⟩$-COOH$ → H_3C-⟨benzene⟩$-CHO$ → H_3C-⟨benzene⟩$-CH_2OH$

(b)

$CH_3CH_2CHCH_2CHCH_3$ with COOH and CH₃ → $CH_3CH_2CHCH_2CHCH_3$ with CHO and CH₃ → $CH_3CH_2CHCH_2CHCH_3$ with CH₂OH and CH₃

(c)

$CH_3CH=CHCOOH$ → $CH_3CH=CHCHO$ → $CH_3CH=CHCH_2OH$

16.39

| | *Carboxylic acid* | *Aldehyde* | *Primary alcohol* |

(a)

HO-⟨benzene⟩-COOH → HO-⟨benzene⟩-CHO → HO-⟨benzene⟩-CH₂OH

(b)

CH_3COOH → CH_3CHO → CH_3CH_2OH

(c)

$CH_3COCOOH$ → CH_3COCHO → CH_3COCH_2OH

or CH_3CHCHO (OH) → *or* CH_3CHCH_2OH (OH)

16.40

(a)

(b)

(c)

(d)

16.41

(a)

(b)

(c)

(d)

16.42

5-Hydroxypentanal

16.43

Galactose

16.44

16.45

16.46

hemiacetal

alcohol

ketone

ketone

Aldosterone

C–C double bond

The hemiacetal group is derived from an aldehyde because the hemiacetal carbon has a hydrogen atom bonded to it.

16.47

C–C double bond

CH$_3$

ketone

Ionone

Applications

16.48

HO— —OH + H$_2$O$_2$ ⟶ O= =O + 2 H$_2$O

When *p*-dihydroxybenzene is oxidized, hydrogen peroxide is reduced.

16.49 The cyanohydrin that decomposes to form HCN is nontoxic and is stable inside the millipede's body.

16.50 Vanillin is an aromatic molecule with a polar hydroxyl group. The solvent of choice for extraction of vanillin from vanilla beans should also be polar, organic and nontoxic. Ethanol is a good choice.

16.51 Benzaldehyde can be identified by its reaction with Tollens' reagent, which forms a silver mirror on the wall of the reaction flask.

16.52 (a) There are several advantages to using *in vitro* testing for acute toxicity. *In vitro* testing is relatively inexpensive, and many more tests can be performed for the same cost. In addition, animals don't have to be sacrificed for *in vitro* testing.
(b) Since *in vitro* testing is performed on cultured cells that are identical, the results of testing may not be reliable for organisms that have many different kinds of cells.

16.53 The largest LD$_{50}$ corresponds to the lest toxic compound. Thus, (a) (LD$_{50}$ = 23 g/kg) is the least toxic, and (c) (LD$_{50}$ = 18 mg/kg) is the most toxic.

General Questions and Problems

16.54

CH$_3$O— —CH   *p*-Methoxybenzaldehyde

16.55 The alcohol pictured, 2,2-dimethyl-1-propanol, can't be formed from reduction of an aldehyde or ketone because it is a tertiary alcohol. Only primary and secondary alcohols result from reduction of aldehydes and ketones, respectively.

16.56 The portion of the odor due to aldehyde is less stable because aldehydes are easily oxidized to carboxylic acids.

16.57 Formaldehyde in the air can cause bronchial pneumonia and dermatitis. Ingestion of formaldehyde can cause kidney damage, coma and death.

16.58

OH
|
Cl₃C—C—OH   Chloral hydrate
|
H

16.59

(a)

$$CH_3CH_2CCH(CH_3)_2$$
(with O double bonded to the C)
2-Methyl-3-pentanone

(b)

$$CH_2{=}CHCH_2CH_2CH{=}CH_2$$
1,5-Hexadiene

(c)

m-Bromotoluene

(d)

$$(CH_3)_3CCHCCH_2CH_3$$
(with O double bonded to C, and CH₃ substituent)
CH₃
4,5,5-Trimethyl-3-hexanone

16.60

(a)

OCH₃
o-Isopropylmethoxybenzene
or
o-Isopropylanisole

(b)

$$CH_3CH_2C{\equiv}CC(CH_2CH_3)_3$$
5,5-Diethyl-3-heptyne

(c)

—NH₂⁺ Br⁻
|
CH₂CH₃
N-Ethylcyclopentyl-
ammonium bromide

(d)

$$(CH_3CH_2)_2N(CH_2)_5CH_3$$
N,N-Diethylhexylamine

16.61

(a)

NO$_2$

CH

o-Nitrobenzaldehyde

(b)

Cl

Cl

O

2,3-Dichlorocyclopentanone

(c)

CH$_3$CH$_2$CH$_2$CH$_2$OCH$_3$

Butyl methyl ether

(d)

OH

CH$_3$CHCHCHCH$_3$

CH$_3$ CH$_3$

2,4-Dimethyl-3-pentanol

16.62

(a)

I O

CH$_3$CCHCH

I I

2,3,3-Triiodobutanal

(b)

O

BrCH$_2$CCHBr$_2$

1,1,3-Tribromoacetone

(c)

NH$_2$ O

CH$_3$CCH$_2$CCH$_3$

CH$_3$

4-Amino-4-methyl-2-pentanone

16.63

(a)

CH$_3$CH=C(CH$_3$)$_2$ + H$_2$ $\xrightarrow{\text{Pd}}$ CH$_3$CH$_2$CH(CH$_3$)$_2$

(b)

CH$_2$OH

CH$_3$CH$_2$CCH$_2$CH$_3$ $\xrightarrow{\text{[O]}}$

CH$_2$CH$_3$

CHO

CH$_3$CH$_2$CCH$_2$Cl I$_3$ $\xrightarrow{\text{[O]}}$

CH$_2$CH$_3$

COOH

CH$_3$CH$_2$CCH$_2$CH$_3$

CH$_2$CH$_3$

(c)

O

CH$_3$CCH$_2$CH$_2$CH$_3$ $\xrightarrow[\text{agent}]{\text{reducing}}$

OH

CH$_3$CHCH$_2$CH$_2$CH$_3$

(d)

O

CH$_2$CH

+ HOCH$_2$CH$_2$CH$_3$ $\underset{\text{catalyst}}{\overset{\text{acid}}{\rightleftharpoons}}$

OH

CH$_2$CH—OCH$_2$CH$_2$CH$_3$

hemiacetal

16.64

(a)

(b)

$$CH_3CH = \overset{\overset{\textstyle CH_2CH_3}{\textstyle |}}{C}CH_2CH_2CH_3 + HCl \longrightarrow CH_3CH_2\overset{\overset{\textstyle CH_2CH_3}{\textstyle |}}{\underset{\underset{\textstyle Cl}{\textstyle |}}{C}}CH_2CH_2CH_3$$

(c)

$$H_3C-\!\!\!\bigcirc\!\!\!-CH_2CH_2OH \xrightarrow{\;H_2SO_4\;} H_3C-\!\!\!\bigcirc\!\!\!-CH=CH_2 + H_2O$$

16.65 Treat samples of the two compounds with Tollens' reagent. The aldehyde reacts to yield a silver mirror, but the alcohol doesn't react.

16.66 1-Butanol (bp 117°C) is the highest boiling of the three compounds because it forms stronger hydrogen bonds than does butylamine (bp 78°C). Butanal (bp 75°C) is polar but doesn't form hydrogen bonds.

16.67 2-Heptanone is less soluble in water than 2-butanone because 2-heptanone has a longer hydrocarbon chain.

Self-Test for Chapter 16

Multiple choice:

1. Which of the following alcohols can't be produced by reduction of an aldehyde or ketone?
   (a) 2-Pentanol (b) Cyclohexanol (c) 2-Methyl-2-pentanol (d) 2-Methyl-1-butanol

2. The term LD_{50} refers to:
   (a) 50% of the amount of a substance that will kill a population (b) the amount of a substance that will kill 50% of a population (c) the name of a substance, 50% of which will kill a population (d) none of the above

3. 3-Pentanone is unlikely to undergo which of the following reactions?
   (a) oxidation (b) reduction (c) acetal formation (d) hemiacetal formation

4. Vanillin contains all of the following functional groups except:
   (a) aldehyde (b) ether (c) aromatic ring (d) ketone

5. How many ketone isomers of the formula $C_6H_{12}O$ are there?
   (a) 4 (b) 5 (c) 6 (d) 7

6. Which of the following aldehydes is least soluble in water?
   (a) Propanal (b) Benzaldehyde (c) Formaldehyde (d) Acetaldehyde

7. Which of the following compounds undergoes reaction with Tollens' reagent?
   (a) 3-Methyl-3-pentanol (b) Glucose (c) Acetone (d) Cyclohexanone dimethyl acetal

8. The main difference between aldehydes and ketones is:
   (a) reactivity (b) solubility (c) flammability (d) polarity

9. Formaldehyde is used for all of the following except:
   (a) polymers (b) disinfectant (c) preservative (d) food additive

10. Which of the following statements about 3-heptanone is true?
    (a) It undergoes reaction with Benedict's reagent. (b) It forms a cyclic acetal with 1,3-propanediol. (c) It is soluble in water. (d) It is a solid at room temperature.

Complete the following statements:

1. Aldehydes, esters, and ketones are all _____ compounds.

2. The shiny product of oxidation of an aldehyde by Tollens' reagent is _____.

3. _____ is a reaction that converts an acetal to an aldehyde or a ketone.

4. A carbonyl group is polarized, with a partial _____ charge on carbon and a partial _____ charge on oxygen.

5. _____ is a ketone that is widely used as a solvent.

6. Chronic exposure to the aldehyde _____ can cause symptoms resembling those of alcoholism.

7. Bonds to the carbonyl carbon of esters and amides are _____ polar than the bonds to the carbonyl carbon of ketones and aldehydes.

8. The conversion of an aldehyde or ketone into an alcohol is said to be a _____ reaction.

9. Formaldehyde is widely used as a _____.

10. The initial product of reaction between a ketone or aldehyde and an alcohol is called a _____.

11. _____ reagent is used to detect sugar in urine.

12. _____ can be detected on the breath during starvation.

Match the entries on the left with their partners on the right:

1. $AgNO_3$, NH_3, H_2O (a) Reagent used to form an acetal

2. $CH_3CH_2COCH_3$ (b) Reduces carbonyl groups to alcohols

3. CH_3CH_2COOH (c) An amide

4. CH_3OH, H^+ catalyst   (d) Product of an aldehyde plus Tollens' reagent

5. CH_3CH_2OH (e) Tollens' reagent

6. $CH_3CH_2COOCH_3$ (f) Colored product of Benedict's test

7. $CH_3CH(OH)CH_3$ (g) Formaldehyde

8. NADH   (h) Product of aldehyde reduction

9. CH_3CHO (i) Yields secondary alcohol when reduced

10. Cu_2O (j) Ester

11. HCHO   (k) Can be oxidized to a ketone

12. CH_3CONH_2 (l) Product of primary alcohol oxidation

Tell whether the following statements are true or false:

1. Glucose contains an acetal link.

2. A bombardier beetle protects itself by secreting benzoquinone.

3. Ketones are oxidized by Tollens' reagent to carboxylic acids.

4. The reduction of aldehydes and ketones is carried out by using NaOH.

5. An acetal is an alternative name for an ester.

6. Only aldehydes form acetals.

7. An aldehyde group always occurs at the end of a carbon chain.

8. In the chemical industry, formaldehyde is used to synthesize polymers.

9. NAD^+ reduces ketones and aldehydes to alcohols.

10. Acetaldehyde results from the oxidation of ethanol.

11. Both aldehydes and ketones can be reduced to alcohols.

12. Aldehydes and ketones are not capable of forming hydrogen bonds.

Chapter Outline

I. Properties and names of carboxylic acids and derivatives (Section 17.1).
  A. General characteristics.
    1. Groups bonded to the carbonyl carbon are electron-attracting.
      a. In carboxylic acids, –OH is bonded to the carbonyl carbon.
      b. In amides, $-NH_2$ is bonded to the carbonyl carbon.
      c. In esters, –OR is bonded to the carbonyl carbon.
    2. All of these functional groups undergo carbonyl group substitution reactions.
  B. Carboxylic acids.
    1. Properties.
      a. All are high-boiling.
      b. Carboxylic acids can hydrogen-bond with each other.
      c. Smaller carboxylic acids are water-soluble.
      d. Volatile carboxylic acids have sharp odors.
    2. Naming carboxylic acids
      a. For simple carboxylic acids, the *-e* of the corresponding alkane is replaced by *-oic acid*.
      b. Many simple carboxylic acids have common names.
      c. For dicarboxylic acids, *-dioic acid* replaces the *-e* of the corresponding alkane.
      d. The group remaining when a carboxylic acid loses -OH is an acyl group.
      e. Unsaturated carboxylic acids are named by using *-enoic acid*.
      f. In some cases, the carbon next to the –COOH group is referred to as the α carbon.
  C. Esters.
    1. Properties.
      a. Esters are lower boiling than carboxylic acids.
      b. Esters have pleasant odors.
      c. Simple esters are liquids.
    2. Naming esters
    Ester names have two parts.
      a. The –OR fragment has the name of the alkyl group R.
      b. The remaining portion is the name of the parent carboxylic acid, with *-ate* replacing *-oic acid*.
  D. Amides.
    1. Properties.
      a. Amides are higher-boiling than carboxylic acids; most are solids.
      b. Amides are not basic.
    2. Naming amides.
      a. An amide has the name of the parent acid, with *-amide* replacing *-oic acid*.
      b. If nitrogen is substituted, the alkyl substituents are specified, preceded by *N-* (to indicate that the substituents are bonded to nitrogen).
II. Carboxylic acids (Sections 17.2–17.4).
  A. Common carboxylic acids (Section 17.2).
    1. Acetic acid.
      a. Acetic acid is a common laboratory solvent.
      b. Acetic acid is formed from fermentation of fruit in the presence of ample O_2.
    2. Citric acid.

B. Acidity of carboxylic acids (Section 17.3).
   1. Carboxylic acids are weak acids, with $pK_a \sim 10^{-5}$.
   2. Carboxylate anions are given the name of the parent carboxylic acid, with -*ate* replacing -*oic acid*.
   3. Carboxylic acids react with base to give carboxylic acid salts.
      a. The amount of salt or acid present depends on pH.
      b. Carboxylic acid salts are much more soluble in water than the parent acids.
C. Reactions of carboxylic acids (Section 17.4).
   1. Ester formation.

      a. carboxylic acid + alcohol $\xrightleftharpoons[\text{catalyst}]{H^+}$ ester + H_2O

      b. Esterification reactions are reversible.
   2. Amide formation.
      a. Carboxylic acid + ammonia (or an amine) $\longrightarrow$ amide + H_2O
      b. Acid anhydride + ammonia (or an amine) $\longrightarrow$ amide + carboxylic acid
III. Esters, amides, and carboxylic acid anhydrides (Sections 17.5–17.7).
   A. Aspirin and other over-the-counter carboxylic acid derivatives.(Section 17.5).
      1. Aspirin.
         a. Aspirin is a salicylic acid ester.
         b. Aspirin causes pain relief, reduces fever and reduces inflammation.
         c. Aspirin's side effects include gastric bleeding and gastric upset.
      2. Acetaminophen is an amide that can be used in place of aspirin.
      3. Benzocaine and lidocaine are amides that are used as topical anesthetics.
   B. Hydrolysis of esters and amides (Section 17.6).
      1. Esters.

         a. Ester + H_2O $\xrightarrow{\text{acid catalyst}}$ carboxylic acid + alcohol

         b. Ester + H_2O $\xrightarrow{\text{base}}$ carboxylate anion + alcohol
      2. Amides.

         Amide + H_2O $\xrightarrow{\text{acid or base}}$ carboxylic acid + amine (or ammonia)
   C. Polyesters and polyamides (Section 17.7).
      1. Nylons are polyamides formed in the reaction of a diacid with a diamine.
      2. Polyesters result from the reaction of a diacid with a dialcohol.
IV. Phosphoric acid derivatives (Section 17.8).
   A. Structure of phosphate esters.
      1. Phosphoric acid has three ionizable hydrogens and can form three different anions.
      2. Phosphates can react with alcohols at 1, 2 or 3 oxygens.
      3. Mono- and diphosphate esters are present as anions.
   B. Phosphate esters in the body.
      1. In the body, phosphate esters exist as anions.
      2. In the body, phosphate esters can form anhydrides.
         a. Diphosphates and triphosphates are the anhydrides that occur in living things.
         b. Triphosphate esters are used for energy storage in the body.

Solutions to Chapter 17 Problems

17.1

(a)

$$CH_3\overset{\overset{\displaystyle O}{\|}}{C}NH_2$$

amide

(b)

$$CH_3OCH_3$$

none
(ether)

(c)

$$CH_3COOH$$

carboxylic acid

(d)

$$CH_3COOCH_2CH_3$$

ester

(e)

$$CH_3COCH_3$$

none
(ketone)

(f)

$$CH_3CH_2CONHCH_3$$

amide

(g)

$$CH_3CH_2NH_2$$

none
(amine)

(h)

$$CH_3CH_2\overset{\overset{\displaystyle O}{\|}}{C}NH_2$$

amide

17.2

(a)

$$\overset{\qquad\quad CH_3\quad\;\; O}{\underset{\;\;6\quad\;\,5\quad\;\,4\quad\;\,3\quad\,2\quad\;1}{CH_3CH_2CH_2CHCH_2COH}}$$

3-Methylhexanoic acid

(b)

o-Nitrobenzoic acid

17.3

$$H-O-\overset{\overset{\displaystyle O}{\|}}{C}-\overset{\overset{\displaystyle H}{|}}{\underset{\underset{\displaystyle H}{|}}{C}}-\overset{\overset{\displaystyle O}{\|}}{C}-O-H$$

Malonic acid

17.4

$$H_2C=CH-\overset{\overset{\displaystyle O}{\|}}{C}-OH \;+\; H_2 \;\xrightarrow{\text{Pd}}\; CH_3CH_2\overset{\overset{\displaystyle O}{\|}}{C}-OH$$

Acrylic acid   Propionic acid
(Propenoic acid)   (Propanoic acid)

17.5

(a)

from benzoic acid

$$\bigcirc\!\!-\overset{\overset{\displaystyle O}{\|}}{C}OCH_2CH_2CH_3$$

from propanol

Propyl benzoate

(b)

from propanoic acid

$$CH_3CH_2\overset{\overset{\displaystyle O}{\|}}{C}OCH_2CH_3$$

from ethanol

Ethyl propanoate

(c)

from acrylic acid

$$H_2C=CH\overset{\overset{\displaystyle O}{\|}}{C}OCH_3$$

from methanol

Methyl acrylate

17.6   (a) CH_3OCH_3 (b) CH_3COOH (c) $CH_3CH_2CH_3$

Low boiling.   Highest boiling.   Lowest boiling.
Polar, but doesn't   Forms strongest   Doesn't form
form hydrogen bonds. hydrogen bonds.   hydrogen bonds.

17.7

More soluble	Less soluble	Reason
(a) CH₃CH₂CH₂COOH	C₈H₁₇COOH	The large hydrocarbon part of C₈H₁₇COOH makes it insoluble in water.
(b) (CH₃)₂CHCOOH	CH₃CH₂COOCH(CH₃)₂	Carboxylic acids form hydrogen bonds with water.

17.8

$$CH_3CH_2\overset{\displaystyle O}{\overset{\|}{C}}OH$$

Propanoic acid
(Propionic acid)

$$CH_3CH_2\overset{\displaystyle O}{\overset{\|}{C}}OCH_3$$

Methyl propanoate
(Methyl propionate)

$$CH_3CH_2\overset{\displaystyle O}{\overset{\|}{C}}NH_2$$

Propanamide
(Propionamide)

$$CH_3CH_2\overset{\displaystyle O}{\overset{\|}{C}}NHCH_3$$

N-Methylpropanamide
(N-Methylpropionamide)

$$CH_3CH_2\overset{\displaystyle O}{\overset{\|}{C}}NCH_3 \atop CH_3$$

N.N-Dimethylpropanamide
(N.N-Dimethylpropionamide)

17.9

(a)

4-Methylpentanoic acid

(b)

p-Chloro-N-methylbenzamide

17.10

(a)

4-Methylpentanamide

(b)

N-Methylbutanamide

17.11

(a)

monosubstituted amide (ii)

(b)

α-amino carboxylic acid (i)

(c)

carboxylic acid (iv)

(d)

methyl ester (iii)

17.12

(a)

CH₃COOCH₃

ester (ii)

(b)

RCONHR

amide (i)

(c)

C₆H₅COOH

carboxylic acid (iii)

(d)

$$CH_3CH_2\overset{\overset{\displaystyle O}{\|}}{C}N(CH_3)_2$$

amide (i)

(e)

CH₃CH₂CH₂CONH₂

amide (i)

(f)

$$\underset{\underset{\displaystyle CH_3}{|}}{HOOCCH_2CHCH_3}$$

carboxylic acid (iii)

17.13

(a)

$$C_6H_5\overset{\overset{\displaystyle O}{\|}}{C}NH_2$$

amide (C₇H₇NO)

(b)

$$CH_3CH_2\overset{\overset{\displaystyle O}{\|}}{C}OH$$

carboxylic acid (C₃H₆O₂)

(c)

$$CH_3\overset{\overset{\displaystyle O}{\|}}{C}OCH_2CH_3$$

ester (C₄H₈O₂)

17.14

(a)

$$CH_3CH_2CH_2\overset{\overset{\displaystyle O}{\|}}{C}-OH + KOH \longrightarrow CH_3CH_2CH_2\overset{\overset{\displaystyle O}{\|}}{C}-O^-K^+ + H_2O$$

(b)

$$2\ \ CH_3CH_2CH_2\underset{\underset{\displaystyle CH_3}{|}}{\overset{\overset{\displaystyle O}{\|}}{CHC}}-OH + Ba(OH)_2 \longrightarrow \left[CH_3CH_2CH_2\underset{\underset{\displaystyle CH_3}{|}}{\overset{\overset{\displaystyle O}{\|}}{CHC}}-O^-\right]_2 Ba^{2+} + 2\ H_2O$$

17.15

$$\left[H-\overset{\overset{\displaystyle O}{\|}}{C}-O^-\right]_2 Ca^{2+} \qquad H_2C=CH\overset{\overset{\displaystyle O}{\|}}{C}-O^-Na^+$$

Calcium formate   Sodium acrylate

17.16 When sodium acetate and disodium glutarate are dissolved in water, acetate ion, glutarate ion and sodium ion are present.

$$CH_3\overset{\overset{\displaystyle O}{\|}}{C}-O^- \qquad {}^-O-\overset{\overset{\displaystyle O}{\|}}{C}CH_2CH_2CH_2\overset{\overset{\displaystyle O}{\|}}{C}-O^- \qquad Na^+$$

acetate ion   glutarate ion   sodium ion

17.17 Redraw the structures so that the alcohol hydroxyl group and the –OH group of the carboxylic acid are facing each other. Remove water, and draw the ester bond.

$$H-\overset{\overset{\displaystyle O}{\|}}{C}-(OH + H)-O-CH_2\underset{\underset{\displaystyle CH_3}{|}}{C}HCH_3 \underset{catalyst}{\overset{H^+}{\rightleftharpoons}} H-\overset{\overset{\displaystyle O}{\|}}{C}-O-CH_2\underset{\underset{\displaystyle CH_3}{|}}{C}HCH_3 + H_2O$$

17.18

(a)

Cyclohexanol   4-Methylpentanoic acid

(b)

CH₃CH₂CH₂CH₂C─OH + H─O─CHCH₃ ⇌ CH₃CH₂CH₂CH₂C─O─CHCH₃ + H₂O

Pentanoic acid   2-Propanol

17.19 Use the technique shown in Problem 17.17 to draw the amide product.

(a)

CH₃CHC─OH + H─NHCH₃ ⟶ CH₃CHC─NHCH₃ + H₂O

(b)

17.20

p-Ethoxyaniline   Acetic acid   Phenacetin

17.21

Salicylic acid   Salsalate

17.22

17.23 Moisture in the air causes hydrolysis of the ester bond of aspirin, yielding acetic acid.

17.24

17.25

(a)

bond broken

CH₃CH=CHC—NHCH₃ + H₂O $\xrightarrow[\text{base}]{\text{acid or}}$ CH₃CH=CHC—OH + H—NHCH₃

2-Butenoic acid   Methylamine

(b)

bond broken

Cl—⟨benzene⟩—C—NCH₂CH₃ + H₂O $\xrightarrow[\text{base}]{\text{acid or}}$ Cl—⟨benzene⟩—C—OH
    |
    CH₂CH₃   p-Chlorobenzoic acid

    + H—NCH₂CH₃
        |
        CH₂CH₃
    Diethylamine

17.26 As in problems 17.17–17.19, draw the reacting partners so that the atoms involved in the reaction face each other. Remove one molecule of water for each bond formed.

(a)

n HO—CCH₂CH₂C—(OH + n H)—OCH₂CH₂O—H $\xrightarrow[\text{– H}_2\text{O}]{\text{heat}}$

$\left(\text{—CCH}_2\text{CH}_2\text{C—OCH}_2\text{CH}_2\text{O—} \right)_n$

(b)

n HO—C—⟨benzene⟩—C—(OH + n H)—NHCH₂CH₂NH—H $\xrightarrow[\text{– H}_2\text{O}]{\text{heat}}$

$\left(\text{—C—⟨benzene⟩—C—NHCH}_2\text{CH}_2\text{NH—} \right)_n$

17.27

HO—P—OH + H—OCH₂CH₂CH₂CH₃ ⟶ HO—P—OCH₂CH₂CH₂CH₃ + H₂O
    | |
    OH   OH

                                    Butyl phosphate (unionized)

⁻O—P—OCH₂CH₂CH₂CH₃
    |
    O⁻

Butyl phosphate (ionized)

17.28

(a)

CH$_3$C—NH$_2$ + H$_2$O $\xrightarrow{\text{acid or base}}$ CH$_3$C—OH + NH$_3$

amide   Acetic acid   Ammonia

(b)

CH$_3$CH$_2$OPO$_3^{2-}$ + H$_2$O $\longrightarrow$ CH$_3$CH$_2$OH + HOPO$_3^{2-}$

phosphate monoester   Ethanol   Hydrogen phosphate anion

(c)

CH$_3$CH$_2$C—OCH$_3$ + H$_2$O $\xrightarrow{\text{acid or base}}$ CH$_3$CH$_2$C—OH + HOCH$_3$

carboxylic acid ester   Propanoic acid   Methanol

17.29

Understanding Key Concepts

17.30

(a) At physiological pH (7.4), pyruvic acid exists as the pyruvate anion, and lactic acid exists as the lactate anion.

(b)

CH$_3$—C—COOH $\xrightarrow{\text{[H]}}$ CH$_3$—CH—COOH

Pyruvic acid   Lactic acid

(c) Hydrogen bonds between the carboxylate oxygen and water are shown. In addition, the carbonyl oxygens can also hydrogen-bond with water. For lactate, hydrogen bonding takes place between the hydroxyl hydrogen and water (shown below), as well as between molecules of lactate. You would expect pyruvate and lactate to have comparable solubility in water.

17.31

(a) Under conditions that favor amide hydrolysis (H₂O, plus either acid or base), the acetyl group can be removed from *N*-acetylglucosamine.

(b)

17.32

(a) Glycerate and phosphate are connected by a phosphate ester linkage.

(b)

1,3-Bisphosphoglycerate

17.33

Oxalate   Malonate   Succinate   Glutarate

17.34

(a)

2-Amino-4-hydroxybutanoic acid
(2-Amino-4-hydroxybutyric acid)   Homoserine lactone

(b)

2 HOC—CH—CH₂—CH₂OH ⟶ HOC—CH—CH₂—CH₂O—C—CH—CH₂—CH₂OH

                                                          + H₂O

(c)

2 HOC—CH—CH₂—CH₂OH ⟶ HOC—C—N—C—CH—CH₂—CH₂OH + H₂O

                                    CH₂CH₂OH

17.35

(a)(i)   (ii)   (iii)

Acetic acid   Methyl acetate   Acetamide

(b)   *Lowest boiling*   ————————> *Highest boiling*
          Methyl acetate ,   Acetic acid,   Acetamide

Methyl acetate is lowest boiling because it doesn't form hydrogen bonds. Acetamide is higher
boiling than acetic acid because acetic acid forms dimers (pictured below). These dimers do not
form the extensively hydrogen-bonded array of molecules that occurs in acetamide, and they
lower the boiling point of acetic acid, relative to acetamide (See Section 17.1).

17.36

(a)   (b)   (c)

Ethyl benzoate   2,3-Dimethylpentanoic acid   2-Methylpropanamide

(d)

$$CH_3CH_2\overset{\overset{\displaystyle O}{\|}}{N}CH$$
$$\underset{\displaystyle CH_2CH_3}{|}$$

N,N-Diethylformamide

Compound (b) is acidic. The other compounds are neither acidic nor basic.

17.37 The hydrolyzed bonds are indicated on the structure.

$$\downarrow H_2O$$

17-Hydroxylinolenic acid   Glutamic acid   Ammonia

Carboxylic Acids

17.38

17.39

(a)

$$CH_3CH_2\overset{\overset{\displaystyle O}{\|}}{C}-OH$$
in water

(b)

$$CH_3CH_2\overset{\overset{\displaystyle O}{\|}}{C}-OH$$
at pH = 2

(c)

$$CH_3CH_2\overset{\overset{\displaystyle O}{\|}}{C}-O^-$$
at pH = 12

17.40

$$CH_3CH_2CH_2CH_2\overset{\overset{\displaystyle O}{\|}}{C}-OH$$
Pentanoic acid

$$CH_3CH_2\overset{\overset{\displaystyle H_3C}{|}}{C}H\overset{\overset{\displaystyle O}{\|}}{C}-OH$$
2-Methylbutanoic acid

$$CH_3\overset{\overset{\displaystyle CH_3}{|}}{C}HCH_2\overset{\overset{\displaystyle O}{\|}}{C}-OH$$
3-Methylbutanoic acid

2,2-Dimethylpropanoic acid

17.41 There are *17* carboxylic acids with the formula $C_7H_{14}O_2$. Any three will do.

$$CH_3CH_2CH_2CH_2CH_2CH_2\overset{\displaystyle O}{\overset{\|}{C}}-OH$$

Heptanoic acid

$$CH_3CH_2CH_2CH_2\overset{\displaystyle H_3C}{\underset{|}{C}}\overset{\displaystyle O}{\overset{\|}{H}}-OH$$

2-Methylhexanoic acid

$$CH_3CH_2CH_2\overset{\displaystyle CH_3}{\underset{|}{CH}}CH_2\overset{\displaystyle O}{\overset{\|}{C}}-OH$$

3-Methylhexanoic acid

$$CH_3CH_2\overset{\displaystyle CH_3}{\underset{|}{CH}}CH_2CH_2\overset{\displaystyle O}{\overset{\|}{C}}-OH$$

4-Methylhexanoic acid

$$CH_3\overset{\displaystyle CH_3}{\underset{|}{CH}}CH_2CH_2CH_2\overset{\displaystyle O}{\overset{\|}{C}}-OH$$

5-Methylhexanoic acid

$$CH_3CH_2CH_2\overset{\displaystyle H_3C}{\underset{\underset{\displaystyle H_3C}{|}}{C}}-\overset{\displaystyle O}{\overset{\|}{C}}-OH$$

2,2-Dimethylpentanoic acid

$$CH_3CH_2\overset{\displaystyle CH_3}{\underset{\underset{\displaystyle CH_3}{|}}{CH}}\overset{\displaystyle O}{\overset{\|}{CH}C}-OH$$

2,3-Dimethylpentanoic acid

$$CH_3\overset{\displaystyle CH_3}{\underset{\underset{\displaystyle CH_3}{|}}{CH}}CH_2\overset{\displaystyle O}{\overset{\|}{CH}C}-OH$$

2,4-Dimethylpentanoic acid

$$CH_3CH_2\overset{\displaystyle CH_3}{\underset{\underset{\displaystyle CH_3}{|}}{C}}CH_2\overset{\displaystyle O}{\overset{\|}{C}}-OH$$

3,3-Dimethylpentanoic acid

$$CH_3\overset{\displaystyle CH_3}{\underset{\underset{\displaystyle CH_3}{|}}{CH}}CHCH_2\overset{\displaystyle O}{\overset{\|}{C}}-OH$$

3,4-Dimethylpentanoic acid

$$CH_3\overset{\displaystyle CH_3}{\underset{\underset{\displaystyle CH_3}{|}}{C}}CH_2CH_2\overset{\displaystyle O}{\overset{\|}{C}}-OH$$

4,4-Dimethylpentanoic acid

$$CH_3CH_2CH_2\overset{\displaystyle O}{\underset{\underset{\displaystyle CH_2CH_3}{|}}{\overset{\|}{CH}C}}-OH$$

2-Ethylpentanoic acid

$$CH_3CH_2\overset{\displaystyle O}{\underset{\underset{\displaystyle CH_2CH_3}{|}}{\overset{\|}{CH}CH_2C}}-OH$$

3-Ethylpentanoic acid

$$CH_3\overset{\displaystyle H_3C}{\underset{\underset{\displaystyle CH_3}{|}}{CH}}\overset{\displaystyle CH_3}{\underset{|}{C}}-\overset{\displaystyle O}{\overset{\|}{C}}-OH$$

2,2,3-Trimethylbutanoic acid

$$CH_3\overset{\displaystyle CH_3}{\underset{\underset{\displaystyle H_3C}{|}}{C}}-\overset{\displaystyle CH_3}{\underset{\underset{\displaystyle CH_3}{|}}{CH}C}-OH$$

2,3,3-Trimethylbutanoic acid

$$CH_3CH_2\overset{\displaystyle H_3C}{\underset{\underset{\displaystyle CH_2CH_3}{|}}{C}}-\overset{\displaystyle O}{\overset{\|}{C}}-OH$$

2-Ethyl-2-methylbutanoic acid

$$CH_3\overset{\displaystyle CH_3}{\underset{\underset{\displaystyle CH_2CH_3}{|}}{CH}CH}-\overset{\displaystyle O}{\overset{\|}{C}}-OH$$

2-Ethyl-3-methylbutanoic acid

17.42

(a)

$$CH_3CH_2CH_2CH_2CH_2\overset{\overset{\displaystyle O}{\|}}{C}OH$$

Hexanoic acid

(b)

$$CH_3CH_2CH_2\underset{\underset{\displaystyle COOH}{|}}{C}HCH_3$$

2-Methylpentanoic acid

(c)

$$CH_3CH_2\underset{\underset{\displaystyle |}{|}}{\overset{\overset{\displaystyle COOH}{|}}{C}}HCH_2CH_3$$

2-Ethylbutanoic acid

(d)

$$\triangleright\!\!-CH_2CH_2\overset{\overset{\displaystyle O}{\|}}{C}OH$$

3-Cyclopropylpropanoic acid

17.43

(a)

$$BrCH_2CH_2\underset{\underset{\displaystyle CH_3}{|}}{C}H\overset{\overset{\displaystyle O}{\|}}{C}OH$$

4-Bromo-2-methylbutanoic acid

(b)

—COOH with CH$_3$

o-Methylbenzoic acid

(c)

$$(CH_3CH_2)_3CCOOH$$

2,2-Diethylbutanoic acid

(d)

$$CH_3(CH_2)_5COOH$$

Heptanoic acid

17.44

(a)

$$CH_3CH_2\underset{\underset{\displaystyle CH_2CH_3}{|}}{C}HCH_2\overset{\overset{\displaystyle O}{\|}}{C}O^-\,K^+$$

Potassium 3-ethylpentanoate

(b)

$$\text{—}\overset{\overset{\displaystyle O}{\|}}{C}O^-\,NH_4^+$$

Ammonium benzoate

(c)

$$\left[CH_3CH_2\overset{\overset{\displaystyle O}{\|}}{C}O^-\right]_2 Ca^{2+}$$

Calcium propanoate

17.45

(a)

$$CH_3\overset{\overset{\displaystyle O}{\|}}{C}O^-\,NH_4^+$$

(b)

$$HO\overset{\overset{\displaystyle O}{\|}}{C}\underset{\underset{\displaystyle CH_2CH_3}{|}}{C}H(CH_2)_2\overset{\overset{\displaystyle O}{\|}}{C}O^-\,Na^+$$

(c)

$$O\!=\!\!\overset{O^-}{\underset{O^-}{C\text{—}C}}\!=\!O \quad Ca^{2+}$$

Systematic name:

Ammonium ethanoate   Monosodium 4-ethylpentanedioate   Calcium ethanedioate

Common name:

Ammonium acetate   Monosodium 4-ethylglutarate   Calcium oxalate

17.46

(a)

CH₃CHCHCH₂COH with CH₃ and CH₃ groups

3,4-Dimethylpentanoic acid

(b)

Triphenylacetic acid

(c)

CH₃CH₂ ... COH

m-Ethylbenzoic acid

(d)

CH₃CH₂CH₂CO⁻ ⁺NH₃CH₃

Methylammonium butanoate

17.47

(a)

CH₃CH₂C—COH with Cl and Cl

2,2-Dichlorobutanoic acid

(b)

CH₃CH₂CH₂CHCH₂COH with OH

3-Hydroxyhexanoic acid

(c)

CHCCH₂COH with CH₃ and H₃C CH₃

3,3-Dimethyl-4-phenyl-pentanoic acid

17.48

HOCCH₂CH—COH with OH   Malic acid

17.49

Fumaric acid

17.50

Na⁺ ⁻OCCH₂CH—CO⁻ Na⁺ with OH   Disodium malate

17.51

[CH₃CO⁻]₃ Al³⁺   Aluminum acetate

Esters and Amides

17.52 There are many answers to this question. Here are some possibilities:

(a)

CH₃CH₂CH₂CH₂CNH₂
Pentanamide

CH₃CH₂CNHCH₂CH₃
N-Ethylpropanamide

HCNCH₂CH₃
CH₂CH₃
N,N-Diethylformamide

(b)

CH₃CH₂CH₂CH₂COCH₃
Methyl pentanoate

CH₃CH₂COCH₂CH₂CH₃
Propyl propanoate

HCOCH₂CH₂CH₂CH₂CH₃
Pentyl formate

17.53 There are many possible answers.

(a)

CH₃ O
CH₃CHCHCNH₂
CH₃
2,3-Dimethylbutanamide

CH₃CHCNHCH₂CH₃
CH₃
N-Ethyl-2-methylpropanamide

CH₃CNCH₂CH₃
CH₂CH₃
N,N-Diethylacetamide

(b)

CH₃COCH₂CH₂CH₃
Propyl acetate

CH₃COCHCH₃
CH₃
Isopropyl acetate

CH₃CHCOCH₃
CH₃
Methyl 2-methylpropanoate

17.54

(a)

CH₃COCH₂CH₂CHCH₃
CH₃
3-Methylbutyl acetate

(b)

CH₃CHCH₂CH₂COCH₃
CH₃
Methyl 4-methylpentanoate

(c)

CH₃CO⎯⟨cyclohexyl⟩
Cyclohexyl acetate

(d)

Phenyl *o*-hydroxybenzoate

17.55

(a)

CH₃CH₂CH₂CH₂COCH₃

Methyl pentanoate

(b)

CH₃CH₂CHCOCHCH₃
  | |
  CH₃   CH₃

Isopropyl 2-methylbutanoate

(c)

(CH₃)₃CCOCH₂CH₃

Ethyl 2,2-dimethylpropanoate

(d)

—COCH₂CH₃

Ethyl benzoate

(e)

CH₃CH₂CO—⬠

Cyclopentyl propanoate

17.56

(a)

CH₃C(OH + H)O—CH₂CH₂CHCH₃ ⇌ (acid catalyst) CH₃C—OCH₂CH₂CHCH₃ + H₂O

3-Methylbutyl acetate

(b)

CH₃CHCH₂CH₂C(OH + H)O—CH₃ ⇌ (acid catalyst) CH₃CHCH₂CH₂C—OCH₃ + H₂O

Methyl 4-methylpentanoate

(c)

CH₃C(OH + H)O—⬡ ⇌ (acid catalyst) CH₃C—O—⬡ + H₂O

Cyclohexyl acetate

(d)

C(OH + H)O— ⇌ (acid catalyst) C—O— + H₂O

Phenyl *o*-hydroxybenzoate + H₂O

17.57

(a)

CH$_3$CH$_2$CH$_2$CH$_2$C—(OH + H)—OCH$_3$ $\underset{\text{catalyst}}{\overset{\text{acid}}{\rightleftharpoons}}$ CH$_3$CH$_2$CH$_2$CH$_2$C—OCH$_3$ + H$_2$O

Methyl pentanoate

(b)

CH$_3$CH$_2$CHC—(OH + H)—OCHCH$_3$ $\underset{\text{catalyst}}{\overset{\text{acid}}{\rightleftharpoons}}$ CH$_3$CH$_2$CHC—OCHCH$_3$ + H$_2$O

Isopropyl 2-methylbutanoate

(c)

(CH$_3$)$_3$CC—(OH + H)—OCH$_2$CH$_3$ $\underset{\text{catalyst}}{\overset{\text{acid}}{\rightleftharpoons}}$ (CH$_3$)$_3$CC—OCH$_2$CH$_3$ + H$_2$O

Ethyl 2,2-dimethylpropanoate

(d)

C—(OH + H)—OCH$_2$CH$_3$ $\underset{\text{catalyst}}{\overset{\text{acid}}{\rightleftharpoons}}$ C—OCH$_2$CH$_3$ + H$_2$O

Ethyl benzoate

(e)

CH$_3$CH$_2$C—(OH + H)—O— $\underset{\text{catalyst}}{\overset{\text{acid}}{\rightleftharpoons}}$ CH$_3$CH$_2$C—O— + H$_2$O

Cyclopentyl propanoate

17.58

(a)

CH$_3$CH$_2$CHCNH$_2$
  |
  CH$_2$CH$_3$

2-Ethylbutanamide

(b)

C—NH

N-Phenylbenzamide

(c)

C—NCH$_2$CH$_3$
    |
    CH$_3$

N-Ethyl-N-methylbenzamide

(d)

     Br O
     | ||
CH$_3$CH$_2$CH$_2$CHCHCNH$_2$
          |
          Br

2,3-Dibromohexanamide

17.59

(a)

3-Methylpentanamide

(b)

N-Phenylacetamide

(c)

HCN(CH₃)₂

N,N-Dimethylformamide

(d)

N-Isopropylpropanamide

17.60

(a)

2-Ethylbutanamide

(b)

N-Phenylbenzamide + H₂O

(c)

N-Ethyl-N-methylbenzamide

(d)

2,3-Dibromohexanamide

17.61

(a)

3-Methylpentanamide → 3-Methylpentanoic acid Ammonia

(b)

N-Phenylacetamide   Acetic acid   Aniline

(c)

N,N-Dimethylformamide   Formic acid   Dimethylamine

(d)

N-Isopropylpropanamide   Propanoic acid   Isopropylamine

Reactions of Carboxylic Acids and their Derivatives

17.62

acid catalyst

aromatic ring

Procaine

amine   ester   amine

17.63

Lidocaine

aromatic ring

amide   amine

17.64

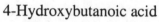

Butyrolactone   4-Hydroxybutanoic acid

17.65

Caprolactam

17.66

ester

amine   aromatic ring

ester   Cocaine

17.67

Polyesters and Polyamides

17.68

17.69

Phosphate Esters and Anhydrides

17.70

The products of hydrolysis are dihydroxyacetone and hydrogen phosphate anion.

17.71

anhydride   ester
bond   bond

17.72

Acetyl phosphate

17.73

Ethanol   Acetyl phosphate   Ethyl phosphate   Acetic acid

17.74

A cyclic phosphate diester

A cyclic phosphate diester is formed when one phosphate forms ester bonds with two hydroxyl groups in the same molecule.

17.75

a phosphate diester

A phosphate diester is formed when one phosphate group reacts with two alcohol hydroxyl groups.

Pyrophosphoric acid   a diphosphate

A diphosphate is formed when a phosphoric acid anhydride (pyrophosphate) reacts with an alcohol.

Applications

17.76

O
‖
CCl₃COH   Trichloroacetic acid   CH₃CHCOH   Lactic acid
|
OH

Trichloroacetic acid is a strong acid used for chemical peeling of the skin, and for removing scars and wrinkles. Lactic acid is a weaker acid used for wrinkle removal and skin moisturizing.

17.77 Malic acid is an α-hydroxy acid. The electron-withdrawing –OH group makes malic acid a stronger acid than succinic acid.

17.78

Trisodium citrate   Citric acid

17.79 Sodium benzoate prevents the growth of microorganisms in acidic food. Potassium sorbate inhibits the growth of mold and fungus.

17.80 Kevlar is a polyamide formed from *p*-benzenedicarboxylic acid and *p*-diaminobenzene. Because it is an amide, it can be hydrolyzed by strong acids and bases.

General Questions and Problems

17.81

O   O   O
‖   ‖   ‖
HC—N(CH₃)₂   CH₃C—NHCH₃   CH₃CH₂C—NH₂

N,N-Dimethylformamide   *N*-Methylacetamide   Propanamide
        A   **B**   **C**

A is the lowest boiling isomer. Since no hydrogens are bonded to nitrogen, no hydrogen bonding between molecules of **A** can take place. Hydrogen bonding can occur between molecules of **B**, and thus **B** is higher boiling than **A**. **C** is the highest boiling isomer.

17.82

Salol (Phenyl salicylate)

17.83

$$CH_3CH_2\overset{O}{\overset{\|}{C}}NH_2 \qquad\qquad CH_3\overset{O}{\overset{\|}{C}}OCH_3$$

Propanamide   Methyl acetate

Propanamide and methyl acetate are both soluble in water because both are polar molecules and can hydrogen bond with water. Propanamide is higher boiling because molecules of propanamide can hydrogen-bond with each other.

17.84 (1) Measure the pH of solutions of the two compounds. Benzoic acid is acidic; benzaldehyde is non-acidic.

(2) Benzaldehyde reacts with Tollens' reagent to form a silver mirror; benzoic acid doesn't react with Tollens' reagent.

17.85

17.86

(a)

$$\underset{\underset{\displaystyle CH_3}{|}}{CH_3CH_2C}=\underset{\underset{}{}}{CCHCH_3}$$
with H₃C and Cl above

2-Chloro-3,4-dimethyl-3-hexene

(b)

$$CH_3CH_2\overset{O}{\overset{\|}{C}}NCH_3$$

N-Methyl-*N*-phenylpropanamide

(c)   (d)

Phenyl 2,2-diethylbutanoate   *N*-Ethyl-*o*-nitrobenzamide

Self-Test for Chapter 17

Multiple choice:

1. Which of the following amides does not form hydrogen bonds?
   (a) Benzamide   (b) Formamide   (c) *N*-Methylformamide   (d) *N,N*-Dimethylformamide

2. Which of the following statements about phosphoric acid anhydrides is untrue?
   (a) Energy is released when triphosphate anhydrides react with water.
   (b) Both mono- and dianhydrides occur in the body.
   (c) Hydrolysis of phosphate ester anhydrides yields caustic products.
   (d) Two molecules of water are necessary to completely hydrolyze a triphosphate anhydride.

3. Which class of compounds is lowest boiling?
   (a) carboxylic acid esters   (b) amides   (c) carboxylic acids   (d) carboxylic acid salts

4. The common name of an -enoic acid is:
   (a) succinic acid   (b) benzoic acid   (c) oxalic acid   (d) acrylic acid

5. Amide bonds occur in all of the following except:
   (a) Nylon   (b) Dacron   (c) urea   (d) proteins

6. In the reaction $CH_3COOH + CH_3OH \rightleftharpoons CH_3COOCH_3 + H_2O$, the yield of CH_3COOCH_3 can be improved by :
   (a) distilling off the CH_3COOCH_3 (b) removing the water   (c) using more CH_3COOH and CH_3OH (d) all of the above

7. Reaction of methanol with oxalic acid in the presence of an acid catalyst forms:
   (a) methyl oxalate   (b) dimethyl oxalate   (c) methyl acetate   (d) reaction doesn't occur

8. Polypropylene and Nylon resemble each other in which respect?
   (a) They are both polymers.   (b) They are both hydrocarbons.   (c) Concentrated acid will dissolve them.   (d) An initiator is needed for polymerization to occur.

9. Which of the following compounds is an α-amino acid?
   (a)   (b)   (c)   (d)

$$H_2NCH_2CH_2COH \qquad H_2NCCH_2CH_3 \qquad H_2NCH_2COCH_3 \qquad H_2NCH_2COH$$

10. How many amides of the formula C_3H_7NO can be drawn?
    (a) 3   (b) 4   (c) 5   (d) 6

Complete the following sentences:

1. The most common general reaction of carboxylic acids, esters, and amides is called a _____ _____ reaction.

2. Kevlar is a type of _____.

3. A carboxylic acid can be dissolved in water by converting it into its _____ ____.

4. The reaction of a carboxylic acid with an alcohol in the presence of an acid catalyst is called an _____ reaction.

5. In carboxylic acids, esters, and amides, the carbonyl-group carbon is bonded to an atom that strongly _____ electrons.

6. Carboxylic acids are named by using the family-name ending ___ ____.

7. $CH_3CH_2COOCH_2CH_2CH_3$ is named _____ _____.

8. Many flavors and fragrances are due to _____.

9. _____ is the transfer of a —PO_3^{2-} group from one molecule to another.

10. Long-chain carboxylic acids can be found in nature as components of _____.

11. The reaction of an ester with aqueous NaOH to yield a salt and an alcohol is called a _____ reaction.

12. Malonic acid is also known as _____ acid.

Tell whether the following statements are true or false:

1. A carboxylic acid salt is more soluble in water than a carboxylic acid.

2. A *saponification* reaction is the acid-catalyzed hydrolysis of an ester.

3. Amides and amines are both basic.

4. A carboxylic acid is higher boiling than an ester of the same molecular weight.

5. Basic hydrolysis of ethyl acetate yields acetic acid and ethanol.

6. The compound $HCON(CH_3)_2$ is named dimethylformamide.

7. Nitrate esters are important in living systems.

8. Acetic acid is about 1% dissociated in a 1 M aqueous solution.

9. Carboxylic acids are either solids or liquids at room temperature.

10. Esterification can be brought about by treating a carboxylic acid with an alcohol in the presence of NaOH.

11. Pyrophosphoric acid is a phosphate ester.

12. Propanamide is higher boiling than methyl acetate.

Match the entries on the left with their partners on the right:

1. $CH_3COOH + CH_3OH + HCl$ (a) Amide hydrolysis

2. $HOOCCH_2COOH$ (b) Ester hydrolysis

3. $(CH_3COO^-)_2Mg^{2+}$ (c) Thioester

4. $CH_3COOCH_3 + NaOH, H_2O$ (d) -enoic acid

5. $HCOOH$ (e) Phosphate ester

6. $CH_3CH=CHCOOH$ (f) Dioic acid

7. $CH_3CONH_2 + NaOH, H_2O$ (g) Amide

8. CH_3OPO_3H (h) Polyester

9. Nylon   (i) Formic acid

10. Dacron   (j) Ester formation

11. Acetyl-SCoA   (k) Acid salt

12. Benzocaine   (l) Polyamide

Chapter 18 – Amino Acids and Proteins

Chapter Outline

I. Introduction to biochemistry and proteins (Sections 18.1–18.2).
  A. Biochemistry (Section 18.1).
    1. Biochemistry is the study of the structure and function of biomolecules.
    2. The principal classes of biomolecules are proteins, carbohydrates, lipids and nucleic acids.
    3. Biomolecules range in size from small organic molecules to polymers with millions of subunits.
    4. The three-dimensional shape of biomolecules is critical to their ability to function.
  B. Proteins (Section 18.2).
    1. Proteins are polymers of amino acids.
    2. The bonds that form between amino acids are amide bonds (peptide bonds).
      a. Two amino acids bond together to form a dipeptide.
      b. Three amino acids bond together to form a tripeptide.
      c. A chain with 10–100 amino acids is a polypeptide.
      d. The atoms that form a peptide bond have a planar relationship.
    3. There are four levels of protein structure.
      a. Primary structure refers to the sequence of amino acids that form peptide bonds.
      b. Secondary structure refers to the organization of polypeptide chains into a regular pattern.
      c. Tertiary structure refers to the overall shape of the protein molecule.
      d. Quaternary structure refers to the organization of proteins composed of several polypeptide chains.
    4. Proteins have numerous functions in living things.
       Among these functions are structure, support, storage, transport, and control of biochemical reactions.
II. Amino acids (Sections 18.3–18.6).
  A. Structure of amino acids (Section 18.3).
    1. Twenty amino acids commonly occur in nature.
      a. All twenty are α-amino acids.
      b. Nineteen of the twenty amino acids are primary amines.
    2. Each amino acid is represented by a three-letter code.
    3. Amino acids are classified as neutral, acidic or basic.
       Of the common amino acids, fifteen are neutral, three are basic, and two are acidic.
    4. Amino acid side chains are classified as hydrophilic (polar) or hydrophobic (nonpolar).
      a. Hydrophobic side chains cluster in the middle of a protein.
      b. Hydrophilic side chains are positioned on the surface of the protein.
  B. Acid-base properties of amino acids (Section 18.4).
    1. Amino acids exist as dipolar zwitterions.
      a. Amino acids have properties similar to salts: they are high-melting and soluble in water.
      b. Amino acids can react as acids or bases.
    2. The pH at which the number of positive charges on an amino acid equals the number of negative charges is called the isoelectric point (pI).
      a. Neutral amino acids have pIs in the range 5.0–6.5.
      b. Acidic amino acids are negatively charged at physiological pH.

   C. Chirality and amino acids (Sections 18.5–18.6).
      1. Chirality (Section 18.5).
         a. Chirality is the property of handedness.
         b. An object that lacks a plane of symmetry is chiral.
      2. Molecular handedness (Section 18.6).
         a. A carbon that is bonded to four different atoms or groups of atoms is a chiral carbon atom.
         b. The two mirror-image forms of a chiral molecule are enantiomers, or optical isomers.
            i. Optical isomers are one kind of stereoisomer.
            ii. Optical isomers are identical in all properties except for their effect on polarized light.
         c. All amino acids except for glycine are chiral.
         d. Only one of a pair of enantiomeric amino acids occurs naturally.
III. Proteins (Sections 18.7–18.12).
   A. Primary protein structure (Sections 18.7–18.8).
      1. The repeating chain of peptide bonds and α-carbons is known as the protein backbone (Section 18.7).
         a. The atoms that form the peptide bond lie in a plane.
         b. The amino-terminal end of the peptide is written on the left, and the carboxy-terminal end is on the right.
         c. A peptide is named by citing the residues in order, from left to right.
      2. Protein function is dependent on the exact sequence of amino acids in protein primary structure.
      3. Primary structure is responsible for the shape of a protein molecule.
         In sickle-cell anemia, a change in only one amino acid is responsible for the disease.
      4. Several types of interactions determine protein shape (Section 18.8).
         a. Noncovalent interactions.
            i. Hydrogen bonds can occur between atoms on the protein backbone
            ii. Hydrogen bonds can occur between side-chains of amino acids or between side-chain amino acids and the polypeptide backbone.
            iii. Ionic interactions can occur between ionized acidic and basic amino acids; these are called salt bridges.
            iv. Hydrophobic interactions occur between nonpolar side chains.
         b. Covalent interactions. The thiol groups of cysteine residues form disulfide bonds.
   B. Secondary protein structure (Section 18.9).
      1. Secondary structure refers to the ordered relationships of backbone atoms resulting from hydrogen bonding.
      2. There are two types of secondary structures.
         a. The α-helix is a right-handed coil formed by hydrogen bonds between an N–H group and a carbonyl group four amino acids away.
         b. The β–sheet occurs when polypeptide chains line up next to each other, and hydrogen bonds form between adjacent chains.
      3. Fibrous and globular proteins show examples of secondary structure.
         a. Some fibrous proteins are composed almost entirely of α–helices.
         b. Globular proteins have smaller regions of α-helix and β–sheet secondary structure.
      4. The parts of the polypeptide chain not involved in a secondary structural element are called random coil segments.
   C. Tertiary protein structure (Section 18.10).
      1. Tertiary structure.
         a. Tertiary structure describes the overall shape of proteins.
         b. The interactions responsible for tertiary structure may be between amino acids many units apart.

c. Interactions described in Section 18.7 give each protein its unique three-dimensional shape.
2. Examples.
  a. Ribonuclease – a globular protein.
      Hydrophobic side-chains congregate in the middle, and hydrophilic side chains are distributed on the outside.
  b. Myoglobin – a globular protein.
    i. Myoglobin has eight α-helix segments.
    ii. A heme group is embedded within the polypeptide chain.
D. Quaternary structure (Section 18.11).
  1. Quaternary structure describes the noncovalent interactions between the polypeptide chains of proteins that consist of more than one chain.
  2. Examples.
    a. Collagen is formed by several tropocollagen strands overlapping lengthwise.
    b. Hemoglobin consists of four polypeptide chains held together by hydrophobic interactions.
  3. Classification of proteins.
    a. Proteins can be classified as simple or conjugated.
    b. Proteins can be classified as fibrous or globular.
F. Chemical properties of proteins (Section 18.12).
  1. Hydrolysis.
     Polypeptide amide bonds can be cleaved by acid or enzymes to yield amino acids.
  2. Denaturation.
    a. Denaturation disturbs a protein's shape without disrupting primary structure.
    b. Denaturation changes the properties of proteins.
    c. Denaturation can be caused by various agents.
      i. Heat disturbs side-chain interactions.
      ii. Mechanical agitation.
      iii Detergents disrupt the interactions of hydrophobic side chains.
      iv. Organic compounds disrupt hydrogen bondss.
      v. pH changes disrupt salt bridges.
      vi. Inorganic salts disrupt salt bridges.
  3. Occasionally, denatured proteins can undergo renaturation.

Solutions to Chapter 18 Problems

18.1 Amino acids containing an aromatic ring: phenylalanine, tyrosine, tryptophan

Phenylalanine   Tyrosine   Tryptophan

Amino acids containing sulfur: cysteine, methionine

Cysteine   Methionine

Amino acids that are alcohols: serine, threonine, tyrosine (a phenol)

Serine   Threonine   Tyrosine

Amino acids with alkyl group side chains: alanine, valine, leucine, isoleucine

Alanine   Valine   Leucine   Isoleucine

18.2

Alanine

18.3 Two dipeptides of alanine (nonpolar) and serine (polar) can be drawn.

Serine   Alanine   Alanine   Serine

18.4

(a)

α-amino acid
(Threonine)

(b)

not an α-amino acid
(amide)

(c)

not an α-amino acid
(amino alcohol)

(d)

α-amino acid
(Leucine)

18.5

		Side Chain Functional Groups:	Hydrogen Bonding?
(a)	Phe, Thr		no
(b)	Asn, Ser		yes
(c)	Thr, Tyr		yes
(d)	Gly, Trp		no

Amino acids that have amine, amide, alcohol or phenol groups are capable of hydrogen bonding to other amino acids having these groups. Only in (b) and (c) do both amino acids have groups that can participate in hydrogen bonding.

18.6

amino group / "R" group / carboxylic acid group

Valine

18.7

Glutamic acid

at low pH   at high pH

At low pH, both of the carboxylic acid groups and the amino group are protonated. At high pH, the carboxylic acid groups exist as carboxylate anions and the amino group is not protonated.

18.8 In the zwitterionic form of an amino acid, the $-NH_3^+$ group is an acid (because it can donate H^+), and the $-COO^-$ group is a base (because it can accept H^+).

18.9 Chiral: (a) chair   (b) jar   (d) scissors   (e) glove   (g) wood screw

18.10 Handed: wrench, beanstalk, bottle cap
Not handed: thumb tack, pencil, eraser

18.11

2-Aminopropane   2-Aminobutane

2-Aminopropane is achiral because no carbon has four different groups bonded to it. 2-Butanol is chiral because four different groups are bonded to carbon 2 (–H, –CH$_3$, –NH$_2$ and –CH$_2$CH$_3$).

18.12

(a)

(a) CH₃CH₂CCH₂CH₃ with Cl above and H below — **achiral**

(b) CH₃CH₂CH₂CCH₃ with Cl above (starred) and H below — **chiral**

(c) CH₃CHCH₂CCH₂CH₃ with CH₃ CH₃ (starred) above and H below — **chiral**

The starred carbon atoms in (b) and (c) each have four different groups bonded to them.

18.13 Threonine and isoleucine each have two chiral carbon atoms (starred in the following structures).

Threonine   Isoleucine

18.14

The starred carbon in the second isomer is chiral because four different groups (–H, –Cl, –Br, –CH₃) are bonded to it.

18.15 (a) Gly–Ser–Tyr   Tyr–Ser–Gly   Ser–Tyr–Gly
Gly–Tyr–Ser   Tyr–Gly–Ser   Ser–Gly–Tyr

(b)

Gly–Ser–Tyr   Gly–Tyr–Ser

18.16 Val–His–Ala   His–Ala–Val   Ala–His–Val
Val–Ala–His   His–Val–Ala   Ala–Val–His

18.17

(a)

Leu–Asp

Leucine (Leu)   Aspartate (Asp)

(b)

Tyr–Ser–Lys

Serine (Ser)   Lysine (Lys)

Tyrosine (Tyr)

18.18

Tyr–Ser–Lys

18.19 Chymotrypsin breaks peptide bonds on the carboxylate side of aromatic amino acids. Table 18.3 shows that Phe, Tyr and Trp are the three aromatic acids that are found in proteins. Vasopressin contains Phe and Tyr, and three fragments result from treatment of vasopressin with chymotrypsin.

Asp–Tyr⊱Phe⊱Glu–Asn–Cys–Pro–Lys–Gly

↓ Chymotrypsin

Asp–Tyr + Phe + Glu–Asn–Cys–Pro–Lys–Gly

18.20 (a) Glutamine and tyrosine interact through *hydrogen bonds* between the terminal –NH$_2$ group of glutamine and the –OH of tyrosine.

(b) Leucine and proline are pulled together through *hydrophobic interactions* between the alkyl side chain of leucine and the ring portion of proline.

(c) A *salt bridge* occurs between the negatively charged aspartate carboxyl group and the positively charged terminal group of arginine.

(d) The alkyl side chain of isoleucine and the aromatic ring of phenylalanine are held together by *hydrophobic interactions*.

18.21 (a) Hydrogen bonds from side chains: tyrosine, asparagine, serine.

(b) Hydrophobic group interactions: alanine, isoleucine, valine, leucine.

18.22 In an α-helix, a carbonyl oxygen forms a hydrogen bond with an amide hydrogen twelve atoms away. Thus, 11 backbone atoms lie between the atoms that take part in an α-helix hydrogen bond.

18.23 The secondary structure of proteins is stabilized by hydrogen bonds between amide nitrogens and carbonyl oxygens of the polypeptide backbone. Tertiary structure is stabilized by hydrogen bonds between groups on the side chains of amino acids.

18.24 (a) This statement describes tertiary structure, which is stabilized by hydrogen bonds, hydrophobic interactions, salt bridges and disulfide bonds between side chains on the same polypeptide chain.

(b) This statement describes secondary structure (α-helix), which is stabilized by hydrogen bonds between amide hydrogen atoms and carbonyl oxygen atoms on the polypeptide backbone.

(c) This statement describes quaternary structure, which is stabilized by hydrophobic interactions, hydrogen bonds and salt bridges.

Understanding Key Concepts

18.25 Peptides that contain neither acidic nor basic amino acids have a net charge of +1 at pH = 1 because both the *N*–terminal amino group and the *C*–terminal carboxylic acid group are protonated. At pH = 11, these peptides have a net charge of –1, because the *N*–terminal group is uncharged and the *C*–terminal group is a carboxylate anion. At pH = 7, these peptides have a net charge of zero.

(a) Val–Gly–Leu

(b) Arg–Lys–His

(c) Tyr–Pro–Ser

at pH = 1

at pH = 11

(d) Glu–Asp–Phe

at pH = 1

at pH = 11

(e) Gln–Ala–Asn

(f) Met–Trp–Cys

18.26 In order for two amino acids to interact, they must both be of the same type (both polar or both nonpolar, for example).
(a) The pairs Pro...Leu and Ile...Val show hydrophobic interactions because they are both nonpolar. The pair Tyr ...Phe also shows hydrophobic interactions.
(b) Arg...Asp and His...Glu show ionic interactions because they are both charged.
(c) Thr...Glu form hydrogen bonds.

18.27

Asp–Gly–Phe–Leu–Glu–Ala

Hydrogen bonds in an α-helix are indicated by dashed lines.

18.28

Phe–Glu–Phe
    Glu–Phe
    Glu–Phe–Asp
            Asp–His–Tyr
               His–Tyr
                  Tyr–Glu–His

The complete peptide:
Phe–Glu–Phe–Asp–His–Tyr–Glu–His

18.29

	Fibrous protein	*Globular protein*
Biological function:	Structural proteins	Enzymes, hormones, transport
Water solubility:	Water-insoluble	Usually water-soluble
Amino acid composition:	Contains many Gly and Pro residues	Varies; hydrophilic groups on the outside account for solubility
Secondary structure:	Large regions of α-helix or β-sheet	Smaller regions of α-helix or β-sheet
Tertiary Structure:	Few interactions between side chains on the same backbone	Complex: determined by hydro-phobic and hydrophilic groups on side chains, as well as by disulfide bonds.
Examples:	Collagen (connective tissue) α-Keratin (hair) Fibroin (silk)	Ribonuclease (enzyme) Hemoglobin (oxygen transport) Insulin (hormone)

Amino Acids

18.30 When referring to an amino acid, the prefix "α" means that the amino group is bonded to the carbon next to the –COOH carbon. In other words, the –NH₂ and –COOH groups are bonded to the same carbon.

18.31 The prefix "L" refers to the handedness of the carbon to which the –COOH and –NH₂ groups are bonded. Most naturally-occurring amino acids are L-amino acids.

18.32

(a)

Serine (Ser)

(b)

Threonine (Thr)

(c)

Proline (Pro)

18.33

(a)

Phenylalanine (Phe)

(b)

Lysine (Lys)

(c)

Glutamine (Gln)

18.34

(a)

Valine (Val)

(b)

Threonine (Thr)

18.35

(a)

Cysteine (Cys)

(b)

Tyrosine (Tyr)

18.36 At a neutral pH (pH = 5 – 8), an amino acid with a pI less than 5 is negatively charged, and an amino acid with a pI greater than 8 is positively charged. Otherwise, an amino acid has no net charge at neutral pH and is neutral.

(a) Lysine (pI = 9.7) is positively charged. (b) (c) Phenylalanine (pI = 5.5) and leucine (pI = 6.0) are neutral.

18.37 (a) Glutamic acid (pI = 3.2) is negatively charged. (b) (c) Proline (pI = 6.3) and alanine (pI = 6.0) are neutral.

18.38

(a)

This structure represents aspartic acid at pH = 3, its isoelectric point.
(low pH)

(b)

This structure represents aspartic acid at pH = 13.
(high pH)

18.39

(a)

at pH = 7
(neutral pH)

(b)

at pH = 3
(low pH)

Handedness in Molecules

18.40 A chiral object is one that has handedness. Examples include a glove and a car.

18.41 An achiral object has no handedness and possesses a plane of symmetry such that one half of the object is an exact mirror image of the other half. Examples include a spoon and a pencil.

18.42 Chiral: (a) shoe   (c) light bulb (because of screw threads)
Achiral: (b) bed

18.43 Achiral: (a) flower pot
Chiral: (b) house key   (c) pair of scissors

18.44 2-Bromo-2-chloropropane has a symmetry plane and is achiral. 2-Bromo-2-chlorobutane and 2-bromo-2-chloro-3-methylbutane don't have a symmetry plane and are chiral because each has a carbon atom bonded to four different atoms or groups of atoms. A star indicates a chiral carbon atom.

(a)

symmetry plane

2-Bromo-2-chloropropane
achiral

(b)

2-Bromo-2-chlorobutane
chiral

(c)

2-Bromo-2-chloro-3-methylbutane
chiral

18.45 First, draw the structure and find the number of different groups bonded to each carbon. A carbon atom bonded to four different groups is chiral. A dashed line represents a symmetry plane.

(a)　　　　　　　　　　(b)　　　　　　　　　　(c)

18.46

18.47

H$_3$C — (chiral, achiral, chiral, achiral)

Peptides and Proteins

18.48 A simple protein is composed only of amino acids. A conjugated protein consists of a simple protein associated with one or more nonprotein molecules.

18.49 (a) Nucleoproteins contain nucleic acids and protein.
(b) Lipoproteins contain lipids and protein.
(c) Glycoproteins contain carbohydrates and protein.
(d) Hemoproteins contain a heme group and protein.

18.50

Type of protein	*Function*	*Example*
Enzymes:	Catalyze biochemical reactions	Ribonuclease
Hormones:	Regulate body functions	Insulin
Storage proteins:	Store essential substances	Myoglobin
Transport proteins:	Transport substances through body fluids	Serum albumin
Structural proteins:	Provide shape and support	Collagen
Protective proteins:	Defend the body against foreign matter	Immunoglobulins
Contractile proteins	Do mechanical work	Myosin and actin

18.51 (a) *Primary structure* refers to the sequence of connection of amino acids in a protein.

(b) *Secondary structure* refers to the orientation of segments of the protein chain into a regular pattern, such as an α-helix or a β-sheet, by hydrogen bonding between backbone atoms.

(c) *Tertiary structure* refers to the coiling and folding of the entire protein chain into a three-dimensional shape as a result of interactions between amino acid side chains.

(d) *Quaternary structure* refers to the aggregation of several protein chains to form a larger structure.

18.52 The disulfide bonds between two cysteine residues help to stabilize a protein's tertiary structure.

18.53 In the presence of an oxidizing agent, thiol groups of two different cysteine residues can come together to form a disulfide bond. Disulfide bonds can connect two different peptide chains or can connect two distant parts of the same chain, introducing a loop in the chain.

18.54 (a) *Hydrophobic interactions* occur between hydrocarbon side chains of amino acids. In a protein, these side chains cluster in the center of the molecule to exclude water, and are responsible for the nearly spherical tertiary shape of globular proteins. Alanine and isoleucine take part in hydrophobic interactions.

(b) *Salt bridges* occur between negatively charged and positively charged amino acid side chain groups. They can stabilize the tertiary structure of a protein by connecting two distant parts of a polypeptide chain or by pulling the protein backbone together in the middle of the chain. They can also stabilize quaternary structure by bringing together two polypeptide chains. Lysine and aspartate can form salt bridges.

18.55 (a) Side chains that can form *hydrogen bonds* are located on the outside of a protein, where they can stabilize tertiary structure by forming hydrogen bonds with water. Hydrogen bonds stabilize quaternary protein structure by holding together several protein strands. Threonine and glutamine can form hydrogen bonds.

(b) *Disulfide bonds* connect distant parts of a polypeptide chain and introduce loops into the chain. Two cysteine residues form disulfide bridges.

18.56 When a protein is denatured, its three-dimensional structure is disrupted, and its ability to catalyze reactions is impaired. Primary structure is not affected by denaturation.

18.57 (a) *Heat* denatures proteins by disrupting side-chain interactions.

(b) *Addition* of a *strong base* disrupts side chain interactions and interferes with salt bridges.

(c) *Detergents* disrupt the association of hydrophobic side chains.

18.58 Met–Ile–Lys   Ile–Met–Lys   Lys–Met–Ile

Met–Lys–Ile   Ile–Lys–Met   Lys–Ile–Met

18.59

Phe – Glu   Glu –Phe

18.60 Amino acids with polar side chains (aspartate and asparagine, for example) are likely to be found on the outside of a globular protein, where they can form hydrogen bonds with water and with each other. Amino acids with nonpolar side chains (valine and leucine, for example) are likely to be found on the inside of globular proteins, where they can escape from water.

18.61 Phenylalanine and tryptophan, nonpolar amino acids, are found on the inside of a globular protein, where they can avoid water. Glutamate and lysine (polar amino acids) are found on the outside of a globular protein, where they can hydrogen-bond with water.

18.62 If a diabetic took insulin orally, digestive enzymes would catalyze its hydrolysis, and the individual amino acids would be absorbed as food.

18.63 Aspartame, when hydrolyzed by digestive enzymes, produces phenylalanine, which is harmful to people who have PKU.

18.64

N–terminal   Tyr – Gly – Gly – Phe – Met   C–Terminal
amino acid   amino acid

18.65

N–terminal   Tyr – Gly – Gly – Phe – Leu   C–terminal
amino acid   amino acid

Properties and Reactions of Amino Acids and Proteins

18.66

(a)

(b)

an ester

18.67 Coupling of glycine molecules produces not only glycylglycine but also glycylglycylglycine and larger polymers. The most abundant product is the following cyclic dipeptide, formed when coupling takes place at both ends of two glycine molecules.

18.68

N-terminal amino acid

C-terminal amino acid

Valine   Glycine   Serine   Alanine   Aspartate

18.69

N-terminal amino acid

C-terminal amino acid

Cysteine   Lysine   Glutamate   Proline

18.70 A peptide rich in Asp and Lys residues is more soluble in water than a peptide rich in Val and Ala residues. The side chains of Asp and Lys are polar and are better solvated by water than the nonpolar, hydrophobic side chains of Val and Ala.

18.71 At its isoelectric point, a protein has the same number of positive and negative charges and is thus electrically neutral. On either side of the isoelectric point, the protein is charged and is more soluble in a polar solvent such as water.

Applications

18.72

(a)

Tyrosine   Tyramine

Decarboxylation is the removal of CO_2 from a molecule.

(b)

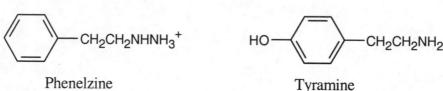

Phenelzine   Tyramine

Like tyramine, phenelzine has an amino group on a two-carbon chain that is bonded to an aromatic ring. Phenelzine resembles tyramine, and it inhibits the enzyme that removes the amino group from tyramine.

18.73 People need a daily source of protein in the diet because the human body doesn't store the protein or amino acids needed for its continuous synthesis of proteins. The body does store fats and carbohydrates.

18.74 An incomplete protein lacks one or more of the nine essential amino acids.

18.75 Food from animal sources is more likely to contain complete protein than food from plant sources because the proteins in animals contain all of the common amino acids.

18.76 Casein and egg white protein are well-balanced proteins because they must provide complete nutrition to newborn and embryonic organisms. It is thus not surprising that they are also well-balanced proteins for human growth and development.

18.77

C = collagen
BI = bovine insulin
HH = human hemoglobin

At pH=6.6, collagen (isoelectric point = 6.6) has as many positive charges as negative charges and does not migrate. Bovine insulin (pI = 5.4) is negatively charged and migrates to the positively charged electrode. Human hemoglobin (pI = 7.1) is positively charged and migrates to the negative electrode.

18.78 You need to remember these facts to answer this question.
(1) In a peptide, the acidic and basic amino acids determine the charge of the peptide.
(2) An amino acid that is acidic is negatively charged at a neutral pH, and a basic amino acid is positively charged at a neutral pH.
(3) A positively charged molecule migrates to the cathode (–), and a negatively charged molecule migrates to the anode (+).

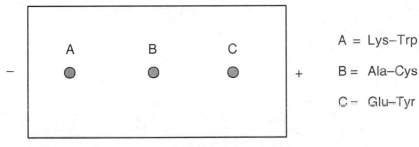

A = Lys–Trp

B = Ala–Cys

C = Glu–Tyr

18.79 A change in protein secondary structure from α-helix to β-pleated sheet alters the shape of the prion and causes groups that were close together in the normal prion to be farther apart in the altered prion. This change disrupts hydrogen bonds and salt bridges that were present in the normal protein and results in the formation of new tertiary interactions.

18.80 It was hard to believe that a protein could duplicate itself and cause disease. It was also hard to accept that a form of protein might be responsible for inherited disease, might be transmitted between individuals and might arise spontaneously.

General Questions and Problems

18.81 Pineapple that is canned has been heated to inactivate enzymes. Thus, no enzymatic hydrolysis occurs when canned pineapple is added to gelatin.

18.82 In α-keratin, pairs of α-helixes twist together into small fibrils that are twisted into larger bundles. In tropocollagen, three coiled chains wrap around each other to form a triple helix.

18.83 (a) Bradykinin:

(b) The rigid proline rings introduce kinks and bends in bradykinin and prevent hydrogen bonds from forming (because proline has no hydrogens to form hydrogen bonds).

18.84 Hydrophobic interactions: (b) methionine, (f) phenylalanine, (h) valine
Hydrogen bonding: (a) glutamate, (c) glutamine, (d) threonine, (e) histidine
Salt bridges: (a) glutamate, (e) histidine
Covalent bonding: (g) cysteine

18.85 After oxidation, the formerly chiral carbon is no longer bonded to four different groups and thus isn't chiral.

18.86 Denaturation disrupts a protein's shape without disrupting its primary structure; hydrolysis breaks bonds and thus destroys a protein's primary structure.

18.87

Oxytocin

18.88 The sulfur in methionine is a sulfide ($-SCH_3$) sulfur instead of a thiol ($-SH$) sulfur and can't form disulfide bridges.

18.89 Amino acids that can form hydrogen bonds contain the following functional groups: amine, alcohol, amide, carboxylic acid (carboxylate). These amino acids are arginine, aspartic acid, asparagine, glutamic acid, glutamine, histidine, lysine, serine, threonine, and tyrosine. Shown below is hydrogen bonding between asparagine and serine.

Hydrogen bonds between the amino acids and water:

18.90 Leucine, alanine, glycine, and valine all have nonpolar side chains and are likely to be found in the interior of proteins, where they can avoid water.

18.91 Polar, hydrophilic amino acids that can form hydrogen bonds with water are found on the outside of globular proteins. Examples: (b) Glu (e) Ser.
Nonpolar amino acids that have small side chains are found in fibrous proteins. Examples: (a) Ala (f) Val. Phe and Leu are nonpolar but are too bulky to be often found in fibrous proteins.

18.92 Glycine is found in bends because of its small size. Proline, because of its rigid structure, is often the initiator of bends.

18.93 If an aspartate residue were substituted for a glutamate residue, a health problem might not occur because both amino acids have similar physical properties and chemical behavior.

Self-Test for Chapter 18

Multiple choice:

1. Which level of protein structure doesn't involve hydrogen bonds?
    (a) primary   (b) secondary   (c) tertiary   (d) quaternary

2. Which of the following amino acids has a hydrophobic side chain?
    (a) Asparagine   (b) Threonine   (c) Histidine   (d) Phenylalanine

3. The isoelectric point of an amino acid is 7.6. Which of the following statements about it is untrue?
    (a) At pH = 7.6, the number of positive charges equals the number of negative charges.
    (b) It is a basic amino acid.
    (c) At pH = 5.5, both the carboxylic acid group and the amine group are protonated.
    (d) It forms salt bridges when it is part of a polypeptide chain.

4. Which of the following organic molecules is chiral?
    (a) 1-Pentanol   (b) 2-Pentanol   (c) 3-Pentanol   (d) 2-Methyl-2-butanol

5. How many tetrapeptides can be formed from alanine, lysine, and two valines?
    (a) 6   (b) 12   (c) 18   (d) 24

6. Which of the following is an amino acid with a nitrogen heterocyclic ring?
    (a) Histidine   (b) Threonine   (c) Tyrosine   (d) Cysteine

7. Addition of heavy metal ions to a protein disrupts which structural element?
    (a) hydrogen bonds   (b) primary structure   (c) hydrophobic interactions   (d) disulfide bonds

8. A table in which proteins are described as collagens and immunoglobulins classifies them by:
    (a) size   (b) shape   (c) function   (d) the type of non-protein associated with them

9. In a nucleoprotein, the protein is conjugated with:
    (a) carbohydrate   (b) metal ions   (c) RNA   (d) lipids

10. Substitution of one amino acid for another in a polypeptide chain disrupts;
    (a) secondary structure   (b) tertiary structure   (c) isoelectric point   (d) all or none of the above, depending on the amino acids involved

Complete the following sentences:

1. The isoelectric point of a neutral amino acid is near pH = _____.

2. Two molecules that differ only in the arrangement of groups around a chiral carbon atom are called _____.

3. Amino acids exist as dipolar ions called _____.

4. The repeating chain of amide bonds in a peptide is called the _____.

5. A disulfide bond between two cysteines in the same chain produces a _____ in the peptide.

6. A protein bonded to a carbohydrate is called a _____.

7. _____ structure refers to how the entire protein is folded and coiled into a specific three-dimensional shape.

8. In the secondary structure called a _____ _____, polypeptide chains line up in a parallel arrangement held together by hydrogen bonds.

9. The tripeptide Ser-Gln-Lys contains side chains that are _____.

10. The amino acids methionine and cysteine are the only two that contain the element _____.

11. A chain with fewer than 50 amino acids is called a _____.

12. _____ interactions pull nonpolar side chains together to exclude water.

Tell whether the following statements are true or false:

1. All amino acids have at least one chiral carbon atom.

2. Tyrosine and valine can react to form a dipeptide.

3. Protein denaturation disrupts the primary structure of a protein.

4. Lysylalanine is identical to alanyllysine.

5. Some amino acids have an isoelectric point near 10.

6. Simple proteins are more common than conjugated proteins.

7. β–Sheets and α-helices occur mostly in fibrous proteins.

8. Amino acids are quite water-soluble.

9. Proteins, as well as amino acids, have isoelectric points.

10. Both fibrous and globular proteins are water-soluble.

11. Proteins may be classified by biological function.

12. 2-Butanol has a chiral carbon atom.

Match the entries on the left with their partners on the right:

1. Isoleucine

2. Insulin

3. Glycylglycine

4. Glycine

5. β–Sheet

6. Aspartic acid

7. Collagen

8. Cysteine

9. Albumin

10. Arginine

11. Proline

12. Tryptophan

(a) Achiral amino acid

(b) Secondary structure

(c) Fibrous protein

(d) Amino acid that is a secondary amine

(e) Amino acid with hydrocarbon side-chain

(f) Globular protein

(g) Peptide hormone

(h) Basic amino acid

(i) Aromatic amino acid

(j) Dipeptide

(k) Acidic amino acid

(l) Can form disulfide bridges

Chapter 19 – Enzymes and Vitamins

Chapter Outline

I. Introduction to enzymes (Sections 19.1–19.3).
  A. Catalysis by enzymes (Section 19.1).
    1. Enzymes are globular proteins that catalyze biochemical reactions.
      a. The active site is the region of the enzyme where catalysis takes place.
      b. The reactant in an enzyme-catalyzed reaction is called the substrate.
      c. Some enzymes are specific for one particular substrate, whereas others catalyze reactions involving a number of substrates.
      d. Most enzymes are specific with respect to stereochemistry.
    2. Enzymes affect only the rate of reaction and not the position of equilibrium.
    3. The catalytic efficiency of an enzyme is measured by its turnover number.
  B. Enzyme cofactors (Section 19.2).
    1. Many enzymes include protein portions and nonprotein portions that are called cofactors.
    2. The cofactors, called coenzymes, are either metal ions or small organic molecules.
    3. Enzymes can obtain from cofactors chemically reactive groups not available as side chains.
    4. Some cofactors are covalently bonded; others serve as cosubstrates.
  C. Enzyme classification (Section 19.3).
    1. Classes of enzymes.
      a. Oxidoreductases catalyze oxidation reduction reactions.
      b. Transferases catalyze the transfer of a specific group from one substrate to another.
      c. Hydrolases catalyze the hydrolysis of substrates.
      d. Isomerases catalyze the isomerization of substrates.
      e. Lyases catalyze the addition or elimination of small molecules.
      f. Ligases catalyze the bonding of two substrate molecules.
    2. Naming enzymes.
      a. The first part of the name identifies the substrate.
      b. The second part of the name identifies the enzyme subclass.
II. Enzyme function (Sections 19.4–19.6).
  A. How enzymes work (Section 19.4).
    1. Models for representing enzyme action.
      a. The shape of the active site is complementary to the shape of the substrate. This description of enzyme–substrate is called the lock-and-key model.
      b. A more modern interpretation of enzyme–substrate interaction is the induced-fit model.
        i. In this model, an enzyme is flexible enough to change shape to fit the spatial requirement of the substrate.
        ii. The enzyme and substrate induce each other to change shape.
    2. Mechanism of enzyme catalysis.
      a. An enzyme–substrate complex is formed when the substrate migrates to the active site, and atoms that will take part in the reaction are held in place (proximity effect).
      b. Reactants are positioned at the exact distance necessary for reaction to occur (orientation effect).
      c. The active site provides the kinds of functional groups necessary for catalysis (catalytic effect).
      d. The activation energy for reaction is lowered by introducing strain into the bonds of the substrate (energy effect).

C. Effect of concentration on enzyme activity (Section 19.5).
    1. When substrate concentration varies, and enzyme concentration remains constant:
        a. Additional substrate increases the rate until all active sites are occupied.
        b. At this point, reaction rate becomes constant.
        c. The enzyme is said to be saturated.
    2. Under most conditions, reaction rate is controlled by enzyme efficiency.
        The upper limit to reaction rate is about 10^8 collisions per mole per second.
    3. When substrate concentration is high, and enzyme concentration varies:
        a. Additional enzyme increases the reaction rate.
        b. The increase in reaction rate is directly proportional to enzyme concentration.
D. Influence of temperature and pH on enzymes (Section 19.6).
    1. Temperature.
        a. All enzymes have an optimum temperature for greatest catalytic efficiency. In the human body, this temperature is 37°C.
        b. At temperatures above 50–60°C, enzymes denature.
    2. pH.
        a. Enzymes also have an optimum pH.
        b. If pH is too high or too low, enzymes lose their ability to catalyze reactions.
III. Enzyme regulation (Sections 19.7–19.9).
A. General strategies of control (Section 19.7).
    1. Activation is any process that increases the action of an enzyme.
    2. Inhibition is any process that slows or stops the action of an enzyme.
B. Feedback and allosteric control.
    1. Feedback control.
        a. The product of a series of reactions is an inhibitor for the first reaction.
        b. This strategy keeps excessive amounts of products from accumulating.
    2. Allosteric control.
        a. Most enzymes are regulated by allosteric control.
        b. Allosteric enzymes have more than one polypeptide chain.
        c. Allosteric enzymes have catalytic sites and regulatory sites.
        d. Binding of a positive regulator increases reaction rate.
        e. Binding of a negative regulator decreases reaction rate.
C. Enzyme inhibition (Section 19.8).
    1. Reversible noncompetitive inhibition.
        a. An inhibitor binds to the enzyme at a site other than the active site and changes the shape of the enzyme.
        b. The enzyme is a less effective catalyst, and reaction rate is slowed.
        c. The inhibitor doesn't compete with the substrate.
    2. Reversible competitive inhibition.
        a. In competitive inhibition, a substrate that resembles the normal substrate occupies the enzyme's active site.
        b. Competitive inhibition is reversible.
            i.   The degree of inhibition can be regulated by controlling the amounts of substrate and inhibitor.
            ii. Increasing the concentration of substrate displaces inhibitor from the active site.
    3. Irreversible inhibition.
        The inhibitor bonds covalently to the active site, and the enzyme is irreversibly inhibited.
D. Covalent modification and genetic control (Section 19.9).
    1. Zymogens.
        a. Some enzymes(zymogens) are synthesized in a form that differs from their catalytic form.
        b. Zymogens are activated by enzymatic addition or removal of a part of the zymogen.

      c. Enzymes that might injure the body if constantly present in their active form are synthesized as zymogens.

    2. Phosphorylation/dephosphorylation.

       Phosphate groups can be added to serine and threonine side chains to activate certain enzymes.

    3. Genetic control.

      a. Synthesis of some enzymes is regulated by genes.

      b. Genetic control is used for enzymes needed only at certain stages of development.

IV. Vitamins (Section 19.10).

  A. Vitamins are small organic molecules that must be supplied in the diet.

  B. Vitamins are classified by solubility.

    1. Water-soluble vitamins are either coenzymes or precursors to coenzymes.

       Water-soluble vitamins include vitamin C and the B vitamins.

    2. Fat-soluble vitamins are stored in the body's fatty tissues.

      a. Vitamin A is important for vision.

      b. Vitamin D regulates calcium absorption.

      c. Vitamin E is an antioxidant.

      d. Vitamin K is involved in blood-clotting.

Solutions for Chapter 19 Problems

19.1 Kinases catalyze a maximum of 1000 (10^3) reactions per second.

19.2 There are two reasons: (1) The enzyme might catalyze reactions within the eye if it were not removed. (2) Saline is sterile and is isotonic with body fluids.

19.3 Most vitamin/mineral supplements contain the listed metal ion cofactors (iron, zinc, copper, manganese, molybdenum, vanadium, cobalt, and nickel), as well as containing selenium and boron.

19.4 Vitamin-derived coenzymes are not synthesized in the body and must be provided in the diet. Other coenzymes are normally synthesized in the body.

19.5 (a) Retinal isomerase catalyzes the isomerization of retinal.
(b) Squalene oxidase catalyzes the oxidation of squalene.
(c) Glucose kinase catalyzes the transfer of a phosphate group to glucose.
(d) Cellulose hydrolase catalyzes the hydrolysis of cellulose.

19.6 Pyruvate decarboxylase is a lyase and catalyzes the elimination of CO_2 from pyruvate.

19.7 In an isomerization catalyzed by triose phosphate isomerase, a terminal hydroxyl group is converted to an aldehyde group, and the adjacent ketone group is converted to a hydroxyl group.

19.8 Reaction (a) might be catalyzed by a decarboxylase because it involves a loss of CO_2. Reaction (b) isn't catalyzed by a decarboxylase.

19.9 Acidic, basic and polar side chains can take part in catalytic activity and in holding the substrate in the active site. Nonpolar side chains can take part in holding the enzyme in the active site but are not likely to be involved in catalytic activity.

19.10 If an enzyme is saturated with substrate, substrate molecules are bound to all of the active sites. (a) Increasing the substrate concentration has no effect on the rate because there are no empty sites where the added substrate can bind. (b) Adding more enzyme increases the rate because more enzyme-substrate complexes can form.

19.11 The rate of the reaction shown in Figure 19.7a is greater at 30°C than at 20°C. The rate is somewhat greater at 40°C than at 25°C.

19.12 The rate of the reaction catalyzed by trypsin is much greater at pH = 8 than at pH = 10.

19.13

(a)   (b)

p-Aminobenzoate

Structure (b) is a possible competitive inhibitor for the enzyme that has p-aminobenzoate (PABA) as a substrate because it resembles PABA both in shape and in the type of functional groups present.

19.14 A product of an enzyme-catalyzed reaction that resembles the substrate might be a competitive inhibitor for the enzyme.

19.15 (a) *Covalent modification*, either by activation of a zymogen or by phosphorylation-dephosphorylation, is a type of enzyme regulation that occurs when an enzyme must be quickly activated.
(b) *Competitive inhibition* by use of a drug can regulate an overactive enzyme.
(c) *Genetic control* regulates enzymes that are needed only during certain stages of development.
(d) *Covalent modification* by phosphorylation-dephosphorylation can regulate enzymes that are needed for quick energy. Alternatively, *feedback control* can regulate glucose production. When glucose levels are adequate, glucose inhibits the enzyme that catalyzes its formation. When glucose levels drop, the enzyme is no longer inhibited, and glucose is formed.

19.16 Vitamin A is fat-soluble because it has a long hydrocarbon chain. Vitamin C is water-soluble because it has polar hydroxyl groups.

19.17 The difference among these compounds occurs at the functional group at the end of the hydrocarbon chain. In retinal, a –CHO group (aldehyde) replaces the –CH₂OH group; in retinoic acid, the –CH₂OH group becomes a –COOH group.

19.18 Vitamins can be enzyme cofactors; some are antioxidants; they aid absorption of calcium and phosphate ions; they are used in synthesis of visual pigments; they are involved in the synthesis of blood clotting factors.

Understanding Key Concepts

19.19

---- hydrogen bonds

ɪɪɪɪɪ salt bridges

19.20

L–Lactate   Pyruvate

(a) The enzyme that catalyzes the above reaction is an oxidoreductase.
(b) The enzyme belongs to the dehydrogenase subclass.
(c) L-Lactate is the substrate for the above enzyme.
(d) The enzyme is named L-lactate dehydrogenase.

19.21 The above enzyme will most likely not use D-lactate as a substrate because most enzymes are "handed" and catalyze the reaction of only one enantiomer of a pair of enantiomers. It is possible that D-lactate might act as a competitive inhibitor of the enzyme.

19.22 The coenzyme needed for the above reaction is NAD^+ (nicotinamide adenine dinucleotide), which is an oxidizing agent and includes the vitamin niacin.

19.23 (a) Increasing the substrate concentration at constant inhibitor concentration increases the rate when substrate concentration is low. Very soon, however, a maximum rate is reached, and adding more substrate does not change the rate of reaction. This maximum rate is always lower than the rate of the uninhibited reaction.
(b) Decreasing the inhibitor concentration at constant substrate concentration increases the rate of reaction. As inhibitor concentration is decreased, more inhibitor dissociates from the enzyme, leaving active enzyme that is free to react with substrate.

19.24 (a) *Allosteric regulation* (either positive or negative) occurs when a regulator binds to the enzyme at a site other than the active site. This binding changes the shape of the enzyme and alters the catalytic ability of the enzyme.

(b) In *covalent modification*, the activity of an enzyme is influenced by the addition or removal of a group that is covalently bonded to the enzyme.

(c) *Inhibition* is any process that stops or slows down an enzyme's ability to catalyze a reaction. Noncompetitive inhibition can be a type of allosteric regulation (see part (a)). Competitive inhibition occurs when an inhibitor reversibly occupies an enzyme's active site. Irreversible inhibition results when an inhibitor covalently binds to an enzyme and destroys its ability to catalyze a reaction.

(d) In *genetic control,* hormones control the synthesis of enzymes.

19.25 The amino acids (from left to right): aspartate, serine, glutamine, arginine, histidine. Arginine and histidine are basic, and aspartate is acidic.

Structure and Classification of Enzymes

19.26 (a) A *hydrolase* catalyzes the hydrolysis (bond-breaking by addition of water) of a substrate.

(b) An *isomerase* catalyzes the isomerization of a substrate.

(c) A *lyase* catalyzes the addition of a small molecule to a double bond of a substrate, or the elimination of a small molecule from a substrate to form a double bond.

19.27 (a) An *oxidoreductase* catalyzes the oxidation or the reduction of a substrate.

(b) A *ligase* catalyzes the formation of a bond between two substrates, with the participation of a high-energy molecule.

(c) A *transferase* catalyzes the transfer of a functional group from one substrate to another.

19.28 An enzyme is a large three-dimensional molecule with a catalytic site into which a substrate can fit. Enzymes are specific in their action because only one or a few molecules have the appropriate shape and functional groups to fit into the catalytic site.

19.29 An enzyme forms an enzyme-substrate complex with a substrate at the enzyme's active site. The substrate is in the proper orientation for functional groups at the active site to carry out a reaction. Strain is introduced into the substrate to lower the energy barrier to reaction. After the reaction, the enzyme and products separate.

19.30 (a) This reaction is catalyzed by a *transferase*, because it involves the transfer of an amino group between substrates.

(b) An *isomerase* catalyzes this reaction.

(c) Formation of oxaloacetate from pyruvate and CO_2 is catalyzed by a *ligase*, which catalyzes the formation of a new bond with participation of ATP.

19.31 (a) A *hydrolase* catalyzes this reaction, which is the hydrolysis of a peptide bond.

(b) A *lyase* catalyzes this reaction.

(c) An *oxidoreductase* catalyzes the introduction of a double bond into a molecule by removal of H_2.

19.32 (a) A *protease* catalyzes the hydrolysis of peptide (amide) bonds in proteins.

(b) A *DNA ligase* catalyzes the formation of a new bond between two small DNA chains.

(c) A *transmethylase* catalyzes the transfer of a methyl group between substrates.

19.33 (a) A *reductase* catalyzes the reduction of a substrate.
(b) A *kinase* catalyzes the transfer of a phosphate group between substrates.
(c) A *synthetase* catalyzes the formation of a bond between two substrates.

19.34 A urease is a hydrolase, since it catalyzes the hydrolysis of urea to ammonia and carbonic acid.

19.35 Alcohol dehydrogenase is an oxidoreductase because it catalyzes the oxidation of an alcohol to an aldehyde.

Enzyme Function and Regulation

19.36 In the lock-and-key model of enzyme action, the active site of an enzyme has a specific shape (lock) into which only a specific substrate (key) can fit. In the induced-fit model, the shape of the active site changes to accommodate the substrate.

19.37 The induced-fit model is a more likely model for enzyme function because it accounts for the fact that enzymes are not rigid but can change their shape to some extent in order to accommodate a substrate and to catalyze a reaction.

19.38 The amino acid residues involved in the active site can be brought close to each other by protein folding without being near each other in the polypeptide chain.

19.39 The active site of an enzyme, where catalysis takes place, is only a small part of the enzyme. Other regions of the enzyme are needed to stabilize the three-dimensional structure of the enzyme, to align the active-site functional groups that catalyze the reaction, to hold the substrate in place, and to provide sites for enzyme control and regulation.

19.40 To function in the very acidic environment of the stomach, an enzyme must be active at a low pH. To function in the intestine, an enzyme must have high catalytic activity at a pH near neutral. Each enzyme has an optimum pH for catalysis, and an enzyme that is most active at neutral pH will not be active in a strongly acidic environment.

19.41 Recall from Chapter 18 that an amino acid with a pI of less than 4 is negatively charged at physiological pH and can act as a base, and an amino acid with a pI greater than 7 is positively charged at physiological pH and can act as an acid. Thus, at physiological pH, glutamate and aspartate can accept H^+, and lysine and arginine can donate H^+. Histidine (pI = 7.6) can both accept H^+ and donate H^+.

19.42

19.43 At a high substrate concentration relative to enzyme concentration, the rate of reaction increases as the enzyme concentration increases.

19.44 The rate of reaction increases as the substrate concentration increases, up to a point where all enzyme catalytic sites are occupied. The reaction rate then levels off, and adding more substrate doesn't increase the reaction rate.

19.45 Increasing enzyme concentration at high, fixed substrate concentration always increases the rate of reaction because more sites are available for catalysis. Increasing substrate concentration at constant enzyme concentration increases the reaction rate until all catalytic sites are occupied, and the reaction rate levels off.

19.46 (a) Lowering the temperature of the enzyme-catalyzed reaction from 37°C to 27°C decreases the rate of reaction.
(b) Raising the pH of the enzyme-catalyzed reaction from 7.5 to 10.5 will probably decrease the rate of reaction, since most enzymes have their optimum rates at close to neutral pH. However, if the enzyme has a rate optimum near 10.5, then the increase in pH from 7.5 to 10.5 will increase the rate of reaction.
(c) Adding a heavy-metal salt either stops the reaction or decreases the rate of the enzyme-catalyzed reaction because heavy metals bind to enzymes, causing irreversible inhibition.

19.47 (a) If the enzyme has maximum activity at 37°C, raising the reaction temperature from 37°C to 40°C should decrease the rate of reaction by a small amount.
(b) Adding an oxidizing agent will most likely denature the enzyme and thus will stop the reaction or greatly decrease its rate.
(c) Adding a drop of dilute $AgNO_3$ could either slow down or stop the enzyme-catalyzed reaction because Ag^+ is a heavy metal that binds to the –SH groups of enzymes, causing irreversible inhibition.

19.48 *Competitive inhibition* occurs when the structure of a second substrate closely resembles that of the normal substrate for an enzyme. The second substrate can occupy the active site and thereby inhibit binding at the active site of the usual substrate. Competitive inhibition is usually reversible.

Noncompetitive inhibition occurs when an inhibitor binds to the enzyme at a location other than the active site. The conformation of the enzyme changes, and the enzyme is inactivated or its catalytic ability is reduced. Noncompetitive inhibition is reversible.

Irreversible inhibition occurs when a molecule covalently bonds to the active site of an enzyme. The active site is thus irreversibly inactivated, and enzyme activity stops.

In competitive inhibition, the inhibitor bonds noncovalently to the active site. In noncompetitive inhibition, the inhibitor binds noncovalently with a group away from the active site. In irreversible inhibition, the inhibitor forms a covalent bond at the active site.

19.49 Irreversible inhibition is the most difficult to treat medically because it occurs at the active site and because of the strength of the bond between the inhibitor and the enzyme.

19.50 Papain is effective as a meat tenderizer because it catalyzes the hydrolysis of peptide bonds and partially digests the proteins in the meat and softens tough connective tissue.

19.51 Papain works by catalyzing hydrolysis of the bee toxin responsible for swelling.

19.52 Allosteric enzymes have two types of binding sites – one site is for catalysis of the enzymatic reaction and one site is for regulation of the reaction. Having two kinds of sites allows for greater regulation and control of enzyme activity.

19.53 Positive regulators change the shape of the active site so that the rate of the enzyme-catalyzed reaction increases. Negative regulators change the shape of the active site so that the enzyme is a less effective catalyst.

19.54 Feedback inhibition occurs when the end product of a series of reactions is an inhibitor for an earlier reaction. When this product accumulates, it inhibits an enzyme that catalyzes an earlier step in the series, and the rate of product formation slows down. When the amount of product decreases, inhibition stops, and product formation is resumed.

19.55 "Feed–forward activation" occurs when the first product of a series of reactions activates enzymes needed for later steps in the sequence. "Feed–forward activation" is a mechanism of enzyme regulation that might be useful when it is important to quickly activate an enzyme or to remove a rapidly accumulating product.

19.56 A zymogen is an enzyme that is synthesized in a form different from its active form and is activated when needed by removal of a covalently bonded portion of the enzyme. Some enzymes are secreted as zymogens because they would digest or otherwise injure the body if they were secreted in their active form.

19.57 Phosphorylation of a serine or threonine residue of an enzyme replaces a polar –OH group with a charged phosphate group. If this replacement occurs near the active site of an enzyme, the activity of the enzyme might be either enhanced or inhibited, depending on the enzyme mechanism.

Vitamins

19.58 Vitamins are small organic molecules that the body can't manufacture and that must be obtained in trace amounts from the diet.

19.59 Water-soluble vitamins act as cofactors for enzymes and make it possible for enzymes to catalyze biochemical reactions. The relationship between fat-soluble vitamins and enzymes is less clear.

19.60 Vitamin C (water-soluble) is excreted in the urine and must be replenished daily, whereas vitamin A (fat-soluble) can be stored in fatty tissue.

19.61 The four fat-soluble vitamins are vitamins A, D, E, and K. All except vitamin E are stored in the body and are toxic when ingested in large amounts.

Applications

19.62 Lead poisons enzymes by bonding to cysteine residues or by displacing an essential metal from an active site. Bonding to cysteine is irreversible and denatures the enzyme, and addition of EDTA can't restore enzyme activity. EDTA can form a coordinate covalent complex with lead when it has displaced a metal from an active site. This complex is water-soluble and can be excreted in the urine.

19.63 The target molecule, *p*-hydroxyphenylglycine is chiral. Since enzymes are specific in their action, only the desired enantiomer is formed.

19.64 (1) Enzymes produce only one enantiomer of a desired product. (2) Enzymes can be used to synthesize products that are difficult to produce by nonbiological pathways. (3) Enzyme-catalyzed reactions often take place without producing dangerous or wasteful by-products.

19.65 The enzymes creatine phosphokinase (CPK), aspartate transaminase (AST) and lactate dehydrogenase (LDH_1) are increased in the blood after a heart attack because they leak from cells damaged in the heart attack.

19.66 Enzyme activity must be monitored under standard conditions because activity is affected by pH, temperature and substrate concentration. The standard is the unit (u), which is the amount of enzyme that converts one micromole of substrate to product at defined standard conditions of pH, temperature and substrate concentration.

19.67 A mild ACE inhibitor allows for more careful control of blood pressure. If a very potent ACE inhibitor were used to control blood pressure, blood pressure might drop drastically and cause serious medical problems. If pit viper peptide were modified so that it caused irreversible inhibition of ACE, it would be a more powerful inhibitor, but it would also be a more dangerous drug. A possible modification to pit viper peptide might be the inclusion of an –SH group near proline that binds irreversibly to the zinc atom at the active site.

19.68 The body excretes excess water-soluble vitamins, but fat-soluble vitamins accumulate in tissues.

19.69 (no answer)

19.70 Listings for vitamin A, vitamin C, iron and calcium are mandatory on food labels because they are considered to be of greatest importance in maintaining good health.

General Questions and Problems

19.71

19.72

$$1.6 \text{ mg riboflavin} \times \frac{100 \text{ mL apple juice}}{0.014 \text{ mg riboflavin}} = 11,000 \text{ mL} = 11 \text{ L apple juice}$$

19.73 Blanching denatures enzymes that would cause slow deterioration of food quality in frozen food.

19.74 Because competitive inhibition is reversible, addition of a large amount of the normal substrate will reverse the binding of the inhibitor, and the rate of reaction of the normal substrate will return to its usual value. The effects of noncompetitive inhibition can't be reversed by addition of excess substrate.

19.75 Look for Arg, His and Lys (basic amino acids) in the polypeptide, and break the bond between the basic amino acid and the amino acid to its right.

Leu–Gly–Arg⁅Ile–Met–His⁅Tyr–Trp–Ala

↓ Trypsin

Leu–Gly–Arg + Ile–Met–His + Tyr–Trp–Ala

19.76 If valine replaced serine, the enzyme would be inactivated because the –OH functional group of serine is essential for enzyme activity. If aspartate replaced glutamate, the effect would probably be minor because both amino acids have the same functional groups.

Self-Test for Chapter 19

Multiple choice:

1. A subclass of enzyme that catalyzes cleavage of peptide bonds is a:
   (a) lipase   (b) dehydrase   (c) protease   (d) reductase

2. Which of the following is an enzyme cofactor?
   (a) thiamine   (b) tocopherol   (c) hexokinase   (d) trypsin

3. The ability of enzymes to bring reactants together is known as the:
   (a) orientation effect   (b) catalytic effect   (c) proximity effect   (d) energy effect

4. Fat-soluble vitamins serve all of the following functions except:
   (a) promotion of bone growth   (b) antioxidant   (c) aiding night vision
   (d) anemia prevention

5. Which of the following enzymes probably requires a coenzyme that is reduced during reaction?
   (a) transferase   (b) oxidase   (c) isomerase   (d) dehydrase

6. The most likely control mechanism for reactions that occur during embryonic development is:
   (a) feedback control   (b) genetic control   (c) zymogens   (d) allosteric control

7. Snake venom probably causes its effects by:
   (a) noncompetitive inhibition   (b) competitive inhibition   (c) allosteric control
   (d) irreversible inhibition

8. Why does the rate of enzymatic reactions decrease as temperature is lowered?
   (a) Salt bridges are disrupted.   (b) The shape of the active site is changed.   (c) Reactions are slower at lower temperatures.   (d) The enzyme begins to denature.

9. If an enzyme is saturated, adding more substrate will:
   (a) increase reaction rate   (b) have no effect on reaction rate   (c) decrease reaction rate
   (d) have varying effects, depending on the enzyme

10. In which of the following types of enzyme regulation can adding large amounts of substrate restore an enzyme's reaction rate to its maximum value?
    (a) feedback inhibition   (b) irreversible inhibition   (c) noncompetitive inhibition
    (d) competitive inhibition

Complete the following sentences:

1. An enzyme called a _____ catalyzes the isomerization of a chiral center.

2. _____ are enzymes that have slightly different structures but that catalyze the same reaction.

3. Vitamin __ is necessary for the synthesis of blood-clotting factors.

4. In the _____ - _____ model of enzyme action, an enzyme can change its shape slightly to fit different substrates.

5. In _____ inhibition, an inhibitor changes the shape of an enzyme by binding at a location other than the active site.

6. If the temperature becomes too high, enzymes begin to _____.

7. The catalytic activity of an enzyme is measured by its _____ _____.

8. A type of covalent modification of an enzyme involves addition or removal of a _____ group.

9. The _____ effect is responsible for bringing substrate and catalytic sites together.

10. The upper limit of any enzyme's rate of reaction is ___collisions per mole per second.

11. An _____ enzyme has more than one chain and has binding sites for both substrate and regulator.

12. An enzyme that is synthesized in a form different from its active form is called a _____.

Tell whether the following statements are true or false:

1. 98.6°F is the optimum temperature for most enzymes.

2. In an enzyme-substrate complex, the substrate is in its lowest energy shape.

3. Noncompetitive inhibition is irreversible.

4. A dehydrogenase catalyzes the loss of H_2O from a substrate.

5. At the active site, the enzyme and substrate are held together by covalent bonds.

6. Vitamins may be small organic molecules or inorganic ions.

7. Chymotrypsinogen is a zymogen.

8. β-Carotene is the active form of vitamin A.

9. Copper, cobalt, and selenium are essential enzyme cofactors.

10. Heavy metals cause irreversible inhibition of enzymes.

11. As enzyme concentration is increased, the reaction rate eventually levels off.

12. The side chains of serine and threonine are sites of covalent modification.

Match the entries on the left with their partners on the right:

1. Papain   (a) Deficiency causes anemia

2. Vitamin D   (b) Occurs away from an enzyme's active site

3. Competitive inhibition   (c) Nonspecific enzyme

4. Kinase   (d) Catalyzes hydrolysis of ester groups in lipids

5. Alanine transaminase   (e) Protein part of enzyme, plus cofactor

6. Cofactor   (f) Deficiency causes scurvy

7. Noncompetitive inhibition   (g) Transfers a phosphate group between substrates

8. Vitamin B_6 (h) Fat-soluble vitamin

9. Lipase   (i) Occurs at an enzyme's active site

10. Vitamin C   (j) Metal ion or small organic molecule

11. Active enzyme   (k) Specific enzyme

12. Lyase   (l) Catalyzes loss of small molecule from substrate

Chapter 20 – Chemical Messengers

Chapter Outline

I. Introduction to chemical messengers (Section 20.1).
    A. Control of vital functions is accomplished by chemical messengers.
        1. The messengers interact with the cells of a target tissue.
        2. The message is delivered by interaction between the chemical messengers and receptors.
        3. Noncovalent interactions draw messengers and receptors together.
        4. The results of the interaction are chemical changes within the target cell.
    B. Two kinds of chemical messengers are important in the body.
        1. Hormones are the chemical messengers of the endocrine system.
            a. Hormones travel through the bloodstream.
            b. The responses produced by hormones are slow but long-lasting.
        2. The chemical messengers of the nervous system are neurotransmitters.
            a. Signals travel very quickly along nerve fibers.
            b. Neurotransmitters carry the message of the signal across the gap that separates one nerve fiber from the next fiber.
            c. The effects of neurotransmitters are very short-lived.

II. Hormones (Sections 20.2–20.5).
    A. Hormones and the endocrine system (Section 20.2).
        1. The endocrine system consists of all the glands that secrete hormones.
        2. The endocrine glands are managed by the hypothalamus in three different ways.
            a. Direct neural control by a nervous system pathway from the hypothalamus.
            b. Direct release of hormones from the hypothalamus.
            c. Indirect control by release of regulatory hormones.
        3. There are three types of hormones.
            a. Polypeptide hormones.
            b. Steroid hormones.
            c. Amino acid derivatives.
        4. The signal of a hormone enters cells in either of two ways.
            a. Steroid hormones pass through the hydrophobic cell membrane.
            b. Other hormones bind with receptors in the cell wall.
    B. How hormones work: epinephrine (Section 20.3).
        1. Epinephrine carried in the bloodstream binds to a receptor on the surface of a cell.
        2. The hormone–receptor complex interacts with a nearby G protein, causing it to bind GTP.
        3. This complex activates the enzyme adenylate cyclase, which resides in the cell membrane.
        4. Adenylate cyclase catalyzes production within the cell of the second messenger, cyclic AMP.
        5. Cyclic AMP initiates reactions that activate glycogen phosphorylase, which catalyzes release of glucose from storage.
        6. After the emergency, a phosphodiesterase catalyzes hydrolysis of cyclic AMP to AMP.
    C. Types of hormones (Sections 20.4–20.5).
        1. Amino acid derivatives (Section 20.4).
            a. Many amino acid derivatives are also neurotransmitters.
                Examples include epinephrine, dopamine and norepinephrine.
            b. Thyroxine is an iodine-containing hormone that regulates the synthesis of various enzymes.

  2. Polypeptide hormones.
   a. TRH and TSH control the thyroid gland.
   b. Vasopressin and oxytocin are small cyclic polypeptides.
   c. Insulin regulates glucose metabolism.
  3. Steroid hormones (Section 20.5).
   a. Mineralocorticoids (such as aldosterone) regulate ionic balance in cellular fluid.
   b. Glucocorticoids (such as cortisone) regulate inflammation.
   c. Sex hormones.
    i. Androgens (male hormones) include testosterone and androsterone.
    ii. Female hormones include estrogens and progestins.
    iii. There are also hundreds of synthetic hormones of all types.

III. Neurotransmitters (Sections 20.6–20.10).
 A. General features of neurotransmitters (Section 20.6).
  1. A nerve impulse is transmitted along a neuron by variations in electric potential.
  2. Neurotransmitters convey the impulse across the synaptic cleft from a presynaptic neuron to a postsynaptic neuron.
  3. The impulse is transmitted down the next neuron, and the above process is repeated.
  4. Neurotransmitters are synthesized and stored in vesicles in the presynaptic neuron.
  5. After transmission, the neurotransmitter is inactivated in one of two ways.
   a. A chemical change inactivates the neurotransmitter.
   b. The neurotransmitter is returned to the presynaptic neuron.
  6. Most neurotransmitters are amines.
  7. Some neurotransmitters act directly, and others rely on second messengers.
 B. How neurotransmitters work: acetylcholine (ACh) (Section 20.7).
  1. Events of neurotransmission.
   a. An impulse arrives at the presynaptic neuron.
   b. The vesicles move to the cell membrane, fuse with it, and release ACh.
   c. ACh crosses the synaptic cleft and binds to receptors on the postsynaptic neuron.
   d. A change in the permeability of the postsynaptic neuron initiates the nerve impulse in that neuron.
   e. Acetylcholinesterase in the synaptic cleft catalyzes the decomposition of ACh.
   f. Choline is reabsorbed into the presynaptic neuron, and new ACh is synthesized.
  2. Interactions of drugs at ACh synapses.
   a. To have an effect a drug must connect with a receptor.
   b. Drugs that are agonists prolong the biochemical response of a receptor.
    Nicotine at a low dose is an example of an agonist.
   c. Drugs that are antagonists block the normal response of a receptor.
    Antagonists can be either competitive (tubocurarine) or irreversible (nerve gas).
 C. Histamine and antihistamines (Section 20.8).
  1. Histamine is the neurotransmitter responsible for the symptoms of allergic reactions.
  2. Antihistamines are drugs that are histamine receptor antagonists.
 D. Monoamines (Sections 20.9–20.10).
  1. Serotonin, norepinephrine, and dopamine are neurotransmitters active in the brain (Section 20.9).
  2. Since these neurotransmitters affect mood, drugs have been created to affect the concentration of these neurotransmitters at synapses.
   a. Tricyclic antidepressants (Elavil) prevent the reuptake of serotonin and norepinephrine from the synaptic cleft.
   b. MAO inhibitors (Nardil) inhibit the enzyme that breaks down monoamine neurotransmitters.
   c. SSRI antidepressants (Prozac) inhibit only the reuptake of serotonin.

3. Dopamine.
   a. Dopamine plays a role in emotion, thought and behavior through interactions with five different kinds of receptors in the brain.
   b. Dopamine levels are responsible for many types of behaviors.
      i. An oversupply of dopamine is associated with schizophrenia.
      ii. An undersupply of dopamine is responsible for Parkinson's disease.
      iii. An ample supply of dopamine is responsible for a feeling of well-being.
   c. Drugs such as heroin, cocaine, marijuana, and alcohol increase dopamine levels.
   E. Neuropeptides (Section 20.10).
   The brain has receptors for small polypeptides (enkephalins) that also act as receptors for opiates.
IV. Drug discovery and drug design (Section 20.11).
   A. Plants were the first source of drugs.
   Today, ethnobotanists seek new plant sources of drugs in remote regions.
   B. In the 19th century, simple drugs (benzocaine, phenacetin) were synthesized in chemical laboratories.
   C. Combinatorial chemistry generates large masses of related compounds and screens them for possible effectiveness as drugs.
   D. Supercomputers and molecular graphics are increasingly used in drug design.

Solutions to Chapter 20 Problems

20.1

If you redraw the reaction shown in Figure 20.3, you can see the anion that is a byproduct of the conversion of ATP to cyclic AMP. The anion (PP_i) is $P_2O_7^{4-}$.

20.2 The heterocyclic rings of caffeine and theobromine resemble the heterocyclic rings of cyclic AMP. It is possible that these two molecules could act as inhibitors to one of the enzymes that inactivates cAMP.

20.3

Glu   His   Pro

The tripeptide is Glu–His–Pro.

20.4

Thyroxine

Thyroxine is hydrophobic because its aromatic, hydrophobic part is larger than its zwitterionic, hydrophilic part.

20.5

Testosterone   Nandrolone

Nandrolone and testosterone are identical except for the presence in testosterone of a methyl group between the first two rings that is absent in nandrolone.

20.6

5-Hydroxytryptophan → (a) decarboxylation → CO_2 → Serotonin → (b) acetylation

N-Acetylserotonin → (c) methylation → Melatonin

(a) decarboxylation (2)
(b) acetylation (3)
(c) methylation (1)

20.7

ether, secondary amine, secondary alcohol, aromatic rings — Propanolol

aromatic ring, secondary amine, phenol, secondary alcohol — Epinephrine

Both structures have aromatic rings and have secondary alcohol and secondary amine functional groups. Propranolol has a naphthalene aromatic ring system and has an ether group. Epinephrine has an aromatic ring with two phenol groups. The compounds have different carbon skeletons in their side chains.

20.8 Malathion, with an LD_{50} of 1000-1375 mg/kg, is the best choice because its lethal dose is highest, and it is thus the least harmful pesticide of the three.

20.9 An agonist (black widow spider venom) prolongs the biochemical response of a receptor. An antagonist (botulinus toxin) blocks or inhibits the normal response of a receptor.

20.10

Tetrahydrocannabinol (THC)

THC is likely to be hydrophobic (because the phenol hydroxyl group is the only polar functional group in the molecule), and it might be expected to accumulate in fatty tissue.

20.11 (a) This structure represents an antihistamine because it has the general antihistamine structure pictured in Section 20.8.
(b) This structure represents an antidepressant. It is similar to Prozac, an SSRI, but there are noticeable differences; the aromatic rings have different substituents, and a third ring is present in the compound pictured.

Understanding Key Concepts

20.12 (a) Insulin, a polypeptide hormone, is involved in type I diabetes.
(b) In unaffected individuals, insulin is released by the pancreas. The pancreas fails to produce insulin in individuals with type I diabetes.
(c) Insulin is transported through the bloodstream to cells that need it.
(d) Insulin doesn't enter cells because it is a polypeptide hormone and can't pass through the hydrophobic cell membrane. Instead, it binds with a cell surface receptor, which generates a second messenger within the cell.

20.13 (a) Luteinizing hormone (LH) is a polypeptide hormone that is produced in the anterior pituitary gland.
(b) Progesterone is a steroid hormone that is produced in the ovaries.
(c) LH doesn't enter progesterone-producing cells because it is a polypeptide hormone. Instead, LH interacts on the cell surface with LH receptors that generate second messengers, which carry out the function of LH.
(d) Progesterone enters the cell directly because it is a steroid hormone and can pass through the hydrophobic cell membrane.

20.14 Since a small amount of epinephrine produces a massive response, at least one step in the sequence that results in the release of glucose must be amplified many fold. Although amplification occurs in all steps of the sequence of events, two steps have the greatest amplification. (1) Adenylate cyclase is capable of catalyzing the production of a great number of cAMP molecules. (2) The kinase enzymes phosphorylated as a result of cAMP activation (Section 19.9), quickly catalyze the breakdown of glycogen to release large amounts of glucose.

20.15 The transmission of a nerve impulse may be terminated by an enzyme that converts the neurotransmitter to an inactive form. It is also possible for the neurotransmitter to be returned to the presynaptic neuron.

20.16 Neurotransmitters can act either by binding to receptors or by activating second messengers.

20.17 Elevated concentrations of dopamine in the brain result in a "high" feeling. All of these drugs increase the concentration of dopamine in the brain. The brain attempts to return to its normal state by decreasing the number of dopamine receptors and by decreasing their sensitivity. Consequently, more of the drug is required to achieve the same effect, leading to addiction.

Chemical Messengers

20.18 Hormones are molecules of different sizes and types that travel through the bloodstream and regulate the rates of biochemical reactions without directly taking part in the reactions. A hormone is detected by a receptor, either at a cell surface or within the cell.

20.19 A chemical messenger is a molecule that travels from one part of the body to another location, where it delivers a signal or acts to control metabolism. The target tissue is the cell or group of cells whose activity is regulated by the messenger. A hormone receptor is the molecule with which the chemical messenger interacts if it is a hormone.

20.20 A vitamin is usually an enzyme cofactor, whereas a hormone regulates enzyme activity.

20.21 A hormone transmits a chemical message from an endocrine gland to a target tissue. A neurotransmitter carries an impulse between neighboring nerve cells. Neurotransmitters act rapidly and with short duration, whereas hormones act more slowly and produce effects of longer duration.

20.22 Like allosteric regulation, hormone binding is noncovalent and serves to control the rate of a reaction, rather than to take part in a reaction.

20.23 Neither a hormone nor its receptor are changed as a result of binding to each other. The binding forces between hormone and receptor are noncovalent.

Hormones and the Endocrine System

20.24 The three major classes of hormones are polypeptide hormones, steroid hormones and hormones that are derivatives of amino acids.

20.25 *Polypeptide hormones:* insulin, oxytocin, vasopressin, thyrotropin-releasing hormone, thyroid-stimulating hormone.
Steroid hormones: aldosterone, cortisone, hydrocortisone, estrone, estradiol, progesterone, testosterone, androsterone.
Amino acid derivatives: epinephrine, dopamine, norepinephrine, thyroxine.

20.26 The body's endocrine system manufactures and secretes hormones, which regulate the functioning of biochemical reaction pathways.

20.27 Endocrine glands include the pituitary, the adrenals, the pancreas, ovaries, testes, pineal, thymus, thyroid, and parathyroid glands.

20.28 Enzymes are proteins, whereas hormones vary greatly in structure. Some hormones are polypeptides, some are proteins, some are steroids, and some are derivatives of amino acids.

20.29 The same type of specificity exists for both an enzyme/substrate complex and a hormone/receptor complex.

20.30 Polypeptide hormones travel through the bloodstream and bind to cell receptors, which are on the outside of a cell. The receptors cause production within cells of "second messengers" that activate enzymes.

20.31 Steroid hormones travel through the bloodstream to target tissues. Because they are lipids, they are able to pass through the cell membrane. Receptors for steroid hormones occur either in intracellular fluid or in the nucleus.

How Hormones Work: Epinephrine

20.32 Epinephrine is produced in the adrenal medulla and released as a result of a nervous system signal from the hypothalamus. It is produced when the body needs an instant response to danger. At target tissues, epinephrine stimulates the production of glucose as a source of energy to deal with whatever stress is at hand.

20.33 The three membrane-bound proteins that transmit the epinephrine message are, in order of involvement, the hormone receptor, G protein and adenylate cyclase, which produces cyclic AMP, the "second messenger". The ratio of epinephrine molecules to cyclic AMP molecules is less than 1:1 because each epinephrine molecule stimulates the production of more than one cyclic AMP molecule.

20.34 The second messenger initiates reactions that activate glycogen phosphorylase, the enzyme responsible for releasing glucose from storage. When the message is ready to be terminated, the enzyme phosphodiesterase converts cyclic AMP to AMP.

20.35 Epinephrine is used to treat anaphylaxis, a life-threatening allergic response whose symptoms include lowered heart rate and blood pressure, and difficulty in breathing.

Hormones

20.36 Insulin is a polypeptide hormone that contains 51 amino acids in two chains that are linked by disulfide bridges. It is stored in the pancreas and is released in response to high glucose levels in the blood. The hormone stimulates cells to take up glucose for use or storage.

20.37 Estradiol has a tetracyclic ring structure. The first ring is a phenol, and the fourth ring has a hydroxyl group. Estradiol is released from the ovaries and acts on most cells. It is responsible for the development of female secondary sex characteristics.

Estradiol

20.38 *Mineralocorticoids* include aldosterone.
Glucocorticoids include hydrocortisone and cortisone.
Sex hormones include testosterone, androsterone, estrone, estradiol and progesterone.

20.39 *Male sex hormones*: androsterone, testosterone.
Female sex hormones: estrone, estradiol, progesterone.

20.40 Both thyroxine and steroid hormones have large nonpolar regions and can cross a cell membrane to activate the synthesis of enzymes.

20.41 Epinephrine, norepinephrine and dopamine can function as both hormones and as neurotransmitters.

20.42   *Hormone*   *Class*
      (a)   amino acid derivative

Dopamine

      (b)   Insulin   polypeptide hormone

      (c)   steroid hormone

Testosterone

20.43

	Hormone	*Class*
(a)	Glucagon	polypeptide hormone
(b)		amino acid derivative

Thyroxine

(c) steroid hormone

Estradiol

Neurotransmitters

20.44 A synapse is the gap between two nerve cells (neurons). Neurotransmitters released by one neuron cross the synapse to receptors on a second neuron and transmit the nerve impulse.

20.45 A nerve impulse arrives at the presynaptic end of a neuron. The nerve impulse stimulates the movement of a vesicle, containing neurotransmitter molecules, to the cell membrane. The vesicle fuses with the cell membrane and releases the neurotransmitter, which crosses the synaptic cleft to a receptor site on the postsynaptic end of a second neuron. After reception, the cell transmits an electrical signal down its axon and passes on the impulse. Enzymes then deactivate the neurotransmitter so that the neuron can receive the next impulse. Alternatively, the neurotransmitter may be returned to the presynaptic neuron.

20.46 The signal from a neurotransmitter might be received by another nerve cell, a muscle cell or an endocrine cell.

20.47 (1) Neurotransmitter molecules are released from a presynaptic neuron in response to an impulse. (2) The neurotransmitter molecules cross the synaptic cleft. (3) The neurotransmitter molecules bind to receptors on the target cell.

20.48 (1) The neurotransmitter can be enzymatically inactivated. (2) The neurotransmitter may be returned to the presynaptic neuron and stored until it is needed again.

20.49

$$CH_3\overset{O}{\overset{\|}{C}}-OCH_2CH_2\overset{+}{N}(CH_3)_3 \xrightarrow[\text{H}_2\text{O}]{\text{Acetylcholinesterase}} CH_3\overset{O}{\overset{\|}{C}}-O^- + HOCH_2CH_2\overset{+}{N}(CH_3)_3$$

Acetylcholine   Acetate   Choline

20.50 (1) An impulse arrives at the presynaptic neuron.
(2) Vesicles containing acetylcholine(ACh) move to the cell membrane, fuse with it, and release ACh.
(3) ACh crosses the synaptic cleft and binds to receptors on the postsynaptic neuron.
(4) The resulting change in the permeability of the postsynaptic neuron to ions initiates the nerve impulse in that neuron.
(5) After the message is delivered, acetylcholinesterase catalyzes the breakdown of acetylcholine.
(6) Choline is reabsorbed into the presynaptic neuron, where new ACh is synthesized by reaction with acetyl coenzyme A.

20.51 Enkephalins are called "neurohormones" because they are secreted in the central nervous system and have receptors in brain tissue.

Chemical Messengers and Drugs

20.52 Drugs that are agonists interact with receptors to produce or prolong the normal response of the receptor. Antagonists block or inhibit the normal response of a receptor.

20.53 Antihistamines such as doxylamine counteract allergic responses caused by histamine by blocking histamine receptors in mucous membranes. Antihistamines such as cimetidine block receptors for histamine that stimulate production of stomach acid.

20.54 The three major monoamine neurotransmitters are serotonin, norepinephrine and dopamine.

20.55 Three families of drugs used to treat depression are tricyclic antidepressants (Elavil), monoamine oxidase inhibitors (Nardil), and selective serotonin reuptake inhibitors (Prozac).

20.56 Both cocaine and amphetamines increase dopamine levels in the brain. Cocaine blocks reuptake of dopamine, and amphetamines accelerate release of dopamine.

20.57 Tetrahydrocannabinol (THC) increases dopamine levels in the same brain areas where dopamine levels increase after administration of heroin and cocaine.

20.58 When it was discovered that the brain had receptors for neurotransmitters that came from plants, scientists reasoned that there must also be animal neurotransmitters that acted on the same receptors. It seems to be a coincidence that the brain receptors that respond to animal neurotransmitters also respond to plant neurotransmitters.

20.59 All of these complex behaviors involve enkephalins.

20.60 An ethnobotanist works in remote regions of the world to learn what indigenous people have discovered about the healing power of plants.

20.61 Combinatorial chemistry begins with the belief that a defined set of chemical subunits may yield an effective drug. These subunits are allowed to react in every possible combination, many reactions at a time, on a microscale. Computers keep track of the vast number of results and screen the products for pharmaceutical usefulness. The combinatorial approach provides many more drug candidates, in a much shorter time period and at a lower cost, than traditional methods of drug design.

20.62 Studies of the exact size and shape of biomolecules give scientists information about receptor sites of molecules of interest. This information allows scientists to design drugs with properties suitable for the desired drug-receptor interaction with the target biomolecule.

20.63 Computers serve many purposes in the development of new drugs. They can be used to consult a database for information about drug-receptor interactions and about the physical properties of both drugs and biomolecules. Computers can be used to make models of the interaction of a drug with a receptor; these models can be rotated in order to examine the drug-receptor fit from many angles. All of this information enables chemists to design a drug with the desired physical and chemical properties.

Applications

20.64 Homeostasis is the maintenance of a constant internal environment in the body.

20.65 Clinical chemistry analyzes the concentrations of significant ions and compounds in tissues and bodily fluids to determine which bodily systems are failing to maintain homeostasis.

20.66 Plants must synthesize hormones in the cells where they are needed because plants don't have endocrine systems nor do they have a continuously circulating fluid like blood.

20.67 Plant growth is controlled by an auxin (a plant growth hormone). The weed-killer 2,4-D mimics the effect of this hormone by promoting excessive plant growth, which kills the weed.

20.68 Epibatidine acts as a painkiller by binding to an acetylcholine receptor in the central nervous system (like nicotine) rather than to an opioid receptor (like morphine).

20.69 Modifications to epibatidine that could be tested as painkillers might include adding or changing substituents on the two epibatidine rings. These compounds with modified rings might be able to act at the same receptor as epibatidine.

General Questions and Problems

20.70 The *hormone receptor* recognizes the hormone and sets into motion the series of reactions that result in the response of the cell to hormonal stimulation.
The hormone-receptor complex interacts with the *G protein* and causes it to bind GTP. The G-protein mediates the reaction between the receptor and adenylate cyclase.
The G protein–GTP complex activates *adenylate cyclase*, which catalyzes the formation of the second messenger, cyclic AMP. Cyclic AMP initiates the reactions that the hormone is designed to stimulate.

20.71 It is important for the second messenger (cyclic AMP) to break down rapidly after synthesis for two reasons. First, once the message has been delivered, cyclic AMP is no longer needed to activate reactions. Second, the precursor of cyclic AMP must be ready for the next signal.

20.72 Signal amplification is the process in which a small signal induces a response much larger in magnitude than the original signal. For hormones, this amplification begins with the activation of the G-protein; one hormone–receptor complex can activate many G-protein–GTP complexes. Each G-protein–GTP complex, in turn, can activate many molecules of adenylate cyclase, which can stimulate production of many molecules of cyclic AMP. The importance of signal amplification is that a small amount of hormone can cause a very large response.

20.73 When caffeine inhibits the enzymatic hydrolysis of cyclic AMP, response to a hormonal signal is prolonged.

20.74 With the exception of the circled groups, testosterone and progesterone are identical.

Testosterone   Progesterone

20.75

Ethynyl estradiol   Norethindrone

Ethynyl estradiol and norethindrone differ only in the ring on the left. Ethynyl estradiol has a phenolic ring, and norethindrone has a ketone group and a double bond in that ring.

Estradiol   Progesterone

The only difference between ethynyl estradiol and estradiol is in the five-membered ring, where a –C≡CH group that is present in ethynyl estradiol is absent in estradiol. Norethindrone and progesterone differ in two respects. (1) The five-membered ring of norethindrone contains a —C≡CH group and an –OH group, whereas the five-membered group of progesterone contains a methyl ketone (acetyl) group. (2) A methyl group between the first two rings is present in progesterone and absent in norethindrone.

20.76 The craving for chocolate might be explained by the stimulation of dopamine receptors by anandamides, producing feelings of satisfaction similar to those produced by THC. The effect of chocolate consumption may be a milder version of marijuana's effects.

20.77 The first step in the conversion of tyrosine to epinephrine (substitution of –OH for –H on the aromatic ring) is catalyzed by tyrosine hydroxylase, an oxidoreductase (subclass: hydroxylase). The second step (loss of CO_2) is catalyzed by dopa decarboxylase, a lyase (subclass: decarboxylase).

20.78 Testosterone can be converted to androsterone by reduction of the ketone group and the double bond in the first ring, and by oxidation of the hydroxyl group in the five-membered ring. Estradiol can be converted to estrone by oxidation of the –OH group in the five-membered ring. Most of these changes occur as a result of oxidations and reductions.

Self–Test for Chapter 20

Multiple Choice:

1. Which of the following compounds is an acetylcholine agonist?
   (a) Nicotine   (b) Succinylcholine   (c) Tubocurarine   (d) Atropine

2. Which of the following hormones regulates the balance of Na^+ and K^+ ions in cellular fluid?
   (a) Androsterone   (b) Progesterone   (c) Aldosterone   (d) Cortisone

3. Cocaine affects the brain because it:
   (a) accelerates the release of dopamine   (b) blocks reuptake of dopamine   (c) raises the level of endorphins   (d) all of the above

4. An effective antihistamine has all of the structural elements listed except:
   (a) an ethylamine skeleton   (b) a tertiary amine   (c) an ether oxygen   (d) two bulky –R groups.

5. Which of the following compounds is a neurotransmitter but not a hormone?
   (a) dopamine   (b) norepinephrine   (c) epinephrine   (d) acetylcholine

6. Which of the following compounds does not reside in the cell membrane?
   (a) cyclic AMP   (b) epinephrine receptor   (c) adenylate cyclase   (d) G protein

7. Hormones and neurotransmitters have all of the following in common except:
   (a) They both regulate reaction rates.   (b) They both can be amino acid derivatives.   (c) They both interact with receptors at target tissues.   (d) They both travel through the bloodstream.

8. Which of the following events doesn't occur in "fight or flight"?
   (a) Epinephrine crosses the cell membrane.   (b) Epinephrine stimulates production of cyclic AMP.   (c) Glucose is released from storage.   (d) Cyclic AMP is converted to AMP.

9. Control of the endocrine system occurs in the:
   (a) pancreas   (b) pituitary gland   (c) adrenal glands   (d) hypothalamus

10. Which of the following isn't a site for hormone receptors?
    (a) outer cell surface   (b) cytoplasm within the cell   (c) cell nucleus   (d) blood stream

Complete the following sentences:

1. _____ is a life-threatening allergic response.

2. In direct neural control, the hypothalamus controls the release of hormones by the _____ gland.

3. Neurotransmitter molecules are stored in _____.

4. _____ is the neurotransmitter responsible for the symptoms of allergic reactions.

5. Nerves that rely on acetylcholine as their neurotransmitter are referred to as _____ nerves.

6. The hormone _____ prepares the uterus to receive a fertilized egg.

7. An _____ is a neuropeptide that acts at opiate receptors.

8. A person who studies the healing powers of plants from remote regions is a _____.

9. One neuron is separated from another by a gap called a _____ _____.

10. Heroin, alcohol, and cocaine all produce an elevated level of the neurotransmitter _____.

11. The hormone _____ contains iodine atoms.

12. After an emergency, the enzyme _____ catalyzes hydrolysis of cyclic AMP to AMP.

Tell whether the following statements are true or false:

1. Only steroid hormones can cross the cell membrane to activate enzymes.

2. Cocaine accelerates the release of dopamine.

3. In direct release of hormones, hormones move through the bloodstream to the posterior pituitary gland, where they are stored until needed.

4. Some neurotransmitters can act directly; others use second messengers.

5. Acetylcholine is synthesized at postsynaptic neurons.

6. Choline is a quaternary ammonium ion.

7. Epinephrine reduces blood pressure and slows the heart rate.

8. An enlarged thyroid gland is a symptom of excess iodine in the diet.

9. Polypeptide hormones vary greatly in size.

10. Succinylcholine is a competitive antagonist for acetylcholine.

Match the entries on the left with their partners on the right.

1. Androgen

2. Tricyclic antidepressant

3. Acetylcholine agonist

4. Natural estrogen

5. Second messenger

6. Oxytocin

7. Regulatory hormone

8. MAO inhibitor antidepressant

9. Synthetic estrogen

10 Acetylcholine antagonist

11. Glucocorticoid

12 SSRI inhibitor antidepressant

(a) Polypeptide hormone

(b) Progesterone

(c) Cortisone

(d) ACTH

(e) Testosterone

(f) Norethindrone

(g) Cyclic AMP

(h) Amitriptyline (Elavil)

(i) Fluoxetine (Prozac)

(j) Phenelzine (Nardil)

(k) Nicotine

(l) Atropine

Chapter Outline

I. Energy and cells (Sections 21.1–21.3).
   A. Energy requirements for living things (Section 21.1).
      1. Energy must be released from food gradually.
      2. Energy must be stored in a readily accessible form.
      3. The rate of release of energy from storage must be finely controlled.
      4. Just enough energy must be released as heat to maintain body temperature.
      5. Energy in a form other than heat must be available to drive reactions that aren't spontaneous at body temperature.
   B. Free energy and biochemical reactions (Section 21.2).
      1. In favorable chemical reactions, free energy is released.
         a. Favorable reactions occur when heat is released and/or disorder increases.
         b. These reactions are described as exergonic.
         c. In favorable reactions, the products are more stable than the reactants.
         d. Favorable reactions have a negative value for ΔG.
      2. Free energy must be provided for unfavorable chemical reactions to take place.
         a. Unfavorable reactions are described as endergonic.
         b. Energy must be supplied in order for endergonic reactions to proceed.
         c. In unfavorable reactions, the products are less stable than the reactants.
         d. Unfavorable reactions have a positive value for ΔG.
   C. The cell and energy (Section 21.3).
      1. Simple organisms have prokaryotic cells.
      2. More complicated organisms have eukaryotic cells.
         These cells have membrane-enclosed nuclei and organelles.
      3. Structure of eukaryotic cells.
         a. Everything between the cell membrane and the nuclear membrane is the cytoplasm.
         b. The fluid of the cytoplasm is the cytosol.
         c. The most important organelles are the mitochondria.
            i. Mitochondria consist of a smooth outer membrane and a folded inner membrane.
            ii. The space between the two membranes is the intermembrane space.
            iii. The space enclosed by the inner membrane is the mitochondrial matrix.
            iv. Most of the energy-producing reactions of the cell begin in the mitochondrial matrix.
II. Metabolism (Sections 21.4–21.7).
   A. Overview of metabolism (Section 21.4).
      1. A sequence of reactions in metabolism is known as a metabolic pathway.
         a. Pathways may be linear, cyclic or spiral.
         b. Pathways that break molecules apart are known as catabolic pathways.
         c. Pathways that build molecules are known as anabolic pathways.
      2. Catabolism consists of four phases.
         a. Digestion occurs in the mouth and small intestine.
         b. Small molecules are degraded in the cell to yield acetyl-SCoA.
         c. Acetyl groups are oxidized to yield CO_2, H_2O and energy.
         d. Some of the energy is transferred to ATP and reduced coenzymes.

B. Strategies of metabolism (Sections 21.5–21.7).
  1. ATP and energy transfer (Section 21.5).
    a. ATP contains two phosphoric anhydride bonds and a phosphate ester bond.
    b. Hydrolysis of one phosphate anhydride bond provides –7.3 kcal/mol of energy.
    c. Synthesis of ATP from ADP and phosphate requires +7.3 kcal/mol of energy.
    d. Synthesis of ATP occurs when there is energy to store, and hydrolysis of ATP occurs when energy is needed.
  2. Metabolic pathways and coupled reactions (Section 21.6).
    a. In any reaction, the amount of energy consumed or released is the same, no matter what the path.
    b. The overall energy change for a series of reactions can be found by adding up the free energy changes for the individual steps.
    c. A reaction that is energetically unfavored can take place if it is coupled with a reaction that is energetically favored.
      i. The phosphorylation of glucose can take place by coupling with the conversion of ATP to ADP.
      ii. ATP can be synthesized by coupling with the transfer of a phosphoryl group from phosphoenolpyruvate.
  3. Oxidized and reduced coenzymes (Section 21.7).
    a. Many biochemical reactions are redox reactions.
      i. Oxidation may be loss of electrons, loss of hydrogen or addition of oxygen.
      ii. Reduction may be gain of electrons, gain of hydrogen or removal of oxygen.
      iii. Reductions and oxidations always occur together.
    b. Common redox coenzymes are NAD^+, $NADP^+$ and FAD (written in the oxidized form).
      i. NAD^+ and $NADP^+$ are used to oxidize alcohols to carbonyl compounds.
      ii. FAD catalyzes the formation of a double bond.
    c. The energy stored in $FADH_2$, $NADH/H^+$ and $NADPH/H^+$ can be passed on to ATP.
III. Metabolic pathways (Sections 21.8–21.10).
  A. The citric acid cycle (Section 21.8).
    1. Oxidation of two-carbon acyl groups from acetyl-SCoA to CO_2 occurs in the citric acid cycle.
    2. The citric acid cycle is a closed loop of eight reactions in which the product of step 8 is a reactant in step 1.
    3. The cycle operates only if:
      a. Acetyl groups are available.
      b. NAD^+ and FAD are in their oxidized form.
      c. Oxygen is available.
    4. A summary of steps:
      a. Steps 1, 2 : Preparation.
        i. Acetyl-SCoA + oxalate —> citrate.
        ii. Citrate is isomerized to isocitrate.
      b. Steps 3, 4 : Oxidative decarboxylation.
        i. Isocitrate is oxidized and decarboxylated to form α-ketoglutarate, with reduction of NAD^+.
        ii. α-Ketoglutarate is decarboxylated to form succinyl–SCoA and reduced NAD^+.
      c. Step 5 : Phosphorylation.
        Succinyl-SCoA + GDP —> succinate + HSCoA + GTP.
      d. Step 6 : Oxidation of succinate.
        Succinate + FAD —> fumarate + $FADH_2$.
      e. Steps 7, 8 : Regeneration of oxaloacetate.
        i. Fumarate + H_2O —> malate.
        ii. Malate + NAD^+ —> oxaloacetate + $NADH/H^+$.

5. Net result of citric acid cycle:
   a. Production of four reduced coenzyme molecules.
   b. Conversion of an acetyl group to two CO_2 molecules.
   c. Production of one ATP.
B. The electron transport chain and production of ATP (Section 21.9).
   1. The end product of the electron transport chain is water in the reaction :
      $$O_2 + 4\ e^- + 4\ H^+ \longrightarrow 2\ H_2O$$
   2. The reactions of the electron transport chain are coupled to oxidative phosphorylation.
   3. Enzymes for electron transport are embedded in the mitochondrial membrane.
   4. Features of the electron transport chain:
      a. Hydrogen and electrons from NADH and $FADH_2$ enter the respiratory chain from the mitochondrial matrix.
      b. Electrons pass from weaker to stronger electron acceptors.
      c. Some of the energy released is used to transport H^+ into the intermembrane space.
      d. The H^+ concentration gradient creates a potential energy difference that is crucial for ATP synthesis.
      e. H^+ ions can return to the complex only by passing through a channel that is part of the ATP synthase complex.
         The energy that they release drives the phosphorylation of ATP.
   5. Various cofactors, including iron–sulfur clusters and cytochromes, are involved in electron transport.
   6. Ultimately, electrons are passed on to oxygen, which combines with H^+ to form H_2O.
   7. The energy needed for ATP synthesis is provided by the passage of H^+ ions through the ATP synthase enzyme complex.
   8. The passage of electrons from one mol NADH produces from 2.5–3 mol ATP.
C. Superoxide and other oxygen byproducts (Section 21.10).
   1. Oxygen can be consumed in other redox reactions besides electron transport.
   2. The products of these reactions may be H_2O_2, the $\cdot OH^-$ radical, or superoxide ion O_2^- .
   3. People are protected from the harmful effects of these species by several enzymes, as well as by antioxidants and vitamins A, C and E.

Solutions to Chapter 21 Problems

21.1 Use two facts to solve this problem:

(1) A reaction with a negative ΔG is exergonic, and a reaction with a positive ΔG is endergonic.
(2) A reaction with a larger negative ΔG releases more energy than a reaction with a smaller negative ΔG.

Thus, reactions (a) and (c) are exergonic, and reaction (b) is endergonic. Reaction (a) releases the most energy, because its ΔG has a larger negative value than the ΔG's of the other reactions.

21.2 The amount of energy produced by both processes is the same.

21.3 (a) Oxidation of glucose is exergonic, and photosynthesis is endergonic.
(b) Sunlight provides the energy for the endergonic pathway.

21.4 (a) Carbohydrates are digested in the mouth, stomach and small intestine to yield sugars, which are degraded in the cytosol to pyruvate. Pyruvate is converted to acetyl-SCoA, which enters the citric acid cycle and is oxidized to CO_2. The reduced coenzymes that are generated by oxidation of acetyl-SCoA enter the electron-transport chain and are used in the production of ATP by oxidative phosphorylation.

(b) The products of amino acid catabolism can enter the central metabolic pathway as pyruvate, acetyl-SCoA and as citric acid cycle intermediates.

21.5

Acetyl phosphate

21.6 This strategy ensures that an exergonic reaction only occurs when the energy it releases is needed.

21.7

Glycerol   Glycerol 1-phosphate

21.8 If a metabolic pathway that breaks down a molecule is exergonic, the reverse of that pathway (synthesis) *must* be endergonic. The only way to synthesize the product is to couple the energetically unfavorable reactions with other reactions that are energetically favorable in a pathway that differs from the reverse of the breakdown pathway.

21.9 Acetyl phosphate + H_2O $\longrightarrow$ Acetate + $HOPO_3^{2-}$ + H^+ $\Delta G = -10.3$ kcal/mol

ADP + $HOPO_3^{2-}$ + H^+ $\longrightarrow$ ATP + H_2O $\Delta G = +7.3$ kcal/mol

_____

Acetyl phosphate + ADP $\longrightarrow$ Acetate + ATP $\Delta G = -3.0$ kcal/mol

The reaction is favorable because ΔG is negative.

21.10 Yes. If you look at the structure of FAD shown in Section 21.7, you will see that ADP appears on the right side of the FAD molecule.

21.11 The hydrogen atoms removed are circled.

Step 3:

Step 6:

Step 8:

21.12 Citrate and isocitrate are the anions of tricarboxylic acids.

21.13 Reduced coenzymes are produced in steps 3, 4, 6, and 8.

21.14 In Step 6 of the citric acid cycle, succinate dehydrogenase catalyzes the removal of two hydrogens from succinate to yield fumarate. The hydrogens are transferred to the coenzyme FAD to produce the reduced coenzyme $FADH_2$.

21.15 α-Ketoglutarate and oxaloacetate are α-keto acids.

21.16 Isocitrate has two chiral carbon atoms.

21.17 Steps 1-4 correspond to the first stage, and steps 5-8 correspond to the second stage.

21.18 The pH is higher in the mitochondrial matrix.

21.19 O_2 is the final electron acceptor. When H^+ ions move from a region of high concentration to a region of low concentration, energy is released that is used in ATP synthesis.

Understanding Key Concepts

21.20 (a) Exergonic reaction:

Succinyl phosphate + H_2O ⟶ Succinate + $HOPO_3^{2-}$ + H^+

(b) Endergonic reaction:

$ADP + HOPO_3^{2-} + H^+$ ⟶ $ATP + H_2O$ $\Delta G = +7.3$ kcal/mol

21.21 (a) The digestion of starch to glucose occurs in Stage 1 of food metabolism.
(b) The synthesis of ATP takes place in Stage 4 of digestion.
(c) The reactions shown represent the citric acid cycle and occur in Stage 3 of food metabolism.
(d) Production of acetyl-SCoA from glucose is a result of Stage 2 of food metabolism.

21.22 When ATP "drives" a reaction, energy from ATP hydrolysis is used to allow another reaction to proceed. In this case, the reaction that forms fatty acid-SCoA from a fatty acid and coenzyme A is endergonic and is unfavorable in the absence of ATP. When the energy from hydrolysis of ATP is used to drive the reaction, the formation of fatty acid-SCoA can take place. Coupling is the metabolic strategy in which the energy from an energetically favorable reaction can be used to allow an energetically unfavorable reaction to take place.

21.23 In the steps of the citric acid cycle in which acetyl groups are oxidized to CO_2, NAD^+ is an acceptor of hydride ions, forming NADH. The hydrogen ions that are removed in an oxidation using NAD^+ are released to the mitochondrial matrix. NADH transfers electrons to the enzymes and coenzymes of the electron transport chain in the fourth stage of metabolism. Ultimately, the hydrogen ions combine with reduced oxygen to form H_2O.

21.24

(a) The coenzyme NAD^+ is involved with reaction **A**.
(b) CO_2 is evolved and an H^+ is added in reaction **B**.
(c) Reaction **A** is catalyzed by an oxidoreductase, and reaction **B** occurs spontaneously.
(d) The product of step **A** is a β–keto acid because its ketone group is two carbons away from the carboxylic acid group bonded to the middle carbon.

21.25

Step	Reaction	Reaction Type	Type of enzyme
1.	Oxaloacetate —> Citrate	Addition	Lyase
2.	Citrate —> Isocitrate	Isomerization	Isomerase
3.	Isocitrate —> α-Ketoglutarate	Oxidation, loss of CO_2	Oxidoreductase
4.	α-Ketoglutarate—>Succinyl-SCoA	Oxidation, loss of CO_2	Oxidoreductase; lyase
5.	Succinyl-SCoA —> Succinate	Hydrolysis, phosphorylation	Ligase
6.	Succinate —> Fumarate	Oxidation	Oxidoreductase
7.	Fumarate —> Malate	Addition of H_2O	Lyase
8.	Malate —> Oxaloacetate	Oxidation	Oxidoreductase

21.26 Metals are better oxidizing and reducing agents. Also, they can accept and donate electrons in one-electron increments.

Free Energy and Biochemical Reactions

21.27 An endergonic reaction requires energy, and an exergonic reaction releases energy.

21.28 For a reaction to be favorable, it must release energy and thus have a negative ΔG.

21.29 The sign of ΔG predicts whether a reaction is favorable (negative ΔG) or unfavorable (positive ΔG).

21.30 Enzymes only increase the rate of reaction and have no effect on either the magnitude or the sign of ΔG.

21.31 Reactions (a) and (b) are exergonic, and reaction (c) is endergonic. Reaction (a) proceeds farthest toward products at equilibrium because it has the largest negative value for ΔG. Reaction (b) produces a phosphate (GTP) that can later yield energy by giving up a phosphoryl group.

21.32 Reactions (a) and (c) are exergonic; reaction (b) is endergonic. Reaction (a) proceeds farthest toward products at equilibrium because it has the largest negative value for ΔG.

Cells and their Structure

21.33

Prokaryotic Cells	Eukaryotic Cells
Quite small	Relatively large
No nucleus	Nucleus
Dispersed DNA	DNA in nucleus
No organelles	Organelles
Occur in single-celled organisms	Occur in single-celled and higher organisms

21.34 Prokaryotic cells are found in bacteria and algae. Eukaryotic cells are found in all other organisms.

21.35 Organelles are subcellular structures that perform specialized tasks within the cell.

21.36 The cytoplasm consists of everything between the cell membrane and the nuclear membrane. The cytosol is the medium that fills the interior of the cell and contains electrolytes, nutrients and many enzymes, in aqueous solution.

21.37 A mitochondrion is egg-shaped and consists of a smooth, outer membrane and a folded inner membrane. The intermembrane space lies between the outer and inner membranes, and the space enclosed by the inner membrane is called the *mitochondrial matrix*.

21.38 Mitochondria are called the body's "power plant" because 90% of the body's supply of ATP is synthesized there.

Metabolism

21.39 Metabolism refers to all reactions that take place inside cells. Digestion is a part of metabolism in which food is broken down into small organic molecules.

21.40 Metabolic processes that break down molecules are called *catabolism*. Metabolic processes that assemble larger molecules from smaller molecules are known as *anabolism*.

21.41 Acetyl-SCoA is formed from the catabolism of all three major classes of food.

21.42 *First* ——> *Last*
digestion, citric acid cycle, electron transport, oxidative phosphorylation

Strategies of Metabolism

21.43 Adenosine triphosphate (ATP) is formed during catabolism to store chemical energy.

21.44 ATP is called a high-energy molecule because energy is released when ATP transfers a phosphoryl group to other molecules.

21.45 ATP has a triphosphate group bonded to C5 of ribose, and ADP has a diphosphate group in that position.

21.46 An ATP molecule transfers a phosphoryl group to another molecule in exergonic reactions.

21.47 A reaction that is energetically unfavorable can be combined with a reaction that is energetically favorable so that the overall reaction is energetically favorable. The two reactions are then said to be coupled.

21.48

1,3-Bisphosphoglycerate + H_2O ⟶
  3-Phosphoglycerate + $HOPO_3^{2-}$ + H^+ $\Delta G = -11.8$ kcal/mol

$ADP + HOPO_3^{2-} + H^+$ ⟶ $ATP + H_2O$ $\Delta G = +7.3$ kcal/mol

———

1,3-Bisphosphoglycerate + ADP ⟶
  3-Phosphoglycerate + ATP $\Delta G = -4.5$ kcal/mol

The reaction is favorable because ΔG is negative.

21.49

$$\text{1,3-Bisphosphoglycerate} \xrightarrow[\quad\quad]{\text{ADP}\quad\text{ATP}} \text{3-Phosphoglycerate}$$

21.50 The hydrolysis of fructose 6-phosphate ($\Delta G = -3.3$ kcal/mol) is not favorable for phosphorylating ADP ($\Delta G = +7.3$ kcal/mol) because the overall value of ΔG (+ 4.0 kcal/mol) is positive.

21.51 (a) NAD^+ is reduced when a molecule is dehydrogenated.
(b) NAD^+ is an oxidizing agent because it oxidizes substrates and is itself reduced.
(c) NAD^+ oxidizes secondary alcohols to ketones.
(d) After dehydrogenation, NAD^+ becomes $NADH/H^+$.
(e)

$$\underset{\displaystyle |}{\overset{\displaystyle |}{\text{H}-\text{C}-\text{OH}}} \xrightarrow[\quad\quad]{NAD^+ \quad NADH/H^+} \underset{\displaystyle |}{\text{C}=\text{O}}$$

21.52 (a) FAD is reduced when a molecule is dehydrogenated.
(b) FAD is an oxidizing agent.
(c) FAD oxidizes –CH$_2$CH$_2$– to –CH=CH–.
(d) Dehydrogenation converts FAD to FADH$_2$.
(e)

The Citric Acid Cycle

21.53 The citric acid cycle takes place in cellular mitochondria.

21.54 The citric acid cycle is also known as the Krebs cycle or the tricarboxylic acid cycle.

21.55 Oxaloacetate is the starting point for the citric acid cycle.

Oxaloacetate

21.56 The two acetyl-SCoA carbons are oxidized to CO$_2$ in the citric acid cycle.

21.57 (a) Oxidations occur in the steps where NAD$^+$ and FAD are reduced (steps 3, 4, 6, and 8).
(b) Decarboxylations occur in steps 3 and 4.
(c) A hydration occurs in step 7.

21.58 Three molecules of NADH/H$^+$ and one molecule of FADH$_2$ are produced in each turn of the citric acid cycle.

The Electron Transport Chain / Oxidative Phosphorylation

21.59 One complete citric acid cycle produces four reduced coenzymes, which enter the electron transfer chain and ultimately generate ATP.

21.60 The two primary functions of the electron transport chain are the conversion of ADP to ATP and the oxidation of the coenzymes NADH and FADH$_2$.

21.61 The coenzymes NADH and FADH$_2$ initiate the events of the electron transport chain.

21.62 The ultimate products of the electron transport chain are water, energy in the form of ATP, and the oxidized coenzymes FAD and NAD.

21.63 (a) FAD = flavin adenine dinucleotide
(b) CoQ = coenzyme Q
(c) NADH/H$^+$ = reduced nicotinamide adenine dinucleotide, plus hydrogen ion
(d) Cyt c = Cytochrome c

21.64 The iron atoms of the cytochromes are oxidized and reduced in the electron transport chain. The –OH and =O atoms in the CoQ ring undergo oxidation and reduction.

21.65 *First* $\xrightarrow{\hspace{7cm}}$ *Last*

NADH,   coenzyme Q,   cytochrome *c*

21.66

21.67 If $FADH_2$ and NADH weren't reoxidized, the body's supply of the oxidized forms of these coenzymes would be depleted, and the citric acid cycle would stop.

21.68 A pH differential is caused by the movement of H^+ ions across the inner mitochondrial membrane. There are more H^+ ions in the intermembrane space than in the mitochondrial matrix.

21.69 Oxidative phosphorylation refers to formation of ATP from the reactions of reduced coenzymes as they are oxidized in the electron-transport chain.

21.70 In oxidative phosphorylation, reduced coenzymes are oxidized, and ADP is phosphorylated.

Applications

21.71 In the light-dependent reaction of photosynthesis, H_2O interacts with the electron-transport system in chloroplasts to produce O_2 and the H^+ ions and electrons necessary for the formation of ATP and NADPH. For the bacteria surrounding black smokers, H_2S corresponds to H_2O, and the products of electron transport are sulfur and the H^+ ions and electrons necessary for the formation of ATP and NADPH.

21.72 Basal metabolic rate is the minimum amount of energy per unit time needed for breathing, maintaining body temperature, circulating blood and keeping all body organs functioning.

21.73 (no answer)

21.74 Daily activities such as walking use energy, and thus the body requires a larger caloric intake than that needed to maintain basal metabolism.

21.75 ADP and phosphate ions from the mitochondrial matrix bind in the loose stage. ADP and phosphate are converted to ATP in the tight stage. In the open stage the ATP molecule is released into the matrix.

21.76 The energy is provided by the movement of hydrogen ions from a region of high concentration to a region of lower concentration as they pass through a channel in the ATP synthase complex.

21.77 Chlorophyll contains a Mg^{2+} ion instead of a Fe^{2+} ion.

21.78 The light-dependent reaction of photosynthesis occurs in the chloroplasts and is used to produce O_2, NADPH, and ATP. The NADPH and ATP are used in the light-independent reaction to produce carbohydrate molecules from water and carbon dioxide.

21.79 Ribulose 5-phosphate + CO_2 + H_2O —> 2 3-Phosphoglycerate
The reaction is exergonic.

General Questions and Problems

21.80 The breakdown of molecules for energy must occur in several steps to avoid the production of large amounts of heat, to allow for storage of energy, and to control the rate of metabolism. Stepwise breakdown also allows energetically favorable steps to be coupled with other energetically unfavorable reactions.

21.81

21.82 Evidently, the isomer with a cis double bond cannot act as a substrate for the enzyme that is responsible for the next step in the citric acid cycle.

21.83 NAD^+ and FAD are associated with oxidoreductases.

21.84 Electrons from the oxidation of reduced coenzymes pass through the electron-transport chain. Ultimately, the electrons are used to reduce O_2, which combines with H^+ ions to form H_2O.

21.85 This reaction requires FAD because it involves the removal of two hydrogen atoms to introduce a double bond. The enzyme involved is an oxidoreductase.

21.86 Enzymes at the site of injury (catalase, in particular) catalyze the decomposition of hydrogen peroxide to oxygen, which bubbles from the wound.

21.87 Isocitrate and malate are chiral.

21.88 Energy from combustion is released to the surroundings as heat and is wasted. Energy from metabolic oxidation is released in several steps and is stored in each step so that is available for use in other metabolic processes.

21.89 The reactive species are $O_2^-\cdot$, $OH^-\cdot$, and H_2O_2. The enzymes superoxide dismutase and catalase and Vitamins E, C, and A can inactivate these species.

Self-Test for Chapter 21

Multiple choice:

1. Which of the following oxygen byproducts isn't produced in the human body?
   (a) O_2^- (b) O_3 (c) $HO\cdot$ (d) H_2O_2

2. The hydrolysis of which of the following substrates can be coupled with the reaction
   ADP + phosphate —> ATP to produce an energetically favorable reaction?
   (a) glucose 6-phosphate   (b) glucose 1-phosphate   (c) creatine phosphate
   (d) fructose 6-phosphate

3. Which of the following cofactors isn't held in a fixed position in electron transport?
   (a) Coenzyme Q   (b) FMN   (c) Iron–sulfur clusters   (d) Cytochrome a

4. Which of the following reactions is an oxidation?
   (a) Fe^{3+} —> Fe^{2+} (b) CH_3COOH —> CH_3CHO
   (c) $CH_3CH_2CH_2COOH$ —>$CH_3CH=CHCOOH$ (d) CH_3COOCH_3—> $CH_3COOH + CH_3OH$

5. All of the following statements about electron transport are true except:
   (a) A concentration gradient is established between the inner membrane and the mitochondrial
   matrix.   (b) Electrons are passed from weaker electron acceptors to stronger electron
   acceptors.   (c) A greater amount of energy is produced from oxidation of NADH than from
   oxidation of $FADH_2$.   (d) Some of the enzyme cofactors in the electron transport chain are
   mobile.

6. All of the following reactions are oxidations except:
   (a) Isocitrate —> α-Ketoglutarate   (b) α-Ketoglutarate —> Succinyl-SCoA
   (c) Succinate —> Fumarate   (d) Fumarate —> Malate

7. Which of the following citric acid cycle enzymes is an isomerase?
   (a) Citrate synthetase   (b) Aconitase   (c) Succinyl-SCoA synthetase   (d) Fumarase

8. Which coenzyme is not an oxidizing agent?
   (a) FAD   (b) Coenzyme Q   (c) Acetyl-SCoA   (d) NAD^+

9. All of the following reactions have positive ΔG except:
   (a) photosynthesis   (b) hydrolysis of acetyl-SCoA   (c) formation of ATP from ADP
   (d) formation of glucose 6-phosphate

10. Which of the following metabolic pathways doesn't occur in mitochondria?
    (a) oxidative phosphorylation   (b) ATP synthesis   (c) citric acid cycle   (d) degradation of
    carbohydrates

Complete the following sentences:

1. _____ cells are found in higher organisms.

2. $A \rightarrow B \rightarrow C$ is known as a _____ _____.

3. ATP is synthesized from _____ and _____.

4. A reaction that requires energy in order to take place is said to be energetically _____.

5. The citric acid cycle is also known as the _____ and as the _____ - _____ cycle.

6. α-Ketoglutaric acid reacts with acetyl-SCoA to yield _____ and _____.

7. Reactions that use the coenzyme _____ remove two hydrogens from an alcohol to yield a ketone.

8. A complete citric acid cycle yields _____ molecules of ATP.

9. _____ is the material that fills the interior of a cell.

10. _____ is a fast-acting enzyme that catalyzes the decomposition of reactive oxygen species.

11. The reaction succinate —> fumarate is catalyzed by _____ _____ .

12. _____ _____ is the minimal amount of energy required to stay alive.

Tell whether the following statements are true or false:

1. ATP is a higher-energy molecule than ADP.

2. Both prokaryotic and eukaryotic cells are found in higher organisms.

3. Anabolism is the breakdown of high energy molecules.

4. In a reaction that is energetically unfavorable, the energy of the products is less than the energy of the reactants.

5. The third and fourth stages of energy production take place in the mitochondria.

6. A reaction that is energetically unfavorable can use ATP as an energy source.

7. $FADH_2$ donates two electrons to cytochrome c in the respiratory chain.

8. FAD removes two hydrogens from a carbon chain to yield a double bond.

9. Release of heat and increase in order contribute to making a reaction favorable.

10. ATP is synthesized only in the respiratory chain.

11. In the synthesis of ATP from ADP, a phosphate ester bond is formed.

12. The reactions of the citric acid cycle may be exergonic or endergonic.

Match the entries on the left with their partners on the right:

1. Mitochondrion

2. Oxidative phosphorylation

3. Isocitrate

4. Anabolic reaction

5. Succinyl-SCoA → succinate

6. Citric acid cycle

7. Malate → oxaloacetate

8. Catabolic reaction

9. Respiratory chain

10. Cytochrome

11. Succinate → fumarate

12. Organelle

(a) Uses energy

(b) Yields one molecule of H_2O

(c) Releases energy

(d) Site of energy production in cell

(e) Reduces NAD^+ to $NADH/H^+$

(f) Tricarboxylic acid

(g) Contains an iron atom

(h) Subcellular structure

(i) Reduces FAD to $FADH_2$

(j) ATP synthesis

(k) Yields 2 molecules of CO_2

(l) Yields acetyl–SCoA plus ATP

Chapter 22 – Carbohydrates

Chapter Outline

I. General information about carbohydrates (Sections 22.1–22.3).
   A. Classification of carbohydrates (Section 22.1).
      1. By complexity.
         a. Monosaccharides don't yield smaller molecules when hydrolyzed.
         b. Disaccharides are composed of two monosaccharides.
         c. Polysaccharides are composed of a large number of monosaccharides.
      2. By carbonyl group.
         a. Aldoses contain an aldehyde carbonyl group.
         b. Ketoses contain a ketone carbonyl group.
      3. By number of carbons in a monosaccharide unit.
         Prefixes (tri-, tetra-, penta-) indicate the number of carbons in the monosaccharide.
   B. Handedness (Section 22.2–22.3).
      1. General characteristics of handed molecules (Section 22.2).
         a. Compounds having a carbon bonded to four different groups are chiral.
            i. A compound with a chiral carbon can exist in either a right-handed form (D) or a left-handed form (L).
            ii. These two forms are called enantiomers.
            iii. An "optically active" compound rotates the plane of plane-polarized light.
            iv. Enantiomers rotate the plane of plane-polarized light to the same extent but in opposite directions.
         b. Compounds having n chiral centers can have 2^n possible stereoisomers.
            i. Some of these isomers are enantiomers.
            ii. Stereoisomers that are not mirror images are diastereomers.
            iii. Some chiral compounds have fewer than the predicted number of stereoisomers because of symmetry.
      2. D and L sugars (Section 22.3).
         a. Stereoisomers can be drawn as Fischer projections.
            i. In these projections, the chiral carbon is drawn as the intersection of two perpendicular lines.
            ii. Bonds that point out of the page are shown as horizontal lines.
            iii. Bonds that point back into the page are vertical lines.
            iv. In sugars, the carbonyl group is at or near the top of a Fischer projection.
         b. Monosaccharides are divided into two families.
            i. In D sugars, the –OH group bonded to the chiral carbon farthest from the carbonyl group points to the right.
            ii. In L sugars, the –OH group bonded to the chiral carbon farthest from the carbonyl group points to the left.
            iii. Most of the carbohydrates that occur naturally are D stereoisomers.
         c. Fischer projections of molecules with more than one chiral carbon are drawn by stacking the chiral centers on top of each other.
         d. The enantiomer of a Fischer projection can be drawn by reversing the horizontal substituents on each chiral carbon.
II. Monosaccharides (Sections 22.4–22.6).
   A. Structure of monosaccharides (Section 22.4).
      1. Monosaccharides with five or more carbons can form cyclic internal hemiacetals.

a. The hemiacetal carbon (C1) can have two stereoisomeric forms.
b. Stereoisomers that differ in configuration only at the hemiacetal carbon are called anomers and are diastereomers.

2. Fischer projections can be converted to cyclic Haworth projections.
a. In a Haworth projection of the β anomer, the –CH$_2$OH group and the anomeric –OH group are on the same side of the ring.
b. In a Haworth projection of the α anomer, the –CH$_2$OH group and the anomeric –OH group are on opposite sides of the ring.
c. Groups that are on the left in a Fischer projection point up in a Haworth projection.
d. Groups that are on the right in a Fischer projection point down in a Haworth projection.
e. The –CH$_2$OH group at C6 points up in D sugars.

3. In solution, glucose exists as a mixture of open chain glucose (0.02%), the α anomer (36%) and the β anomer (64%).
a. Any mixture of glucose anomers achieves the same percent of anomers in solution.
b. This phenomenon is called mutarotation.

B. Important monosaccharides (Section 22.5).
1. Glucose is the most important monosaccharide in human metabolism.
2. Galactose.
a. Galactose differs from glucose only in the configuration at C4.
b. Galactose is a component of the disaccharide lactose.
c. Galactosemia is an inherited disorder of galactose metabolism.
3. Fructose.
a. Fructose is a component of the disaccharide sucrose.
b. Fructose is a ketohexose.
4. Ribose and 2-deoxyribose.
a. These monosaccharides are aldopentoses.
b. In 2-deoxyribose, the –OH group at C2 is replaced by –H.
c. Both of these sugars occur as components of nucleic acids.

C. Reactions of monosaccharides (Section 22.6).
1. Reaction with oxidizing agents.
a. Aldoses can be oxidized to carboxylic acids.
b. In basic solution, ketoses can also be oxidized to carboxylic acids.
    Ketoses and aldoses are in equilibrium with an intermediate enediol.
c. Carbohydrates that react with oxidizing agents are called reducing sugars.
2. Reaction with alcohols.
a. Hemiacetals react with alcohols to form acetals that are called glycosides.
b. The bond between the anomeric carbon atom and the oxygen of the –OR group is a glycosidic bond.
3. Formation of a bond between two monosaccharides.
a. Glycosidic bonds can form between two monosaccharides or between a monosaccharide and another molecule.
    i. These bonds may have either α or β orientation.
    ii. Glycosides are not reducing sugars.
b. Bonds between monosaccharides in more complex carbohydrates are also glycosidic bonds.
    The bond is described by specifying the positions of the connected carbon atoms and by using α or β to indicate the orientation.
c. Hydrolysis is the cleavage of a glycosidic bond.

III. Important disaccharides (Section 22.7).
    A. Maltose.
        1. Maltose consists of two glucose molecules joined by an α-1,4 glycosidic bond.
        2. Maltose occurs in prepared foods and occurs in the body as a product of starch digestion.
        3. Maltose is a reducing sugar.
    B. Lactose.
        1. Lactose consists of a β-D-glucose molecule joined to a β-D-galactose molecule by a β-1,4 glycosidic linkage.
        2. Lactose is a reducing sugar.
        3. Lactose occurs in milk.
        4. Lactose intolerance is a metabolic disorder in which lactose can't be digested.
    C. Sucrose.
        1. Sucrose consists of an α-D-glucose molecule joined to a β-D-fructose molecule by a glycosidic bond connecting the two anomeric carbons.
        2. Sucrose isn't a reducing sugar.
        3. Sucrose is the most common disaccharide.
IV. Important biomolecules derived from carbohydrates (Section 22.8).
    A. Chitin is a polymer of *N*-acetyl-D-glucosamine that occurs in the shells of shellfish and in insects.
    B. Cartilage and tendons consist of protein fibers and polysaccharides composed of β-D-glucuronic acid and *N*-acetyl-D-glucosamine or galactose derivatives.
    C. Hyaluronate and chondroitin 6-sulfate are present in joints, tendons and cartilage.
    D. Heparin is a polysaccharide that contains sulfate groups and that functions as an anticoagulant.
    E. Glycoproteins contain carbohydrates bonded to proteins and have important functions at cell surfaces.
V. Polysaccharides (Section 22.9)
    A. Polysaccharides consist of hundreds to thousands of monosaccharides connected by glycosidic bonds.
    B. Cellulose.
        1. Cellulose consists of thousands of β-D-glucose units connected by glycosidic bonds.
        2. Chains of cellulose fibers can form hydrogen bonds.
        3. Humans can't digest cellulose.
    C. Starch.
        1. Starch consists of glucose units joined by α-1,4 glycosidic bonds.
        2. There are two kinds of starch.
            a. Amylose consists of hundreds of glucose units joined by α-1,4 glycosidic bonds and is soluble in hot water.
            b. Amylopectin is much larger than amylose, also contains α-1,6 branches every 25 units, and is insoluble in water.
            c. Starch is digested in the small intestine by α-amylase.
    D. Glycogen.
        1. Glycogen resembles amylopectin but is larger and has more branches.
        2. In humans and animals, glycogen is used for carbohydrate storage.

Solutions to Chapter 22 Problems

22.1   The name of a monosaccharide consists of three parts:
(1) the prefix *aldo-* (if the carbonyl group is an aldehyde) or *keto-*(if the carbonyl group is a ketone);
(2) a number prefix, such as *tri-, tetr-, pent-, hex-* (to show the number of carbons in the monosaccharide);
(3) the suffix *-ose*, which indicates that the compound is a sugar).

22.2

22.3   An aldopentose (see illustration in Sec. 22.1) has three chiral carbon atoms. Using the fact that a molecule with n chiral carbons has 2^n stereoisomers, we calculate that an aldopentose has a maximum of $2^3 = 8$ stereoisomers.

22.4

If the monosaccharide shown on the left were to look in the mirror, it would see monosaccharide (d), its enantiomer.

22.5   The bottom carbon is not chiral. The orientations of the hydroxyl groups bonded to the chiral carbons must be shown in order to indicate which stereoisomer is pictured.

22.6   The enantiomers are mirror images. The –OH bonded to the chiral carbon farthest from the carbonyl group points to the right in the D enantiomer and to the left in the L enantiomer.

(a)   (b)

A D-aldopentose   An L-aldopentose   An L-ketohexose   A D-ketohexose

22.7   First, coil D-talose into a circular shape:

Next, rotate around the indicated single bond between C4 and C5 so that the –CH$_2$OH group (C6) points up.

Finally, form a hemiacetal bond between the aldehyde and the –OH group at C5.

β-anomer

α-anomer

22.8 Reverse the series of steps shown in Problem 22.7. First, break the hemiacetal bond.

Rotate around the single bond between C4 and C5 so that the hydroxyl group on C5 points down.

Uncoil D-mannose to arrive at the Fischer projection.

D-Mannose

22.9 (a) The monosaccharide is a hexose. (b) The tetracyclic ring system resembles the ring system of a steroid. (c) A lactone is a cyclic ester.

Ouabain

22.10

anomeric carbon (2)

The drawing represents the β anomer because the –OH group bonded to the anomeric carbon is on the same side of the ring as carbon 6.

22.11 Chiral carbons are starred. Remember that anomeric carbons and all other carbons bonded to four different groups are chiral.

(a)   (b)   (c)

α-D-Fructose   α-D-Ribose   β-D-2-Deoxyribose

22.12

cyclic AMP   ATP

from ribose

22.13

L-Fucose   α-D-Galactose   β-D-Galactose

(a) L-Fucose is an α anomer because the anomeric hydroxyl group is on the opposite side of the hemiacetal ring from carbon 6.

(b) L-Fucose is missing a hydroxyl group on carbon 6.

(c) The –OH group at carbon 2 that is below the plane of the ring in D-galactose is above the plane of the ring in L-fucose. The –OH groups that are above the plane of the ring in D-galactose are below the plane of the ring in L-fucose.

(d) 6-Deoxy-L-galactose is a correct name for L-fucose.

22.14

α-D-Ribose   +   CH₃OH $\xrightarrow[\text{catalyst}]{\text{H}^+}$ Methyl α-D-riboside   +   H₂O

β-D-Ribose   Methyl β-D-riboside

The two products are acetals because reaction with methanol occurs at the hemiacetal hydroxyl group, producing a compound with two –OR groups.

22.15 Cellobiose has a β-1,4 glycosidic link.

22.16

Cellobiose   β-D-Glucose   β-D-Glucose

22.17

(a)

α-D-Glucose   α-D-Glucose

Maltose

(b)

α-D-Glucose   β-D-Fructose

Sucrose

(c)

β-D-Galactcose   β-D-Glucose

Lactose

22.18 Glutamine and asparagine are the two amino acids with side-chain amide groups.

22.19 The two subunits of heparin are joined by an α-1,4 glycosidic link.

22.20 Starch has so few hemiacetal units per molecule (only the one at the end of a very long chain) that a positive reducing-sugar reaction with Tollens' reagent or Benedict's reagent is undetectable.

Understanding Key Concepts

22.21

$$\text{Starch} \xrightarrow{\text{Amylase}} \text{Maltose} \xrightarrow{\text{Maltase}} \text{Glucose}$$

polysaccharide   disaccharide   monosaccharide

Starch is a large polysaccharide consisting of many glucose subunits connected by α-1,4 glycosidic bonds. α-Amylase hydrolyzes these bonds to yield maltose, a disaccharide, and maltase cleaves the α-1,4 glycosidic bond of maltose to give the monosaccharide glucose.

22.22 (a) The two fructose molecules are diastereomers and anomers; they are stereoisomers that aren't mirror images. (b) D-Galactose and L-galactose are enantiomers. (c) L-Allose and D-glucose are diastereomers.

22.23 (a), (b)

    α anomer   β anomer   β anomer

(c) The linkage between monosaccharide **A** and monosaccharide **B** is an α-1,4 link that connects carbon 1 of **A** to carbon 4 of **B**.

(d) The linkage between monosaccharide **B** and monosaccharide **C** is an β-1,4 link that connects carbon 1 of **B** to carbon 4 of **C**.

22.24 (a) None of the three monosaccharides are identical, and none are enantiomers.

hydrolysis

A B C

L-Fucose D-Glucose D-Galactose

22.25 Monosaccharide **C** (D-galactose) is oxidized by an oxidizing agent because it is the only one of the three monosaccharides that has a hemiacetal in equilibrium with an open-chain aldehyde. Isolation and identification of the resulting carboxylic acid also identifies the terminal hemiacetal monosaccharide.

22.26 Monosaccharides **B** and **C** are the components of lactose, but **B** and **C** would have to be connected **C–B**, instead of **B–C**, in order for lactose to be part of the trisaccharide.

22.27

Polysaccharide	Linkage	Branching?
Cellulose	β-1,4	no
Amylose	α-1,4	no
Amylopectin	α-1,4	yes: α-1,6 branches occur ~ every 25 units
Glycogen	α-1,4	yes: even more α-1,6 branches than in amylopectin

22.28 In solution, an equilibrium exists between open-chain glucose and its cyclic hemiacetal forms. The open chain form reacts with the oxidizing agent, and, according to Le Châtelier's Principle, the equilibrium shifts to produce more of the open-chain form, which is also oxidized. Ultimately, all of the glucose is oxidized to gluconate.

Classification and Structure of Carbohydrates

22.29 A carbohydrate is a polyhydroxylated aldehyde or ketone (or a derivative of one of these) that belongs to one of the biologically most important classes of compounds.

22.30 The family-name ending for a sugar is -ose.

22.31 An aldose contains an aldehyde carbonyl group, and a ketose contains a ketone carbonyl group.

22.32

(a)	(b)	(c)	(d)
Threose	Ribulose	Xylose	Tagatose
an aldotetrose	a ketopentose	an aldopentose	a ketohexose

22.33

a ketoheptose

22.34

oxygen missing here

a four-carbon deoxy sugar

22.35 *Glucose* occurs in most food, especially fruits and vegetables, and in all living organisms.
Galactose occurs in brain tissue and as a component of lactose (milk sugar).
Fructose occurs in honey and in many fruits.
Ribose occurs in nucleic acids.

22.36 *Dextrose* is another name for glucose.

Handedness in Carbohydrates

22.37 *Enantiomers* are stereoisomers that are mirror images.

22.38 L-Glucose and D-glucose are mirror images (enantiomers).

22.39

enantiomers

The third stereoisomer doesn't have an enantiomer because it has a symmetry plane and is not chiral.

22.40

D Threose   chiral   D-Erythrose   achiral

The reduction product of D-erythrose has a symmetry plane and is achiral.

22.41 An optically active compound rotates the plane of plane-polarized light.

22.42 A polarimeter measures the degree of rotation of plane-polarized light by a solution of an optically active compound.

22.43 (a) Fructose rotates light to the left to a greater degree than glucose rotates light to the right.
(b) The mixture is called invert sugar because the sign of rotation of the fructose–glucose mixture is inverted from (opposite to) the sign of rotation of sucrose.

22.44 Equimolar solutions of enantiomers rotate light to the same degree but in opposite directions.

Reactions of Carbohydrates

22.45 A reducing sugar is a sugar that gives a positive reaction when treated with an oxidizing agent such as Tollens' reagent or Benedict's reagent. A sugar must have an aldehyde carbonyl group or a group that can isomerize to an aldehyde in order to give this reaction.

22.46 Mutarotation occurs when either a pure anomer or a mixture of anomers is dissolved in water. In either case, if the rotation of plane-polarized light is measured, the degree of rotation changes until it reaches a constant value. At this point, an equilibrium mixture of both anomers is present in the solution.

22.47 Most sugars exist in the cyclic hemiacetal form, in which a sugar hydroxyl group has added to the sugar carbonyl group in the same molecule. *Anomer* is the name given to each of the two stereoisomers formed. Anomers differ in the orientation of substituents at the hemiacetal carbon.

22.48 In the β form of a carbohydrate hemiacetal, the –OH group attached to C1 (the hemiacetal carbon) is on the same side of the ring as the –CH₂OH group. In the α form, the –OH group at C1 and the –CH₂OH group are on opposite sides of the ring.

22.49 The α form of D-gulose is shown, because the anomeric –OH group at C1 is on the opposite side of the hemiacetal ring from the –CH₂OH group at C6.

22.50

 =

β-D-Mannose   α-D-Mannose

22.51

D–Gulose

22.52

β-D-Ribulose

22.53–22.54

β-D-Allose

22.55

D-Glucose   Sorbitol

22.56

D-Fructose   Sorbitol   Mannitol

22.57

D-Glucose   Gluconic acid

22.58

D-Ribose   Ribonic acid

22.59 In a hemiacetal, an –OH group and an –OR group are bonded to a carbon atom that was formerly a carbonyl carbon. In an acetal, the carbon is bonded to two –OR groups.

a hemiacetal   an acetal

22.60 A *glycoside* is the acetal product that results from reaction of the hemiacetal –OH group of a carbohydrate with an alcohol.

22.61

22.62

The product in this problem has a cyclic hemiacetal carbon and is in equilibrium with an open-chain aldehyde that is a reducing sugar. The glycosides in Problem 22.61 are acetals and are not in equilibrium with an aldehyde.

Disaccharides and Polysaccharides

22.63

Disaccharide	occurs in:	made from:
maltose	fermenting grains	glucose + glucose
lactose	milk	glucose + galactose
sucrose	many plants	glucose + fructose

22.64 Lactose and maltose have hemiacetal linkages that give positive Tollens' test results. Sucrose has no hemiacetal group and is thus unreactive toward Tollens' reagent.

22.65 Amylose, a major component of the human diet, consists of α-D-glucose units linked together by α-1,4 glycosidic bonds. Cellulose, used by plants as a structural material, consists of β-D-glucose units linked together by β-1,4 glycosidic bonds.

22.66 Amylose and amylopectin are both components of starch and both consist of long polymers of α-D-glucose linked by α-1,4 glycosidic bonds. Amylopectin is much larger and has α-1,6 branches every 25 units or so along the chain.

22.67

22.68 Gentiobiose contains both an acetal grouping and a hemiacetal grouping. Gentiobiose is a reducing sugar because it has a hemiacetal group on the right-hand monosaccharide unit. A β-1,6 linkage connects the two monosaccharides.

22.69

22.70 Trehalose is a nonreducing sugar because it contains no hemiacetal linkages. The two D-glucose monosaccharides are connected by an α-1,1 acetal link

22.71 Amylopectin and glycogen are both polymers that are composed of α-D-glucose units linked by α-1,4 glycosidic bonds. Both amylopectin and glycogen have α-1,6 branches, but glycogen has many more branches and is much larger (1 million glucose units per molecule) than amylopectin (100,000 glucose units per molecule). Amylopectin is the major component of starch, which is used for carbohydrate storage in plants, and glycogen is used for carbohydrate storage in animals.

22.72

Amygdalin

Applications

22.73 In many cases, only one enantiomer of a molecule has the desired effect; the other enantiomer might be biologically inactive or might cause harmful side effects. A drug manufacturer might be able to patent a single enantiomer of a drug that has been on the market for a number of years and thus retain its market for the drug. In most cases, it is difficult and costly to synthesize a single-enantiomer drug.

22.74 Enzyme-catalyzed reactions are usually stereospecific and produce only one enantiomer of the compound of interest.

22.75

$$\frac{4 \text{ kcal}}{1 \text{ g}} \times 400 \text{ g} = 1600 \text{ kcal}: \frac{1600 \text{ kcal}}{2000 \text{ kcal}} \times 100\% = 80\%$$

80% of calories in a 2000 kcal daily diet would be digestible carbohydrate.

22.76 Starch, a polysaccharide, is an example of a complex carbohydrate in the diet. Glucose and fructose are simple carbohydrates found in the diet. Soluble and insoluble fiber are complex carbohydrates that can't be hydrolyzed to simple carbohydrates, and most of them pass undigested through the body.

22.77 Water forms hydrogen bonds with the hydroxyl groups of the carbohydrate portion of the glycoprotein.

22.78 The antifreeze in our cars lowers the freezing point of water. Antifreeze proteins slow the formation of ice crystals by forming hydrogen bonds with water molecules at the surface of ice crystals that are starting to form.

22.79 All blood groups have *N*-acetylglucosamine, galactose and fucose as components of their antigenic determinants. Blood group O is the universal donor because it has components common to all blood groups. The other blood groups have additional components of their antigenic determinants that provoke an immune response if blood with incompatible groups is mixed.

22.80 People with type O blood can receive blood only from other donors that have type O blood. People with type AB blood can give blood only to other people with type AB blood because antibodies to AB blood are present in the blood of people having any of the other blood types.

22.81 In a healthy diet, cellulose provides fiber, which aids in the passage of food through the digestive system.

22.82 Pectin and vegetable gum are two kinds of soluble fiber, which can be found in fruits, barley, oats and beans.

General Questions and Problems

22.83

D-Ribose and L-ribose are enantiomers that are identical in all properties (melting point, density, solubility and chemical reactivity) except for the direction that they rotate plane-polarized light (b).

22.84

D-Ribose and D-xylose are diastereomers and differ in all properties listed.

22.85

22.86

α-D-Fructose

22.87 The α and β hemiacetal forms of monosaccharides are diastereomers because they are not mirror images.

22.88

Raffinose

22.89 Raffinose is not a reducing sugar because it has no hemiacetal groups.

22.90 The sweet taste of a partially chewed cracker is due to the enzymatic breakdown of starch to glucose.

22.91

$$HOCH_2CCH_2OH \qquad \text{1,3-Dihydroxyacetone}$$

1,3-Dihydroxyacetone has no optical isomers because it has no chiral carbons.

22.92 Symptoms of the disease galactosemia, which results when the body lacks an enzyme needed to digest galactose, include:
In infancy: vomiting, enlarged liver, failure to thrive.
Eventual: liver failure, mental retardation, cataracts.

22.93

Dulcitol is optically inactive because it has a plane of symmetry and thus doesn't have an enantiomer.

22.94 Lactose intolerance is an inability to digest lactose. Symptoms include bloating, cramps and diarrhea.

22.95 Enzymes produced by the bacteria in yogurt predigest most of the lactose, making it possible for lactose-intolerant people to eat yogurt without symptoms.

22.96

```
        H    O
         \  //
          C
          |  *
    HO —  C — H
          |
     H —  C — OH
          |  *
     H —  C — OH
          |  *
    HO —  C — H
          |
         CH3
```

L-Fucose has four chiral carbons.

Self-Test for Chapter 22

Multiple choice:

1. One of these disaccharides is not a reducing sugar. Which one?
    (a) Sucrose   (b) Maltose   (c) Lactose   (d) Cellobiose

2. Which one of the following bonds doesn't occur in common polysaccharides?
    (a) α-1,4 bonds   (b) α-1,6 bonds   (c) β-1,4 bonds   (d) β-1,6 bonds

3. The compound shown is :
    (a) The α anomer of a ketopentose   (b) the α anomer of an aldohexose   (c) the β anomer of an aldopentose   (d) the β anomer of a ketohexose

4. Oxidation of the aldotetroses pictured in Section 22.2 can be controlled to produce dicarboxylic acids known as tartaric acids. How many stereoisomeric tartaric acids are there?
    (a) 1   (b) 2   (c) 3   (d) 4

5. *N*-Acetyl-D-glucosamine is a component of all of the following, except:
    (a) chitin   (b) blood group determinants   (c) tendons   (d) heparin

6. Humans can't digest cellulose because:
    (a) Its molecules are too big.   (b) Humans don't produce enzymes to digest polysaccharides.
    (c) Humans can't digest branched polysaccharides.   (d) Human enzymes that digest
    carbohydrates can only hydrolyze α glycosidic bonds.

7. Which blood group is the "universal donor"?
    (a) A   (b) B   (c) AB   (d) O

8. Which of the following polysaccharides consists of only α-1,4 glycosidic bonds?
    (a) amylopectin   (b) cellulose   (c) amylose   (d) glycogen

9. Which of these errors of carbohydrate metabolism is not life-threatening?
    (a) galactosemia   (b) lactose intolerance   (c) diabetes mellitus   (d) blood-group incompatibility

10 How many stereoisomers does an open-chain 2-ketopentose have?
    (a) 2   (b) 4   (c) 6   (d) 8

Complete the following sentences:

1. An object that has handedness is said to be _____.

2. Starch molecules are digested by enzymes called _____.

3. The two mirror image forms of a chiral molecule are called _____.

4. A reaction between an aldehyde carbonyl group and an alcohol hydroxyl group in the same
    molecule yields a _____.

5. *Levulose* is another name for _____.

6. _____ and _____ are two kinds of starch.

7. The reaction of a monosaccharide with an alcohol yields a _____.

8. _____ is used for food storage in animals.

9. D-Glucose can be classified as a _____.

10. 3-Pentanol is an _____ molecule.

11. A _____ is a stereoisomer that is not an enantiomer.

12. _____ have important functions at cell surfaces.

Tell whether the following statements are true or false:

1. All naturally-occurring carbohydrates are chiral.

2. Glucose is a reducing sugar.

3. In an L sugar, the –OH on the carbon nearest to the carbonyl group points to the left.

4. Humans can digest polysaccharides containing β-1,4 acetal links but not α-1,4 acetal links.

5. Achiral objects possess a plane of symmetry.

6. Crystalline glucose is a mixture of α anomer, β anomer, and open-chain forms.

7. Sucrose contains both acetal and hemiacetal groups.

8. Amylopectin and glycogen contain 1,4 and 1,6 acetal links.

9. An acetal is an ester.

10. Maltose is a disaccharide composed of glucose and galactose.

11. Two diastereomers rotate plane-polarized light in equal amounts but in opposite directions.

12. Not all compounds with n chiral carbons have 2^n stereoisomers.

Match the entries on the left with their partners on the right:

1. Maltose   (a) Aldohexose

2. Cellulose   (b) Glucose

3. Methyl glucoside   (c) Aldotriose

4. Ribose   (d) Glucose + fructose

5. Fructose   (e) Glucose + glucose

6. Glycogen   (f) Polysaccharide of α-D-glucose

7. Dextrose   (g) Glucose + galactose

8. Glucose   (h) Aldopentose

9. Sucrose   (i) Ketohexose

10. Lactose   (j) Acetal

11. Glyceraldehyde   (k) Animal starch

12. Amylose   (l) Polysaccharide of β-D-glucose

Chapter 23 – Carbohydrate Metabolism

Chapter Outline

I. Introduction to carbohydrate metabolism (Sections 23.1–23.2).
    A. Digestion of carbohydrates (Section 23.1).
        1. Digestion is the breakdown of food into small molecules.
        2. The products of digestion are absorbed from the intestinal tract.
        3. Digestion of carbohydrates.
            a. α–Amylase in the mouth breaks starch into smaller polysaccharides and maltose.
            b. α–Amylase in the small intestine further breaks down polysaccharides.
            c. Disaccharides are broken down to monosaccharides in the small intestine.
    B. Overview of glucose metabolism (Section 23.2).
        1. *Glycolysis* is the conversion of glucose to pyruvate; it occurs when energy is needed.
        2. *Glycogenesis* is the synthesis of glycogen from glucose; it occurs when excess glucose is present.
        3. The *pentose phosphate pathway* supplies other monosaccharides; it occurs when these are in short supply.
        4. *Glycogenolysis* is the breakdown of glycogen to glucose units; it occurs when the body needs glucose.
        5. Pyruvate has several fates:
            a. Under normal circumstances, pyruvate is converted to acetyl-SCoA.
            b. When oxygen is lacking, pyruvate is converted to lactate.
            c. When the body is starved for glucose, pyruvate is converted to glucose via *gluconeogenesis*.
II. Glycolysis and pyruvate metabolism (Sections 23.3–23.6).
    A. Glycolysis is the breakdown of glucose to two pyruvates (Section 23.3).
        Glycolysis occurs in the cytosol.
    B. Steps in glycolysis:
        1. Steps 1–3: Phosphorylation.
            a. Step 1: Glucose moves into the cell and is converted to glucose 6-phosphate, with the expenditure of one ATP.
            b. Step 2: Glucose 6-phosphate is isomerized to fructose 6-phosphate.
            c. Step 3: Fructose 6-phosphate is converted to fructose 1,6-bisphosphate, with the expenditure of one ATP.
        2. Steps 4,5: Cleavage and isomerization.
            a. Step 4: Fructose 1,6-bisphosphate is cleaved to glyceraldehyde 3-phosphate and dihydroxyacetone phosphate.
            b. Step 5: Dihydroxyacetone phosphate is isomerized to glyceraldehyde 3-phosphate.
        3. Steps 6–10: Energy generation.
            a. Step 6: Glyceraldehyde 3-phosphate is phosphorylated and oxidized to 1,3-bisphosphoglycerate: NAD^+ —> $NADH/H^+$.
            b. Step 7: 1,3-Bisphosphoglycerate transfers a phosphate to ADP to yield 3-phosphoglycerate.
            c. Step 8: 3-Phosphoglycerate is isomerized to 2-phosphoglycerate.
            d. Step 9: 2-Phosphoglycerate is dehydrated to phosphoenolpyruvate.
            e. Step 10: Phosphoenolpyruvate transfers a phosphate group to ADP to yield ATP and pyruvate.
    C. End results of glycolysis.
        1. Conversion of glucose to 2 pyruvates.
        2. Production of 2 ATP.
        3. Production of 2 $NADH/H^+$.

D. Entry of other sugars into glycolysis (Section 23.4).
   1. Fructose is converted to fructose 6-phosphate and enters glycolysis.
   2. Mannose is converted to fructose 6-phosphate and enters glycolysis.
   3. Galactose is converted to glucose 6-phosphate and enters glycolysis.
E. Pyruvate metabolism (Section 23.5).
   1. When oxygen is available, pyruvate is converted to acetyl-SCoA, with the conversion of NAD^+ to $NADH/H^+$ and the production of CO_2.
   2. When glucose is in short supply, pyruvate can be converted back to glucose by gluconeogenesis.
   3. Under anaerobic conditions, pyruvate is reduced to lactate, and $NADH/H^+$ is converted to NAD^+.
   4. In yeast, pyruvate is converted to ethanol and CO_2.
F. Energy output in complete catabolism of glucose (Section 23.6).
   1. The total energy output from glucose metabolism is the combined result of:
      a. Glycolysis.
      b. Pyruvate —> acetyl-SCoA.
      c. Citric acid cycle of two acetyl-SCoA molecules (and passage of the resulting reduced coenzymes through the respiratory chain).
      d. Passage of two reduced coenzymes from glycolysis through the respiratory chain.
   2. The number of ATP produced depends on:
      a. The number of electrons that enter the respiratory chain from reduced coenzymes.
      b. The number of ATP produced per reduced coenzyme.
      c. An estimated 30–38 ATP are produced per mol glucose catabolized.
III. Regulation of glucose metabolism (Sections 23.7–23.9).
   A. Regulation of glucose concentration in the blood (Section 23.7).
      1. Hypoglycemia: low blood sugar.
         The hormone glucagon stimulates breakdown of glycogen to glucose to raise blood sugar.
      2. Hyperglycemia: high blood sugar.
         The hormone insulin stimulates passage of glucose into cells to be used in energy production.
   B. Fasting and starvation (Section 23.8).
      1. First, glucose is released from glycogen.
      2. Then, glucose is synthesized from proteins via gluconeogenesis.
      3. Then, fats are metabolized to acetyl-SCoA, which enters the citric acid cycle.
      4. As the citric acid cycle is overloaded, acetyl-SCoA is removed by formation of ketone bodies.
      5. Ultimately, the body produces 50% of ATP from ketone bodies.
      6. The body can endure this state for months.
   C. *Diabetes mellitus* (Section 23.9).
      1. There are two types of *diabetes mellitus*.
         a. In Type I (juvenile), the pancreas produces insufficient insulin.
            i. Juvenile diabetes is an autoimmune disease, in which insulin-producing cells are destroyed.
            ii. Juvenile diabetes is treated by supplying insulin.
         b. In Type II (adult-onset), insulin doesn't aid the passage of glucose across the cell membrane.
            i. Adult-onset diabetes results when cell receptors fail to recognize insulin.
            ii. Drugs that increase insulin levels are an effective treatment.
      2. Complications of diabetes
         a. Cataracts may result from buildup of sorbitol in the eye.
         b. Ketoacidosis is caused by buildup of acidic ketones.
         c. Hypoglycemia may be due to an overdose of insulin or to failure to eat.

IV. Other pathways of carbohydrate metabolism (Sections 23.10, 23.11).
    A. Glycogen metabolism (Section 23.10).
        1. Glycogenesis.
           a. Glycogenesis occurs when glucose levels are high.
           b. The pathway to glycogen synthesis:
                Glucose —> Glucose 6-phosphate —> Glucose 1-phosphate —>
                Glucose-UDP —> Glycogen
        2. Glycogenolysis.
           a. Glycogenolysis occurs when there is an immediate need for energy.
           b   The pathway of glycogenolysis:
                Glycogen —> Glucose 1-phosphate —> Glucose 6-phosphate —> Glucose
    B. Gluconeogenesis (Section 23.11).
        1. Gluconeogenesis is the synthesis of glucose from any of several small molecules,
           including lactate, pyruvate, amino acids and glycerol.
        2. Gluconeogenesis occurs when the body is starved for glucose.
        3. Seven of the steps of gluconeogenesis are reversals of glycolysis steps.
           a. The other three steps are too endergonic, and alternate pathways must be used.
           b. Step 1 of gluconeogenesis:
                Pyruvate —> Oxaloacetate —> Phosphoenolpyruvate
           c. Oxaloacetate is an intermediate that allows amino acids to enter gluconeogenesis.

Solutions to Chapter 23 Problems

23.1 (a) *Glycogenolysis* is the release of glucose units from glycogen.

      (b) *Gluconeogenesis* is the synthesis of glucose from lactate or other noncarbohydrates.

      (c) *Glycogenesis* is the synthesis of glycogen from glucose.

23.2 The following synthetic pathways have glucose 6-phosphate as their first reactant:
      Glycogenesis: synthesis of glycogen from glucose
      Pentose phosphate pathway: synthesis of five-carbon sugars from glucose
      Glycolysis: conversion of glucose to pyruvate

23.3 (1) In *Step 6*, 1,3-bisphosphoglycerate is synthesized. In *Step 7*, the energy is harvested in ATP as 3-phosphoglycerate is formed.

      (2) In *Step 9*, phosphoenolpyruvate is synthesized. In *Step 10*, the energy is harvested in ATP as pyruvate is formed.

23.4 The following steps of glycolysis are isomerizations:

      Step 2: Glucose 6-phosphate → Fructose 6-phosphate

      Step 5: Dihydroxyacetone phosphate → Glyceraldehyde 3-phosphate

      Step 8: 3-Phosphoglycerate → 2-Phosphoglycerate

23.5

Glucose 6-phosphate   Fructose 6-phosphate

23.6 (a) Pyruvate is oxidized to a greater extent than glucose because it has two carbon-oxygen double bonds.
(b) Oxidation occurs in step 6, in which glyceraldehyde 3-phosphate is oxidized and phosphorylated to give 1,3 bisphosphoglycerate. NAD^+ is the oxidizing agent.

23.7

Fructose   Fructose 6-phosphate

Fructose 6-phosphate enters glycolysis at step 3.

23.8

D-Glucose   D-Galactose

Glucose and galactose differ in configuration at carbon 4.

23.9 One molecule of CO_2 is formed when one molecule of pyruvate is converted to acetyl-SCoA. Two more molecules of CO_2 are formed in the citric acid cycle; one is formed in the conversion isocitrate —> α-ketoglutarate (Step 3), and the other is formed in the conversion α-ketoglutarate —> succinyl-SCoA (Step 4). Since each glucose provides two pyruvates (and thus two acetyl-SCoAs), a total of 6 CO_2 are formed.

23.10 (a) The remaining energy is dissipated as heat.

(b) The exergonic nature of the reaction makes it very favorable in the forward direction and unfavorable in the reverse direction. Also, escape of the gaseous product drives the reaction to completion in the forward direction.

23.11 As starvation begins, insulin starts to decrease as glucagon starts to increase, while liver glycogen begins a rapid decrease. After several hours, the levels of insulin and glucagon continue to change, and blood glucose drops significantly. As glycogen is used up, fatty acids and ketone bodies appear in the bloodstream. At the end of 24 hours, liver glycogen is depleted, the levels of glucose and insulin are reduced, and the levels of glucagon, free fatty acids and ketone bodies are elevated.

23.12

```
        CH2OH
         |
   H — C — OH
         |
  HO — C — H
         |
   H — C — OH
         |
   H — C — OH
         |
        CH2OH
```

Sorbitol

Sorbitol can't form a cyclic hemiacetal because it doesn't have a carbonyl group.

23.13 (a) The increase in [H$^+$] drives the equilibrium shown in Section 23.9 to the right, causing the production of CO_2.

(b) This effect is an example of Le Châtelier's Principle.

23.14 UTP + Glucose 1-phosphate → Glucose-UDP + $OP_2O_6{}^{4-}$ $\Delta G = +1.1$ kcal/mol

$OP_2O_6{}^{4-}$ + H$_2$O → 2 HOPO$_3{}^{2-}$ $\Delta G = -8.0$ kcal/mol

——

UTP + Glucose 1-phosphate + H$_2$O → Glucose-UDP + 2 HOPO$_3{}^{2-}$ $\Delta G = -6.9$ kcal/mol

The common intermediate for these two reactions is $OP_2O_6{}^{4-}$ (pyrophosphate). ΔG for the coupled reactions is –6.9 kcal/mol, indicating an exergonic overall reaction and a favorable free-energy change.

23.15

Glycerol   Glycerol 3-phosphate   Dihydroxyacetone
                                                            phosphate

Understanding Key Concepts

23.16 Most of the enzymes involved with digestion are hydrolases, which catalyze the hydrolysis bonds in large molecules to produce smaller molecules.

23.17 (a) The *pentose phosphate pathway* operates when either ribose 5-phosphate or the reduced coenzyme NADPH is needed.
(b) *Glycogenesis* occurs when the concentration of glucose in the blood is high and the body doesn't need glucose for energy production.
(c) *Hydrolysis to free glucose* takes place in the liver when free glucose is needed in cells in other parts of the body. (Only free glucose can be transported in the blood.)
(d) *Glycolysis* occurs when the body needs energy and the supply of glucose is adequate.

23.18 The energy investments made when glucose is converted to glucose 6-phosphate (Step 1) and when fructose 1-phosphate is converted to fructose 1,6-bisphosphate (Step 3) produce the phosphorylated intermediates needed in later stages of glycolysis. These intermediates take part in the reactions that ultimately repay the initial energy investment. Cleavage of fructose 1,6-bisphosphate at Step 4 generates the two three-carbon molecules whose transformations result in the formation of pyruvate.

23.19 (a) Pyruvate is directed to *gluconeogenesis* when the body needs glucose and both glucose and glycogen are in short supply. Gluconeogenesis takes place in the liver.
(b) Pyruvate is *converted to lactate* in muscles and in red blood cells, under anaerobic conditions.
(c) Pyruvate enters into the *citric acid cycle* when the body needs energy. To enter the cycle, pyruvate is first converted to acetyl-SCoA in mitochondria.
(d) In yeast, pyruvate yields *ethanol and CO_2* in the absence of oxygen.

23.20

Step	Enzyme	Class
1	Hexokinase	transferase
2	Glucose 6-phosphate isomerase	isomerase
3	Phosphofructokinase	transferase
4	Aldolase	lyase
5	Triose phosphate isomerase	isomerase
6	Glyceraldehyde 3-phosphate dehydrogenase	oxidoreductase, transferase
7	Phosphoglycerate kinase	transferase
8	Phosphoglycerate mutase	isomerase
9	Enolase	lyase
10	Pyruvate kinase	transferase

Transferases are the most common class of enzymes in glycolysis because several reactions involve phosphate transfers to ADP and from ATP. Ligases are not represented among the enzymes of glycolysis because ligases are involved with the synthesis of larger molecules from smaller molecules, with the expenditure of ATP. Glycolysis is a pathway for the breakdown of larger molecules to smaller molecules, with the eventual generation of ATP.

23.21 (1) Insulin levels rise (d).
(2) Glucose is taken up by cells (f).
(3) Glycolysis occurs to replenish ATP supplies (a).
(4) Glycogen synthesis occurs (glycogenesis) if there is excess glucose (g).
(5) Blood levels pass through normal to below normal (hypoglycemic) (c).
(6) Glucagon is secreted (b).
(7) The liver releases glucose into the bloodstream (e).

23.22 In the absence of oxygen, the pyruvate product of catabolism of glucose in wine is fermented by yeast enzymes to ethanol and CO_2, which increased the pressure in the bottle and popped the cork.

23.23 Compounds available for gluconeogenesis include pyruvate, lactate, many amino acids, glycerol and intermediates of the citric acid cycle, especially oxaloacetate. The conversion of fatty acids to glucose occurs in plants, where fatty acids stored in seeds can be used as a source of carbohydrates after germination. Unlike plants, animals don't need carbohydrates as structural materials and are able to obtain all the carbohydrates they need from food.

23.24 (a) No. Molecular oxygen is not involved in any of the steps of glycolysis.
(b) Molecular oxygen is used in electron transport, where it combines with hydrogen ions and with electrons from coenzymes (reduced in the citric acid cycle) to produce water. The reoxidized coenzymes can reenter the citric acid cycle or can be used in glycolysis.

Digestion and Metabolism

23.25 Digestion occurs primarily in the mouth, stomach, and small intestine; it involves the enzyme-catalyzed hydrolysis of food components into small molecules.

23.26 Maltose + H_2O $\xrightarrow{\text{Maltase}}$ 2 Glucose

This process occurs in the mucous lining of the small intestine.

23.27

Type of food molecules	Products of digestion
Proteins	Amino acids
Triacylglycerols	Glycerol and fatty acids
Sucrose	Glucose and fructose
Lactose	Glucose and galactose
Starch	Glucose

23.28 The major monosaccharide products of digestion are glucose, fructose and galactose.

23.29 The word *aerobic* describes a condition in which oxygen is plentiful; the word *anaerobic* describes a condition where oxygen is absent.

23.30 Under aerobic conditions, pyruvate forms acetyl-SCoA.
Under anaerobic conditions, pyruvate forms lactate.
Under fermentation conditions, pyruvate forms ethanol and CO_2.

23.31 *Glycolysis* is the metabolic pathway that catabolizes glucose to pyruvate.
Gluconeogenesis is the process that synthesizes glucose from small molecules when glucose is in short supply.

23.32 In *glycogenolysis*, the breakdown of glycogen produces glucose when it is needed.
In *glycogenesis*, glycogen is synthesized from glucose when glucose is in excess.

23.33 The pentose phosphate pathway is used to provide the coenzyme NADPH and to produce ribose 5-phosphate, a sugar used in nucleic acid synthesis.

23.34 *If the body needs*:   then   *Fate of intermediates in pentose phosphate pathway*:

NADPH	Pentose phosphate intermediates are recycled to glucose 6-phosphate for further production of NADPH.
ATP	Fructose 6-phosphate and glyceraldehyde 3-phosphate (pentose phosphate intermediates) enter glycolysis.
Nucleic acid synthesis	Ribose 5-phosphate is the major product.

Glycolysis

23.35 Pyruvate is the final product of glycolysis. ATP is also formed in the final reaction. NADH is a byproduct of an earlier reaction of glycolysis.

$$CH_3-\underset{\underset{O}{\|}}{C}-\underset{\underset{O}{\|}}{C}-O^-$$ Pyruvate

23.36 The NADH generated in glycolysis can enter two pathways under anaerobic conditions. (1) NADH can be reoxidized to NAD^+ in the conversion of pyruvate to lactate. (2) In the fermentation reaction (in yeast) of pyruvate to ethanol and CO_2, NADH can also be reoxidized. Under aerobic conditions, NADH can enter the electron transport chain, where it is reoxidized to NAD^+ and ATP is produced.

23.37 Glycolysis occurs in the cytosol of all cells.

23.38 Gluconeogenesis occurs in the cytosol of liver cells.

23.39 (a) Phosphorylation:

Step 1: Glucose → Glucose 6-phosphate

Step 3: Fructose 6-phosphate → Fructose 1,6-bisphosphate

Step 6: Glyceraldehyde 3-phosphate → 1,3-Bisphosphoglycerate

(b) Oxidation:

Step 6: Glyceraldehyde 3-phosphate → 1,3-Bisphosphoglycerate

(c) Dehydration:

Step 9: 2-Phosphoglycerate → Phosphoenolpyruvate

23.40 Note: "Direct (or substrate-level) phosphorylation" is formation of ATP as a byproduct of a reaction, as opposed to formation of ATP as a byproduct of electron transport.
(a) Glycolysis of 1 mol glucose produces 2 mol ATP as a result of direct phosphorylation. (Actually, 4 mol ATP are produced by phosphorylation, but 2 mol ATP are consumed in steps 1 and 3 of glycolysis.)
(b) Aerobic conversion of pyruvate to acetyl-SCoA doesn't produce ATP by direct phosphorylation.
(c) In the citric acid cycle, one mol of acetyl-SCoA produces 1 mol ATP by direct phosphorylation (Step 5). Most of the ATP produced in the citric acid cycle results from passage of the reduced coenzymes NADH and $FADH_2$ through the electron-transport chain.

23.41 Under anaerobic conditions, NADH can't enter the respiratory chain. Instead, in order to replenish the body's supply of NAD^+, NADH reacts with pyruvate to form lactate and NAD^+.

23.42

Lactate — Lactate dehydrogenase → Pyruvate

23.43 The complete catabolism of one mole of sucrose yields 12 moles of CO_2.

23.44 Catabolism of one mole of sucrose produces four moles of acetyl-SCoA.

Regulation of Glucose Metabolism / Metabolism in Diabetes Mellitus

23.45

Condition	Blood sugar level	Symptoms
Hypoglycemia	low	weakness, sweating, rapid heartbeat, confusion, coma, death
Hyperglycemia	high	increased urine flow, low blood pressure, coma, death

23.46 Insulin is released when blood glucose levels are high and results in passage of glucose into cells, where it is metabolized. Glucagon is released when blood glucose levels are low and results in breakdown of glycogen in the liver to produce glucose.

23.47 Glucose is initially formed from glycogen during starvation or fasting. When glycogen is used up, glucose is formed from pyruvate, lactate, amino acids and other small molecules via gluconeogenesis.

23.48 Acetyl-SCoA is converted to ketone bodies to prevent buildup in the cells.

23.49 Symptoms of diabetes include excessive thirst, frequent urination, high concentrations of glucose in the urine and blood, and weight loss.

23.50 In diabetes, excess glucose in the eyes and extremities is converted to sorbitol, which can't be transported out of cells. This elevated sorbitol level changes the osmolarity of tissues and causes cataracts and gangrene.

23.51 In juvenile diabetes, the β-cells in the pancreas, which produce insulin, are recognized as foreign substances and are attacked and destroyed by antibodies.

23.52 *Juvenile diabetes* is caused by insufficient production of insulin in the pancreas. *Adult-onset diabetes* is caused by the failure of cell membrane receptors to recognize insulin.

23.53 Most of the glycogen in the body is stored in muscle cells and in the liver.

23.54 Unlike liver cells, muscle cells lack an enzyme that converts glucose 6-phosphate to glucose, which can pass into the bloodstream. Consequently, the glucose 6-phosphate product of glycogenolysis in muscle cells enters directly into glycolysis.

23.55 UTP reacts with glucose to form the high-energy compound UDP-glucose, which carries glucose to a growing glycogen chain.

23.56 The exact reverse of an energetically favorable reaction must be energetically unfavorable. Since glycogenolysis is energetically favorable, its exact reverse must be energetically unfavorable. Thus, glycogenesis must occur by an alternate pathway that is energetically favorable.

Glucose Anabolism

23.57 *Gluconeogenesis* is the anabolic pathway for making glucose.

23.58 Lactate and pyruvate are two molecules that can serve as starting materials for glucose synthesis.

23.59 In glucose anabolism, pyruvate is initially converted to oxaloacetate and then to phosphoenolpyruvate.

23.60 Several steps of the exact reverse of the energetically favorable conversion of glucose to pyruvate are energetically unfavorable.

Applications

23.61 Dextran adheres to teeth and allows bacterial colonies to stick to teeth without being washed away by water or saliva.

23.62 Plaque is composed of glycoproteins from saliva, bacteria, dextran and polysaccharide storage granules released by the bacteria.

23.63 The bacteria associated with plaque secrete products that are toxic to the gums.

22.64 Benedict's test detects all reducing sugars in the bloodstream and is thus not specific for glucose.

22.65 Glucose is oxidized by glucose oxidase to yield gluconate and H_2O_2, which reacts with a dye in a peroxidase-catalyzed reaction to yield a colored oxidized dye (and H_2O). The color change, which can be measured, is specific for glucose.

23.66 The fasting level of glucose in a diabetic is 140 mg/dL or greater, as compared to an average level of 90 mg/dL for a nondiabetic.

23.67 After drinking a glucose solution, both a diabetic person and a nondiabetic person experience a great increase in blood sugar level in the first hour. After two hours, the glucose level in a nondiabetic person returns to near fasting level, while the level in a diabetic person remains high.

23.68 Creatine phosphate quickly provides ATP in one step, whereas glucose metabolism takes many steps to provide ATP.

23.69 The distance a person can sprint is limited by readily available energy that comes from creatine phosphate and glycogen, both of which are quickly used up.

23.70 *First used*   ——————————————————————————>   *Last used*
        ATP, creatine phosphate, glucose, glycogen, fatty acids from triacylglycerols

23.71 Cotton fabric, paper, and rayon are all made from cellulose. Cotton fabric and paper are made from unmodified cellulose. In rayon, the hydroxyl groups of cellulose are converted to acetate groups.

General Questions and Problems

23.72 Pyruvate can cross the mitochondrial membrane because it is the only molecule in glycolysis that is not a phosphate. (Phosphates can't cross the mitochondrial membrane.)

23.73 Kinase enzymes are associated with phosphoryl group transfers.

23.74 Fructose and glucose have the same net ATP production because fructose can be phosphorylated to form fructose 6-phosphate, which can enter glycolysis directly as a glycolysis intermediate.

23.75 Glucose obtained from the hydrolysis of glycogen is phosphorylated by reaction with inorganic phosphate ion and enters the glycolysis pathway as glucose 6-phosphate. Thus, one fewer ATP is needed (at step 1), and one more ATP is produced.

Self-Test for Chapter 23

Multiple choice:

1. The synthesis of glucose from small molecules is called:
   (a) glycolysis   (b) glucogenesis   (c) gluconeogenesis   (d) glycogenesis

2. Which one of the following substances can cross cell membranes?
   (a) glucose 6-phosphate   (b) ATP   (c) glucose   (d) acetyl-SCoA

3. The synthesis of glycogen occurs in the:
   (a) liver and bloodstream   (b) liver and muscles   (c) liver and pancreas   (d) muscles and pancreas

4. The exact reverse of which of the following steps of glycolysis also occurs in gluconeogenesis?
   (a) glucose —> glucose 6-phosphate   (b) phosphoenolpyruvate —> pyruvate
   (c) fructose 6-phosphate —> fructose 1,6-bisphosphate
   (d) 3-phosphoglycerate —> 2-phosphoglycerate

5. When the body needs to synthesize nucleic acids:
    (a) The oxidative phase of the pentose phosphate path is bypassed.   (b) The synthesis of
    NADPH is increased.   (c) Glucose 6-phosphate enters glycolysis.   (d) Three-, four-, or
    seven-carbon sugars are produced.

6. After several weeks of starvation, the body's principal energy source is:
    (a) protein   (b) fat   (c) carbohydrate   (d) all three

7. Type I *diabetes mellitus* is a disorder of:
    (a) insufficient insulin production   (b) faulty glucose metabolism   (c) autoimmune response
    (d) all three

8. Which of the following is not a route for pyruvate metabolism in the human body?
    (a) conversion to acetyl-SCoA   (b) reduction to lactate   (c) fermentation to alcohol
    (d) reformation of glucose

9. Glycogenesis resembles glycogenolysis in that:
    (a) both require the coenzyme UTP   (b) both occur when glucose is in good supply
    (c) both are stimulated by the hormone epinephrine   (d) both involve glucose 6-phosphate as
    an intermediate

10. Which of the following monosaccharides doesn't enter glycolysis?
    (a) ribose   (b) mannose   (c) galactose   (d) fructose

Complete the following sentences:

1. The _____ – _____ pathway is another name for glycolysis.

2. Step __ of glycolysis involves an oxidation and a phosphorylation.

3. _____ _____ _____catalyzes the formation of acetyl-SCoA from pyruvate.

4. _____ aids in the passage of blood glucose across cell membranes.

5. The first step of glycogenolysis is the formation of _____.

6. Steps ___ are known as the energy investment part of glycolysis.

7. The metabolic response to _____ resembles starvation.

8. _____ and _____ supply the energy for gluconeogenesis.

9. When pyruvate is converted to acetyl-SCoA, one molecule of _____ is lost.

10. The isomerization of glucose 6-phosphate to fructose 6-phosphate is catalyzed by _____.

11. The hormone _____ stimulates breakdown of glycogen.

12. _____ may be due to an overdose of insulin.

Tell whether the following statements are true or false:

1. The pentose phosphate pathway is important because it produces NADH.

2. Fructose, galactose, and mannose can all enter the glycolysis pathway.

3. Conversion of glucose 6-phosphate to fructose 6-phosphate requires ATP.

4. Glycogenesis is the exact reverse of glycogenolysis.

5. Hyperglycemia is a high level of blood glucose.

6. The reactions of glycolysis occur in the mitochondria.

7. 36 ATP are produced for each glucose that passes through the glycolysis pathway.

8. Glucagon is the storage form of glucose.

9. All four transformations of pyruvate occur in the human body.

10. Cleavage of fructose 1,6-diphosphate yields two molecules of glyceraldehyde 3-phosphate.

11. Pyruvate is converted to lactate under anaerobic conditions.

12. Each conversion of glyceraldehyde 3-phosphate to pyruvate requires two ADP.

Match the entries on the left with their partners on the right:

1. Glycolysis   (a) Formed by fermentation of pyruvate

2. Hyperglycemia   (b) Formed from pyruvate under anaerobic conditions

3. Enolase   (c) Intermediate in glycogen synthesis

4. Glycogenolysis   (d) Synthesis of glucose from pyruvate

5. UDP-glucose   (e) Catalyzes the cleavage of fructose 1,6-diphosphate

6. Ribose 5-phosphate   (f) Low blood sugar

7. Gluconeogenesis   (g) Synthesis of glycogen from glucose

8. Ethanol   (h) Product of pentose phosphate pathway

9. Hypoglycemia   (i) Catalyzes loss of water from 2-phosphoglyceric acid

10. Glycogenesis   (j) Breakdown of glycogen to glucose

11. Lactate   (k) High blood sugar

12. Aldolase   (l) Breakdown of glucose to pyruvate

Chapter 24 – Lipids

Chapter Outline

I. Structure and classification of lipids (Section 24.1).
  A. Lipids are defined by solubility in nonpolar solvents.
  B. Classification of lipids.
    1. Waxes.
    2. Triacylglycerols.
    3. Glycerophospholipids.
    4. Sphingolipids.
    5. Steroids and eicosanoids.
II. Fatty acids and their esters (Sections 24.2–24.4).
  A. Fatty acids (Section 24.2).
    1. Fatty acids are long-chain carboxylic acids.
    2. Fatty acids are classified by the number of double bonds they have.
       a. Fatty acids with no double bonds are saturated.
       b. Fatty acids with one double bond are monounsaturated.
       c. Fatty acids with more than one double bond are polyunsaturated.
  B. Waxes are esters of long-chain alcohols with fatty acids.
  C. Fats and oils.
    1. Fats and oils are mixtures of esters of glycerol with three fatty acids and are known as triacylglycerols.
    2. Properties of fats and oils (Section 24.3).
       a. Hydrophobic.
       b. Uncharged.
       c. Melting point is determined by the length of the fatty acid side chains and the number of double bonds.
          i. Solid fats have saturated fatty acid side chains.
          ii. Liquid fats have unsaturated fatty acid side chains.
    3. Reactions of triacylglycerols (Section 24.4).
       a. Hydrogenation.
             Control of hydrogenation determines the consistency of a fat.
       b. Hydrolysis.
          i. In the body, enzymes catalyze hydrolysis of triacylglycerols.
          ii. In the laboratory, strong aqueous base is used.
          iii. The resulting fatty acid salts are called soaps.
          iv. Soaps clean because the polar end dissolves in water and the nonpolar end dissolves in grease.
          v. Soap molecules cluster together in water to form micelles; grease is trapped in the middle of a micelle.
III. Cell membrane lipids (Sections 24.5–24.6).
  A. Phospholipids (Section 24.5).
    1. Glycerophospholipids
       a. Glycerophospholipids are esters of glycerol with two fatty acids and a phosphate group that is bonded to one of a number of different compounds containing an –OH group.
       b. The phospholipid with choline as a phosphate ester is a lecithin.
          i. Lecithins are components of cell membranes.
          ii. Lecithin is often used as an emulsifying agent.

2. Sphingolipids and other membrane lipids.
    a. Sphingolipids are derivatives of the amino alcohol sphingosine.
    b. Sphingolipids consist of:
        i. An amide bond between a fatty acid and sphingosine.
        ii. A phosphate ester also bonded to choline.
    c. Sphingomyelins are sphingolipids that are constituents of the coating around nerve fibers.
  B. Glycolipids resemble sphingolipids, except that the phosphate group at C1 is replaced by a carbohydrate.
    1. Cerebrosides have a monosaccharide at C1.
        Cerebrosides are found in cell membranes.
    2. Gangliosides have a small polysaccharide at C1.
        Gangliosides are components of neurotransmitters and receptors.
  C. Cholesterol (Section 24.6).
    1. Cholesterol has a tetracyclic steroid structure.
    2. Cholesterol serves as a starting material for steroid hormones.
    3. Cholesterol is a component of cell membranes that helps maintain the structure of the membrane.
IV. Cell membranes (Sections 24.7–24.8).
  A. Structure of cell membranes (Section 24.7).
    1. Cell membranes are composed of two parallel layers of phospholipids, called a *lipid bilayer.*
    2. The nonpolar tails are clustered in the middle, and the polar heads point inward and outward.
    3. The fluid-mosaic model of a cell membrane explains the more complex structural details.
        a. Glycolipids and cholesterol are in the lipid part and provide membrane structure.
        b. Glycoproteins (20%) mediate the action of cell contents with the outer environment.
            i. Some proteins form channels to allow specific molecules to enter or leave.
            ii. Glycoproteins that extend through the bilayer are called integral proteins.
            iii. Glycoproteins that are partially embedded are peripheral proteins.
            iv. The carbohydrate portions act as receptors for enzymes and neurotransmitters.
        c. The membrane is fluid and doesn't rupture.
            Fluidity of the membrane increases with the amounts of saturated and unsaturated fatty acids in the lipid portion.
  B. Transport across cell membranes (Section 24.8).
    1. Passive transport.
        a. Simple diffusion.
            i. Gases and small nonpolar molecules diffuse through the bilayer.
            ii. Small hydrophilic molecules pass through channels formed by integral proteins.
        b. Facilitated diffusion.
            Facilitated diffusion is passive transport, but proteins help solutes to pass across the membrane.
    2. Active transport.
        a. Ions and other substances that maintain concentration gradients inside and outside the cell move by active transport.
        b. Active transport requires an expenditure of energy and involves changing the shape of an integral protein.
V. Eicosanoids (Section 24.9).
  A. General information.
    1. Eicosanoids are derivatives of 20-carbon fatty acids.
    2. Eicosanoids are synthesized from arachidonic acid.
    3. Eicosanoids are short-term messengers.

B. There are three classes of eicosanoids.
   1. Thromboxanes promote aggregation of blood platelets during clotting.
   2. Prostaglandins.
      a. Prostaglandins consist of a five-membered ring with two side chains.
      b. Biological effects include blood pressure lowering, stimulation of uterine contractions, and lowering the extent of gastric secretions.
   3. Leukotrienes mediate inflammatory and allergic responses.

Solutions to Chapter 24 Problems

24.1 The circled groups can be used to identify lipid families.

(a)   (b)

an eicosanoid

a glycerophospholipid

(c)

$CH_3(CH_2)_{16}C-OCH_2(CH_2)_6CH=CH(CH_2)_6CH_3$

a wax

24.2

from C_{20} carboxylic acid   from C_{32} alcohol

24.3

$CH_2-O-\overset{O}{\overset{\|}{C}}-CH_2CH_2CH_2CH_2CH_2CH_2CH_2CH=CHCH_2CH_2CH_2CH_2CH_2CH_2CH_2CH_3$

$CH-O-\overset{O}{\overset{\|}{C}}-CH_2CH_2CH_2CH_2CH_2CH_2CH_2CH=CHCH_2CH_2CH_2CH_2CH_2CH_2CH_2CH_3$

$CH_2-O-\overset{O}{\overset{\|}{C}}-CH_2CH_2CH_2CH_2CH_2CH_2CH_2CH=CHCH_2CH_2CH_2CH_2CH_2CH_2CH_2CH_3$

Glyceryl trioleate

24.4 (a) Butter has the largest percentage of saturated fatty acids.
(b) Soybean oil has the largest percentage of polyunsaturated fatty acids.

24.5

Arachidonic acid

24.6 Fatty acid (b) has a higher melting point because it is more saturated. Fatty acid (a) has more double bonds, which make it difficult for molecules of (a) to form crystals and which lower its melting point.

24.7 The starred carbon of the triacylglycerol pictured below is bonded to four different groups and is chiral. (Whenever two different fatty acids are bonded to carbon 1 and carbon 3 of glycerol, carbon 2 is chiral.)

24.8 London forces bind the nonpolar segments of lipids together. These forces are generally weak, but when there are many such interactions, their total contribution is relatively large. Lipids don't mix with water because the hydrogen bonds between water molecules are stronger than the forces between lipid molecules or between water molecules and lipid molecules.

24.9   Glyceryl trioleate (Problem 24.3)

$$\Big| \begin{array}{l} 3\ H_2 \\ \text{catalyst} \end{array}$$

CH$_2$-O-C-CH$_2$CH$_2$CH$_2$CH$_2$CH$_2$CH$_2$CH$_2$CH$_2$CH$_2$CH$_2$CH$_2$CH$_2$CH$_2$CH$_2$CH$_2$CH$_2$CH$_3$

CH-O-C-CH$_2$CH$_2$CH$_2$CH$_2$CH$_2$CH$_2$CH$_2$CH$_2$CH$_2$CH$_2$CH$_2$CH$_2$CH$_2$CH$_2$CH$_2$CH$_2$CH$_3$

CH$_2$-O-C-CH$_2$CH$_2$CH$_2$CH$_2$CH$_2$CH$_2$CH$_2$CH$_2$CH$_2$CH$_2$CH$_2$CH$_2$CH$_2$CH$_2$CH$_2$CH$_2$CH$_3$

Glyceryl tristearate

The acyl groups of the above triacylglycerol are derived from stearic acid.

24.10

24.11

(a)

R' is an unsaturated hydrocarbon group, and R is a saturated hydrocarbon group.

(b)

24.12

Choline

Phosphate

Myristic acid

Hydrophilic head   Hydrophobic tails

A sphingomyelin

24.13

Stearic acid acyl group

Oleic acid acyl group

Phosphate   Ethanolamine

A glycerophospholipid

24.14

The illustrated structure is a phospholipid (a) because it contains a phosphate group. It is a sphingolipid (c) because it has a sphingosine backbone. It is a lipid (e) because it is soluble in nonpolar solvents. It contains a phosphate ester group (f).

24.15 Integral membrane proteins must be hydrophobic to remain in the hydrophobic environment of a cell membrane. They must contain many amino acids with nonpolar side chains and must be folded so that the hydrophobic regions face outward.

24.16 You would predict that NO would cross a lipid bilayer by simple diffusion because it is small and relatively nonpolar.

24.17 Glucose 6-phosphate has a charged phosphate group and can't pass through the hydrophobic lipid bilayer.

24.18 The inner and outer surfaces of the lipid bilayer are in different environments and serve different functions. For example, the outer surface must receive signals from the cell's surroundings and must contain groups that allow the cell to be identified. The inner surface must include groups needed to pass messages to other parts of the cell.

24.19

The carboxylic acid group and the hydroxyl group are capable of forming hydrogen bonds. The molecule has both polar and nonpolar regions.

Understanding Key Concepts

24.20 The triacylglycerol that has the highest melting point has the greatest percent of saturated fatty acids. Of the four fatty acids listed, palmitic acid and stearic acid are saturated, and oleic acid and linoleic acid are unsaturated. Thus, if you add the percentages in the table, you arrive at a new table.

Triacylglycerol	Percent saturated fatty acids	Percent unsaturated fatty acids
Triacylglycerol A	49.2%	47.5%
Triacylglycerol B	28.9%	70.8%
Triacylglycerol C	19.5%	76.8%

This table shows that Triacylglycerol A has the highest melting point. Triacylglycerols B and C are probably liquids at room temperature because their fatty acid composition more closely resembles that of the oils in Table 24.2 than that of the animal fats.

24.21 Three of the fatty acids in the table shown in the previous problem are C_{18} fatty acids (stearic acid, oleic acid, and linoleic acid). When the triacylglycerols are hydrogenated, the unsaturated fatty acids are converted to stearic acid. The composition of the triacylglycerols after hydrogenation can be found by adding the percentages of C_{18} fatty acids.

Triacylglycerol	Percent C_{16} fatty acids	Percent C_{18} fatty acids
Triacylglycerol A	21.4%	75.3%
Triacylglycerol B	12.2%	87.5%
Triacylglycerol C	11.2%	85.1%

After hydrogenation, triacylglycerol B would be composed of 12.2% palmitic acid and 87.5% stearic acid. The hydrogenation product of triacylglycerol B closely resembles the hydrogenation product of triacylglycerol C because they have similar percentages of C_{16} fatty acids and C_{18} fatty acids.

24.22

The membrane lipid is a glycerophospholipid that is a phosphatidylserine.

24.23 Because the membrane is fluid, rather than rigid, it is able to flow together after an injury, instead of shattering.

24.24

The two fatty acids are 16-carbon saturated straight-chain fatty acids. The polar head is situated in lung tissue, and the nonpolar groups protrude into the air space within the alveoli.

Waxes, Fats and Oils

24.25 A lipid is a naturally occurring organic molecule that dissolves in nonpolar solvents.

24.26 There are many different structural kinds of lipids because many different types of naturally occurring molecules dissolve in nonpolar solvents.

24.27 A fatty acid is a long-chain (C_{12}–C_{22}) carboxylic acid having an even number of carbon atoms.

24.28 *Saturated fatty acids* are long-chain carboxylic acids that contain no carbon–carbon double bonds. *Monounsaturated fatty acids* contain one carbon–carbon double bond. *Polyunsaturated fatty acids* contain two or more carbon–carbon double bonds.

24.29 An essential fatty acid can't be synthesized by the human body and must be part of the diet.

24.30 Linoleic acid and linolenic acid are two essential fatty acids. Vegetable oils and nuts are good sources of these acids.

24.31 The double bonds in naturally occurring fatty acids are cis.

24.32 Saturated fatty acids are straight and can easily order themselves in a crystal. A double bond in a fatty acid produces a kink, which makes it more difficult for molecules to be arranged in a crystal, and thus a double bond lowers the melting point of the fatty acid. A cis fatty acid is lower melting than a trans fatty acid because a cis double bond produces a larger kink in a fatty acid hydrocarbon chain than a trans double bond produces.

24.33 A fat or oil is a triester of glycerol with three fatty acids – a triacylglycerol.

24.34 Fats are composed of triacylglycerols containing both saturated and unsaturated fatty acids, are solids at room temperature, and are usually obtained from animal sources. Oils are made up of triacylglycerols containing mainly unsaturated fatty acids, are liquids at room temperature, and are obtained from plant sources.

24.35

$$CH_2-O-\overset{\overset{\displaystyle O}{\|}}{C}-CH_2CH_2CH_2CH_2CH_2CH_2CH_2CH_2CH_2CH_2CH_3$$

$$CH-O-\overset{\overset{\displaystyle O}{\|}}{C}-CH_2CH_2CH_2CH_2CH_2CH_2CH_2CH_2CH_2CH_2CH_3$$

$$CH_2-O-\overset{\overset{\displaystyle O}{\|}}{C}-CH_2CH_2CH_2CH_2CH_2CH_2CH_2CH_2CH_2CH_2CH_3$$

Glyceryl trilaurate

24.36

In one isomer, palmitic acid forms an ester with the middle hydroxyl group of glycerol; in the other, palmitic acid forms an ester with a terminal hydroxyl group. (The first isomer is chiral.)

24.37 In animals, fats are used for energy storage, as components of cell membranes, and as precursors for steroid hormones.

24.38 A wax serves as a protective coating for fruits, berries, leaves, animal fur, and feathers.

24.39

$$CH_3(CH_2)_{13}CH_2\overset{O}{\underset{\|}{C}}-OCH_2(CH_2)_{14}CH_3$$

Cetyl palmitate

24.40 Spermaceti is a wax.

Chemical Reactions of Lipids

24.41 A vegetable oil can be converted into a solid cooking fat by hydrogenating all of its double bonds.

24.42 If some, but not all, of the double bonds in corn oil were hydrogenated, the resulting product would be a semisolid fat that could be used as margarine.

24.43 All double bonds are cis.

24.44

$$
\begin{array}{l}
CH_2-O-\overset{\overset{\displaystyle O}{\|}}{C}-(CH_2)_{16}CH_3 \\
| \quad\quad\quad \overset{\displaystyle O}{\|} \\
CH-O-C-(CH_2)_7CH=CH(CH_2)_7CH_3 \\
| \quad\quad\quad \overset{\displaystyle O}{\|} \\
CH_2-O-C-(CH_2)_7CH=CHCH_2CH=CHCH_2CH=CHCH_2CH_3
\end{array}
\xrightarrow{\text{H}_2,\ \text{Pd catalyst}}
$$

$$
\begin{array}{l}
CH_2-O-\overset{\overset{\displaystyle O}{\|}}{C}-(CH_2)_{16}CH_3 \\
| \quad\quad\quad \overset{\displaystyle O}{\|} \\
CH-O-C-(CH_2)_{16}CH_3 \quad\quad \text{Glyceryl tristearate} \\
| \quad\quad\quad \overset{\displaystyle O}{\|} \\
CH_2-O-C-(CH_2)_{16}CH_3
\end{array}
$$

Glyceryl tristearate is higher melting than the original lipid because it has no double bonds and can solidify more easily.

Phospholipids, Glycolipids, and Cell Membranes

24.45 A triacylglycerol is an ester of glycerol and three fatty acids; a phospholipid contains a phosphate group. There are two main kinds of phospholipids. A *glycerophospholipid* is an ester of glycerol 3-phosphate, two fatty acids, and an amino alcohol bonded to the phosphate group. A *sphingolipid* is an amide of sphingosine and a fatty acid, and has an amino alcohol bonded to a phosphate group, which is attached to C1 of sphingosine.

24.46 Glycerophospholipids have an ionic part (the *head*) and a nonpolar part (the *tail*). The ionic head protrudes outward toward the aqueous environment of the cell or inward toward the cell contents, and the nonpolar tails cluster together to form the membrane. Triacylglycerols don't have an ionic head and thus can't function as membrane components.

24.47 A sphingomyelin and a cerebroside are similar in that both have a sphingosine backbone. The difference between the two occurs at C1 of sphingosine. A sphingomyelin has a phosphate group bonded to an amino alcohol at C1; a cerebroside has a glycosidic link to a monosaccharide at C1.

24.48 Sphingomyelins and glycolipids are two different kinds of sphingosine-based lipids.

24.49 Glycerophospholipids are more soluble in water than triacylglycerols because they have an ionic phosphate group that is solvated by water.

24.50 In a soap micelle, the polar hydrophilic heads are on the exterior, and the hydrophobic tails cluster in the center. In a membrane bilayer, hydrophilic heads are on both the exterior and interior surfaces of the membrane, and the region between the two surfaces is occupied by hydrophobic tails.

24.51 Glycolipids, cholesterol, and proteins are present in cell membranes in addition to phospholipids.

24.52 If cell membranes were freely permeable, the concentrations of all substances would be the same on both sides of the cell membrane, and it would be impossible for cells to maintain concentration gradients.

24.53

a cerebroside

24.54

a sphingomyelin

24.55

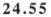

a glycerophospholipid

24.56 Aqueous NaOH cleaves all ester bonds, including phosphate esters.

Cardiolipin

NaOH, H₂O

24.57 Active transport requires energy because it is a process in which substances are transported across a membrane in a direction opposite to their tendency to diffuse.

24.58 In both simple diffusion and facilitated diffusion, substances cross cell membranes from areas of high concentration to areas of low concentration. In facilitated diffusion, substances are helped by proteins in crossing cell membranes.

Eicosanoids

24.59 Eicosanoids are called "local hormones" because they are synthesized near their site of action.

24.60 A prostaglandin that stimulates uterine contractions is an example of an eicosanoid serving as a local hormone.

24.61 Arachidonic acid is synthesized from linolenic acid, an essential fatty acid.

24.62

Thromboxane A₂   Arachidonic acid

Thromboxane A₂ is an eicosanoid. Arachidonic acid is the precursor of thromboxane A₂, just as it is the precursor of all other eicosanoids.

24.63 Leukotrienes are responsible for triggering asthmatic attacks, inflammation and allergic reactions, and thus it is desirable to inhibit their synthesis.

24.64 By transferring its acetyl group, aspirin inhibits the enzyme that is responsible for the first step in the conversion of arachidonic acid to prostaglandins.

Applications

24.65 In addition to fats and oils, other foods with high lipid content are meat, fish, poultry, dairy products, nuts, seeds, whole-grain cereals and prepared foods.

24.66 According to the FDA, no more than 30% of daily caloric intake should come from fats and oils.

24.67 Detergents and soaps both have hydrocarbon "tails" and polar "heads," and both form micelles, in which the hydrocarbon "tails" surround greasy dirt and aggregate in the center of a cluster. The polar "heads" protrude into the aqueous medium and make the cluster soluble.

24.68 Cationic detergents are used in fabric softeners and disinfecting soaps.

24.69 Branched-chain hydrocarbons are no longer used for detergents because they aren't biodegradable. Bacteria in sewage treatment plants can't digest detergents made from branched-chain hydrocarbons, and the undecomposed detergents produce suds in waterways.

24.70 Fog, homogenized milk and smoke are colloidal dispersions.

24.71 Loss of plasma proteins decreases the osmotic pressure of blood. If the osmotic pressure of blood is lower than normal, less water from tissues will be drawn into the plasma in the venous end of capillaries, resulting in fluid retention.

24.72 Unlike butter, margarine contains no cholesterol.

24.73 Peanut oil and olive oil are the best sources of monounsaturated fatty acids.

24.74 The liposome might carry a group that recognizes glycolipids or proteins on the exterior surface of the tumor cell.

24.75 The liposome fuses with a skin cell and delivers the moisturizer directly to the inside of the skin cell. This is more efficient than applying the moisturizer to the surface of the cell.

General Questions and Problems

24.76 A lecithin (b), a sphingomyelin (d), a cerebroside (e) and glyceryl trioleate (f) are saponifiable lipids.

24.77

Lipid	Backbone	Groups attached:
(b) A lecithin	Glycerol	A saturated fatty acid, an unsaturated fatty acid, a phosphate group, choline
(d) A sphingomyelin	Sphingosine	A fatty acid, a phosphate group, choline or ethanolamine
(e) A cerebroside	Sphingosine	A fatty acid, a monosaccharide
(f) Glyceryl trioleate	Glycerol	Three oleic acids

24.78

$$CH_2-O-\overset{\overset{O}{\|}}{C}-(CH_2)_7CH=CHCH_2CH=CHCH_2CH=CHCH_2CH_3$$

$$CH-O-\overset{\overset{O}{\|}}{C}-(CH_2)_7CH=CHCH_2CH=CHCH_2CH=CHCH_2CH_3$$

$$CH_2-O-\overset{\overset{O}{\|}}{C}-(CH_2)_{12}CH_3$$

or

$$CH_2-O-\overset{\overset{O}{\|}}{C}-(CH_2)_7CH=CHCH_2CH=CHCH_2CH=CHCH_2CH_3$$

$$CH-O-\overset{\overset{O}{\|}}{C}-(CH_2)_{12}CH_3$$

$$CH_2-O-\overset{\overset{O}{\|}}{C}-(CH_2)_7CH=CHCH_2CH=CHCH_2CH=CHCH_2CH_3$$

24.79 The fat described in the previous problem is lower melting than a fat composed of linolenic, myristic and stearic acids, because the fat in Problem 24.78 is more unsaturated and thus solidifies at a lower temperature.

24.80 Cholesterol isn't saponifiable because it contains no ester linkages.

24.81

$$CH_3(CH_2)_{16}\overset{\overset{\displaystyle O}{\|}}{C} - OCH_2(CH_2)_{20}CH_3 \quad \text{Jojoba wax}$$

from stearic acid   from a C_{22} alcohol

Jojoba wax is the ester formed by a C_{22} alcohol and a C_{18} carboxylic acid. Spermaceti is the ester formed by a C_{18} alcohol and a C_{16} carboxylic acid. It might be possible to substitute jojoba wax for spermaceti in the cosmetic industry as long as its greater molar mass and resulting higher melting point were unimportant.

24.82 Sphingomyelins, cerebrosides, and gangliosides are abundant in brain tissue.

24.83 Cholesterol, a steroid, is a component of cell membranes and is the starting material for the synthesis of all other steroids.

24.84 Prostaglandins can lower blood pressure, assist in blood clotting, stimulate uterine contractions, lower gastric secretions, and cause some of the pain and swelling associated with inflammation.

24.85 Lecithins emulsify fats in the same way as soaps dissolve grease; the fats are coated by the nonpolar part of a lecithin, and the polar part of lecithins allows fats to be suspended in aqueous solution.

24.86

$$
\begin{array}{l}
CH_2-O-\overset{\overset{\displaystyle O}{\|}}{C}-R \\
CH-O-\overset{\overset{\displaystyle O}{\|}}{C}-R' \ + \ 3\ NaOH \xrightarrow{\ H_2O\ } \\
CH_2-O-\overset{\overset{\displaystyle O}{\|}}{C}-R''
\end{array}
\quad
\begin{array}{l}
CH_2OH \\
CHOH \quad + \\
CH_2OH
\end{array}
\quad
\begin{array}{l}
Na^+\ {}^-O-\overset{\overset{\displaystyle O}{\|}}{C}-R \\
Na^+\ {}^-O-\overset{\overset{\displaystyle O}{\|}}{C}-R' \\
Na^+\ {}^-O-\overset{\overset{\displaystyle O}{\|}}{C}-R''
\end{array}
$$

Molar mass of fat = 1500 g

Molar mass of NaOH = 40 g

$$5.0 \text{ g oil } \times \ \frac{1 \text{ mol}}{1500 \text{ g}} \ = 3.3 \times 10^{-3} \text{ mol oil}$$

Since 3 mol of NaOH are needed to saponify 1 mol of oil, 9.9×10^{-3} mol of NaOH is needed to saponify 3.3×10^{-3} mol of oil.

$$9.9 \times 10^{-3} \text{ mol NaOH } \times \ \frac{40 \text{ g}}{1 \text{ mol}} \ = 0.39 \text{ g NaOH, or approximately 0.4 g NaOH}$$

24.87

$$\frac{200 \text{ mg cholesterol}}{1 \text{ dL}} \times \frac{10 \text{ dL}}{1 \text{ L}} \times 5.75 \text{ L} \times \frac{1 \text{ g}}{1000 \text{ mg}} = 11.5 \text{ g cholesterol}$$

An average person has approximately 11–12 grams of cholesterol in their blood.

Self-Test for Chapter 24

Multiple choice:

1. Small polar molecules pass through the lipid bilayer by:
    (a) simple diffusion through the lipid bilayer   (b) facilitated transfer   (c) active transport
    (d) simple diffusion through channels

2. Cholesterol is :
    (a) a male sex hormone   (b) a saponifiable lipid   (c) a component of cell membranes
    (d) common to plants and animals

3. Which of the following is not an effect of prostaglandins?
    (a) stimulation of allergic response   (b) lowering of blood pressure   (c) reduction of gastric
    secretions   (d) stimulation of uterine contractions

4. Active transport requires all of the following except:
    (a) the solutes to be nonpolar organic molecules   (b) the expenditure of ATP   (c) the need for
    cells to maintain a concentration gradient between the inside and the outside   (d) the assistance
    of integral proteins

5. Which of the following contain a glycosidic bond?
    (a) triacylglycerols   (b) sphingomyelins   (c) lecithins   (d) cerebrosides

6. The basic hydrolysis of which of the following triacylglycerols produces only polyunsaturated
    fatty acids?
    (a) glyceryl trioleate   (b) glyceryl tristearate   (c) glyceryl linoleate dioleate   (d) glyceryl
    trilinolenate

7. How many different triacylglycerols (including enantiomers!) can be formed from glycerol,
    two stearic acids and one oleic acid?
    (a) 1   (b) 2   (c) 3   (d) 4

8. Which of the following molecules aren't components of glycolipids?
    (a) sphingosine   (b) phosphate groups   (c) fatty acids   (d) sugars

9. A cell membrane is composed of all of the following except:
    (a) triacylglycerols   (b) phosphoglycerides   (c) sphingomyelins   (d) glycolipids

10. Waxes:
    (a) are triacylglycerols   (b) can be hydrolyzed by base   (c) contain no more than thirty carbons
    (d) are only produced by plants

Complete the following sentences:

1. A glycolipid contains an _____ link between sphingosine and a sugar.

2. _____ is a mixture of long-chain fatty acid salts.

3. The carboxylate end of a fatty acid is _____ and the organic chain end is _____.

4. _____ and _____ are two components of cell membranes.

5. The common model of a cell membrane is called the _____ _____ model.

6. Steroid structures are based on a _____ ring system.

7. Prostaglandins are synthesized in the body from a fatty acid called _____ acid.

8. Clusters of soap molecules in water are called _____.

9. _____ are phospholipids that are abundant in brain tissue.

10. Phospholipids aggregate in a closed, sheetlike membrane called a _____ _____.

11. _____ are a group of compounds derived from 20-carbon unsaturated fatty acids.

12. _____ proteins are involved with active transport across cell membranes.

Tell whether the following statements are true or false:

1. Lipids are defined by their physical properties, not by their structure.

2. Saturated fats are lower melting than unsaturated fats.

3. Sphingolipids contain a carboxylic acid ester group.

4. Cholesterol is synthesized by the human body.

5. Sphingosine is a component of both phospholipids and glycolipids.

6. When soap molecules are dissolved in water, they form a lipid bilayer.

7. Cholesterol is a hormone.

8. The main difference between fats and oil is in their melting points.

9. Cerebrosides are a major constituent of the coating around nerve fibers.

10. Waxes and fats are both carboxylic acid esters.

11. Leukotrienes are synthesized in the cells where they act.

12. Facilitated diffusion requires an energy investment.

Match the entries on the left with their partners on the right:

1. Decyl stearate

2. Prostaglandin

3. Choline

4. Stearic acid

5. Integral protein

6. Glyceryl trilaurate

7. Cerebroside

8. Oleic acid

9. Lecithin

10. Linoleic acid

11. Sphingomyelin

12. Peripheral protein

(a) Extends completely through the cell membrane

(b) Monounsaturated fatty acid

(c) Partially embedded in the cell membrane

(d) Phosphoglyceride

(e) Amino alcohol

(f) Saturated fatty acid

(g) Polyunsaturated fatty acid

(h) C_{20} acid with a five-membered ring

(i) Sphingolipid

(j) Fat

(k) Glycolipid

(l) Wax

Chapter Outline

I. Triacylglycerols (Sections 25.1–25.4).
    A. Digestion of triacylglycerols (Section 25.1).
        1. Triacylglycerols (TAGs) pass through the mouth unchanged.
        2. In the stomach, TAGs are broken down into small droplets.
        3. As TAGs pass into the intestines, lipases and bile are produced.
            a. Bile acids solubilize lipid droplets.
            b. Lipases hydrolyze lipids to mono- and diacylglycerols, fatty acids, and glycerol.
        4. Products of TAG digestion are absorbed through the intestinal wall.
            a. Smaller molecules are transported to the liver.
            b. Free fatty acids and acylglycerols are reconverted to triacylglycerols and packaged into lipoproteins (chylomicrons).
    B. Lipoproteins for lipid transport (Section 25.2).
        1. Triacylglycerols and fatty acids enter metabolism from 3 sources:
            a. Diet.
            b. Storage in adipose tissue.
            c. Synthesis in the liver.
        2. These lipids must be made soluble by association with lipoproteins.
        3. A lipoprotein is a globule of TAGs and fatty acids surrounded by a layer of phospholipids.
        4. Five kinds of lipoproteins are important.
            a. Chylomicrons carry lipids in the diet through the lymphatic system into the blood.
            b. VLDLs carry TAGs from the liver to tissues for storage or energy production.
            c. IDLs carry remnants of VLDLs from peripheral tissues back to the liver for use in synthesis.
            d. LDLs carry cholesterol from the liver to tissues.
            e. HDLs carry cholesterol from cells to the liver, where it is converted to bile acids.
    C. Metabolism of triacylglycerols (Section 25.3–25.4).
        1. Overview (Section 25.3).
            a. TAGs are hydrolyzed.
                i.   TAGs in the diet are hydrolyzed to glycerol and fatty acids by lipoprotein lipase in capillary walls in adipose tissue.
                ii. TAGs in adipocytes are hydrolyzed within the cells, and the fatty acids travel into the bloodstream with albumins.
            b. Glycerol is carried to the liver or kidneys.
                Glycerol is converted to dihydroxyacetone phosphate, which enters glycolysis or gluconeogenesis.
            c. Fatty acids have two fates.
                i.   When energy is in good supply, fatty acids are converted to TAGs for storage.
                ii. When energy is needed, fatty acids are metabolized to acetyl-SCoA.
            d. Acetyl-SCoA is used for:
                i.   Generation of energy via the citric acid cycle and oxidative phosphorylation.
                ii. Biosynthesis of fatty acids.
                iii. Production of ketone bodies.
                iv. Synthesis of steroids.

2. Storage and mobilization of TAGs (Section 25.4).
   a. When blood glucose are high, TAGs are synthesized for storage.
      i. The glycerol 3-phosphate needed is made from dihydroxyacetone phosphate, which comes from glycolysis.
      ii. The fatty acyl-SCoAs needed come from digestion or biosynthesis.
      iii. Two fatty acyl-SCoA are added to glycerol 3-phosphate.
      iv. After removal of phosphate from glycerol 3-phosphate, the third fatty acyl-SCoA is added.
   b. When blood glucose levels are low, fatty acids and glycerol are released from adipocytes and enter the bloodstream.
II. Fatty acid oxidation (Sections 25.5–25.7).
   A. Steps in fatty acid oxidation (Section 25.5).
      1. Activation.
         a. Fatty acids react with HSCoA to form fatty acyl-SCoA.
         b. At the same time, ATP is converted to AMP + 2 $HOPO_3^{2-}$.
      2. Transport.
         Fatty acyl-SCoAs are transported across the mitochondrial membrane.
      3. Oxidation (β Oxidation).
         a.

         e. An n-carbon fatty acid produces $n/2$ acetyl-SCoA.
   B. Energy from fatty acid oxidation (Section 25.6).
      1. The number of molecules of ATP produced from a fatty acid that yields n acetyl-SCoA molecules is $14n–6$.
      2. Fats produce more than twice the amount of energy per unit weight than carbohydrates do.
   C. Production of ketone bodies (ketogenesis) (Section 25.7).
      1. Ketone bodies are formed when the body produces excess acetyl-SCoA.
      2. Synthesis of ketone bodies.
         a. 2 Acetyl-SCoA —> acetoacetyl-SCoA + HSCoA.
         b. Acetoacetyl-SCoA + acetyl-SCoA —> 3-hydroxy-3-methylglutaryl-SCoA + HSCoA.
         c. 3-Hydroxy-3-methylglutaryl-SCoA —> acetyl-SCoA + acetoacetate.
         d. Acetoacetate + $NADH/H^+$ —> 3-hydroxybutyrate + NAD^+.
         e. Acetoacetate —> acetone + CO_2

3. Catabolism of ketone bodies during starvation produces much of the energy that the body needs.

4. When ketone bodies are formed faster than the body can utilize them, ketoacidosis occurs.

   In ketoacidosis, blood pH drops, ketone bodies are excreted in the urine, and coma and death may result.

III. Fatty acid biosynthesis (lipogenesis) (Section 25.8).

   A. Lipogenesis occurs when amino acids and carbohydrates are in good supply.

   B. Lipogenesis resembles fatty acid oxidation but isn't its exact reverse.

   Lipogenesis occurs in the cytosol, and intermediates are carried by ACP.

   C. Mechanism of lipogenesis.

   1. Condensation.
      a. Acetyl-SCoA + HCO_3^- —> H_2O + malonyl-SCoA.
      b. Malonyl-SCoA + HSACP —> malonyl-SACP + HSCoA.
      c. Acetyl-SCoA + HSACP —> acetyl-SACP + HSCoA.
      d. Acetyl-SACP + malonyl-SACP —> acetoacetyl-SACP + SACP.
   2. Reduction, using NADPH/H$^+$.
   3. Dehydration.
   4. Reduction, using the coenzyme NADPH/H$^+$.
   5. Addition of acetyl-SACP units, followed by steps 2–5, occurs until the chain is the correct length.

Solutions to Chapter 25 Problems

25.1 Both cholate and cholesterol have the tetracyclic ring structure of a steroid. Cholate has more polar functional groups (three –OH groups and one carboxylate group) and is better able to emulsify fats than cholesterol (one –OH group). The hydrophobic side of cholate interacts with TAGs, and the hydrophilic side interacts with the aqueous environment. The less polar cholesterol is more suitable for incorporation into cell membranes. Thus, the two molecules can't change roles.

Cholate   Cholesterol

25.2 The enzyme *triose phosphate isomerase* catalyzes the isomerization of dihydroxyacetone phosphate to glyceraldehyde 3-phosphate, which proceeds through the last 5 steps of glycolysis to yield pyruvate.

25.3 (a), (b) In *Step 1*, a C=C double bond is introduced, using FAD as the oxidizing agent.
   In *Step 3*, an alcohol is oxidized to a ketone, using NAD$^+$ as the oxidizing agent.
   (c) In *Step 2*, water is added to a carbon-carbon double bond.
   (d) In *Step 4*, HSCoA displaces acetyl-SCoA, producing a chain-shortened acyl-SCoA fatty acid.

25.4

(a)

Seven β oxidations are needed.

(b)

$$10\ CH_3C\!-\!SCoA$$

Nine β oxidations are needed.

25.5   In the citric acid cycle, steps 6 (dehydrogenation of succinate to produce fumarate), 7 (hydration of fumarate to produce malate), and 8(oxidation of malate to produce oxaloacetate) are similar to the first three reactions of the β oxidation of a fatty acid.

25.6   The formation of 3-hydroxybutyrate from acetoacetate is a reduction (iii).

25.7   (a) Acetyl-SCoA provides the acetyl groups used in the synthesis of the ketone bodies. (b) Three acetyl-SCoA molecules are used. (c) During prolonged starvation, the body, including the brain, uses ketone bodies as an energy source.

Understanding Key Concepts

25.8   The NADH and FADH$_2$ produced in β oxidation must be reoxidized in the electron transport system in order for β oxidation to continue. Since oxygen is required to reoxidize these reduced coenzymes in the electron transport system, β oxidation is an aerobic pathway even though oxygen isn't directly involved.

25.9   (a) HDL has the highest ratio of protein to lipid.
(b) Chylomicrons have the lowest density because they have the highest percentage of lipids, and lipids are less dense than protein.
(c) VLDL carries TAGs from the liver to peripheral tissue, where they are used either for storage or for energy generation.
(d) Chylomicrons carry TAGs from the diet.
(e) LDL carries cholesterol from the liver to peripheral tissue.
(f) HDL removes cholesterol from circulation and transports it to the liver, where it is converted to bile acids and excreted.
(g) LDL contains "bad" cholesterol, which is deposited in tissues and contributes to atherosclerosis.

25.10

A	B	C
high blood glucose	high glucagon / low insulin	fatty acid and TAG synthesis
low blood glucose	high insulin / low glucagon	TAG hydrolysis and fatty acid oxidation

25.11 Fatty acid + HSCoA + ATP $\longrightarrow$ Fatty acyl-SCoA + AMP + 2 PO$_4^{3-}$

The above reaction, which is used to activate fatty acids for β oxidation, requires the energy expenditure of the equivalent of two ATPs. This energy is later recaptured in β oxidation of the fatty acid.

25.12 When oxaloacetate in liver is used for gluconeogenesis, less oxaloacetate is available for the citric acid cycle, and less acetyl-SCoA is able to enter the cycle. Instead, there is a buildup of acetyl-SCoA in the bloodstream. Heart and muscle use the excess acetyl-SCoA for synthesis of ketone bodies. Buildup of ketone bodies leads to ketoacidosis, in which blood pH is lowered and the odor of acetone is noticeable in urine and on the breath. Ketoacidosis can lead to dehydration, labored breathing, and death.

25.13 Catabolism of one gram of stored TAG provides more energy than does catabolism of one gram of glycogen. Another reason that stored fats have a higher "energy density" than stored carbohydrates is the association of water with the hydrophilic glycogen molecules, which further reduces the energy yield per gram of glycogen.

Digestion and Catabolism of Lipids

25.14 Lipids make you feel full because they slow the rate of movement of food through the stomach.

25.15 Digestion of triacylglycerols occurs in the small intestine, where pancreatic lipase partially hydrolyzes emulsified triacylglycerols. Short-chain fatty acids are absorbed into the bloodstream. In the intestinal lining, longer-chain fatty acids and acylglycerols are recombined to form triacylglycerols, which are bound in chylomicrons that travel through the lymphatic system to enter the bloodstream.

Hydrolysis of stored triacylglycerols occurs in fat cells. Hydrolysis of triacylglycerols from food occurs at capillary walls of adipose tissue, muscles and liver.

25.16 Bile emulsifies lipid droplets so that they can be attacked by enzymes.

25.17 The products of pancreatic lipase hydrolysis of triacylglycerols (TAGs) are mono- and diacylglycerols, plus fatty acids and glycerol. The products of lipoprotein lipase (in adipocytes) are fatty acids and glycerol.

25.18 Acylglycerols, fatty acids, and protein are combined to form *chylomicrons*, which are lipoproteins used to transport lipids from the diet into the bloodstream.

25.19 Very-low-density lipoproteins originate in the liver and are used to transport TAGs that have been synthesized in the liver to tissues where they will be used or stored.

25.20 Fatty acids from adipose tissue are carried in the bloodstream by albumins.

25.21 Steps 6–10 of the glycolysis pathway are necessary for converting glyceraldehyde 3-phosphate to pyruvate. These steps include an oxidation (Step 6), a phosphorylation (Step 6), two phosphate transfers to ADP (Steps 7 and 10), an isomerization (Step 8), and a dehydration (Step 9).

25.22 For each molecule of glycerol, 5.5 molecules of ATP are released in forming pyruvate. One ATP results from the conversion of glycerol to glyceraldehyde-3-phosphate, and 4.5 more arise from the conversion of glyceraldehyde-3-phosphate to pyruvate (2 direct phosphorylations, which produce 2 ATP, and production of one NADH, which enters the electron transport chain to produce 2.5 more ATP).

25.23 Eight molecules of ATP are formed in the catabolism of glycerol to yield acetyl SCoA — the 5.5 mentioned in Problem 25.21 and an additional 2.5 in the conversion of pyruvate to acetyl SCoA (Section 23.5).
A maximum of 18 molecules of ATP are released in the complete catabolism of glycerol to CO_2 and H_2O — the 8 molecules mentioned above and an additional 10 molecules formed when acetyl SCoA is degraded in the citric-acid cycle.

25.24 An adipocyte is a cell, almost entirely filled with fat globules, in which TAGs are stored and mobilized.

25.25 Adipose tissue is located under the skin and in the abdominal cavity and is used for storage and mobilization of triacylglycerols.

25.26 Fatty acid oxidation occurs primarily in heart, liver and muscle cells.

25.27 β Oxidation occurs in the mitochondrial matrix of cells.

25.28 A fatty acid is converted to its fatty acyl-SCoA in order to activate it for catabolism.

25.29 The activated fatty acid must be transported from the cytosol into the mitochondrial matrix.

25.30 Stepwise oxidation of fatty acids is known as β oxidation because the carbon β to the thioester group (2 carbons away from the thioester group) is oxidized in the process.

25.31 The sequence is a spiral because the same reaction series is repeated on a two-carbon-shortened fatty acid until the original acid is consumed. In a cycle, the product of the final step is a reactant in the first step.

25.32 Each cycle of β oxidation produces 4 molecules of ATP (2.5 ATPs from the formation of the reduced coenzyme NADH and 1.5 ATPs from the formation of the reduced coenzyme $FADH_2$), plus one molecule of acetyl-SCoA, which enters into the citric acid cycle to yield 10 more molecules of ATP, for a total of 14.

25.33 In the previous problem, we calculated that each cycle of β oxidation produced 14 ATP. Since the last acetyl-SCoA doesn't undergo β oxidation, 4 fewer ATP are produced from that cycle. Two ATP are also used for activation, and when they are subtracted, we arrive at the formula:

ATP produced per fatty acid = $14n - 6$, where n = the number of acetyl-SCoA produced

For a 10-carbon acid, $n = 5$; thus, the energy content of $CH_3(CH_2)_8COOH$ (capric acid) is a maximum of 64 ATP per mole. For a 14-carbon acid, $n = 7$ and the energy content is a maximum of 92 ATP.

Least energy/mole ⟶ *Greatest energy/mole*

Molecule	Glucose	Sucrose	$CH_3(CH_2)_8COOH$	$CH_3(CH_2)_{12}COOH$
ATP content/mole	32 ATP	64 ATP	64 ATP	92 ATP

25.34

25.35

25.36 The number of moleculess of acetyl-SCoA produced from one molecule of fatty acid is half the number of carbons in the acid. The number of cycles of β oxidation is one fewer than the number of moleculess of acetyl-SCoA produced.

Acid	Acetyl-SCoA Produced	Number of cycles
(a) $CH_3(CH_2)_6COOH$	4	3
(b) $CH_3(CH_2)_{12}COOH$	7	6

25.37 Three cycles of β oxidation catabolize caprylic acid (a C_8 acid), and 6 cycles of β oxidation catabolize myristic acid (a C_{14} acid).

Fatty Acid Anabolism

25.38 The anabolic pathway for synthesizing fatty acids is called *lipogenesis*.

25.39 Since β oxidation is an energetically favorable reaction, its exact reverse is energetically unfavorable and thus doesn't occur.

25.40 Acetyl-SCoA is the starting material for fatty-acid synthesis.

25.41 Fatty acids have an even number of carbons because they are synthesized from a starting material (acetyl-SCoA) that has an even number of carbons.

25.42 Palmitic acid has 16 carbons and is synthesized from 8 acetyl-SCoA units through 7 rounds of the lipogenesis spiral.

25.43 Each cycle of lipogenesis uses two NADPH molecules. For the synthesis of palmitic acid, which requires 7 cycles of lipogenesis, 14 molecules of NADPH are needed.

Applications

25.44 Total cholesterol: 200 mg/dL or lower.
          LDL: 160 mg/dL or lower.
          HDL: 60 mg/dL or higher.

25.45 Atherosclerosis is the formation of deposits composed of cholesterol and other lipid-containing materials in the arteries of the brain and heart.

25.46 LDL carries cholesterol from the liver to tissues; HDL carries cholesterol from tissues to the liver, where it is converted to bile and excreted.

25.47 A cholesterol/HDL ratio of 3.5 is ideal, a ratio of 4.5 indicates an average risk, and a ratio of 5.5 shows a high risk.

25.48 Malabsorption is an inability to absorb lipids into the bloodstream, and it is detected by large amounts of fat in the feces.

25.49 Medium-chain triacylglycerols are composed of fatty acids containing ten or fewer carbon atoms. These triacylglycerols can be directly absorbed into the cells lining the small intestine, where they are broken down. The resulting fatty acids can be transported in the bloodstream via albumins.

25.50 Important functions of the liver include:

(a) Synthesis of glycogen, glucose, triacylglycerols, fatty acids, cholesterol, bile acids, plasma proteins, and blood clotting factors.
(b) Catabolism of glucose, fatty acids, and amino acids.
(c) Storage of glycogen, lipids, amino acids, iron, and fat-soluble vitamins.
(d) Inactivation of toxic substances.

25.51 Cirrhosis is the development of fibrous tissue in the liver and is due to excessive deposits of triacylglycerols as a result of alcoholism or metabolic disorders.

General Questions and Problems

25.52 An excess of carbohydrates produces an excess of acetyl-SCoA. If more acetyl-SCoA is produced than is needed in the respiratory chain, it is used to synthesize fatty acids, which are used to produce the triglycerides that are deposited in adipose tissue. Once carbohydrates have been catabolized to acetyl-SCoA, it is not possible to resynthesize carbohydrates, because animals don't have enzymes to synthesize carbohydrates from acetyl-SCoA.

25.53 In β oxidation, the alcohol intermediate is chiral because the hydroxyl carbon is bonded to four different groups.

25.54 Acetone, acetoacetate and 3-hydroxybutyrate are ketone bodies, which are produced when blood sugar is low and the body metabolizes fats. If more acetyl-SCoA is produced than can enter the citric acid cycle, it is converted to ketone bodies, in the process known as ketogenesis, to be used as an alternate energy source. Ketone bodies are so named because they either contain the ketone functional group or are directly derived from ketones.

25.55 Ketosis is a condition in which ketone bodies accumulate in the blood faster than they can be metabolized. Since two of the ketone bodies are carboxylic acids, they lower the pH of the blood, producing the condition known as ketoacidosis. Symptoms of ketoacidosis include dehydration, labored breathing and depression; prolonged ketoacidosis may lead to coma and death.

25.56

Glyceryl trimyristate

Glycerol is converted to glyceraldehyde 3-phosphate, which enters glycolysis, is converted to pyruvate and yields one acetyl-SCoA. Each myristate produces 7 acetyl-SCoA molecules; three myristates yield 21 acetyl-SCoA molecules. A total of 22 acetyl-SCoA molecules are thus formed.

25.57 Consider a carbohydrate and a fatty acid with similar molar masses. Glucose (molar mass = 180 g) yields a maximum of 32 ATP/mole; $CH_3(CH_2)_8COOH$ (molar mass = 172 g) yields a maximum of 64 ATP/mole (Problem 25.33). Thus, the energy yield per mole from a fat is about twice the yield from a sugar. There are two principal reasons for this difference. (1) A carbohydrate has fewer carbons than a fatty acid of similar molar mass and thus produces fewer moles of acetyl-SCoA per mole of carbohydrate. (2) Only 2/3 of a carbohydrate's carbons are used to form acetyl-SCoA; the other carbons are released as CO_2 in the transformation pyruvate —> acetyl-SCoA.

25.58 (a) HDL, which transports cholesterol from tissue to the liver, is endogenous.
(b) Chylomicrons, which carry dietary triacylglycerols in the bloodstream, are exogenous.

25.59 The body synthesizes cholesterol when no cholesterol is present in the diet. Thus, eliminating exogenous sources of cholesterol won't eliminate cholesterol in the bloodstream. A certain amount of cholesterol is essential for membrane function and as the starting material for synthesis of steroid hormones.

25.60 Ketones have little effect on pH, but the two other ketone bodies are acidic, and they lower the pH of urine.

25.61

$$H_2C=CH-\overset{\overset{\textstyle CH_3}{|}}{C}=CH_2 \qquad \text{2-Methyl-1,3-butadiene}$$

Since cholesterol contains 27 carbon atoms, at least 6 molecules of 2-methyl-1,3-butadiene would be needed for its synthesis.

Self-Test for Chapter 25

Multiple choice:

1. ATP is ultimately produced in all of the following steps of fatty acid catabolism except:
   (a) fatty acid activation   (b) introduction of a double bond into a fatty acid   (c) oxidation of an alcohol to a ketone   (d) entry of acetyl-SCoA into the citric acid cycle

2. An excess of ketone bodies in the blood is known as:
   (a) ketosis   (b) ketonuria   (c) ketoacidosis   (d) ketonemia

3. The reactants for TAG synthesis are:
   (a) glycerol and fatty acids   (b) glycerol 3-phosphate and fatty acids   (c) glyceraldehyde 3-phosphate and fatty acyl-SCoA   (d) glycerol and fatty acyl-SCoA

4. Production of ketone bodies occurs in:
   (a) the liver   (b) adipose tissue   (c) muscle   (d) all of the above

5. Which of the following statements about lipogenesis is false?
   (a) Synthesis occurs two carbons at a time.   (b) Formation of acyl-SACP intermediates requires ATP.   (c) The coenzyme NADPH is needed.   (d) Lipogenesis occurs when acetyl-SCoA is in abundance.

6. Chylomicrons transport all of the following except:
   (a) acylglycerols   (b) small-chain fatty acids   (c) phospholipids   (d) cholesterol

7. Fatty acids from storage in adipose tissue are transported :
   (a) by chylomicrons   (b) by VLDL   (c) by serum albumin   (d) free in the bloodstream

8. Acetyl-SCoA is the starting material for synthesis of all of the following except:
   (a) steroids   (b) fatty acids   (c) ketone bodies   (d) glycerol

9. β Oxidation of $CH_3(CH_2)_8COOH$ produces a maximum of how many ATPs?
   (a) 78   (b) 72   (c) 64   (d) 60

10. When glucose is in good supply, the body:
    (a) synthesizes ketone bodies from acetyl-SCoA   (b) hydrolyzes TAGs from adipocytes   (c) breaks down fatty acids via β-oxidation   (d) synthesizes TAGs for storage

Complete the following sentences:

1. One _____ and one _____ are needed for each β oxidation cycle.

2. Bile acids solubilize lipids by forming _____.

3. Triacylglycerols are stored in _____.

4. TAG synthesis begins with the conversion of glycerol to _____ _____.

5. An alternate name for β oxidation is the ___ - ____ ____.

6. The first step in β oxidation involves introduction of a _____ _____.

7. _____ is the presence of ketone bodies in the urine.

8. _____ is a coenzyme for fatty-acid biosynthesis.

9. _____ is a ketone body containing a hydroxyl group.

10. Chylomicrons are transported in the _____ _____ and in the bloodstream.

11. TAGs that are released from storage are said to be _____.

12. All fatty acids are synthesized from _____.

Tell whether the following statements are true or false:

1. Bile acids are steroids.

2. TAGs are hydrolyzed by pancreatic lipases to glycerol and fatty acids.

3. Activation of fatty acids for fatty-acid oxidation requires two phosphates to be cleaved.

4. A chylomicron is a type of lipoprotein.

5. Chylomicrons carry fatty acid-SCoA across the mitochondrial membrane.

6. A fatty acid with n carbons requires $n/2 - 1$ cycles of β-oxidation for complete breakdown.

7. TAGs are synthesized from glycerol and fatty acyl-SCoAs.

8. HDL transports cholesterol to tissues, where it can accumulate.

9. A fatty acid with a molecular weight similar to that of glucose yields more ATPs per molecule than glucose.

10. Fatty acid synthesis occurs in mitochondria.

11. The terminal $-CH_3$ group of a fatty acid comes from malonyl-SCoA.

12. Most naturally-occurring fatty acids have an even number of carbon atoms.

Match the entry on the left with its partner on the right:

1. Chylomicron

2. Lipogenesis

3. LDL

4. Acetone

5. Malonyl-SCoA

6. Fatty-acid spiral

7. Micelle

8. Lipoprotein lipase

9. HDL

10. Albumin

11. Bile

12. Acetoacetate

(a) Lipoprotein rich in cholesterol

(b) Protein that carries fatty acids in the bloodstream

(c) Solubilizcs fats

(d) Hydrolyzes TAG in adipose tissue

(e) Lipoprotein that aids in lipid transport of fats in the diet

(f) Lipoprotein rich in protein

(g) Starting material in lipogenesis

(h) Acidic ketone body

(i) Fatty acid biosynthesis

(j) Breakdown of fatty acids into acetyl-SCoA

(k) Formed from bile and lipids

(l) Nonacidic ketone body

Chapter Outline

I. Nucleic acids (Sections 26.1–26.4).
   A. Introduction (Section 26.1).
      1. When a cell isn't dividing, its nucleus consists of chromatin, a tangle of fibers composed of protein and DNA.
      2. Just before dividing, the DNA is duplicated.
      3. During division, chromatin organizes itself into chromosomes, each of which is a huge DNA molecule.
      4. The chromosomes are made up of genes, individual segments of DNA that contain instructions for synthesizing a single protein.
      5. The human body has 23 pairs of chromosomes.
   B. Composition of nucleic acids (Section 26.2).
      1. Nucleic acids are polymers of nucleotides.
         DNA and RNA are the two types of nucleic acids.
      2. Nucleotides consist of:
         a. A heterocyclic base.
            i. The bases for DNA are the purines adenine and guanine, and the pyrimidines cytosine and thymine.
            ii. For RNA, uracil replaces thymine.
         b. A pentose.
            i. For DNA, the pentose is D-ribose.
            ii. For RNA, the pentose is D-2-deoxyribose.
            ii. The pentose is connected to the base by a β-N-glycosidic bond to the anomeric carbon.
         c. A phosphate group.
            The phosphate group is attached at C5 of the pentose.
      3. The combination of sugar + base is known as a nucleoside.
         a. Nucleosides are named by replacing the *-ine* of the base name by *-osine* for purines and *-idine* for pyrimidines.
         b. If the pentose is 2-deoxyribose, the prefix "deoxy" is added to the name.
         c. To indicate position, numbers without primes are used for bases, and numbers with primes are used for the pentose.
         d. Nucleosides have important biochemical functions other than as components of nucleic acids.
      4. Nucleotides.
         a. Nucleotides are named by adding "5'-monophosphate" to the nucleoside name.
         b. Nucleotides can form di- and triphosphates.
            ATP plays an important role in biochemical energetics.
   C. The structure of nucleic acid chains (Section 26.3).
      1. Nucleotides are joined by phosphate ester bonds between the 5' phosphate and the 3' –OH group of the sugar of the next nucleotide.
      2. Vast numbers of nucleotides can be connected by these bonds to form immense polynucleotides.
      3. The structure and function of nucleic acids depends on the sequence of nucleotides.
      4. The sequence is described by starting at the 5' end and identifying the bases by one-letter abbreviations.

    D. Base-pairing in DNA (Section 26.4).
       1. In DNA, two polynucleotide strands coil around each other in a double helix.
         a. The sugar–phosphate backbone is on the outside.
         b. The bases are inside.
       2. The two strands run in opposite directions.
       3. The two strands are held together by H-bonding between bases.
         a. A and T form two hydrogen bonds to each other.
         b. C and G form three hydrogen bonds to each other.
       4. The two strands are complementary.
         a. A and T always occur in DNA in the same percentage.
         b. C and G always occur in DNA in the same percentage.
II. The function of nucleic acids (Sections 26.5–26.11).
    A. The central dogma of molecular genetics (Section 26.5).
       1. The function of DNA is to store genetic information.
       2. The function of RNA is to read and decode DNA and use the information to synthesize proteins.
       3. Nucleic acids take part in three major processes.
         a. Replication is the process in which DNA makes a copy of itself.
         b. Transcription is the process in which RNA reads the genetic message.
         c. Translation is the process in which the genetic message is used to make proteins.
    B. Replication of DNA (Section 26.6).
       1. Mechanism of replication.
         a. The double helix partially unwinds.
         b. Bases line up and hydrogen-bond with their complements.
         c. DNA polymerase catalyzes bond formation between the 5' phosphate group on the arriving nucleotide and the 3' –OH of the old strand.
       2. Two identical new copies of the double helix are formed.
       3. Because strand growth occurs in one direction (5' —> 3'), only one strand of DNA is synthesized continuously.
         a. The other strand is synthesized in segments, beginning at the replication fork.
         b. DNA ligase attaches the segments of the other strand.
       4. The copying of DNA requires several hours, involves many replication forks, and proceeds virtually without error.
    C. RNA (Section 26.7).
       1. Structure of RNA.
         a. RNA resembles DNA but has the following differences;
           i. The pentose is ribose.
           ii. Uracil replaces thymine.
         b. RNA chains are shorter than DNA chains.
         c. RNA chains may be single-stranded or double-stranded.
       2. Types of RNA.
         a. Ribosomal RNA has a molecular weight of 5×10^6 amu and occurs in ribosomes, which are the site of protein synthesis.
         b. Messenger RNA reads DNA and carries the message to the ribosomes.
         c. Transfer RNA delivers amino acids to the growing protein chain.
    D. Transcription (Section 26.8).
       1. mRNA is synthesized by transcription of DNA.
         a. RNA polymerase recognizes a control segment of DNA that precedes the nucleotides to be transcribed.
         b. A small section of DNA unwinds.
         c. Complementary bases are attached.

    d. Transcription stops when RNA polymerase recognizes a "stop" nucleotide sequence.

    e. All RNA is synthesized in the same way, although we will focus on mRNA in this description.

  2. Only one DNA strand is transcribed — the template strand.

    a. The other strand is the information strand.

    b. mRNA is a copy of the information strand (with U replacing T).

  3. Not all genes are continuous strands of DNA.

    a. The coding sections of DNA (exons) are interrupted by noncoding sections (introns).

    b. In the final mRNA, the intron sections are cut out.

  4. Each mRNA controls the synthesis of one protein.

E. Translation (Sections 26.9–26.10).

  1. The genetic code (Section 26.9).

    a. A sequence of three mRNA bases codes for a specific amino acid.

    b. The codes are written in the 5' —> 3' direction.

    c. Each amino acid is represented by one or more codes.

  2. Transfer RNA (Section 26.10).

    a. The message carried by mRNA is decoded by tRNA.

    b. Each amino acid is transported by its own tRNA to the ribosome.

    c. Amino acids are bonded to tRNA by an ester bond between the –COOH group of an amino acid and C3' of ribose at the end of the tRNA.

    d. Each tRNA has an anticodon that corresponds to a codon sequence on mRNA.

  3. Protein synthesis.

    a. Initiation.

      i. The first AUG codon on the 5' end of mRNA is a "start" codon (which also codes for methionine).

      ii. When the Met tRNA comes together with the mRNA codon and occupies one of the two binding sites in the ribosome, elongation can start.

      iii. If Met isn't the first amino acid in the protein, it is removed after protein synthesis.

    b. Elongation.

      i. A tRNA with an anticodon complementary to the second mRNA codon occupies the second binding site.

      ii. An enzyme in the ribosome catalyzes peptide bond formation and breaks the bond between the first amino acid and its tRNA.

      iii. This tRNA leaves the ribosome.

      iv. The ribosome shifts one position along the mRNA chain (translocation).

      v. The second site is free to accept the next tRNA.

      vi. A single mRNA can be read by many ribosomes.

    c. Termination.

      i. A "stop" codon signals the end of translation.

      ii. An enzyme called "releasing factor" frees the polypeptide chain from the last tRNA, and the mRNA is released from the ribosome.

Solutions to Chapter 26 Problems

26.1

2'-Deoxythymidine

26.2 D-Ribose has one more oxygen atom than 2-deoxy-D-ribose.

β-D-Ribose
($C_5H_{10}O_5$)

β-2-Deoxy-D-ribose
($C_5H_{10}O_4$)

26.3

2'-Deoxyadenosine 5'-monophosphate

26.4

Guanosine 5'-triphosphate (GTP)

26.5   dCMP – 2'-Deoxycytidine 5'-monophosphate
CMP – Cytidine 5'-monophosphate
UDP – Uridine 5'-diphosphate
AMP – Adenosine 5'-monophosphate
ATP – Adenosine 5'-triphosphate

26.6   G-G-T-A = guanine-guanine-thymine-adenine

26.7

26.8   (a) Original strand: 5'   G-C-C-T-A-G-T   3'
: : : : : : :
Complement: 3'   C-G-G-A-T-C-A   5'

(b) Original strand: 5'   A-A-T-G-G-C-T-C-A   3'
: : : : : : : : :
Complement: 3'   T-T-A-C-C-G-A-G-T   5'

26.9

Adenine   Uracil

26.10 The phosphate groups cause the DNA molecule to be negatively charged.

26.11 (a) A longer strand of DNA has a higher "melting temperature" because larger molecules have greater numbers of hydrogen bonds.
(b) A strand of DNA containing a higher percentage of C/G base pairs has a higher "melting temperature". A C/G base pair has three hydrogen bonds, whereas an A/T pair has only two hydrogen bonds. A DNA strand with a higher percent of C/G base pairs has more hydrogen bonds, and more heat is required to separate the two strands.

26.12 (a) DNA template strand: 5' G-A-T–T–A-C-C-G-T 3'
⋮ ⋮ ⋮ ⋮ ⋮ ⋮ ⋮ ⋮ ⋮
mRNA complement: 3' C-U-A-A-U-G-G-C-A 5'

(b) DNA template strand: 5' T-A–T-G-G-C-T–A-G-G-C-A 3'
⋮ ⋮ ⋮ ⋮ ⋮ ⋮ ⋮ ⋮ ⋮ ⋮ ⋮ ⋮
mRNA complement   3' A-U-A-C-C-G-A-U-C-C-G-U 5'

26.13 *Amino Acid*   *Possible Codons   (5' –> 3')*

(a) Ala	GCU	GCC	GCA	GCG		
(b) Phe	UUU	UUC				
(c) Leu	UUA	UUG	CUU	CUC	CUA	CUG
(d) Val	GUU	GUC	GUA	GUG		
(e) Tyr	UAU	UAC				

26.14 The sequence guanine, uracil, cytosine (GUC) codes for the amino acid valine.

26.15   *Codon*   *Amino Acid*

(a) AUU	Ile
(b) GCG	Ala
(c) CGA	Arg
(d) AAC	Asn

26.16 Three mRNA base triplets code for isoleucine: AUU, AUC, AUA. Six possible DNA informational strands could code for this tripeptide if different codons were used for each Ile.
5' ATTATCATA 3'   5' ATCATTATA 3'   5' ATAATCATT 3'
5' ATTATAATC 3'   5' ATCATAATT 3'   5' ATAATTATC 3'

26.17 - 26.18

mRNA sequence:	5' CUU—AUG—GCU—UGG—CCC—UAA						3'
Amino-acid sequence:	Leu——Met——Ala——Trp——Pro——Stop						
tRNA anticodons:	3' GAA	UAC	CGA	ACC	GGG	AUU	5'
DNA template sequence:	3' GAA—TAC—CGA—ACC—GGG—ATT						5'

Understanding Key Concepts

26.19

Guanosine 5'-monophosphate

26.20

The sequence of the left chain: –A–G–T–C–.
The sequence of the right chain: –G–A–C–T–.

26.21

Segments B and C are joined by the action of a DNA ligase enzyme.

26.22 The sugar-phosphate backbone is found on the exterior of the DNA double helix. Since the phosphate groups are negatively charged, histone proteins should have a large number of positively charged amino acids, such as lysine, arginine and histidine, on their surfaces.

26.23

The nucleotides adenosine 5'-monophosphate, cytidine 5'-monophosphate, guanosine 5'-monophosphate and uridine 5'-monophosphate are used to synthesize messenger RNA.

26.24 Each amino acid has more than one mRNA codon.
Codons for Tyr: UAU, UAC.
Codons for Gly: GGU, GGC, GGA, GGC.
Codons for Phe: UUU, UUC.
Using the first codon listed:

(a) 5' U A U G G U G G U U U U 3' mRNA

(b) 3' A T A C C A C C A A A A 5' DNA template strand

(c) 5' T A T G G T G G T T T T 3' DNA informational strand

The upper strand of DNA is the template for the synthesis of mRNA, and its sequence of bases is the complement of the sequence of bases that make up the enkephalin gene (with T replacing U). The lower strand is the informational strand.
(d) To find the number of DNA sequences, multiply the numbers of different codons for each amino acid.
2 x 4 x 4 x 2 = 64 possible DNA sequences code for the first four amino acids in enkephalins.

Structure and Function of Nucleic Acids

26.25 A nucleotide is a monomer unit of DNA or RNA. It consists of a heterocyclic amine base, an aldopentose, and a phosphate group.

26.26 Ribose is the sugar in RNA, and deoxyribose is the sugar in DNA. The –OH group at carbon 2 of ribose is replaced by –H in deoxyribose.

26.27 Adenine, cytosine, guanine, and thymine are the four heterocyclic bases in DNA. Adenine, cytosine, guanine, and uracil are the four major heterocyclic bases in RNA

26.28 The purine bases (two fused heterocyclic rings) are adenine and guanine. The pyrimidine bases (one heterocyclic ring) are cytosine, thymine (in DNA) and uracil (in RNA).

26.29 *Messenger RNA (mRNA)* carries the genetic message from DNA to ribosomes.
Ribosomal RNA (rRNA) complexes with protein to form ribosomes, where protein synthesis takes place.
Transfer RNA (tRNA) transports specific amino acids to the ribosomes, where they are incorporated into proteins.

26.30 DNA is the largest nucleic acid, mRNA is intermediate, and tRNA is the smallest of the three nucleic acids.

26.31 (a) *Base pairing* is the hydrogen-bonded pairing of two complementary heterocyclic bases in the double helix of DNA and during replication, transcription and translation.
(b) Adenine pairs with thymine (or uracil, in RNA), and guanine pairs with cytosine.
(c) Adenine and thymine (or uracil) form 2 hydrogen bonds with each other. Cytosine and guanine form 3 hydrogen bonds with each other.

26.32 *Similarities:* Replication, transcription and translation are all polymerizations in which a nucleic acid is used as a template for the synthesis of another biopolymer. In all of these processes, hydrogen bonding is used to bring the subunits into the correct position for bond formation and to determine the order of assembly.
Differences: In replication, DNA makes a copy of itself. In transcription, DNA is used as a template for the synthesis of mRNA. In translation, mRNA is used as a template for the synthesis of proteins. Replication and transcription take place in the nucleus of cells, and translation takes place in ribosomes.

26.33 A chromosome is an enormous molecule of DNA. A gene is a part of the chromosome that codes for a single piece of information (that is, a single protein) needed by a cell.

26.34 Chromatin is composed of protein and DNA.

26.35 A gene carries the DNA code needed to synthesize a specific polypeptide.

26.36 There are 46 chromosomes (23 pairs) in a human cell.

26.37 The DNA double helix is held together by hydrogen bonds between base pairs.

26.38 Bases that are complementary form hydrogen bonds with each other and thus always occur in pairs. For example, adenine is always hydrogen-bonded to thymine or uracil, and guanine is always hydrogen-bonded to cytosine.

26.39 The percent of A always equals the percent of T, since A and T are complementary. The same is true for G and C. Thus, sea urchin DNA contains about 32% each of A and T, and 18% each of G and C.

26.40 If a sample of DNA is 28% T, the percent of A is also 28%, since A and T are complementary. The sample contains 22% G and 22% C, because G and C are also complementary.

26.41 The 5' end of a nucleotide is a phosphate group bonded to carbon 5' of ribose. The 3' end is an –OH group bonded to carbon 3' of ribose.

26.42 Polynucleotides are written from 5' to 3'.

26.43–26.45

A phosphate ester bond is formed between the phosphate group and the sugar. Water is removed in the formation of both the sugar–phosphate linkage and the sugar–base linkage.

26.46

26.47 An advantage to this strategy is that the cell can make a biomolecule before it is needed. The biomolecule can be quickly converted to its active form when required.

Nucleic Acids and Heredity

26.48 Transcribed RNA is complementary to the template strand of DNA.

26.49 Numerous replication forks are needed when DNA is duplicated in order to increase the speed of replication of the enormous DNA chain.

26.50 To say that DNA replication is semiconservative means that each of the two new copies of DNA has a strand of DNA that was the original template and one strand that is newly synthesized.

26.51 A codon is a sequence of three nucleotides on mRNA that codes for a specific amino acid in protein synthesis.

26.52 An anticodon is a sequence of three nucleotides that is complementary to a sequence on a codon. The anticodon occurs on tRNA and matches the codon sequence on mRNA when it brings the correct amino acid into position for protein synthesis.

26.53 A tRNA molecule is cloverleaf-shaped and contains 70-100 nucleotides. The tRNA anticodon triplet is on one "leaf," and an amino acid bonds covalently to the 3' end.

26.54 The tRNAs for each amino acid differ in their anticodon sequences.

26.55 Exons and introns are sections of DNA. Exons carry the genetic message, whereas introns do not appear to code for any part of the protein being synthesized.

26.56

Amino Acid	Codons (5' –> 3')			
(a) Pro	CCU	CCC	CCA	CCG
(b) Lys	AAA	AAG		
(c) Met	AUG			

26.57 - 26.58

Codon (5' —> 3')	Amino Acid	tRNA Anticodon (3' —> 5')
(a) ACU	Thr	UGA
(b) GGA	Gly	CCU
(c) CUU	Leu	GAA

26.59

Amino Acid	Codon (5' —> 3')	tRNA Anticodon (3' —>5')
(a) Pro	CCU	GGA
	CCC	GGG
	CCA	GGU
	CCG	GGC
(b) Lys	AAA	UUU
	AAG	UUC
(c) Met	AUG	UAC

26.60–26.62

The DNA sequence of the template strand is complementary to the DNA sequence of the informational strand. The mRNA sequence is identical to the DNA sequence on the informational strand, except that U in mRNA replaces T in DNA.

Informational strand: (5' —> 3')	TAC-CGA
Template strand: (3' —> 5')	ATG-GCT
mRNA: (5' —> 3')	UAC-CGA
Dipeptide:	Tyr—-Arg

26.63

Informational strand: (5' —> 3')	CCT-GAC-GCG-GTT
Template strand: (3' —> 5')	GGA-CTG-CGC-CAA
mRNA: (5' —> 3')	CCU-GAC-GCG-GUU
Tetrapeptide	Pro—Asp—Ala—Val

26.64 Metenkephalin: Tyr—Gly—Gly—-Phe—Met   Stop
mRNA (5' —> 3'):   UAU–GGU–GGU–UUU–AUG–UAA
UAC   GGC GGC UUC   UAG
GGG GGG   UGA
GGA GGA

26.65 Using the first set of base pairs above to solve this problem:

Informational strand (5' —> 3'): TAT–GGT–GGT–TTT—ATG–TAA
Template strand (3' —> 5'): ATA–CCA–CCA–AAA—TAC—ATT

Applications

26.66 Viruses consist of a strand of nucleic acid wrapped in a protein coat. Unlike higher organisms, viruses can't replicate or manufacture protein independent of a host cell.

26.67 In reverse transcription, a host cell uses the RNA of an RNA virus (*retrovirus*) as a template for the synthesis of viral DNA, which is replicated and decoded. The host cell then synthesizes viral proteins.

26.68 To be effective, a drug must be powerful enough to act on viruses within cells without damaging the cells and their genetic material. Also, drugs quickly lose their effectiveness because of the high mutation rate of the AIDS virus.

26.69 An outline of a polymerase chain reaction:
(1) A solution of DNA that is to be copied is heated so that the DNA separates into two strands.
(2) Two oligonucleotide primers, which are complementary to the ends of the segment of DNA to be copied, are attached to the DNA strands.
(3) DNA polymerase and nucleotides are added, and the segment of DNA between the primers is copied.
The process is repeated many times until large amounts of the desired DNA is produced.

26.70 A polymerase chain reaction is used to produce a large number of copies of a specific DNA chain.

General Questions and Problems

26.71 The two mRNA codons for glu are GAA and GAG. Of the 4 codons for val (GUU, GUC, GUA, and GUG), the last two differ from the glu codons by one base. Thus, a change in one base can completely alter the structure and function of a protein.

26.72 To code for preproinsulin, 81 x 3 = 243 bases are needed to code for the protein's 81 amino acids. In addition, a three-base "start" codon and a three-base "stop" codon are needed, for a total of 249 bases .

26.73 <u>Position 9</u>:   Horse amino acid = Gly   Human amino acid = Ser
    mRNA codons (5' —> 3'):
    GGU GGC GGA GGG   UCU UCC UCA UCG AGU AGC

    DNA bases (template strand 3' —> 5'):
    <u>CCA</u> <u>CCG</u> CCT CCC   AGA AGG AGT AGC <u>TCA</u> <u>TCG</u>

The underlined horse DNA base triplets differ from their human counterparts (also underlined) by only one base.

<u>Position 30</u>:   Horse amino acid = Ala   Human amino acid = Thr
    mRNA codons (5' —> 3'):
    GCU GCC GCA GCG   ACU ACC ACA ACG

    DNA bases (template strand 3' —> 5'):
    CGA CGG CGT CGC   TGA TGG TGT TGC

Each group of three DNA bases from horse insulin has a counterpart in human insulin that differs from it by only one base. It is possible that horse insulin DNA differs from human insulin DNA by only two bases out of 159!

26.74 If a protein doesn't have methionine as its first amino acid, the methionine is removed after protein synthesis is complete.

26.75 Recall from problems 26.39 and 26.40 that the percent of A equals the percent of T, the percent of C equals the percent of G, and all percents add to 100%. If a DNA molecule contains 22% A, it will also contain 22% T, 28% C and 28% G. If you check the list of available nucleoside triphosphates, you should notice that only 22% dCTP is available for replication. dCTP is the nucleoside triphosphate that is limiting to the replication, and dTTP is in excess.

Self-Test for Chapter 26

Multiple choice:

1. The name for a nucleoside formed from cytidine and 2'-deoxyribose is:
   (a) deoxycytidine 5'-monophosphate   (b) 2'-deoxycytidine   (c) 2'-deoxycytosine
   (d) 2'-deoxycytosine 5'-monophosphate

2. Adenine and thymine are complementary because:
   (a) they are both purines   (b) they are both pyrimidines   (c) they both occur in DNA
   (d) they form two hydrogen bonds to each other

3. If the base sequence CAC-TTA-GGT appears on the informational strand of DNA, which
   sequence occurs in mRNA?
   (a) CAC-TTA-GGT   (b) CAC-UUA-GGU   (c) GTG-AAT-CCA   (d) GUG-AAU-CCA

4. Which statement about the RNA base sequence CGG-AAA-GUU is true?
   (a) It codes for a basic tripeptide.   (b) It contains a "stop" codon.   (c) Changing the third
   codon from GUU to GUC changes the amino acids in the tripeptide.   (d) The 5' end is on the
   right, and the 3' end is on the left.

5. Which of the following completes the initiation phase of protein synthesis?
   (a) the small subunit of a ribosome   (b) the large subunit of a ribosome   (c) mRNA   (d) tRNA

6. The process by which the genetic message contained in DNA is read is called:
   (a) replication   (b) transcription   (c) translation   (d) translocation

7. Which of the following heterocyclic bases contains a methyl group?
   (a) guanine   (b) cytosine   (c) thymine   (d) uracil

8. An enzyme involved in translation is:
   (a) DNA polymerase   (b) restriction endonuclease   (c) RNA polymerase   (d) releasing factor

9. Which of the following statements about DNA replication is untrue?
   (a) Replication is semiconservative.   (b) Each DNA strand has many replication forks.
   (c) DNA ligase catalyzes bond formation between each arriving nucleotide.
   (d) Replication proceeds in the 5'—>3' direction.

10. Which heterocyclic base contains only carbon, hydrogen and nitrogen?
   (a) adenine   (b) guanine   (c) cytosine   (d) thymine

Complete the following sentences:

1. _____ is the process by which an identical copy of DNA is made.

2. The two strands of DNA have base sequences that are _____.

3. When a cell is not actively dividing, its nucleus is occupied by _____.

4. Another name for an RNA virus is a _____.

5. An _____ is a segment of a gene that does not code for protein synthesis.

6. tRNA binds to an amino acid by an _____ linkage.

7. A _____ consists of a heterocyclic amine base bonded to an aldopentose.

8. An enzyme called a _____ _____ frees the polypeptide chain from the last tRNA during protein synthesis.

9. The point of replication of a DNA chain is called the _____ ____.

10. The sugar _____ has an -H instead of an -OH at its 2' position.

11. The _____ - _____ model describes DNA as two polynucleotide strands coiled about each other in a double helix.

12. The enzyme _____ _____ catalyzes the bonding of nucleotides to form new strands of DNA.

Tell whether the following statements are true or false:

1. There are a total of 64 codons for the 20 amino acids.

2. The amount of adenine in an organism's DNA is equal to the amount of guanine.

3. In transcription, mRNA is a copy of the informational strand of DNA.

4. An amino acid codon occurs on tRNA.

5. The codon AUG initiates protein synthesis.

6. Synthetase enzymes catalyze the formation of ester bonds between amino acids and their tRNAs.

7. The individual units of RNA and DNA are called nucleotides.

8. The two strands of the DNA double helix run in the same direction.

9. Transcription is the process by which the genetic message is decoded and used to make proteins.

10. Most human DNA contains genetic instructions.

11. Each amino acid is specified by more than one codon.

12. The correct name for the RNA nucleotide containing G is guanidine 5'-monophosphate.

Match the entries on the left with their partners on the right:

1. 5' end   (a) Enzyme used in replication

2. A-C-G   (b) Cysteine codon

3. U-G-C   (c) Forms three hydrogen bonds

4. Adenine   (d) Coded for by six codons

5. DNA ligase   (e) Enzyme used in the polymerase chain reaction

6. 3' end   (f) "Stop" codon

7. Leu   (g) Purine

8. Cytosine   (h) Enzyme used in transcription

9. Taq polymerase   (i) –OH group

10. Uracil   (j) Cysteine anticodon

11. U-G-A   (k) May cause hereditary disease

12. RNA polymerase   (l) Phosphate group

Chapter 27 – Genomics

Chapter Outline

I. Mapping the human genome (Section 27.1).
   A. Two research groups have collectively decoded 90% of the human genome.
      1. The Human Genome Project.
         a. The Human Genome Project is made up of 20 international not-for-profit groups.
         b. The technique:
            i. For each chromosome, a genetic map is developed; the map shows the location of markers determined by inheritance.
            ii. A map of finer resolution (physical map) shows markers determined by other methods.
            iii. The chromosome is cut into large segments, and the resulting clones are organized into an overlapping sequence.
            iv. Each clone is fragmented into hundreds of pieces, which are labelled and separated by electrophoresis.
            v. The sequences are assembled into a nucleotide map.
      2. Celera.
         a. Celera is a for-profit research group.
         b. The technique:
            i. The entire genome is broken into fragments, without identifying their origin.
            ii. The fragments are copied many times, sequenced and separated.
            iii. The sequences are reassembled, using a supercomputer.
   B. What is known about the human genome, as a result of these studies.
      1. There are approximately 3.1 billion base pairs in the human genome.
      2. The genome consists of 30,000 - 40,000 genes.
      3. A gene can produce several different proteins.
      4. About 200 genes are common to both humans and bacteria.
      5. Roughly 50% of the genome is devoted to repeat sequences.
      6. Both maps contain interruptions and misoriented sequences.
II. Characteristics of chromosomes (Sections 27.2–27.3).
   A. Chromosome structure (Section 27.2).
      1. Telomeres.
         a. Telomeres are long series of repeating DNA that are found at the ends of each chromosome.
         b. Telomeres protect the ends of chromosomes from accidents.
         c. Telomeres also prevent the ends of chromosomes from pairing with other DNA.
         d. The enzyme telomerase catalyzes the addition of telomeres to DNA.
            Telomerase is more active in young cells than in older cells.
      2. Centromeres.
         a. Centromeres are constrictions that determine the shapes of chromosomes during cell division.
         b. Centromeres contain large repetitive base sequences.
      3. Other noncoding DNA.
         Not all of the functions of noncoding DNA are known.
            i. Some segments are regulatory.
            ii. Other proposed functions: accommodation of DNA folding, evolutionary roles.
      4. Genes.
         The coding sections of a gene (exons) are interspersed with noncoding introns.

B. Mutations and polymorphisms (Section 27.3).
   1. Mutations.
      a. An error in mRNA transcription is not serious.
      b. An error in DNA replication is a mutation and is passed on each time DNA replicates.
         i. Substances that cause mutations are mutagens.
         ii. Each time mRNA is transcribed, the resulting protein will have an error.
         iii. The consequences of a mutation range from insignificant to lethal.
      c. If the error occurs in a somatic cell, cancer may result.
      d. If the error occurs in a germ cell, a genetic defect may be passed on to the offspring.
   2. Polymorphisms.
      a. Polymorphisms are variations in nucleotide sequences that are common within a given population.
      b. Replacement of one nucleotide by another in the same location is a single-nucleotide polymorphism (SNP).
         i. SNPs are responsible for most of the variation among human beings.
         ii. SNPs are responsible for many genetic diseases.
         iii. A catalog of SNPs has been developed; it now has 1.4 million SNPs.
         iv. This catalog has been used to identify SNPs responsible for abnormalities.

III. Recombinant DNA and genomics (Section 27.4–27.5).
   A. Recombinant DNA technology is used to cut a specific gene out of one organism and insert it into the DNA of another organism (Section 27.4).
      1. The second organism is usually a bacterium.
      2. Bacterial DNA is contained in plasmids, which are easy to isolate.
   B. Technique of recombinant DNA.
      1. The plasmid is cleaved by a restriction endonuclease.
         a. There are more than 200 restriction endonucleases.
         b. Cleavage occurs at a specific site in a base sequence.
         c. Each DNA strand is left with a few unpaired bases, called "sticky ends".
      2. The gene to be inserted is also cleaved by the same endonucleases and thus has complementary sticky ends.
      3. The gene and the plasmid are mixed in the presence of a DNA ligase enzyme and the gene is inserted into the plasmid.
      4. The plasmid can be reinserted into a bacterial cell, and the bacteria, which multiply rapidly, manufacture the protein.
   C. Uses of recombinant DNA technology - Genomics (Section 27.5).
      1. Agriculture.
         Transgenic plants and animals have been bred; their DNA includes single genes that code for desirable traits.
      2. Medicine.
         a. Gene therapy might cure inherited diseases by replacing a disease-causing gene with a healthy copy of that gene.
         b. A personal genomic survey might be helpful in drug and therapeutic choices.
         c. DNA chip screening can be used to detect polymorphisms associated with diseases and drug responses.

Solutions to Chapter 27 Problems

27.1 uuiioouoppagfdtttrr**once**trtrnnnaedigop**upon**sldjflsjfxxxbvgfa**qqq**eu**time**abrrxoknuw
(once upon a time)

27.2 Look back to Table 26.4 and note that UGU codes for cysteine, and UGG codes for tryptophan. In the synthesized protein, a tryptophan would replace a cysteine. Since cysteine forms disulfide bridges, the protein's three-dimensional structure would most likely be disrupted and its function might be affected.

27.3 The complementary DNA strand is drawn by pairing the bases and by reversing the labels of the two ends of the strands. The restriction enzyme cleaves the complementary strand at the same location.

$$5'\quad -A- // -G-A-T-C-T-\quad 3'$$
$$3'\quad -T-C-T-A-G- // -A-\quad 5'$$

27.4 To be sticky, base sequences must be complementary. Draw the complement of the first sequence. If the complement you draw is identical to the second sequence, the two sequences are sticky.
(a) The pairs are sticky.
(b), (c) the pairs aren't sticky.

27.5 (a) The field of *comparative genomics* deals with the identification of genes that perform identical functions in mice and humans.
(b) A person working in *genetic engineering* might be involved with creating a variety of wheat that is not harmed by a herbicide that kills weeds that interfere with wheat crops.
(c) *Pharmacogenetics* is used for screening a individual's genome to choose the most appropriate pain-killing medication for that person.
(d) *Bioinformatics* is the computer analysis of base-sequence information from groups of people with and without a certain disease to discover where the disease-causing polymorphism lies.

Understanding Key Concepts

27.6 The working draft of the human genome is the sequence of the nucleotides in about 90% of genes. Further work will include increasing accuracy to 99.9%, sequencing the repetitive noncoding DNA, and identifying the proteins coded for by the genes.

27.7 The variations in DNA sequences occupy only a small part of the genome; the rest is identical among humans.

27.8 *Telomeres* protect the chromosome from mutations, prevent DNA from bonding to other DNA, and are believed to play a role in human aging. *Centromeres* form the constrictions that determine the shapes of chromosomes during cell division. *Promoter sequences* determine which genes will be replicated. *Introns* are noncoding segments that are interspersed with gene-encoding exons and whose function is unknown.

27.9 Both mutations and polymorphisms are variations in base sequences. A mutation is an error in a base sequence that is transferred during DNA replication, occurs in a very small number of individuals, and is caused by a random error or a mutagen. A polymorphism is a variation in DNA sequence that is common within a given population.

27.10 Recombinant DNA contains two or more DNA segments that do not occur together in nature. The DNA that codes for a specific human protein can be incorporated into a bacterial plasmid using recombinant DNA technology. The plasmid is then reinserted into a bacterial cell, where its protein-synthesizing machinery makes the desired protein.

27.11 Major benefits of genomics include creation of disease-resistant and nutrient-rich crops, gene therapy to cure or prevent genetic diseases, and genetic screening that leads to more effective health care. Major negative outcomes are associated with the misuse of an individual's genetic information, and with prediction of a genetic disease for which there is no cure.

The Human Genome Map

27.12 The Human Genome Project is the nonprofit group , and Celera Genomics is the private corporation.

27.13 Competition caused the working draft of the Human Genome Project to be completed in 15 months, rather than in the 4 years originally anticipated.

27.14 Approximately 50% of the human genome is composed of repeat sequences.

27.15 Approximately 3 billion base pairs were identified.

27.16 (a) About 200 genes are identical to bacterial genes.
(b) A single gene may produce several proteins.

27.17 The most surprising result is that humans have between 30,000 and 40,000 genes, a number much smaller than the previous estimate of 100,000 genes.

27.18 The clones used in DNA mapping are multiple identical copies of DNA segments from a single individual. Clone samples large enough for experimental manipulation are essential for mapping.

Chromosomes, Mutations and Polymorphisms

27.19 Telomeres protect the ends of chromosomes from changes that might alter the coding sequence of DNA.

27.20 The youngest cells have long telomeric sequences of DNA, and the telomeres shorten as cells age. Thus, cell age can be predicted by telomere length.

27.21 Telomerase is responsible for adding telomeres to DNA. Telomerase is most active in young cells and least active in older cells.

27.22 The centromere is the constriction that determines the shape of a chromosome during cell division. It is composed of noncoding and repetitive DNA.

27.23 A mutagen is an external agent that can cause an error in base sequence in DNA.

27.24 Ionizing radiation, certain viruses and certain chemicals are mutagens.

27.25 An error in the sequence of RNA affects only one molecule of RNA; other intact molecules of RNA can still carry out protein synthesis. A mutation in DNA is much more drastic, however, because there is only one molecule of DNA per gene, and any error will be copied into all subsequent DNA molecules during replication.

27.26 Some mutations result from random and spontaneous events. Other mutations are caused by exposure to a mutagen.

27.27 A single-nucleotide polymorphism (SNP) is the replacement of one nucleotide by a different nucleotide at the same location in a strand of DNA.

27.28 An SNP can result in the change in identity of an amino acid inserted into a protein a a particular location in a polypeptide chain. The effect of an SNP depends on the function of the protein and the nature of the SNP.

27.29 The effects of some SNPs are negligible. SNPs are responsible for differences in hair and eye color and for genetic diseases such as sickle-cell anemia, a type of epilepsy, and total color blindness. Some SNPs are associated with the risk of developing diseases such as Alzheimer's disease and breast cancer, whereas other SNPs impart resistance to diseases, including AIDS.

27.30 Analysis of an individual's DNA would allow a physician to predict the age at which inherited diseases might become active, their severity, and the response of the individual to various types of treatment.

27.31 Not necessarily. Since many amino acids are coded by several different base sequences, some substitutions cause no change in the amino acid composition of the protein being synthesized.

27.32 A change in the nature of an amino acid's side chain determines whether an amino acid change will create a major or a minor alteration in the protein's shape. Similar side chains will have a lesser effect than very different side chains.

27.33

	Normal Codon	Codes for:	Mutated Codon	Codes for:
(a)	UUU	Phe	UUC	Phe
(b)	CUU	Leu	CGU	Arg

In (a), the mutated mRNA codes for the same amino acid as the nonmutated mRNA, and thus the mutation has no effect. In (b), the mutated mRNA codes for a basic amino acid, instead of a neutral, nonpolar amino acid, and the effect might change the shape and function of the synthesized protein. Mutation (b) is more serious that mutation (a).

27.34

	Normal Codon	Codes for:	Mutated Codon	Codes for:
(a)	GUC	Val	GCC	Ala
(b)	CCC	Pro	CAC	His

In (a), the mutated mRNA codes for an amino acid (Ala) that is somewhat similar to the normal amino acid (Val), and the effect of the mutation may be small. In (b) the mutated mRNA codes for an amino acid that is basic, whereas the normal amino acid is proline, a large, bulky, neutral amino acid. The second mutation is more serious because the mutation changes the type of amino acid in the protein and would probably affect the shape and function of the protein.

Recombinant DNA

27.35 The DNA of bacterial cells occurs in plasmids, each of which carries only a few genes. The plasmids are easy to isolate, and several copies of each plasmid are present in a bacterial cell. The DNA of plasmids replicates rapidly by normal base pairing.

27.36 (1) Proteins can be produced in greater quantity than otherwise possible. (2) The proteins don't carry diseases that might be present in the host organism otherwise used for protein production.

27.37 Sticky ends arc unpaircd bases on each end of each end of the cleaved DNA. Recombinant DNA is formed when the sticky ends of the DNA of interest and of the DNA of the plasmid have complementary base pairs and can be joined by a DNA ligase.

27.38 Electrophoresis and the polymerase chain reaction are important tools in recombinant DNA technology.

27.39 *Unpaired bases:*   (a) CGTAA   (b) TGACC   (c) AGTCT
Sticky sequence: GCATT   ACTGG   TCAGA

27.40 Write out the sticky sequence for the first of the two base sequences. If the sticky sequence agrees with the second sequence shown, the two sequences are sticky.
(a) The sequence TTAGC is sticky with AATCG, not AAACG. Thus, the two sequences shown aren't sticky.
(b) CGTACG isn't sticky with GTACGT.

Genomics

27.41 Pharmacogenomics is practiced by a person in the pharmaceutical industry, who develops new drugs and studies the genetic basis of response to drug therapy. A pharmacogeneticist uses a person's genome to match a patient with the safest and most effective drugs for that individual.

27.42 Proteomics is the study of the complete set of proteins coded for by a genome or synthesized by a given type of cell. It might provide information about the role of a protein in both healthy and diseased cells.

27.43 Both genetic engineering and gene therapy are involved with altering the genetic makeup of an organism. Gene therapy is used on humans, with the goal of curing or preventing disease. Genetic engineering is used for plants or other nonhuman organisms, with the goal of producing a new substance or of changing a genetic trait.

27.44 Corn and soybeans have been genetically altered and improved to provide disease and herbicide resistance.

27.45 Possible advantages include treatment of a genetic defect by gene therapy, choice of the most effective drug for treatment of a disease, and lifestyle adjustments to avoid development of a disease. Major drawbacks include identification of a disease for which there is no cure and discrimination against a person on the basis of genotype.

27.46 A DNA chip could be used to match a patient's DNA fragments with polymorphic sequences linked to known genetic disorders, in order to diagnose inherited diseases.

27.47 A DNA chip is a solid support containing many short single-stranded pieces of DNA of known composition. A fluorescent-labeled DNA sample is applied to the chip, and it sticks to complementary base pairs. The fluorescence pattern shows where complementary bonding has occurred. DNA chips are currently being used to distinguish between two types of pediatric leukemia.

Applications

27.48 A group of anonymous individuals was the DNA donor for these projects.

27.49 When there were variations in the DNA samples, the most common variation was chosen.

27.50 The five steps of DNA fingerprinting:

(1) A sample of DNA is digested with a restriction endonuclease.
(2) The resulting fragments are separated by size using gel electrophoresis.
(3) The RFLP fragments are transferred to a nylon membrane.
(4) The RFLP blot is treated with a radioactive DNA probe, which binds to the sticky ends of the RFLPs.
(5) The radioactive RFLPs can be identified by exposing an X-ray film to the blot.

It is important to standardize DNA fingerprinting techniques because all samples must be analyzed under the same conditions in order to be compared.

27.51 In DNA fingerprinting, it is possible to compare DNA from different tissues because all tissues from the same individual contain identical DNA.

27.52 It might be possible to introduce the salt-tolerant gene into other crops, especially staple crops. Perhaps it might be possible to develop plants that can be irrigated with sea water.

General Questions and Problems

27.53 A monogenic disease is caused by the variation in just one gene.

27.54 A vector is the agent used to carry therapeutic quantities of DNA directly into cell nuclei.

27.55

	Normal	Mutated
DNA:	5' A-T-T-G-G-C-C-T-A 3'	5' A-C-T-G-G-C-C-T-A 3'
mRNA:	5' A-U-U-G-G-C-C-U-A 3'	5' A-C-U-G-G-C-C-U-A 3'
Amino acids:	Ile—Gly—Leu	Thr—Gly—Leu

The mutation would substitute a Thr for an Ile and would affect the tertiary structure of the protein.

27.56 TATGACT is sticky with ATACTGA.

27.57 A hereditary disease is caused by a mutation in the DNA of a germ cell and is passed from parent to offspring. The mutation affects the amino-acid sequence of an important protein and causes a change in the biological activity of the protein.

27.58 A mutation must occur in a germ cell (sperm or egg) in order for it to be passed down to future generations.

Self-Test for Chapter 27

Multiple choice:

1. A field of study that deals with the use of computers to manage and interpret genetic information is:
   (a) genetic engineering   (b) proteomics   (c) bioinformatics   (d) gene therapy

2. Approximately how many genes are in the human genome?
   (a) 3.1 billion   (b) 1.4 million   (c) 100,000   (d) 30,000

3. Which of the following is not a characteristic of a telomere?
   (a) It has a repeating series of nucleotides.   (b) Each chromosome has one telomere.   (c) The nucleotide groups of telomeres are noncoding.   (d) A telomere protects the end of a chromosome from accidental damage.

4. Which of the following mutations is least likely to cause genetic damage?
   (a) AUC to AUA   (b) AUC to AUG   (c) GUU to GGU   (d) CAA to CGA

5. Which of the following mutations is most likely to cause genetic damage?
   (a) AUC to AUA   (b) AUC to AUG   (c) GUU to GGU   (d) CAA to CGA

6. All of the following are composed of noncoding DNA except:
   (a) telomere   (b) centromere   (c) promoter sequence   (d) exon

7. Which of the following is not a characteristic of plasmids?
   (a) They are easy to isolate.   (b) They replicate in the same way as human DNA does.
   (c) They are circular.   (d) Each cell has one plasmid.

8. A hereditary disease caused by a defect in hemoglobin is:
   (a) cystic fibrosis   (b) sickle-cell anemia   (c) Tay-Sachs disease   (d) albinism

9. In which type of map are marker locations determined by inheritance patterns?
   (a) clone map   (b) physical map   (c) chromosome   (d) genetic map

10. DNA fingerprinting uses all of the following except:
    (a) a radioactive DNA probe   (b) restriction endonuclease   (c) a fluorescent marker   (d) gel electrophoresis

Complete the following sentences:

1. Groups of unpaired bases at the end of a DNA chain treated with a restriction endonuclease are known as _____ ____.

2. Repeat sequences in noncoding DNA are often referred to as ____ DNA.

3. In recombinant DNA technology, plasmids are cut open with a _____ _____.

4. Genetically modified tomatoes isolate excess sodium ions in _____.

5. The ELSI program of the National Human Genome Research Institute deals with _____.

6. Mutations may be caused by exposure to _____ _____ or to chemicals called _____.

7. An _____ is a segment of a gene that does not code for protein synthesis.

8. The replacement of one nucleotide by another in the same location along the polynucleotide chain is known as a ____-_____ _____.

9. The field of _____ is directed to the study of the complete set of proteins coded by a genome or synthesized within a given type of cell.

10. A _____ is a constriction that determines the shape of a chromosome during cell division.

11. A point mutation that doesn't change the amino acid incorporated into a protein is a _____ mutation.

12. The film result of DNA fingerprinting is an _____.

Tell whether the following statements are true or false:

1. In a frameshift mutation, the number of inserted or deleted nucleotides is not a multiple of 3.

2. "SNP" stands for single-nucleoside polymorphism.

3. The DNA used for the Human Genome Project came from a single donor.

4. By reorganization of exons during mRNA synthesis, a gene can produce several different proteins.

5. A person working in the field of pharmacogenomics is likely to work at a company that manufactures drugs.

6. Mapping of each chromosome starts at one end and works to the other end.

7. Telomeres consist of a long series of repeats of the nucleotide sequence TTAGGG.

8. The nucleotide sequences -GAACT- and -CTGGA- are "sticky".

9. The mutation of GAU to GAG is a nonsense mutation.

10. A mutation in RNA causes little damage.

11. Telomerase is responsible for removing telomeres from DNA.

12. Human insulin can be manufactured by recombinant DNA technology.

Match the entries on the left with their partners on the right:

1. Silent mutation

2. Exon

3. Human Genome Project

4. Mature somatic cell

5. Missense mutation

6. Plasmid

7. Mutation

8. Nonsense mutation

9. Celera

10. SNP

11. Intron

12. Frameshift mutation

a. UUG —> UAG

b. UUA —> CUA

c. Shows little telomerase activity

d. Addition or loss of a nucleotide

e. Occurs in a very small number of individuals

f. Noncoding DNA

g. Uses a series of "maps" for genome mapping

h. Occurs in at least 1% of population

i. Coding DNA

j. GCU —> GGU

k. "Shotgun" approach to DNA mapping

l. Bacterial DNA

Chapter Outline

I. Introduction to protein and amino acid metabolism (Sections 28.1–28.2).
  A. Protein digestion (Section 28.1).
    1. Proteins are denatured in the stomach.
    2. In the stomach, the enzyme pepsin hydrolyzes proteins to polypeptides.
    3. In the intestine, other enzymes hydrolyze the polypeptides to amino acids.
    4. Amino acids cross the cell membrane of the intestine and are absorbed directly into the bloodstream.
       Active transport is required for amino acids to cross the intestinal lining.
  B. Overview of amino acid metabolism (Section 28.2).
    1. The amino acid pool is the collection of all free amino acids in the body.
       The amino acid pool is the source of amino acids for protein synthesis and of nitrogen for the synthesis of nitrogen-containing biomolecules.
    2. Amino acid catabolism occurs in two steps:
      a. Removal of nitrogen, which can be:
        i. Used for synthesis of nitrogen-containing biomolecules.
        ii. Excreted as urea.
      b. Entry of the remaining carbon atoms into metabolic pathways.
        i. Citric acid cycle.
        ii. Gluconeogenesis.
        iii. Ketogenesis.
        iv. Lipogenesis.
II. Amino acid catabolism (Section 28.3–28.5).
  A. Removal of the amino group (Section 28.3).
    1. Transamination.
      a. In transamination, the amino group of an amino acid and the keto group of an α-keto acid change places.
      b. Transaminase enzymes are usually specific for α-ketoglutarate as the amino group acceptor.
      c. Transamination reactions are equilibria that regulate amino acid concentration.
    2. Deamination.
      a. If the glutamate from transamination is in excess, the $-NH_3^+$ group can be removed and excreted and α-ketoglutarate regenerated.
      b. This reaction is known as oxidative deamination.
      c. Either NAD^+ or $NADP^+$ is required.
      d. The reverse reaction reductive amination, occurs in biosynthesis.
  B. The urea cycle (Section 28.4).
    1. Because ammonia is toxic, the human body converts it to urea in order to excrete it.
    2. The reactions of the urea cycle take place in the liver.
    3. Ammonia is first converted to carbamoyl phosphate.
       $NH_4^+ + HCO_3^- + 2\ ATP \longrightarrow$ carbamoyl phosphate $+ 2\ ADP + HOPO_3^{2-} + H_2O$.
    4. Steps of the cycle:
      a. Step 1: Carbamoyl phosphate + ornithine $\longrightarrow$ citrulline $+ HOPO_3^{2-}$.
      b. Step 2: Citrulline + aspartate + ATP $\longrightarrow$ argininosuccinate $+ AMP + P_2O_7^{4-}$.
      c. Step 3: Argininosuccinate $\longrightarrow$ fumarate + arginine.
      d. Step 4: Arginine $+ H_2O \longrightarrow$ urea + ornithine.

5. Results of the cycle:
    a. Urea is eliminated.
        The urea carbon comes from bicarbonate, the nitrogen comes from aspartate, and the other nitrogen comes from ammonia.
    b. Four phosphate bonds are broken.
    c. Fumarate, a citric acid cycle intermediate, is produced.
        Fumarate is converted to oxaloacetate, which undergoes transamination to yield aspartate, which reenters the cycle. (Fumarate can also enter gluconeogenesis.)
C. Fate of the carbon atoms (Section 28.5).
    1. All amino acid carbon skeletons are either citric acid cycle intermediates or fatty acid metabolism intermediates.
    2. Glucogenic amino acids.
        a. Amino acids that are converted to pyruvate or enter the citric acid cycle as α-ketoglutarate, succinyl-SCoA, fumarate, or oxaloacetate are glucogenic.
        b. These amino acids can be converted to glucose.
    3. Ketogenic amino acids.
        a. Amino acids that are converted to acetyl-SCoA or acetoacetyl-SCoA are known as ketogenic amino acids.
        b. These amino acids can enter either ketogenesis to form ketone bodies or fatty acid biosynthesis.
    4. Some amino acids are both glucogenic and ketogenic.
III. Biosynthesis of nonessential amino acids (Section 28.6).
    A. The human body can synthesize 11 of the 20 common amino acids.
    B. All 11 amino acids derive their amino group from glutamate.
    C. Pyruvate, oxaloacetate, α-ketoglutarate and 3-phosphoglycerate are the precursors of all nonessential amino acids.
    D. Tyrosine is formed from phenylalanine.
        An inability of the body to perform this conversion is the metabolic error in phenylketonuria.

Solutions to Chapter 28 Problems

28.1 (a) False. The amino acid pool is the collection of free amino acids in the body. (b) True (c) True (d) False (e) False. Glycine isn't essential because it can be synthesized in the human body.

28.2 The first reaction is catalyzed by an oxidoreductase (hydroxylase), and the second step is catalyzed by a lyase (decarboxylase).

28.3

Leucine + α-Ketoglutarate → α-Keto-4-methylpentanoate + Glutamate

28.4

28.5   The conversion of glutamate to α-ketoglutarate can be identified as an oxidation by noting the reduction of the coenzymes NAD⁺ or NADP⁺.

28.6   The three branched-chain amino acids are valine, leucine and isoleucine.

Valine + α-Ketoglutarate → α-Keto-3-methylbutanoate + Glutamate

28.7

28.8

28.9

Understanding Key Concepts

28.10

28.11 Catabolism of an amino acid begins with a transamination reaction that removes the amino acid nitrogen.

The carbon atoms:
The resulting α-keto acid, which contains the carbons from the original amino acid, undergoes reactions that convert it to a common metabolic intermediate. This intermediate may be a citric acid cycle intermediate, pyruvate, acetyl-SCoA, or acetoacetyl-SCoA.

The nitrogen atoms:
Glutamate, which contains the amino group from the original amino acid, undergoes an oxidative deamination reaction that converts the amino group to ammonium ion and that regenerates α-ketoglutarate. Either NAD⁺ or NADP⁺ can be used as the enzyme cofactor.

Ammonium ion enters the urea cycle, where it is transformed to urea and is excreted.

28.12

NADPH/H$^+$ can also be used as an enzyme cofactor.

$$^-OOCCH_2CH_2\overset{\overset{\displaystyle NH_3^+}{|}}{C}HCOO^- + CH_3\overset{\overset{\displaystyle O}{\|}}{C}COO^- \underset{\text{aminotransferase}}{\overset{\text{Alanine}}{\rightleftharpoons}} {}^-OOCCH_2CH_2\overset{\overset{\displaystyle O}{\|}}{C}COO^- + CH_3\overset{\overset{\displaystyle NH_3^+}{|}}{C}HCOO^-$$

Glutamate   Pyruvate   α-Ketoglutarate   Alanine

The enzymes for both reactions can catalyze reaction in both directions. The product is the amino acid alanine.

28.13 It is important for ornithine transcarbamoylase to have a high activity in order to remove NH$_4^+$ from the body quickly. It is also important that arginase activity be high in order to release urea for excretion by the kidneys and to provide the ornithine needed to react with carbamoyl phosphate.

28.14 All amino acids are "essential" in the sense that all of them are necessary for protein synthesis. The body, however, can synthesize only about half of them from non-amino acid precursors. The other amino acids must be provided by food, and thus it is "essential" that they be part of the diet.

28.15 The carbon atoms from ketogenic amino acids can be converted to ketone bodies or to acetyl-SCoA. The carbon atoms from glucogenic amino acids can be converted to compounds that can enter gluconeogenesis and can form glucose, which can enter glycolysis and also yield acetyl-SCoA.

Amino Acid Pool

28.16 The digestion of proteins begins in the stomach.

28.17 The body's amino-acid pool, which is the collection of free amino acids that result from diet or tissue breakdown, occurs throughout the body.

28.18 Pyruvate and 3-phosphoglycerate are glycolytic precursors of amino acids.

28.19 Oxaloacetate and α-ketoglutarate are citric acid cycle precursors of amino acids.

Amino Acid Catabolism

28.20 In a transamination reaction, a keto group of an α-keto acid and an amino group of an α-amino acid change places.

28.21

$$\underset{\alpha\text{-amino acid}}{\overset{\overset{+}{N}H_3}{\underset{|}{RCHCOO^-}}} + \underset{\text{Pyruvate}}{\overset{O}{\underset{||}{CH_3CCOO^-}}} \underset{\text{α-Aminotransferase}}{\rightleftharpoons} \underset{\alpha\text{-keto acid}}{\overset{O}{\underset{||}{RCCOO^-}}} + \underset{\text{Alanine}}{\overset{\overset{+}{N}H_3}{\underset{|}{CH_3CHCOO^-}}}$$

$$\underset{\alpha\text{-amino acid}}{\overset{\overset{+}{N}H_3}{\underset{|}{RCHCOO^-}}} + \underset{\text{Oxaloacetate}}{\overset{O}{\underset{||}{^-OOCCH_2CCOO^-}}} \underset{\text{α-Aminotransferase}}{\rightleftharpoons} \underset{\alpha\text{-keto acid}}{\overset{O}{\underset{||}{RCCOO^-}}} + \underset{\text{Aspartate}}{\overset{\overset{+}{N}H_3}{\underset{|}{^-OOCCH_2CHCOO^-}}}$$

28.22

Amino Acid $\xrightarrow[\text{α-Aminotransferase}]{\text{α-Ketoglutarate} \quad \text{Glutamate}}$ α-Keto acid

(a)

$$\underset{\text{Isoleucine}}{CH_3CH_2\overset{\overset{CH_3}{|}}{CH}-\overset{\overset{+}{N}H_3}{\underset{|}{CH}}-COO^-}$$
$$CH_3CH_2\overset{\overset{CH_3}{|}}{CH}-\overset{O}{\underset{||}{C}}-COO^-$$

(b)

$$\underset{\text{Cysteine}}{HSCH_2-\overset{\overset{+}{N}H_3}{\underset{|}{CH}}-COO^-}$$
$$HSCH_2-\overset{O}{\underset{||}{C}}-COO^-$$

28.23

Amino Acid $\xrightarrow[\text{α-Aminotransferase}]{\text{α-Ketoglutarate} \quad \text{Glutamate}}$ α-Keto acid

(a)

$$\underset{\text{Phenylalanine}}{\bigcirc-CH_2-\overset{\overset{+}{N}H_3}{\underset{|}{CH}}-COO^-}$$
$$\bigcirc-CH_2-\overset{O}{\underset{||}{C}}-COO^-$$

(b)

$$\underset{\text{Serine}}{HOCH_2-\overset{\overset{+}{N}H_3}{\underset{|}{CH}}-COO^-}$$
$$HOCH_2-\overset{O}{\underset{||}{C}}-COO^-$$

28.24 In an oxidative deamination reaction, an $-NH_3^+$ group of an amino acid (usually glutamate) is replaced by a carbonyl oxygen, and ammonium ion is eliminated.

28.25 Either NAD^+ or $NADP^+$ is associated with oxidative deamination.

28.26

| Amino Acid | α-Keto acid |

(a)

Phenylalanine

(b)

Tryptophan

28.27 Ammonium ion is the other product of oxidative deamination.

28.28 A glucogenic amino acid is an amino acid that is catabolized to pyruvate or to citric acid cycle intermediates and can enter gluconeogenesis.

28.29 A ketogenic amino acid is catabolized to acetoacetyl-SCoA or acetyl-SCoA, which can be used either in the synthesis of ketone bodies or in fatty acid biosynthesis.

The Urea Cycle

28.30 Ammonia is toxic and must be eliminated as nontoxic urea, which is water-soluble.

28.31 The urea cycle might be called the arginine cycle because urea is formed from the amino acid arginine, its immediate precursor.

28.32 The *urea carbon* comes from carbamoyl phosphate, which is synthesized from bicarbonate produced from CO_2 in the citric acid cycle.

28.33 *One nitrogen* comes from carbamoyl phosphate, which is synthesized from ammonium ion produced from oxidative deamination.
One nitrogen comes from aspartate.

Amino Acid Anabolism

28.34 Nonessential amino acids can be synthesized in 1–3 steps by most organisms. Plants and microorganisms synthesize essential amino acids in many more steps.

28.35 Glutamate is the source of nitrogen for amino acid anabolism because all other amino acids acquire their amino group from glutamate.

28.36 Amino acids are synthesized from non-nitrogen metabolites by transamination reactions with glutamate, which is itself synthesized from α-ketoglutarate and ammonium ion by reductive amination, the reverse of oxidative deamination.

28.37 In the body, tyrosine is biosynthesized from phenylalanine. Tyrosine is an essential amino acid for phenylketonurics, who are unable to synthesize tyrosine from phenylalanine.

28.38 Phenylketonuria (PKU) is caused by a genetic inability to convert phenylalanine to tyrosine, leading to the accumulation of phenylalanine and its metabolites in the body. PKU causes mental retardation if not detected early in life. Treatment consists of a diet restricted in phenylalanine.

28.39 Aspartame is a dipeptide that contains phenylalanine, which must be severely restricted in the diet of phenylketonurics, who can't metabolize phenylalanine.

28.40 All biomolecules that contain nitrogen acquire it from amino acids. These include (b) nitric oxide, (c) collagen, and (d) epinephrine.

Applications

28.41 (a) Gout is a painful inflammation of the joints caused by deposits of insoluble salts of uric acid. These deposits occur because of an excess of purines in the body or because of an impaired ability to excrete the products of purine metabolism. Although the symptoms of gout are often due to metabolic problems that are genetic, some cases of gout are caused by injury or excessive alcohol consumption.
(b) Simple ways to prevent attacks of gout that are not genetic are to limit consumption of alcohol and purine-rich foods.

28.42

Allopurinol   Hypoxanthine   Xanthine   Uric acid

Allopurinol is identical to hypoxanthine in all but one respect: the nitrogen at position 7 of the hypoxanthine ring is at position 8 of the allopurinol ring. Just as hypoxanthine can be oxidized to xanthine, allopurinol can be oxidized to a compound similar to xanthine (alloxanthine). The product of allopurinol oxidation, however, is an inhibitor of the enzyme that converts xanthine to uric acid. Instead of producing uric acid, purine catabolism ends with the formation of the more soluble hypoxanthine and xanthine, which can be easily excreted.

Oxidation of xanthine to uric acid occurs at position 8 of the purine ring system. In allopurinol, this site is occupied by nitrogen.

28.43 A compound that is xenobiotic is foreign to the body.

28.44 The body responds to a xenobiotic compound in two ways. (1) Xenobiotic compounds are hydroxylated to make them less hydrophobic and more water-soluble. (2) Enzyme-catalyzed reactions of xenobiotics with polar molecules yield compounds that are easier to excrete.

28.45 If a biomolecule is inducible, extra amounts of it can be synthesized when more of it is needed.

General Questions and Problems

28.46 Three molecules of ATP are consumed in producing each molecule of urea, making the process energy-intensive.

28.47

The enzyme that catalyzes the transamination is either valine aminotransferase or alanine aminotransferase.

28.48 Amino acids can enter the citric acid cycle as α-ketoglutarate, succinyl-SCoA, fumarate and oxaloacetate. α-Ketoglutarate enters the cycle at step 4, succinyl-SCoA enters at step 5, fumarate enters at step 7 , and oxaloacetate enters at step 1.

28.49 An amino acid can be both glucogenic and ketogenic. After catabolism, certain amino acids yield products that can enter the citric acid cycle and other products that can be intermediates of fatty acid metabolism.

28.50 Carbons from amino acids can be catabolized to acetyl-SCoA, which can be used in fatty acid biosynthesis. The fatty acids can form triacylglycerols, which are transported to adipose tissue. There, the TAGs can be hydrolyzed to fatty acids.

28.51 Tissue is dynamic because its components are constantly being broken down and reformed. Dynamic relationships are common in protein and amino acid metabolism, where proteins are digested and resynthesized, and where amino acids are converted to other amino acids and to carbohydrate intermediates.

28.52 Storage: Unlike fats and carbohydrates, amino acids aren't stored in the body. Instead, when excess amino acids accumulate, amino acid nitrogen is excreted and the resulting compounds are converted to either fats or carbohydrates.

Energy: Fats and carbohydrates that are not stored are catabolized. Surplus amino acids must be converted to either fats or carbohydrates in order to be an energy source.

28.53 The basic scheme of the conversion of glutamate to glycogen is deamination —>
gluconeogenesis —> glycogenesis.
Step 1: Glutamate (b) —> α-Ketoglutarate (e) (deamination or transamination).
Step 2: α-Ketoglutarate (e) —> Oxaloacetate (d) (citric acid cycle).
Step 3: Oxaloacetate (d) —> Phosphoenolpyruvate (f) (gluconeogenesis).
Step 4: Phosphoenolpyruvate (f) —> Glucose (a) (gluconeogenesis).
Step 5: Glucose (a) —> Glycogen (c) (glycogenolysis).
The complete sequence: (b) —> (e) —> (d) —> (f) —> (a) —> (c).

28.54 The activated forms of the proteases would hydrolyze the proteins in the lining of the
pancreas if they were stored there until needed in digestion. They can be stored safely in
their inactive form and still be readily available when needed for digestion.

28.55 Active transport of amino acids across cell membranes is achieved by several transport
systems, each of which is specific for several different amino acids. An excess of one
amino acid might overwhelm its transport system, making it unavailable to transport other
amino acids and causing an amino acid deficiency.

28.56 One of the ATPs in the urea cycle is hydrolyzed to AMP, which is the equivalent of
spending two ATPs.

28.57 The nitrogen may be converted to urea and excreted in the urine, or it may be used in the
synthesis of a new nitrogen-containing compound.

Self-Test for Chapter 28

Multiple choice:

1.   Which of the following amino acids is strictly ketogenic?
      (a) proline   (b) threonine   (c) leucine   (d) isoleucine

2.   The product of transamination of valine is:
      (a) α-keto-3-methylbutanoic acid   (b) α-ketobutanoic acid   (c) α-keto-4-methylpentanoic
      acid   (d) α-ketopentanoic acid

3.   The amino acid proline is probably synthesized by cyclization of:
      (a) arginine   (b) glutamate   (c) leucine   (d) threonine

4.   The urea cycle takes place in the:
      (a) muscles   (b) kidneys   (c) bloodstream   (d) liver

5.   Which of the following proteases is necessary for the activation of other proteases?
      (a) pepsin   (b) chymotrypsin   (c) carboxypeptidase   (d) trypsin

6.   How many grams of protein tissue are broken down in an adult body per day?
      (a) none   (b) 50 g   (c) 300 g   (d) 1000 g

7.   Ornithine is:
      (a) a urea cycle intermediate   (b) an amino acid   (c) an acceptor of a carbamoyl group
      (d) all three

8.   Which of the following nitrogen-containing compounds is used to treat gout?
      (a) hypoxanthine   (b) xanthine   (c) allopurinol   (d) uric acid

9.   Which of the following isn't a precursor in nonessential amino acid biosynthesis?
(a) fumarate   (b) pyruvate   (c) α-ketoglutarate   (d) 3-phosphoglycerate

10.   Glucogenic amino acids enter gluconeogenesis via:
(a) acetyl-SCoA   (b) oxaloacetate   (c) α-ketoglutarate   (d) fumarate

Complete the following sentences:

1.   In the transamination reaction of alanine and α-ketoglutarate, _____ and _____ are formed.

2.   A _____ is a chemical compound foreign to the body

3.   Ketogenic amino acids are catabolized to _____ _____ or _____ _____.

4.   The first step in the urea cycle is the formation of _____ _____ from ammonia, CO_2, and ATP.

5.   A _____ is an enzyme that carries out peptide hydrolysis.

6.   The amino acid serine enters the citric acid cycle as _____.

7.   _____ is the key reaction in amino acid anabolism.

8.   The essential amino acid _____ is part of the urea cycle.

9.   PKU is a metabolic error in converting _____ to _____.

10.   The pain of gout is caused by an inflammatory response to _____ _____ in tissues.

11.   Liver damage is associated with a high level of the enzyme _____.

12.   The carbon in urea comes from _____.

Tell whether the following statements are true or false:

1.   3-Phosphoglycerate is a precursor in the synthesis of nonessential amino acids.

2.   Protein digestion starts in the mouth.

3.   All ketogenic amino acids except lysine and isoleucine are also glucogenic amino acids.

4.   Essential amino acids can neither be synthesized nor catabolized in the human body.

5.   Some organisms can excrete nitrogen as ammonia without undergoing any harm.

6.   Amino acid catabolism occurs in the intestinal lining.

7.   Some intermediates in the urea cycle also occur in the citric acid cycle.

8.   The urea cycle is an endergonic process.

9.   Both nitrogens of urea come from ammonium ion.

10.   Proline is a nonessential amino acid.

11.   Each amino acid is associated with its own transaminase enzyme.

12.   Oxidative deamination is the reverse of reductive amination.

Match the entries on the left with their partners on the right:

1. Oxidative deamination

2. Ornithine

3. α-Ketoglutarate

4. Serine

5. Trypsin

6. Reductive amination

7. Leucine

8. Phenylketonuria

9. Pepsin

10. Uric acid

11. Transamination

12. Threonine

(a) Hydrolyzes proteins in the small intestine

(b) Process for synthesizing glutamate from α-ketoglutarate and NH_4^+

(c) Ketogenic amino acid

(d) End product of purine catabolism

(e) Process that transfers an amino group from an amino acid to α-ketoglutarate

(f) Nonessential amino acid

(g) Intermediate in the urea cycle

(h) Process that regenerates α-ketoglutarate from glutamate

(i) Glucogenic amino acid

(j) Intermediate in both the citric acid cycle and in amino acid metabolism

(k) Hydrolyzes proteins in the stomach

(l) Metabolic disease

Chapter Outline

I. Water (Sections 29.1–29.2).
  A. Body water and its solutes (Section 29.1).
    1. Types of body fluids.
      a. Intracellular fluid is within cells.
      b. Extracellular fluid is outside of cells.
        i. Blood plasma
        ii. Interstitial fluid, which fills the spaces between cells.
    2. Components of body fluids.
      a. Electrolytes (inorganic ions).
      b. Gases — O_2 and CO_2.
      c. Small organic molecules.
      d. Ionized biomolecules.
      e. All body fluids have the same osmolarity, even if they differ in composition.
    3. Movement of body fluids.
      a. Blood travels through peripheral tissues in capillaries.
        i. At the arterial end, blood pressure is higher and pushes solutes into interstitial fluid.
        ii. At the venous end, blood pressure is lower, and solutes reenter blood plasma.
        iii. Blood plasma and interstitial fluid have similar composition.
      b. Lymph capillaries collect excess interstitial fluid and other molecules too large to pass through capillary walls; this combination is called lymph.
        i. Lymph can't return to surrounding tissue.
        ii. Lymph enters the blood stream at the thoracic duct.
      c. Solutes in interstitial and intracellular fluid are exchanged by crossing cell membranes.
        Often, active transport is needed to maintain concentration differences.
  B. Maintenance of fluid balance (Section 29.2).
    1. Fluid balance is controlled by hormones.
    2. Receptors in the hypothalamus monitor concentration of blood solutes.
    3. If the concentration of solutes is too high, secretion of antidiuretic hormone increases.
      a. In SIADH, too much hormone keeps kidneys from excreting enough water.
      b. In *diabetes insipidus*, excessive amounts of dilute urine are excreted.
II. Blood (Sections 29.3–29.6).
  A. Components of blood (Section 29.3).
    1. Whole blood contains:
      a. Plasma.
      b. Blood cells.
    2. Blood serum is the fluid portion that remains after blood has clotted.
  B. Functions of blood.
    1. Transport.
    2. Regulation: redistribution of heat and solutes, and buffering of tissues.
    3. Defense.
      a. Immune response.
      b. Clotting.
  C. Immune response (Section 29.4).
    1. A foreign invader (antigen) is a substance that the body does not recognize as part of itself.

2. The body responds to antigens in three ways.
   a. Inflammatory responses (nonspecific).
      i. Inflammation produces swelling, warmth and pain.
      ii. The chemical messenger histamine is released at the site of injury.
      iii. Histamine dilates capillaries and increases blood flow to the injured area, allowing clotting factors and white blood cells to pass.
      iv. Bacteria are destroyed by phagocytes (white blood cells), which can also initiate specific immune responses.
      v. Inflammation disappears when infectious agents have been removed.
   b. Cell-mediated immune response (specific).
      i. The cell-mediated immune response is under the control of T lymphocytes.
      ii. The cell-mediated immune response guards against abnormal cells due to bacteria, viruses or cancer.
      iii. When a T cell recognizes an invader, it produces killer T cells (that destroy the invader), helper T cells (that enhance defenses), and memory T cells (that remain on guard).
   c. Antibody-mediated immune response (specific).
      i. The antibody-mediated immune response is under the control of B lymphocytes (with the assistance of T lymphocytes).
      ii. A B cell is activated when it binds to an antigen and encounters a helper T cell.
      iii. The B cells divide to produce plasma cells, which form non-cell-bound antibodies called immunoglobulins.
      iv. The antibodies find their antigens and inactivate them by one of several methods.
      v. Memory cells produce more antibodies if the same antigen reappears.
      vi. The body contains thousands of different immunoglobulins, and many have been identified.

D. Blood clotting (Section 29.5).
   1. A blood clot consists of blood cells trapped in a mesh of the protein fibrin. The process of clot formation requires many steps.
   2. The body's mechanism for halting blood loss is called hemostasis.
      a. The first event is constriction of blood vessels and formation of a plug of platelets.
      b. Then, blood clotting occurs by either of two pathways.
         i. In the intrinsic pathway, blood makes contact with the negatively charged surface of collagen.
         ii. In the extrinsic pathway, damaged tissue releases a glycoprotein called tissue factor.
      c. In either pathway, several zymogen clotting factors are released.
      d. After several steps, the enzyme thrombin catalyzes the formation of insoluble fibrin, which forms the clot.
   3. After the injury has healed, the clot is broken down by hydrolysis of its peptide bonds.

E. Red blood cells and blood gases (29.6).
   1. The purpose of red blood cells (erythrocytes) is to transport blood gases.
   2. Hemoglobin is responsible for transporting O_2 and CO_2. Hemoglobin consists of four protein chains and four heme molecules.
   3. Oxygen transport.
      a. Oxygen is transported via bonding with Fe^{2+} through an unshared electron pair.
      b. The percent of heme molecules that carry oxygen is the percent saturation.
      c. The binding curve is s-shaped.
         i. The uptake of the first molecule of oxygen is more difficult than the uptake of the remaining molecules.
         ii. The release of the first O_2 is more difficult than the release of the other three.

4. CO_2 transport.
   a. CO_2 can be transported in three ways.
      i.   Dissolved (about 7%).
      ii. Bonded to Hb.
      iii. As HCO_3^- in solution.
   b. Carbonic anhydrase in erythrocytes catalyzes the formation of HCO_3^- from CO_2.
   c. The HCO_3^- can be transported in blood to the lungs, where it is exhaled as CO_2.
   d. Electrolyte balance in erythrocytes is maintained by entry of one Cl^- for every HCO_3^- removed.
   e. Excess acidity is controlled by binding of H^+ to hemoglobin, with release of O_2.
5. The effects of changes in the oxygen saturation curve with changing pCO_2 and $[H^+]$ are illustrated in Figure 29.12.
6. Acidosis and alkalosis result from disruption of the body's mechanism for maintaining pH and by imbalances in CO_2 metabolism.

III. Urine (Sections 29.7–29.8).
   A. The kidney and urine formation (Section 29.7).
      1. The kidney is composed of nephrons.
      2. Blood enters the nephrons at the glomerulus, where filtration occurs. Plasma and smaller solutes are filtered into the surrounding fluid.
      3. Reabsorption recaptures water and smaller solutes.
      4. In secretion, some solutes are excreted in higher concentration than occurs in the filtrate.
      5. Some substances move by passive diffusion; others move by active transport.
      6. Hormones influence urine composition.
   B. Urine composition and function (Section 29.8).
      1. Composition of urine.
         a. The components of urine are mainly electrolytes and nitrogen-containing wastes.
         b. The concentration of these substances varies with water intake, temperature, exercise and state of health.
      2. Acid–base balance.
         a. Of the 50–100 mEq of H^+ produced in metabolism, very little appears in the urine.
         b. H^+ is produced from CO_2 in the reaction:
            $$CO_2 + H_2O \longrightarrow H^+ + HCO_3^-$$
         c. The resulting H^+ combines with either NH_3 or HPO_4^{2-} and is excreted.
         d. H^+ also combines with HCO_3^- in urine filtrate to produce CO_2, which enters the bloodstream.
      3. Fluid and Na^+ balance.
         a. The amount of H_2O reabsorbed depends on:
            i.   The osmolarity of the fluid passing through the kidney.
            ii. Antidiuretic hormone-controlled membrane permeability.
            iii. The amount of Na^+ reabsorbed.
         b. Reabsorption of Na^+ is under the control of aldosterone.

Solutions to Chapter 29 Problems

29.1 When chloride concentrations are low, the reaction should proceed farther to the right, according to Le Châtelier's principle. When chloride concentrations are high, the reaction proceeds to the left. In order to move passively into a cell, a molecule cannot be charged because a cell membrane is non-polar. Therefore, the form of cisplatin shown on the left enters the cell more readily. Once inside, the equilibrium shifts to the right and forms the charged version of cisplatin, which does not cross back through the cell membrane.

29.2 (a) interstitial fluid - (iii) fluid that fills spaces between cells
(b) whole blood - (ii) fluid, solutes and cells that together flow through veins and arteries
(c) blood serum - (iv) fluid that remains after clotting agents are removed from plasma
(d) intracellular fluid - (v) fluid within cells
(e) blood plasma - (i) fluid that remains when blood cells are removed

29.3 (a) The value of pH goes down because of the formation of carbonic acid from dissolved CO_2, which increases the $[H_3O]^+$ and thus increases acidity.
(b) A blood gas analysis measures $[O_2]$, $[CO_2]$, and pH.

29.4 (a) Pneumonia is a cause of *respiratory acidosis*. In pneumonia, the lungs have difficulty exhaling CO_2, and increased blood acidity results.
(b) Failure of the kidneys to excrete H_3O^+ results in *metabolic acidosis*.
(c) Overdose of an antacid leads to overneutralization of H_3O^+, which raises pH and leads to *metabolic alkalosis*.
(d) Hyperventilation removes CO_2 from the body, raising pH and resulting in *respiratory alkalosis*.
(e) Congestive heart failure is a cause of *respiratory alkalosis*.

Understanding Key Concepts

29.5 (a) The body fluid found inside cells is called intracellular fluid.
(b) The body fluid found outside cells is called extracellular fluid.
(c) Blood plasma and interstitial fluid are the major body fluids found outside of cells.
(d) K^+, Mg^{2+} and HPO_4^{2-} are the major electrolytes found inside cells.
(e) The major electrolytes found outside cells are Na^+ and Cl^-.

29.6

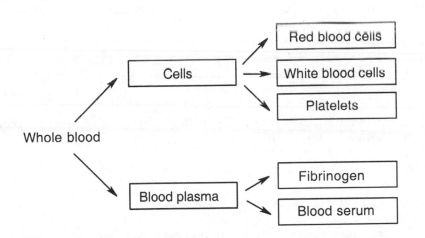

29.7 (a) Blood carries CO_2 (dissolved and as HCO_3^-) from the tissues to the lungs.
(b) Blood carries O_2 from lungs to tissues.
(c) Blood transports nutrients from the digestive system to the tissues.
(d) Blood carries waste products from the tissues to the site of excretion.
(e) Blood transports hormones from endocrine glands to their site of binding.
(f) Blood transports defensive agents such as white blood cells (to destroy foreign material) and platelets (to prevent blood loss).

29.8   Symptoms of inflammation include swelling, redness, warmth and pain. Histamine causes these symptoms by dilating capillaries, causing an increased blood flow that reddens and warms the skin. Pain and swelling occur when blood-clotting factors and defensive proteins enter the intercellular space.

Histamine is produced by the enzymatic decarboxylation of histidine.

29.9   <u>Cell-mediated immune response</u>, which is under the control of T cells, arises when abnormal cells, bacteria or viruses enter cells. The invading cells are killed by T cells that destroy the invader.

<u>Antibody-mediated immune response</u>, which is under the control of B cells, assisted by T cells, occurs when antigenic substances enter cells. When an antigen is recognized, B cells divide to produce plasma cells, which form antibodies to the antigen. These antibodies form an antibody-antigen complex that inactivates the antigen.

Body Fluids

29.10 The three principal body fluids are intracellular fluid, extracellular fluid and interstitial fluid.

29.11 Intracellular fluid contains most of the body's water.

29.12 To be soluble in bodily fluids, a substance must be an ion, a gas, a small molecule, or a molecule with many polar or ionic groups on its surface.

29.13 Substances not soluble in blood are transported by blood proteins.

29.14 Blood pressure in arterial capillaries is higher than interstitial fluid pressure, and blood pressure in venous capillaries is lower than interstitial fluid pressure.

29.15 The difference in blood pressure between arterial capillaries and interstitial fluid pushes solutes and water into interstitial fluid. The difference in blood pressure between interstitial fluid and venous capillaries draws solutes and water into venous capillaries.

29.16 The lymphatic system collects excess interstitial fluid, cellular debris, proteins, and lipid droplets and ultimately returns them to the bloodstream.

29.17 Lymph enters the bloodstream at the thoracic duct.

29.18 Antidiuretic hormone is also known as vasopressin.

29.19 Antidiuretic hormone causes a decrease in the water content of the urine.

29.20 Blood plasma is the fluid portion of blood that contains water-soluble solutes.

29.21 Blood serum is the fluid that remains after blood has completely clotted.

29.22 The three main types of blood cells are erythrocytes (red blood cells), platelets, and white blood cells.

29.23 *Red blood cells* transport blood gases.
White blood cells protect the body from foreign substances..
Platelets assist in blood clotting.

29.24 An eletrolyte is a substance that produces ions.

29.25 Potassium cation, magnesium cation and hydrogen phosphate anion are the major electrolytes inside cells. Sodium cation and chloride anion are the major electrolytes outside of cells.

29.26 An antigen is a foreign substance that the body identifies as an invader. Three types of bodily responses to antigens are inflammation, cell-mediated immune response, and antibody-mediated immune response.

29.27 Antihistamines block attachment of the neurotransmitter histamine to its receptors.

29.28 Specific immune responses, like enzyme-substrate interactions, involve a noncovalent interaction between an antigen and a defender (antibody) specific to that antigen.

29.29 Immunoglobulins are the plasma proteins involved in the antibody-mediated immune response.

29.30 The antibody-directed immune response involves B lymphocytes, a type of white blood cell. These B lymphocytes identify antigens and divide into plasma cells that produce antibodies specific to the antigen present.

29.31 Memory cells, which are produced from B cells, can quickly produce more plasma cells if the same antigen appears in the future. Memory cells "remember" the antigen and are capable of producing antibodies to it for a long time.

29.32 When a T cell recognizes an antigen on the surface of an invader, three kinds of T cells are produced. *Killer* T cells destroy the invader, *helper* T cells enhance defenses against the invader, and *memory* T cells can produce new killer T cells if the invader reappears.

29.33 When T cells recognize an antigen on the surface of an invading cell, they produce killer T cells that destroy the invader, often by releasing a toxic protein that perforates cell membranes.

29.34 A blood clot is a mass of blood cells trapped in a fibrin mesh.

29.35 Vitamin K and calcium ion are needed for blood clotting.

29.36 Blood clotting can be triggered by either the intrinsic pathway, which occurs when blood is exposed to negatively charged surfaces, or by the extrinsic pathway, which occurs when a substance called tissue factor is released by injured cells.

29.37 Blood clotting enzymes are released as zymogens in order to avoid undesirable clotting in noninjured tissues.

29.38 Each hemoglobin subunit can bind one O_2 molecule.

29.39 Hemoglobin iron must be in the +2 oxidation state in order to bind with oxygen.

29.40 Oxyhemoglobin is bright red, whereas deoxyhemoglobin is dark red-purple.

29.41 When the partial pressure of oxygen drops below 10 mm Hg, hemoglobin is unsaturated. When the partial pressure of oxygen is greater than 100 mm Hg, hemoglobin is completely saturated. Between these pressures, hemoglobin is partially saturated.

29.42 Because of oxygen's allosteric interaction with hemoglobin, uptake of the first oxygen facilitates the uptake of the remaining oxygens. In the reverse direction, release of the first oxygen facilitates the release of the other three oxygens.

29.43 Hemoglobin is 50% saturated with oxygen at 30 mm Hg.
Under normal conditions at sea level, the partial pressure of O_2 is:
$$760 \text{ mm Hg } \times 0.21 = 160 \text{ mm Hg}$$
According to Figure 29.11, hemoglobin is 100% saturated with O_2 under normal conditions.

29.44 CO_2 can be transported as a dissolved gas, as bicarbonate ion, or bonded to hemoglobin.

29.45 CO_2 in the blood raises $[H^+]$ in two types of reactions:

(1) Reaction of CO_2 with non-ionized $-NH_2$ groups of hemoglobin amino acids produces H^+.

$$Hb-NH_2 + CO_2 \longrightarrow Hb-NHCOO^- + H^+$$

(2) Carbonic anhydrase catalyzes the reaction of CO_2 with H_2O, producing bicarbonate and H^+.

$$CO_2 + H_2O \underset{\text{anhydrase}}{\overset{\text{Carbonic}}{\rightleftharpoons}} HCO_3^- + H^+$$

29.46 (a)   Increasing the temperature causes hemoglobin to release more O_2 to tissues.
(b) (c) Production of CO_2 brings about an increase of $[H^+]$, which causes the release of O_2.

29.47 A blood serum pH of 7.6 indicates a condition of alkalosis.

29.48 Ketoacidosis due to diabetes is classified as metabolic acidosis because it is caused by increased production of acid as a result of metabolic dysfunction.

29.49 Acidosis due to congestive heart failure is considered to be respiratory acidosis because it is caused by a failure to efficiently remove CO_2 from the blood.

29.50 In addition to filtration, kidneys also recapture water and essential solutes (reabsorption) and excrete excess solutes (secretion).

29.51

$$H^+ + HCO_3^- \rightleftharpoons CO_2 + H_2O$$

$$H^+ + HPO_4^{2-} \rightleftharpoons H_2PO_4^-$$

Applications

29.52 Emollients are fats such as lanolin, vegetable oils or petroleum jelly.

29.53 Humectants are substances such as glycerol, lactic acid, and lecithin that attract moisture from the air and hold it to the skin. Most humectants are compounds capable of forming hydrogen bonds with water.

29.54 Endothelial cells in brain capillaries form tight junctions so that no substances can pass between them.

29.55 In an asymmetric transport system, substances can either be transported into a cell or be transported out of a cell, but not both. For example, there exists a system for transport of glycine out of brain cells, but no system exists for transport of glycine into brain cells.

29.56 Substances that are soluble in membrane lipids can cross the blood-brain barrier. Ethanol crosses this barrier because it's soluble in membrane lipids.

29.57 There are at least four reasons why it would be desirable to have a substitute for human blood:
(1) The need for blood transfusions is growing.
(2) The number of blood donors is declining.
(3) It is possible for blood to be contaminated.
(4) Blood has a short shelf-life, and it must be stored at a low temperature.
Two oxygen-carrying substitutes for human blood are modified hemoglobin and perfluorocarbons.

29.58 *Advantages:*
Modified hemoglobin: Because antigens are left behind when hemoglobin is extracted, blood typing is unnecessary.
Modified hemoglobin has a long shelf-life.
Perfluorocarbons: Perfluorocarbons are relatively inexpensive.
Perfluorocarbons are chemically inert.

Disadvantages:
Modified hemoglobin: The cost of extracting modified hemoglobin is higher than the cost of manufacturing perfluorocarbons.
Modified hemoglobin has a short lifetime in the body.
Modified hemoglobin might be altered in the body by biochemical reactions.
Perfluorocarbons: Perfluorocarbons might be (but probably aren't) toxic.
The amount of oxygen delivered by perfluorocarbons is hard to regulate.

29.59 The substance to be analyzed is combined with a reagent with which it forms a colored product. The quantity of product is determined by using a photometer to measure the amount of visible light of a specific wavelength that the colored product absorbs.

29.60 A change in enzyme level in body fluids may indicate organ damage. An automatic analyzer can reproducibly measure the rate of an enzyme-catalyzed reaction to detect the presence of elevated or reduced levels of enzymes.

29.61 Automated analyzers are quick and inexpensive (after their initial cost). They can reproducibly perform dozens of different tests, and they avoid contamination of the sample by humans and exposure of humans to pathogenic organisms and toxic reagents. They generate few dirty dishes, and they don't take coffee breaks.

General Questions and Problems

29.62 Ethanol is soluble in blood because it is a small, polar molecule.

29.63 A nursing mother's antibodies can be passed to her baby in breast milk.

29.64 When the concentration of sodium in the blood is high, the secretion of antidiuretic hormone (ADH) increases. ADH causes the water content of the urine to decrease, and causes the amount of water retained by the body to increase, causing swelling.

29.65 Active transport is the movement of solutes from regions of low concentration to regions of high concentration, a process that requires energy. Osmosis is the movement of water through a semipermeable membrane from a dilute solution to a more concentrated solution, a process that requires no energy.

29.66 Active transport is necessary when a cell needs a substance that has a higher concentration inside the cell than outside, or when a cell needs to secrete a substance that has a higher concentration outside the cell than inside.

29.67 In the blood, CO_2 from metabolism reacts to form $HCO_3^- + H^+$. The H^+ is bound to hemoglobin, which releases O_2, and is carried to the lungs. There, the H^+ is released and O_2 is bound to hemoglobin.

In the urine, CO_2 reacts to form HCO_3^- and H^+. The HCO_3^- returns to the bloodstream, and the H^+ is neutralized by reaction with HPO_4^{2-} or NH_3.

Whenever excess HCO_3^- accumulates in blood or urine, it can react with H^+ to form $H_2O + CO_2$.

29.68 *Homeostasis* is the maintenance of a constant internal environment in the body. *Hemostasis* is the body's mechanism for preventing blood loss and could be considered a part of homeostasis.

29.69 When blood CO_2 level drops, the following reaction occurs to restore CO_2 supply:

$$H^+ \; + \; HCO_3^- \longrightarrow H_2CO_3 \longrightarrow CO_2 \; + \; H_2O$$

This reaction uses up H^+ ions and leads to alkalosis. Breathing into a paper bag recaptures the expired CO_2 and restores the blood CO_2 level.

Self-Test for Chapter 29

Multiple choice:

1. Which oxygen is taken up by heme with the most difficulty?
   (a) the first oxygen   (b) the second oxygen   (c) the last oxygen   (d) all bind with equal ease

2. Cardiac arrest may result in:
   (a) metabolic alkalosis   (b) metabolic acidosis   (c) respiratory alkalosis   (d) respiratory acidosis

3. Cell-mediated immune response guards against all of the following except:
   (a) cancer cells   (b) transplanted organs   (c) allergens   (d) bacteria

4. Potassium ion is most abundant in:
   (a) interstitial fluid   (b) intracellular fluid   (c) plasma   (d) extracellular fluid

5. All of the following are involved in blood clotting except:
   (a) tissue factor   (b) zymogens   (c) thrombin   (d) memory cells

6. Which of the following disorders is not an autoimmune disease?
   (a) hemophilia   (b) arthritis   (c) lupus erythematosus   (d) diabetes mellitus

7. The amount of water reabsorbed in kidney tubules depends on:
   (a) the amount of sodium reabsorbed   (b) control of membrane permeability by antidiuretic hormone   (c) aldosterone   (d) all three

8. Blood is at its lowest percent saturation with oxygen in:
   (a) peripheral tissue   (b) muscles   (c) veins   (d) arteries

9. All of the following decrease the oxygen affinity of hemoglobin except:
   (a) increased $[H^+]$ (b) increased $[O_2]$ (c) increased $[CO_2]$ (d) increased temperature

10. B cells divide to produce all of the following except:
    (a) memory cells   (b) antibodies   (c) phagocytes   (d) plasma cells

Complete the following sentences:

1. The percentage of heme molecules that carry oxygen is dependent on the _____ _____ of O_2.

2. Antigens can be small molecules known as _____.

3. In the process of blood clotting, _____ are activated to give active clotting factors.

4. Inorganic ions are the major contributors to the _____ of body fluids.

5. Histamine is synthesized from _____.

6. _____ ion and vitamin ____ assist in blood clotting.

7. In _____ _____, substances move from regions of low concentration to regions of high concentration.

8. The three functions of blood are _____, _____, and _____.

9. Bacteria at the site of inflammation are attacked by _____.

10. Arthritis and allergies are known as _____ diseases.

11. _____ is caused by the absence of one or more clotting factors.

12. Fibrin molecules are bound into fibers by cross-links between the side chains of the amino acids _____ and _____.

Tell whether the following sentences are true or false:

1. The walls of lymph capillaries are constricted so that lymph can't return to surrounding tissues.

2. Homeostasis is the body's mechanism for halting blood loss.

3. O_2, H^+, and CO_2 all bond to heme.

4. Secreted H^+ is eliminated in the urine as NH_4^+ or $H_2PO_4^-$.

5. When the partial pressure of CO_2 increases, the percent saturation of hemoglobin decreases.

6. Allergies and asthma are caused by an underproduction of immunoglobulin E.

7. Blood plasma is the fluid remaining after blood has completely clotted.

8. Blood clotting begins with the release of tissue factor from injured tissue.

9. Reabsorption is the movement of solutes and water out of the kidney.

10. The metabolism of food contributes to one's water intake.

11. Lymphocytes surround and destroy bacteria.

12. Caffeine causes increased output of urine.

Match the item on the left with its partner on the right:

1. B cells

(a) Foreign substance

2. Active transport

(b) Enzyme that catalyzes the formation of histamine

3. Fibrin

(c) Movement of solute against a concentration gradient

4. Carbonic anhydrase

(d) White blood cells involved in antibody-directed immune response

5. Erythrocytes

(e) Controls reabsorption of Na^+

6. T cells

(f) Blood protein responsible for clotting

7. Antigen

(g) Enzyme that catalyzes reaction between H_2O and CO_2

8. Histidine decarboxylase

(h) Movement of water in response to a concentration difference

9. Osmosis

(i) White blood cells involved in cell-directed immune response

10. Antidiuretic hormone

(j) Red blood cells

11. Antibody

(k) Protein molecule that identifies a foreign substance

12. Aldosterone

(l) Causes a decrease in the water content of urine

Answers to Self Tests

Chapter One

Multiple choice: 1. b 2. d 3. b 4. d 5. a 6. a 7. c 8. b
Sentence completion: 1. nonmetallic 2. physical 3. Bi 4. condenses 5. mass and volume 6. liquid 7. pure substance 8. chemical formulas 9. malleable 10. carbon, hydrogen, oxygen and nitrogen
True/false: 1. T 2. T 3. T 4. F (physical methods) 5. F (seven atoms) 6. T 7. F (Ag) 8. T 9. F (a gas) 10. T

Chapter Two

Number questions: 1. (a) micrometer (b) deciliter (c) megagram (d) liter (e) nanogram 2. (a) kL (b) pg (c) cm (d) hL 3. (a) 5 (b) 2 (c) 1 (d) exact (e) 3,4,5 or 6 4. (a) 7.03×10^{-5} g; 3 sig. fig. (b) $1.371\,00 \times 10^5$ m; 4,5,or 6 sig. fig. (c) 1.1×10^{-2} L; 2 sig. fig. (d) $1.837\,100\,8 \times 10^7$ mm; 8 sig. fig. 5. (a) 8.07×10^2 L (b) 4.77×10^6 people (c) 1.27×10^{-3} g (d) 1.04×10^4 μm 6. (a) 0.564 lb (b) 0.417 m (c) 7.6 L (d) 85.4 in. (e) 95°F (f) 25°C (g) 5.92 fl oz (h) 6.17×10^{-3} oz 7. 31 cal 8. 217 g
Multiple choice: 1. b 2. d 3. b 4. a 5. c 6. d 7. b 8. c 9. c 10. a
Sentence completion : 1. kilogram, meter, cubic meter, Kelvin 2. number, unit 3. specific heat 4. nano- 5. 3 6. 1 lb/454 g 7. calorie, joule 8. factor-label 9. Specific gravity 10. Celsius, Kelvin
True/false: 1. F (specific gravity is unitless) 2. T 3. F (three sig. fig.) 4. F (0.9464 L/1 qt.) 5. T 6. F 7. F 8. T 9. F 10. T
Matching: 1. e 2. j 3. g 4. i 5. h 6. l 7. f 8. k 9. c 10. a 11. d 12. b

Chapter Three

Multiple choice: 1. c 2. b 3. a 4. c 5. d 6. d 7. a 8. b 9. d 10. d 11. a 12. b
Sentence completion: 1. p 2. dalton 3. protons, neutrons 4. atomic number 5. shells 6. group 7. 13 8. subatomic particles 9. isotopes 10. 18 11. quantized
True/false: 1. T 2. F (5.486×10^{-4} amu) 3. F 4. T 5. F (atomic number indicates only protons) 6. F (They're less reactive.) 7. F (in the same group) 8. T 9. T 10. F (Subshells can contain 2,6,10 ·· electrons.) 11. T 12. F
Matching: 1. h 2. e 3. k 4. a 5. j 6. l 7. c 8. b 9. i 10. d 11. g 12. f

Chapter Four

Multiple choice: 1. d 2. a 3. d 4. c 5. a 6. b 7. b 8. d 9. b 10. d
Sentence completion: 1. Ionization energy 2. potassium phosphate 3. 2 4. polyatomic 5. simplest 6. 8 7. base 8. Hydroxyapatite 9. crystalline 10. 4A or 5A
True/false: 1. F (It forms only Zn^{2+}.) 2. T 3. F (energy needed to form an ion) 4. T 5. F (ions formed may be H^+, $H_2PO_4^-$, and HPO_4^{2-}.) 6. F (Solutions of ions conduct electricity.) 7. T 8. T 9. T 10. F (group 8A) 11. T 12. F
Matching: 1. e 2. l 3. k 4. a 5. h 6. j 7. i 8. b 9. f 10 g 11. d 12. c

Chapter Five

Multiple choice: 1. c   2. d   3. b   4. c   5. a   6. a   7. d   8. b   9. d   10. a
Sentence completion: 1. electronegative   2. biomolecule   3. covalent   4. C≡C, C≡N
5. diatomic   6. planar trigonal   7. *d*   8. triple   9. Binary   10. organic   11. condensed
True/false: 1. T   2. T   3. F   4. F (valence electrons)   5. F (It's planar.)   6. F (covalent
compounds)   7. T   8. F   9. F (Some bent molecules have bond angles that are approx. 109.5°.)
10. T   11. T
Matching: 1. h(or c)   2. j   3. f   4. a   5. k   6. i   7. e   8. c   9. b   10. g   11. d   12. l

Chapter Six

Multiple choice: 1. a   2. a   3. c   4. b   5. d   6. c   7. c   8. b   9. a   10. d
Sentence completion: 1. coefficients   2. precipitate   3. spectator   4. aqueous   5. molar mass
6. percent yield   7. reactants   8. +3   9. reducing   10. neutralization
True/false: 1. F (It has the same number of atoms.)   2. T   3. T   4. F   5. T   6. F (Molar mass
is the conversion factor.)   7. F   8. F (The mole ratio is 1/2.)   9. T   10. T
Matching: 1. h   2. f   3. k   4. a   5. i   6. c   7. j   8. b   9. g   10. l   11. d   12. e

Chapter Seven

Multiple choice: 1. c   2. b   3. d   4. d   5. b   6. a   7. c   8. a   9. d   10. d
Sentence completion: 1. 1   2. Conservation of Energy   3. catalyst   4. reversible   5.
endothermic   6. equilibrium-constant expression   7. temperature, pressure, catalyst
8. metabolism   9. Reaction rate   10. collide
True/false: 1. F (produced)   2. F (At equilibrium, the ratio of concentrations is constant.)   3. T
4. T   5. F (The size of E_{act} and ΔH are unrelated.)   6. F (not always true for biochemical
reactions)   7. T   8. F (Catalysts lower the height of the energy barrier.)   9. F (At equilibrium, the
rate of the forward reaction equals the rate of the reverse reaction.)   10. T
Matching: 1. c   2. j   3. l   4. i   5. a   6. k   7. b   8. f   9. d   10. e   11. g   12. h

Chapter Eight

Multiple choice: 1. b   2. c   3. d   4. a   5. d   6. c   7. a   8. b   9. c   10. d
Sentence completion: 1. pressure, volume   2. definite, indefinite   3. Dalton's   4. standard
temperature and pressure   5. Avogadro's   6. equilibrium   7. atmosphere, Pascal, mm Hg,
pounds per square inch   8. heat of fusion   9. number of atoms, volume   10. temperature
11. change of state   12. volatile
True/false: 1. T   2. F (Only ideal gases have similar physical behavior.)   3. T   4. F (Doubling
pressure halves the volume.)   5. T   6. F (only true in crystals)   7. F (273 K)   8. T   9. F (higher)
10. F (Vapor pressure doesn't depend on quantity of liquid.)   11. F (viscosity)
Matching: 1. g   2. e   3. k   4. f   5. h   6. a   7. j   8. l   9. b   10. d   11. c   12. i

Chapter Nine

Multiple choice: 1. b 2. d 3. a 4. b 5. c 6. d 7. c 8. c 9. a 10. b
Sentence completion: 1. miscible 2. equivalent 3. volumetric flask 4. solubility, partial pressure 5. isotonic 6. hygroscopic 7. $M_1 \times V_1 = M_2 \times V_2$. 8. colloid 9. solvent, small solute molecules 10. saturated 11. glucose 12. lower
True/false: 1. F (solvent) 2. T 3. F (A quantity of the second liquid is added to make 100 mL of solution.) 4. F 5. T 6. F (Weight/weight percent is rarely used.) 7. T 8. F (Effect of temperature is unpredictable.) 9. T (It also differs with respect to particle size.) 10. F (hemolysis) 11. F (raise) 12. T
Matching: 1. h 2. f 3. d 4. j 5. a 6. k 7. b 8. i 9. g 10. l 11. e 12. c

Chapter Ten

Multiple choice: 1. b 2. a 3. c 4. d 5. c 6. c 7. b 8. a 9. b 10. d
Sentence completion: 1. equivalent 2. red 3. diprotic 4. strong 5. Dissociation 6. OH^- ions 7. Neutralization 8. pH 9. 30.0 mL 10. conjugate 11. carbonate / bicarbonate 12. amphoteric
True/false: 1. F (60 mL of 0.1 M NaOH) 2. T 3. F (H_2SO_4 is a strong acid.) 4. F 5. F 6. T 7. T 8. F (According to this definition, an acid donates H^+.) 9. F (Ammonia yields ammonium ion, plus the anion of the acid.) 10. T 11. F 12. T
Matching: 1. d 2. e 3. g 4. l 5. a 6. b 7. i 8. j 9. c 10. f 11. k 12. h

Chapter Eleven

Multiple choice: 1. c 2. d 3. c 4. a 5. c 6. d 7. a 8. d 9. b 10. c
Sentence completion: 1. transmutation 2. Gamma radiation 3. tracer 4. background 5. nucleons 6. ^{14}C 7. curie 8. nuclear fission 9. film badges 10. body imaging 11. nuclear fusion 12. critical mass
True/false: 1. F (3/4 will have decayed after 24 days.) 2. T 3. T 4. F (Becquerel) 5. T 6. F 7. F (Atomic number increases by 1.) 8. F (Hazards are due to emissions of radiation.) 9. F (The rem is more common.) 10. T 11. F (Most are synthetic.) 12. F
Matching: 1. f 2. i 3. l 4. k 5. c 6. j 7. d 8. h 9. b 10. a 11. e 12. g

Chapter Twelve

Multiple choice: 1. a 2. c 3. d 4. c 5. b 6. d 7. c 8. a 9. c 10. a
Sentence completion: 1. paraffins 2. triple 3. oxygen 4. distillation 5. condensed structure 6. quaternary 7. lower 8. ring 9. IUPAC 10. isomers 11. Combustion 12. higher
True/false: 1. F (They have different molecular formulas.) 2. T 3. F (It's puckered.) 4. F (3-Methylhexane) 5. T 6. T 7. F (It's polar covalent.) 8. T 9. T 10. F (Reactivity depends on the nature of the functional groups.) 11. T 12. F
Matching: 1. i 2. j 3. f 4. l 5. h 6. c 7. a 8. k 9. e 10. b 11. g 12. d

Chapter Thirteen

Multiple choice: 1. d 2. b 3. a 4. c 5. a 6. c 7. c 8. c 9. d 10. d
Sentence completion: 1. 2-heptyne 2. hydrogenation 3. *para* 4. more, fewer 5. hydration
6. catalyst 7. carbocation 8. unsaturated 9. Toluene 10. substitution 11. Polycyclic aromatic
compounds 12. thermal cracking
True/false: 1. F 2. T 3. T 4. F (2-bromobutane) 5. F (Halogenation is the reaction of X_2
with an alkene, where X is a halogen.) 6. T 7. F 8. F (Hydration requires a strong acid as a
catalyst.) 9. T 10. F 11. F 12. T
Matching: 1. e 2. k 3. i 4. j 5. b 6. l 7. d 8. c 9. a 10. f 11. g 12. h

Chapter Fourteen

Multiple choice: 1. c 2. b 3. b 4. a 5. d 6. d 7. a 8. b 9. c 10. d
Sentence completion: 1. wood alcohol 2. glycols 3. phenols 4. alkene 5. thiols
6. $KMnO_4$ or $K_2Cr_2O_7$ 7. lower 8. BHT 9. greater 10. free radical 11. peroxide 12. CFC
Matching: 1. j 2. g 3. f 4. h 5. l 6. b 7. e 8. a 9. k 10. d 11. i 12. c
True/false: 1. T 2. F (A ketone is formed from the oxidation of a secondary alcohol.) 3. T
4. F (carbolic acid) 5. T 6. T 7. F (Ethyl chloride is an anesthetic.) 8. F (two hydrogen atoms)
9. T 10. T 11. F 12. T

Chapter Fifteen

Multiple choice: 1. c 2. a 3. d 4. c 5. c 6. a 7. b 8. d 9. a 10. b
Sentence completion: 1. *amino-* 2. quaternary 3. DNA 4. Toxicology 5. heterocycle 6.
Alkaloids 7. hydrogen bonding 8. ammonium 9. free radical 10. nonaromatic amines
True/false: 1. T 2. T 3. F (They're lower boiling.) 4. T 5. F 6. T 7. F (It's synthetic.) 8.
T 9. F (NO lowers blood pressure.) 10. F (*N*-Methylbutylamine)
Matching: 1. d 2. l 3. h 4. i 5. a 6. j 7. b 8. k 9. f 10. g 11. e 12. c

Chapter Sixteen

Multiple choice: 1. c 2. b 3. a 4. d 5. c 6. b 7. b 8. a 9. d 10. b
Sentence completion: 1. carbonyl 2. silver 3. Hydrolysis 4. positive, negative 5. Acetone
6. Acetaldehyde 7. more 8. reduction 9. disinfectant or preservative 10. hemiacetal
11. Benedict's 12. Acetone
True/False: 1. F (a hemiacetal link) 2. T 3. F (Ketones don't undergo Tollens' reaction.) 4. F
($NaBH_4$ is used for reduction.) 5. F 6. F (Both aldehydes and ketones form acetals.) 7. T 8. T
9. F (NADH) 10. T 11. T 12. T
Matching: 1. e 2. i 3. d (or l) 4. a 5. h 6. j 7. k 8. b 9. l 10. f 11. g 12. c

Chapter Seventeen

Multiple choice: 1. d 2. c 3. a 4. d 5. b 6. d 7. b 8. a 9. d 10. a
Sentence completion: 1. carbonyl group substitution 2. polyamide 3. carboxylate salt
4. esterification 5. attracts 6. -oic acid 7. propyl propanoate 8. esters 9. Phosphorylation
10. fats 11. hydrolysis or saponification 12. propanedioic acid
True/false: 1. T 2. F (basic hydrolysis) 3. F (Amides are nonbasic.) 4. T 5. F (The products
are acetate ion and ethanol.) 6. F (*N,N*-dimethylformamide) 7. F 8. T 9. T 10. F
(Esterification is acid-catalyzed.) 11. F (It's an acid anhydride.) 12. T
Matching: 1. j 2. f 3. k 4. b 5. i 6. d 7. a 8. e 9. l 10. h 11. c 12. g

Chapter Eighteen

Multiple choice: 1. a 2. d 3. c 4. b 5. b 6. a 7. d 8. b 9. c 10. d
Sentence completion : 1. 5.0-6.3 2. enantiomers 3. zwitterions 4. backbone 5. loop
6. glycoprotein 7. Tertiary 8. β-sheet 9. polar 10. sulfur 11. polypeptide 12. Hydrophobic
True/false: 1. F (Glycine is achiral.) 2. T 3. F (Denaturation disrupts all structural elements
except primary structure.) 4. F (They're different.) 5. T 6. F 7. T 8. T 9. T 10. F (Fibrous
proteins are insoluble.) 11. T 12. T
Matching: 1. e 2. g 3. j 4. a 5. b 6. k 7. c 8. l 9. f 10. h 11. d 12. i

Chapter Nineteen

Multiple choice: 1. c 2. a 3. c 4. d 5. b 6. b 7. d 8. c 9. b 10. d
Sentence completion: 1. isomerase 2. Isoenzymes 3. K 4. induced-fit 5. noncompetitive
6. denature 7. turnover number 8. phosphoryl 9. proximity 10. 10^9 11. allosteric 12.
zymogen
True/false: 1. T 2. F 3. F 4. F (a dehydrase) 5. F (Enzyme-substrate interactions are
noncovalent.) 6. F (Minerals, not vitamins, are inorganic ions.) 7. T 8. F (Retinol, retinal,
retinoic acid are all active forms of vitamin A.) 9. T 10. T 11. F (Reaction rate increases.) 12. T
Matching: 1. c 2. h 3. i 4. g 5. k 6. j 7. b 8. a 9. d 10. f 11. e 12. l

Chapter Twenty

Multiple choice: 1. a 2. c 3. b 4. c 5. d 6. a 7. d 8. a 9. d 10. d
Sentence Completion: 1. Anaphylaxis 2. adrenal 3. vesicles 4. Histamine 5. cholinergic
6. progesterone 7. enkephalin 8. ethnobotanist 9. synaptic cleft 10. dopamine 11. thyroxine
12. phosphodiesterase
True/false: 1. F (Thyroxine can cross the cell membrane.) 2. F (It blocks reuptake.) 3. T 4.
T 5. F (presynaptic neurons) 6. T 7. F (It increases blood pressure and heart rate.) 8. F (It's a
symptom of iodine deficiency.) 9. T 10. T
Matching: 1. e 2. h 3. k 4. b 5. g 6. a 7. d 8. j 9. f 10. l 11. c 12. i

Chapter Twenty-one

Multiple choice: 1. b 2. c 3. a 4. c 5. a 6. d 7. b 8. c 9. b 10. d
Sentence completion: 1. Eukaryotic 2. metabolic pathway or linear sequence 3. ADP and phosphate 4. unfavorable 5. Krebs cycle, tricarboxylic acid cycle 6. succinyl-SCoA, CO_2 7. NAD^+ 8. one (plus 4 reduced coenzymes) 9. Cytoplasm 10. Catalase 11. succinate dehydrogenase 12. Basal metabolism
True/false: 1. T 2. F (Only eukaryotic cells are found in higher organisms.) 3. F (Anabolism is the synthesis of complicated molecules from simpler molecules.) 4. F 5. T 6. T 7. F ($FADH_2$ donates electrons to coenzyme Q.) 8. T 9. F (decrease in order) 10. F (ATP can be formed in the citric acid cycle) 11. F (a phosphate anhydride) 12. T
Matching: 1. d 2. j 3. f 4. a 5. l 6. k 7. e 8. c 9. b 10. g 11. i 12. h

Chapter Twenty-two

Multiple choice: 1. a 2. d 3. c 4. c 5. d 6. d 7. d 8. c 9. b 10. b
Sentence completion: 1. chiral 2. amylases 3. enantiomers 4. cyclic hemiacetal 5. fructose 6. amylose, amylopectin 7. glycoside 8. Glycogen 9. aldohexose 10. achiral 11. diastereomer 12. Glycoproteins
True/false: 1. T 2. T 3. F (The hydroxyl group on the chiral carbon farthest from the carbonyl group is on the left.) 4. F (α, not β) 5. T 6. F (Crystalline glucose is the α-anomer.) 7. F (Sucrose contains only an acetal bond.) 8. T 9. F (An acetal resembles an ether.) 10. F (Maltose is composed of two glucose molecules.) 11. F (The relationship between the rotations of diastereomers is not predictable.) 12. T
Matching: 1. e 2. l 3. j 4. h 5. i 6. k 7. b 8. a 9. d 10. g 11. c 12. f

Chapter Twenty-three

Multiple choice: 1. c 2. c 3. b 4. d 5. a 6. b 7. d 8. c 9. d 10. a
Sentence completion: 1. Embden-Meyerhof 2. 6 3. Pyruvate dehydrogenase complex 4. Insulin 5. glucose 1–phosphate 6. 1-5 7. diabetes mellitus 8. GTP, ATP 9. CO_2 10. glucose 6-phosphate isomerase 11. glucagon 12. Hypoglycemia
True/false: 1. F (It produces NADPH.) 2. T 3. F 4. F 5. T 6. F (Glycolysis occurs in the cytosol.) 7. F (The yield of ATP was formerly considered to be 38 ATP/ 1 mol glucose. The new estimate is 30-32 ATP/ 1 mol glucose.) 8. F (glycogen) 9. F (Fermentation occurs only in yeasts.) 10. T (but one results from isomerization of dihydroxyacetone phosphate) 11. T 12. F (It produces two ATPs.)
Matching: 1. l 2. k 3. i 4. j 5. c 6. h 7. d 8. a 9. f 10. g 11. b 12. e

Chapter Twenty-four

Multiple choice: 1. d 2. c 3. a 4. a 5. d 6. d 7. c 8. b 9. a 10. b
Sentence completion: 1. glycoside 2. Soap 3. hydrophilic, hydrophobic 4. Glycolipids, cholesterol, glycoproteins 5. fluid-mosaic 6. tetracyclic 7. arachidonic 8. micelles 9. Sphingomyelins 10. lipid bilayer 11. Eicosanoids 12. Integral
True/false: 1. T 2. F 3. F (They contain an amide group.) 4. T 5. T 6. F (They form a micelle.) 7. F (Cholesterol is a steroid component of cell membranes.) 8. F (The major difference is in the quantity of unsaturated fatty acids they contain.) 9. F (Cerebrosides are components of nerve cell membranes in the brain.) 10. T 11. T 12. F (In facilitated diffusion, solutes are transported across cell membranes by proteins, but no energy investment is required.)
Matching: 1. l 2. h 3. e 4. f 5. a 6. j 7. k 8. b 9. d 10. g 11. i 12. c

Chapter Twenty-five

Multiple choice: 1. a 2. d 3. c 4. a 5. b 6. b 7. c 8. d 9. c 10. d
Sentence completion: 1. NAD$^+$, FAD 2. micelles 3. adipocytes 4. dihydroxyacetone phosphate 5. fatty-acid spiral 6. double bond 7. Ketonuria 8. NADPH 9. 3–Hydroxybutyrate 10. lymphatic system 11. mobilized 12. acetyl–SCoA
True/false: 1. T 2. F (The products are mainly mono- and diacylglycerols.) 3. T 4. T 5. F 6. T 7. F (Dihydroxyacetone phosphate, not glycerol) 8. F (LDL transports cholesterol.) 9. T 10. F (It occurs in the cytosol.) 11. F (It comes from acetyl–SCoA.) 12. T.
Matching: 1. e 2. i 3. a 4. l 5. g 6. j 7. k 8. d 9. f 10. b 11. c 12. h

Chapter Twenty-six

Multiple choice: 1. c 2. d 3. b 4. a 5. b 6. b 7. c 8. d 9. c 10. a
Sentence completion: 1. Replication 2. complementary 3. chromatin 4. retrovirus 5. intron 6. ester 7. nucleoside 8. releasing factor 9. replication fork 10. 2'-deoxyribose 11. Watson-Crick 12. DNA polymerase
True/false: 1. F (61 codons code for the 20 amino acids; the other three are "stop" codons.) 2. F (The amount of adenine equals the amount of thymine.) 3. T 4. F (An anticodon occurs on tRNA.) 5. T 6. T 7. T 8. F (They run in opposite directions.) 9. F (translation) 10. F (Most DNA consists of introns.) 11. F (Two have only one codon.) 12. F (guanosine 5'-monophosphate)
Matching; 1. l 2. j 3. b 4. g 5. a 6. i 7. d 8. c 9. e 10. h 11. f 12. k

Chapter Twenty-seven

Multiple choice: 1. c 2. d 3. b 4. a 5. b 6. d 7. c 8. b 9. c 10. b
Sentence completion: 1. "sticky" ends 2. 'junk' 3. restriction endonuclease 4. vacuoles 5. bioethics 6. ionizing radiation, mutagens 7. intron 8. single nucleotide polymorphism 9. proteomics 10. centromere 11. silent 12. autoradiogram
True/false: 1. T 2. F (nucleotide) 3. F (from several people) 4. T 5. T 6. F (starts from base-base sequences at known locations) 7.T 8.T 9. F (missense) 10.T 11. F (adding) 12. T
Matching: 1. b 2. i 3. g 4. c 5. j 6. l 7. e 8. a 9. k 10. h 11. f 12. d

Chapter Twenty-eight

Multiple choice: 1. c 2. a 3. b 4. d 5. a 6. c 7. d 8. c 9. a 10. b
Sentence completion: 1. pyruvate, glutamate 2. xenobiotic 3. acetyl–SCoA, acetoacetyl–SCoA 4. carbamoyl phosphate 5. protease 6. pyruvate 7. Transamination 8. arginine 9. phenylalanine, tyrosine 10. urate crystals 11. ALT 12. bicarbonate
True/false: 1. T 2. F (It starts in the stomach.) 3. F (lysine and leucine) 4. F (The human body can catabolize essential amino acids.) 5. T 6. F (Catabolism occurs in the liver and in the cytosol.) 7. T 8. T 9. F (One is from aspartate; the other is from ammonium ion.) 10. T 11. F (Some transaminases have several amino acid donors.) 12. T
Matching: 1. h 2. g 3. j 4. f 5. a 6. b 7. c 8. l 9. k 10. d 11. e 12. i

Chapter Twenty-nine

Multiple choice: 1. a 2. d 3. c 4. b 5. d 6. a 7. d 8. b 9. b 10. c
Sentence completion: 1. partial pressure 2. haptens 3. zymogens 4. osmolarity 5. histidine 6. calcium, K 7. active transport 8. transport, regulation, defense 9. phagocytes 10. autoimmune 11. Hemophilia 12. lysine, glutamine

True/false: 1. F (constructed) 2. F (hemostasis) 3. F (CO_2 bonds to hemoglobin) 4. T 5. T 6. F (overproduction) 7. F (blood serum) 8. T 9. F (tubule) 10. T 11. F (phagocytes) 12. T
Matching: 1. d 2. c 3. f 4. g 5. j 6. i 7. a 8. b 9. h 10. l 11. k 12. e